PAPERS ON ANIMAL POPULATION GENETICS

PAPERS ON
ANIMAL POPULATION GENETICS

Selected by

ELIOT B. SPIESS

University of Pittsburgh

Boston   Toronto

LITTLE, BROWN AND COMPANY

Published simultaneously in Canada
by Little, Brown & Company (Canada) Limited

PRINTED IN THE UNITED STATES OF AMERICA

FOREWORD

Teaching advanced courses in genetics carries an obligation to make available to students new experimental data and new principles. Textbooks not only cannot keep pace in rapidly changing fields but they rarely cultivate in students enthusiasm derived from first hand acquaintance with facts. The first volumes in this series (*Papers on Bacterial Genetics* and *Bacterial Viruses* selected by Adelberg and Stent respectively) have in my experience given students a realistic sense of discovery, methodology, techniques, and analysis from the most qualified of microbial geneticists.

The field of population genetics shares with that of microbial genetics a rapidly advancing recent history, a decade of discoveries and synthesis of principles. However, the two fields contrast greatly in their order of discovery and theory. Students can be made aware of the contrast by recalling the respective beginnings of the two fields: Microbial genetics was born in the 1940's with discoveries of gene exchange in bacteria and the elaboration of molecular structure for the hereditary material. Population genetics developed first as mathematical generalization based on simple Mendelian principles in the 1920's, followed in the next decade by confirmation of some of those generalizations with observation of natural populations. It has been only within the last fifteen years that the more important function of empirical knowledge from real populations has emerged, namely, the demonstration of selective differences between genotypes, their magnitude, and the subtlety of dynamic elements controlling the genetic potential of populations. Magnitudes of integrating forces, stochastic forces, and non-Mendelian forces (cytoplasmic, meiotic drive and other phenomena) have been measured and have helped to conceptualize population dynamics from which greater generalizations can be made in the future. It is this trend in the genetics of natural or experimental populations which this collection of papers is designed to illustrate.

Three main points of view may be discerned in experimental population genetics today: 1) the evolutionally oriented (secular change in natural populations), 2) the quantitatively oriented (chiefly breeding improved animals and plants for human needs), and 3) the medically oriented (genetic trends in human populations). Each has made major contributions and each is dependent on the others for further development of principles. Papers in this collection have been selected for their evolutionary orientation primarily, particularly papers of current interest in animal experimental population genetics. Some discussions applicable to the other points of view will be found frequently, however.

The bibliography and introduction are intended to preserve continuity and

v

to compensate for the discretionary nature of the selections.   Emphasis has been on providing students with a cross-section of the recent literature.   Comprehensive reviews were excluded from reprinting because they do not fulfill the purpose of acquainting students with analysis and techniques.   Papers already published in book form were also not considered for reprinting.

Finally I would like to acknowledge the excellent cooperation and generosity of all the authors and copyright owners who have permitted the reprinting of their works, and especially to those who contributed rare copies for that purpose. Special thanks are due Professors James F. Crow, Bruce Wallace, Theodosius Dobzhansky, C. C. Li, and Richard C. Lewontin for their helpful comments and criticisms in the choice of papers to be reprinted and the general organization of the book.

ELIOT B. SPIESS
Pittsburgh, Pennsylvania, 1962

CONTENTS

Pagination of the papers in this collection is indicated by the boldface number centered at the bottom of the page. Other page numbers appearing on certain papers refer to original publication.

INTRODUCTION

The extension of Mendel's laws from a concept of individual inheritance mechanisms to the dynamics of genotypes in populations has been very productive indeed. Several genetic disciplines have benefited from the broader view: plant and animal breeding; medical or anthropological studies; and evolutionary mechanism theory. In all these applications of population genetics mathematical treatment of genotypes, phenotypes, deterministic and stochastic forces has been an essential ingredient. To biologists not trained in mathematics, the classic works of Fisher, Haldane, and Wright, while recognized as fundamental amplifications of Mendel's laws on a populational level, were not fully appreciated until recently when magnitudes of dynamic forces were measured in natural and experimental populations on a more extended scale and with more thorough knowledge of genic action.

To be a useful science population genetics must be a synthesis of intelligent observation coupled with mathematical theory. Sewall Wright (383) stressed the synthesis as a reciprocal relation: "The role of the mathematical theory is that of an intermediary between bodies of factual knowledge discovered at two levels, that of the individual and that of the population. It must deduce from postulates at the level of the individual and from models of population structure what is to be expected in populations, and then modify its models and postulates on the basis of any discrepancies with observation and so on." The concrete details of natural population phenomena could hardly have been anticipated by the mathematician. On the other hand, phenomena like random genetic drift were predicted mathematically and later confirmed in the laboratory and field. Several books and symposia have reduced the unfortunate gap between mathematical prediction by models and experimental verification or reinterpretation of those models, notably the books by C. C. Li (11), Dobzhansky (3), Lerner (9, 10), Falconer (4), and symposia on population genetics at Pavia (2), Cold Spring Harbor (1955 through 1959), and Chicago (24). While these volumes are all indispensable to the population geneticist, the recent surge of experimental work has brought forth many principles which must be tested further and for which mathematical models have yet to be developed.

EFFECTS OF SELECTION ON POPULATIONS

Intensity of selection

Perhaps the most significant of long term processes for consideration is the utilization of genetic potential in the adaptation of a species to its environment. There is no doubt that Darwinian-Wallace selection is the central mechanism bringing about adaptation, the perfecting of a species' ability to exploit its environment, or the becoming more fit to exist under specified conditions. Darwin realized that his term, natural selection, was a metaphorical expression for the net effect of two or more variants' differing in reproductive capacity (total expectation of offspring, or "fitness") when living together in the same environment. Given time and the replicating ability of hereditary material, simple arithmetic indicates that any arbitrary initial population would become more "fit" by elimination of harmful variants until maximum fitness has been attained. The magnitude of that process is of considerable interest.

How does one speak of the intensity of selection? Obviously selection is not a tangible force like radiant energy. Nevertheless, the intensity of a differential reproductive capacity can be measured. Simpson (22) has used the term "selection intensity" in the same sense as for selection coefficients commonly used, that is in terms of a genotype's disadvantage relative to another, which he limits to ±1. If a lethal has a −1 "selective intensity" value, it is hard to understand the upper limit +1. It is quite conceivable that the upper limit may be a very large number. Breeders define selection intensity as the amount of culling necessary to make progress towards a goal; more commonly it is defined in terms of a practiced differential "between the average of those selected to be parents and the average of the population in which they were born" (Lush, 12; Lerner, 10). However, the selection differential, while of importance in measuring gains under artificial selection where mean values are expected to progress toward predetermined goals, is not always relevant to natural selection. Haldane has reminded us (157) that natural selection is often directed towards stabilization, the maintenance of the mean value and removal of extreme variants. He mentions that if the mean value of a quantitative character is the same in the survivors as in the original population, the breeder puts the intensity of selection as zero. Intrapopulational selection intensity, then, Haldane measures as the natural logarithm of the ratio between the optimal phenotype's and the total population's survival frequency.

Crow's definition (23) of a population's genetic load as a "proportion by which the population fitness is decreased in comparison with an optimum genotype" amounts to the same sort of measure but expressed non-logarithmically and in terms of genotype rather than phenotype. Haldane gives several examples of phenotype selection including cases in which the standard deviation of x is reduced but the mean is unchanged in survivors compared with the population before selection. If fitness of genetic variables is measured, as in the case of Dobzhansky's (96) karyotypes in *Drosophila pseudoobscura* populations, the Haldane selection intensity ratio is the equivalent of taking the negative log of the population's net fitness ($\overline{W}$ in Wright's terminology = S in Haldane's for this case) if the optimal karyotype's fitness is set equal to one.

In principle, then, the selection intensity for any quantitative effect on phenotype or fitness can be measured. If the genetic basis for the phenotype is known, so much the better; the Haldane method is not limited to phenotypic selection. It is for the geneticist to determine the genetic basis for fitness in order that genetic selection intensity may be measured. Haldane's examples of selection intensity range from near zero to 12%; the upper limit as in a simple balanced lethal system would be 69% (or 50% in non-logarithmic terms). Quite probably natural selection intensities are closer to the higher figure as exemplified in papers following.

If the intensity of selection is very great for many phenotypic characters, the population might become extinct. Haldane (163) discusses the question, "How severe a selection pressure can a population endure if applied at a single time?" Of course the question may also be asked in terms of genetically determined interactions of organism with environment: "How severe may the deleterious genetic load involving fitness characters become before the population suffers loss leading to extinction?"

Haldane's mathematical investigation assumes one or more genes to be rare because of a balance between mutation and selection. After a sudden environmental change the rare genotype becomes beneficial and the common genotype deleterious. A number of genetic deaths (loss of a gene from a population due to impairment of that gene's reproduction) must occur until the beneficial allele substitutes for the more prevalent less fit allele. If the proportion of deaths in any generation due to action of the ith locus (d_i) is summed for all generations, the cost of selection in readjusting the population's genotype to the new conditions is ascertained. Haldane finds that for the principal modes of heredity in haploid and diploid organisms, the cost of selection depends mainly on the small frequency of the beneficial gene at the time of environmental change and relatively little upon the genetic load factor (selective disadvantage of the less fit allele, that is Haldane's "k") as long as that load is small. If the load is large (if the deleterious allele is very low in fitness) it will take fewer generations for selection to accomplish the gene substitution so that fewer total genetic deaths will result. In other words, if the deleterious gene is nearly lethal, it will be wiped out very quickly in a haploid organism by very nearly making the population extinct ($D = 1$ almost), while in the long run a weakly deleterious gene will do more damage in total deaths provided its frequency at the start of selection is high enough, or conversely, that the favored allele is low enough in frequency. Haldane's "D" represents the total proportion of deaths for all generations, ranging from about 9.9 to 100 with 30 as a representative value for autosomal loci, or about 20 for sex-linked loci, that is, about thirty generations' worth of genetic deaths must occur to bring about the substitution of the favored allele for the deleterious one.

A recent paper of Haldane (165) presents more precise expressions for the cost of natural selection for cases of higher intensity (greater differences in fitness between genotypes). The cost is reduced by 30% if the detrimental genotype has half the fitness value of the beneficial genotype. Also, if the intensity of selection is changing slowly from unfavorable through neutral to favorable, almost all the cost (extra deaths due to selection) occurs before the favored gene has reached a frequency of $\frac{1}{2}$, and the total cost is very much reduced; in other words, selection is accomplished quicker with fewer total numbers lost in the process.

If selection pressure is applied by overloading the genotype with too rapid a mutation rate, the total cost of selection may be so great as to bring about extinction. Kimura (189) has discussed mathematically the balance between "a short-term requirement for a low frequency of mutation and a long term requirement for ample store of mutant genes" (Auerbach). His "substitutional, or evolution, load" (see also mutational and balanced loads) is the equivalent of Haldane's "cost of selection" but is expressed as determining an optimal mutation rate, which if too great will bring too much mutational damage for the population. That mutation rate depends on the rate of gene substitution per generation (1/300 in Haldane's estimate), degree of dominance (about 2% for average spontaneous lethal heterozygote fitness depression), and finally total mutational damage per gamete (about 2 for human gametes according to Morton, Crow, and Muller (256). The estimate of optimal mutation rate (5.8%) agrees well with that observed for Drosophila and estimated for man by Muller (262).

Modes of selection

The general ways in which characters or genotypes are favored or eliminated within populations by selection can be distinguished in three principal modes: 1) linear, dynamic, or directional; 2) centrifugal, or disruptive; and 3) centripetal, or stabilizing, selection (Simpson [22], Schmalhausen [20], and Waddington [25, 359]). Briefly, these modes refer respectively to: 1) alteration of the mean from parent to offspring in the direction of applied selection, a mode of greatest significance to breeders; 2) increase in genetic variance brought about by selecting from both extremes and eliminating intermediates, or the favoring of more than one optimum in a population; and 3) reduction in variance by selecting individuals near the mean as parents, or where a single optimum is favored coinciding with the central phenotypes of the distribution.

Examples of directional selection in the breeding of improved plants and animals are illustrated at length in the books of Lush (12), Lerner (10), and Falconer (4). The work of Mather and Harrison (234), the Robertsons (287, 289–298), and their colleagues (281, 282, 285–287) are especially important in establishing fundamentals. Principles discussed may apply equally to characters contributing to fitness in an environment changing in a linear direction. Under an environmental stress such as the presence of DDT in Drosophila populations for example linear selection is effective in both directions (Bennett [37], Crow [82], Merrell [244], and Oshima [267]). Disruptive selection is illustrated in the experiments of Thoday (346–348), Millicent and Thoday (251), and Waddington (356). Stabilizing selection experiments have been carried out by Falconer (139), Robertson (140), Waddington (359), and Thoday (346). Stabilizing selection in natural populations has been emphasized by Schmalhausen (20) with many noteworthy illustrations. Discussion of these experiments, responses and outcome of selection is postponed to the next section below.

It is important to remember that no experiment can be a simple case of only a single mode of selection. Admixture of different modes is unavoidable when ignorance of the fitness characters being selected and their genetic basis is so great.

The levels at which selection may act have been stressed by Sewall Wright (381): selection among genes, cells, clones, biparental organisms, within populations (demes), between populations, and among species must all be considered. It is the biparental level which "gives the great advantage that the evolution of the entire population, rather than a single lineage, is promoted by selection." Under constant selection conditions the multiple adaptive peaks directly result from the multiplicity of genic action (pleiotropy) and multiple allelism. Under changing conditions, it is obvious according to Wright "that the process of continual readaptation would be more effective if it could be based on the adaptiveness of genotypes or systems of these, than merely on the momentary net effects of the separate genes." Consequently, in the adaptations of several gene pools to communities or several demes within a species to the entire species area, interdeme selection leading to several adaptive consequences including races and species is of vast importance. Of course linear, disruptive, and stabilizing selection act at all these levels. The nature of selection, how it is applied, at what level, and for how many generations is critical in determining the response of the population.

Response to selection

The effectiveness of selection in producing a response within a previously unselected population depends on (232): 1) modes and intensity of selective forces, 2) action of genes as displayed in phenotypes being selected, and 3) the amount and architecture of genetic variability in the population. It is the adapted population following the action of natural selection or the "improved" population following artificial selection, the resultant of these three factors, which demonstrates the powerful yet varied nature of the entire process. With numerous genetic pathways available to selection, populations with various genotypes initially may respond with parallel outcome; or conversely under various selective pressures a single population may give diverse responses.

Linear response. Countless examples of linear response can be found (especially in the books cited in the preceding section). Linear adaptational response to a specific environmental stress is illustrated by the experiments of Bennett (37) with insecticide (DDT) resistance in Drosophila populations. His test of the "Darwinian" view (pre-adaptational, that some degree of hereditary variation in resistance must be present before exposure to the toxic agent) vs. the "Lamarckian" view (post-adaptational, that exposure induces physiological and/or hereditary resistance) is basic to selection theory and represents substantiation for biparental dioecious organisms of results obtained by the Lederbergs and Cavalli-Sforza in bacteria (see Adelberg's *Papers on Bacterial Genetics*).

For comparison with the results of sib-selection where flies selected were not exposed to the toxic agent, random mating large populations were maintained with no exposure (control), intermittent exposure, and regular exposure to DDT. While selection was effective in the latter two populations, it was much more so when selection was coupled with inbreeding. Presumably under sib-selection with only a single pair chosen per culture greater intensity is achieved than under random mating, plus a greater probability for exposure of homozygous genotypes, many of which had qualities favoring the direction of selection. The large random mating populations would respond by compromising general fitness with improved reaction to the environmental stress. The fact that after the final sib-selected generation in both high lines a mass unselected culturing brought the mean value of resistance to about half that attained demonstrates that progress had been made with sib-selection at the expense of general fitness. Also, an indication that high resistance was not brought about by selection for general elimination of harmful mutants nor the opposite susceptibility by selection for preservation of such mutants is shown by the statement that high lines had as many or more mutants (both in kind and frequency) than did the low lines. In spite of close inbreeding and intense selection, heterogeneity persisted though the limit for resistance or susceptibility seemed to have been reached. Bennett's demonstration of the genetic basis for the resistance by comparing the dominance relations of his stocks with those from other laboratories makes clear that the final adaptive outcome may be phenotypically the same even when numerous possible genetic pathways are available for the species.

It is also worth noting that in only one out of the four sib-selection lines, namely High Line #1, was progress consistently effective until after the "mass mating hiatus" when divergence became much more rapid. It is quite difficult to account for the relative inefficiency of selection for susceptibility before the mass mating and the improved rate of progress afterwards. Similar phenomena are common to many other selection experiments, the classic study being that of Mather and Harrison (234). These authors demonstrated in selecting for change in bristle number after an extreme drop in fertility and a relaxation of selection allowing for genetic recovery and presumably recombination of hypothetically selected linkages, that further progress could be made to new levels. Their results led to an explicit concept: additive genetic variance for a character is converted into linear response in the direction of applied selection until the variance component reaches zero or until the genetic system determining the population's fitness becomes so unbalanced or disturbed that fitness is lowered excessively. At that point further progress becomes impossible without acquiring new additive variance either by recombination of previously linked complexes (potential variability) or by mutation (although Waddington's findings were negative [360]). F. W. Robertson and Reeve (287, 298) offer an alternative explanation: according to them, Mather places too much reliance on particular linkages of polygenes which seem to resist recombination while under strong selection but which do recombine under mass mating. They feel that pleiotropic actions of iso-alleles in different backgrounds has not been thoroughly examined as a source of genetic variation. Rather than a large number of polygenes, a small number of major genes with varied effects in differing backgrounds which modify the major genes' pleiotropic effects may be responding to selection, that is differences created by selection will be conditional on the genetic background and will disappear when the background is changed. Unfortunately in the Robertson and Reeve model it is difficult to visualize the recovery of fitness following mass mating without a recombination mechanism at work. Doubtless pleiotropy of main complexes selected is important as these authors have shown, but the linkage relations of genes affecting fitness and those affecting the selected character must also be considered. Further discussion of these views will be found in the section on intrapopulational fitness and genetic architecture.

A. Robertson (289) has summarized the response to selection for characters which might be called "trivial" or "peripheral" with regard to fitness and characters of prime importance to fitness. Fisher showed that the rate of change in fitness was proportional to the additive variance in fitness; therefore, a population at selective equilibrium with its present environment has little or no variance in fitness by definition. Characters with minor phenotypic effect and little relation to fitness ("trivial" characters like bristle number in Drosophila) have large amounts of additive variance in natural or unselected populations. The lack of dominance for such characters might be expected from Fisher's theory of the evolution of dominance: selection to reduce the expressivity of deleterious genes in heterozygotes would affect only the fitness component of that heterozygote's expression and would be unlikely to affect that component of expression which has little relation to fitness. Consequently a basic additive pattern of genic action perhaps represents a lack of modification by natural selection. In response to selection for improvement in one of the major components of fitness, such as viability or fertility, there is often some utilizable genetic variation, but this response must be made at the expense of some other component of fitness because by definition we cannot increase over-all fitness. Therefore a negative additive genetic correlation may be expected between the main components of fitness at least as far as the statistical properties of the population is concerned. (Of course some genotypes like heterozygotes might be superior in nearly all major fitness components, so that negative correlation would not be expected for all genotypes.) Robertson then states: "If we take a 'peripheral' character and submit it to intense selection we are altering its position in relation to fitness so that it has now become a major fitness component. We shall eventually reach a new equilibrium position in which there is no further utilizable genetic variance left, in which the genetic situation is similar to that in natural fitness components. We can then expect negative additive genetic correlations between it and the natural fitness components." Cessation of response to selection does not mean genetic fixation necessarily, there may be considerable genetic variance still in potential form, perhaps tied up in linkages, or correlated with fitness in one way or another which might be freed by recombination or mutation.

Dobzhansky has emphasized the correlation between fitness and traits being selected (99): "It cannot be stressed too often that natural selection does not operate with separate 'traits.' . . . Now, the reproductive success of a genotype is determined by the totality of the traits and qualities which it produces in a given environment. . . . When a trait is a part of a complex, a system, or a syndrome of developmentally correlated characters, it is obviously the whole system which is favored or discriminated against by natural selection. This is not contradicted by the fact that some one character may be of paramount significance in deciding the success or failure of a genotype in a given environment and at a given time."

Lerner's model (9) of genetic homeostasis is strikingly similar to Robertson's model of relationship between fitness and characters. Both models reflect the association between individual and populational properties which are of importance to adaptation under natural selection. For further discussion, see the section on homeostasis.

Genetic assimilation. A highly significant response to linear selection was found by Waddington (355, 357, 358) in Drosophila and has been elaborated by Bateman (33, 34) and by Milkman (247–249), namely the response for environmentally evoked expressions of genotypes. In the earlier experiments Waddington selected for phenocopy ability (reduced crossvein making ability as expressed following a heat shock). With increased response, that is greater sensitivity to heat shock, imperfect crossveins became so common that even in the absence of the shock a percentage of flies failed to make perfect crossveins. The crossveinless characters, originally an ostensibly "non-hereditary," or "acquired," character became incorporated into the population's genotype. At the same time selection practiced against ability to phenocopy was also effective. Such results could only mean that 1) genetic variation tending to control highly specific interactions with precisely directed environments was present in the original population and 2) the tendency of selection was to bring about increase in frequency of genotypes with stabilizing developmental control of an originally labile process.

The repeatability of these experiments and the multiple locus nature of crossveinless control after such assimilation by selection has been demonstrated by Bateman and by Milkman. Genes controlling this effect were at least five in number and were located one on the X chromosome and two on each large autosome. Assimilation was brought about by selection of penetrance modifiers of these major genes in addition to increasing the major genes' frequencies. Penetrance has been shifted by bringing about a change in the position of the underlying age-response distribution relative to the thresholds for appearance of the character. Bateman points out that selection within two inbred lines produced no response and that assimilation depends as all selection responses on genetic variation initially present in the population. Such evidence clearly shows that the phenomenon is not a "Lamarckian" one.

Waddington's later experiments (357) on assimilation of the bithorax phenotype using ether treatment uncovered on two successive occasions a single dominant allele of the bithoraxoid-like (Bxl) gene. However, later in the up-selected line an X chromosome recessive which caused a maternal effect of bithorax appeared, plus some polygenic activity for haltere effects on both autosomes. Thereby a variety of genetic pathways disclosing control of apparently one principal phenotype (haltere-effect) were manifested. Another important point can be emphasized: following the second assimilation both up-selected, down-selected, and controls were given the heat shock treatment for crossveinless phenocopy. If lack of bithorax assimilation in the down-selected lines had been brought about by selection for increased homeostatic development, the down-selected line should have produced less crossveinless phenocopy (that is, be more resistant to environmental stress) than the control or up-selected lines. In fact up and down-selected lines were both more sensitive than wild type controls to heat shock. Their ability to withstand deleterious effects of ether treatment on survival had improved as expected, however. Consequently, one can conclude that selection had produced a developmental shift response and a better resistance to ether treatment but not simultaneously, *ipso facto*, an improved homeostasis of development (see Waddington's canalization experiments).

Stabilizing response. It has been pointed out by Waddington (25) that selection for individuals near the mean as parents may lead to two different responses: 1) elimination of genotypes controlling development of abnormal phenotypes (normalizing selection) and 2) elimination of genotypes which "render the developing animal sensitive to the potentially disturbing effects of environmental stresses" (canalizing selection). It would seem that selection of parents near the mean might involve both responses to some extent, but it may not if the environment is unchanging or if no conscious selection is performed to reduce phenotypic variance produced by environmental fluctuation.

Schmalhausen (20) has emphasized production of homeostatic, or developmentally regulated, forms by stabilizing selection, continual elimination of harmful mutants, or accumulation of modifiers which suppress the action of harmful mutants (cf. Fisher's evolution of dominance). His book cites evidence that selection is capable of transforming labile into stable traits as shown in the experiments of Kamshilov (1939): "By means of artificial selection, the mutation eyeless in Drosophila was made to appear equally in a moist culture medium (normal maximum) as well as a dry culture medium (normal minimum). This shows that development of a certain characteristic is rendered autonomous experimentally, and its expression becomes independent of changes in the external environment." Waddington also (359) has had some success in reducing the difference between high and low temperature Bar-eye phenotypes by family selection for genes controlling developmental buffering.

Mather (230) and Thoday (344, 345) have studied asymmetry and its variation in bilateral structures such as sternopleural bristles as a measure of developmental stability (to be discussed under homeostasis later). Selection for high and low asymmetry was effective but the mode of selection applied was linear, not stabilizing in the sense of removing extremes from each end of the parental distribution.

The more general variance reduction effect of stabilizing, or normalizing, selection has been illustrated by many experiments including Thoday's in this collection. Haldane's emphasis on this effect of selection has already been noted. Alan Robertson (290) discusses the general consequences of selection for phenotypic intermediates and the lower survival of extreme deviants: in summary, if the extremes have low fitness merely because they are extreme and not because they are a particular genotype, selection will act to fix loci which control the intermediate character. Such a response would amount to a linear one towards the mean of the phenotypic distribution and genetic variance will be reduced by selection. On the other hand if extremes have low fitness because they are homozygotes (net fitness being unconnected with the "intermediate character of optimal fitness" in the former case) genetic variability will be maintained (see heterosis section).

Falconer (139) and Falconer and Robertson (140) selected intermediates as parents to verify the change in phenotypic variance as a consequence of centripetal selection. In both experiments, on Drosophila bristle number and on mouse body weight respectively, little difference in variance could be ascribed to selection. In Thoday's (346) stabilizing line there was some reduction in phenotypic variance as well as reduction in vigor. Apparently Robertson's prediction that stabilizing selection for phenotypic intermediates will lead to fixation is borne out in Thoday's experiments.

Certainly it is clear that canalizing and normalizing selection can be different in both their responses and final products. If stabilizing selection acts against homozygotes, the familiar heterotic heterozygote is superior in fitness so that genetic variability and often polymorphism is maintained. It has often been demonstrated that heterozygotes may tend to be homeostatic; if homeostasis is a fitness property to be favored, both canalizing and normalizing responses will take place together.

Disruptive response. Response to selection which favors two or more optima in a population may be (Mather, 232) an "adjusted discontinuity at the phenotypic level which is a feature of both isolation and polymorphism. In the case of isolation, however, this is accompanied by disruption of the erstwhile common gene pool, whereas in polymorphism the morphic types continue to share a common gene pool (apart from any switch genes that may be involved), on whose adjustment the polymorphism indeed depends for its efficient working." While the disruption of gene pools is of tremendous significance to the origin of species, it is the polymorphic outcome for a single population which is pertinent to this discussion. Mather gives numerous illustrations of selection for two or more optima, the most ancient being the sex difference: "The males and females in a dioecious population, for example, will be subjected to different forces of selection and will represent different optimal phenotypes. These phenotypes are nevertheless tied together, for neither has any meaning except in relation to the other: each is an integral part of the other's effective environment. Thus there can be no tendency towards isolation because fertility and fitness depend on the cooperation of the two." Other examples include Batesian mimicry in which it benefits the mimetic species to be polymorphic. Since it is obviously disadvantageous for the mimic form to increase too much in frequency lest predators cease to learn to distinguish mimic from model on a "taste" basis, it must increase by becoming polymorphic. Thus, continues Mather, "wherever we can discern a sufficiently strong tie, or cooperation, between structures or entities, we might expect to find all the features of polymorphism." Dempster also (94) has examined the theoretical consequences of variable selective pressures in space or time which can maintain substantial additive genetic variance. This effect is what Mather refers to as cyclical disruptive selection. Levene (203) and Li (225) have also discussed the consequences of having more than one ecological niche available.

Thoday and his colleagues have carried out an especially informative series of experiments on disruptive selection (346–348, 251), the first extensive verification of Mather's discussion. In the account included in this collection, disruptive selection is performed using two mating schemes with the two optima being high and low sternopleural bristle number. Certainly preservation and in fact increase in variance in both D− and D+ lines in contrast with the loss of variance and fitness in the stabilizing line has substantiated theory. Most important was the responsiveness to directional selection in the D lines, showing the increased variance to be indeed due to increased genetic variability in the disruptive lines but due to reduced variability in the stabilized line. Heterogeneity of optima then can not only maintain, but also promote genetic diversity. Provision for initiation of polymorphic mechanisms within a single gene pool without isolation was demonstrated later (348): using a mating scheme which produced divergent directional response into two sub-populations with gene flow between them. In effect the selection applied uncovered a low chaeta-number second chromosome factor in the low sub-population with an allele of intermediate effect and a high chaeta-number third chromosome factor in the high sub-population with an allele of intermediate effect. The two sub-populations maintain their difference because the intermediate factors can migrate from one to the other without greatly affecting the difference in chaeta-number. In further experiments Thoday was able to demonstrate that particular linkages on chromosomes II and III were being maintained by disruptive or stabilizing selection despite considerable recombination of chaeta-number genes. In disruptive selection repulsion products were eliminated while in stabilizing selection they were favored and established in high frequency though linkages were in coupling phase initially (see further discussion under fitness and genetic architecture).

It is not suggested that disruptive selection is the only mechanism by which polymorphism arises; but since it has been shown to be quite possible and efficient, it could easily happen in nature and undoubtedly does take place. Habitat preference by different genotypes can maintain polymorphism (356, 202). In the evolution of dominance in the butterfly *Papilio dardanus* which has both mimetic and non-mimetic females (72) when both homozygote phenotypes are selected for, modifiers will be increased to perfect the dominance of one allele or the other within a local population.

INTEGRATING PROPERTIES OF POPULATIONS

For organisms that "share a common gene pool" in Mendelian populations the continuity of the genetic material is vastly greater than for asexually reproducing forms which have only relationships in lineage with their single parent individuals. The unitary nature of the sexually reproducing biparental population is evidenced in all its basic properties, for example, through the determinacy of random combinations of zygotes from gamete frequencies (Hardy-Weinberg-Chetverikov [68] equilibrium). It is the interrelatedness of combinations manufactured by the sexual processes (meiosis and assortment of gametes to zygotes) that make a fundamental network interconnecting and integrating the components of the population. It is that network upon which selection acts as well as upon the individuals and their component genotypes.

But in addition to these basic properties natural selection has had the opportunity to create closer integration through special interactions which can raise the net fitness of the population as a whole, that is, through heterosis, homeostasis, and epistatic (non-allelic) interactions. (See Dobzhansky [104] for a comprehensive discussion.)

Heterosis and balanced polymorphism

The outcome of selection favoring heterozygotes was worked out by Fisher in 1922. Stabilizing selection response in which homozygotes have lower fitness than heterozygotes permits the maintenance of genetic variation at a constant level determined by the relative fitness values of those homozygotes. Provision for balanced polymorphism, a dynamic equilibrium of genotype frequencies, is thereby established. Clearly both disruptive and stabilizing selection are capable of maintaining polymorphism, but the former depends on multiple optima (of which all optima could be homozygotes) while the second is "balanced" in that it relies on at least one heterozygote's superior fitness to supply homozygotes by segregation.

Examples of heterozygotes relatively superior to their respective homozygotes have been known since balanced lethals were found by H. J. Muller in 1918. Numerous examples of polymorphism in natural populations are given by Ford (1940, 1945) who defines it as "the occurrence together in the same habitat of two or more discontinuous forms of a species in such proportions that the rarest of them cannot be maintained merely by recurrent mutation." The question, however, arises as to how much of this observed polymorphism is stable and attributable to heterozygote superiority, how much to disruptive selection, and how much is unstable being either based upon rapidly changing environmental conditions or transient genotypic changes (random drift in small populations or the incompleted response to selection). Huxley's summary (174) describes quite comprehensively the widespread significance of polymorphism and our relative ignorance of the "nature of selective forces involved in most morphisms and of the genetic stability mechansims underlying them."

An extensive series of good clues to the heterotic basis for maintenance of "cryptomorphism" (Huxley's term for chromosomal arrangement heterogeneity in Drosophila) has emerged through the research of Dobzhansky and his colleagues. With the extensive collecting of flies in the *Drosophila pseudoobscura* complex through Western North America by Sturtevant and Dobzhansky from 1934 to 1939, a widespread polymorphism in the structural arrangement of chromosome III was described. Later in collections by Dobzhansky at Mt.

San Jacinto, California, seasonal changes and long term gradual changes in the relative frequencies of these arrangements were reported; but as late as 1941, Dobzhansky was not certain of the mechanism underlying the chromosomal polymorphism: "The character of the chromosomal variability in *D. pseudo-obscura*, and especially the temporal changes observed in its population, seem best accounted for on the assumption that the genetically effective sizes of these populations are small." It was after an analysis of the cyclic data of seasonal alteration of these arrangement relative frequencies that the hypothesis was put to the test that the frequency changes were a selection response on the part of the fly populations to the environmental cycle. Samples of flies containing the common gene arrangements from Pinon Flats, on the slopes of Mt. San Jacinto, were introduced into population cages as described by Wright and Dobzhansky (384). The results of this historical experiment demonstrated the constant equilibrium outcome of selective response: that the zygotic combinations of chromosomal inversions possessed specific fitness values in the laboratory environment and very probably must be far from neutral in their wild habitat. Constant equilibria at non-zero frequencies for the competing arrangements in population cages indicated that the indefinite persistence of several types in the same locality in nature could very possibly be the result of similar mechanisms. Wright's mathematical analysis offered three alternatives as possible selective modes at work: 1) the favoring of arrangement heterozygotes (now termed "heterokaryotypes" abbreviated "HTK's" to avoid confusion with genic heterozygotes) over both corresponding homozygotes ("homokaryotypes" abbreviated "HOK's") without differences between male and female in fitness; 2) sex differences in fitness but in females the superior HOK could be equal to the HTK; and 3) that HTK's may have been intermediate with fitness values varying with the changes in composition of the population. Within the limits of the data all three hypotheses fitted about equally well, but in view of the stable equilibrium attained with three arrangements the simplest mechanism, namely heterozygote superiority in both sexes was adopted tentatively.

This paper also represents one of the first attempts to estimate selective coefficients from sample data. It is worth noting that Wright's iteration by the least squares method works best if changes in "q" values follow a smooth curve. Unfortunately, sample frequencies may vary from generation to generation because of sampling error, random fluctuations in competing genotypes, and selection determined parameters. A simplified method based on Haldane's gene frequency ratio was worked out by Levene for a single pair of alleles (109), which has the advantage of estimating selection coefficients on segments of the total curve so that by inspection one can see whether the coefficients appear constant throughout or not.

It was plain that until these structural combinations were tested for their specific fitness properties, the exact mechanism bringing about net superiority for HTK's could not be ascertained decisively. In 1947 Dobzhansky reported the needed information: samples of eggs deposited by flies in the population cages and the larvae hatching from those eggs were grown under optimal conditions; at the late larval stage within samples the agreement with the Hardy-Weinberg expectation was good, but there was a slight consistent excess of HTK's surviving to that stage. Adult flies from the population cages when outcrossed to tester stocks for chromosome identification were very appreciably in excess of HTK's and deficient in HOK's. A selective elimination must therefore occur under cage conditions between egg and adult stage. There was no doubt that as far as net survival in preadult stages was concerned HTK's possessed heterosis. Later (1950) in natural populations (Pinon Flats) the same comparisons were made between egg samples laid by wild females and the frequency of adult karyotypes determined from outcrossing wild males to tester females, and again the excess of HTK's among adults was shown to be highly significant, thereby establishing Wright's first hypothesis in the interpretation of population cage outcome as well as a likely mechanism to explain constant frequencies, year after year, in the wild habitat.

Further population cage experiments on the same chromosomal arrangements from many other localities in California and Mexico were performed. Heterosis was again observed, but the adaptive values of the various karyotypes proved to be different for each locality. The mere sequence of chromosomal banding characterizing the particular arrangement then did not determine a constant selective value. Experiments were done in which chromosomes with different arrangements of diverse geographic origins were introduced into the same population cage (96, 109, 112). Heterosis occurred sporadically (heterozygotes were intermediate in viability, for example) and a diversity of selective outcomes was produced; in some cases complete fixation of one arrangement took place while in a few cases after some fluctuation new heterotic equilbria became established. The heterosis was not an intrinsic property of a gene arrangement. "It is the result of interaction of complexes of polygenes carried in chromosomes with different gene arrangements. Within the population of each geographic region, the polygene complexes in the chromosomes have become mutually adjusted, or 'coadapted', by a process of natural selection." Such coadapted complexes do not exist when chromosomes of different geographic origin are mixed in laboratory populations, and consequently adaptive novelties may be created: new races have appeared, which are adapted uniquely, each to its own genotypic background and physical environment (96).

Evolutionists have used the terms "microevolution" and "macroevolution" (Goldschmidt, 1940, see Simpson, 22) as if they were completely unrelated phenomena, but Simpson in 1953 suggested that "clarity might now be improved by abandoning them." However, with new definitions for these terms and insertion of a new one, "mesoevolution," Dobzhansky (96) revived them to describe phenomena which are either creative and unique in evolution (meso- or macroevolution) or repeatable, reversible, and predictable (microevolution). Specifically, "Mesoevolution involves alteration in more or less numerous genetic units, emergence of new adaptively integrated genotypes, and appearance of at least new races, or of new species and genera . . . [It] may be rapid enough to be observed by human observers." The attainment of new equilibria in population cages containing chromosomal arrangements from diverse localities he classifies as mesoevolutionary.

The delicate balance of these coadapted inversion systems has been demonstrated 1) by population cage studies in which temperature, food conditions (yeast species), degree of crowding, and the presence of other gene arrangements in the same population have been varied; and 2) by fitness analysis in which portions of the fly life cycle are tested under various culture conditions. For a summary of this work, see daCunha (90) and (97, 102, 321, 324, 325).

Heterosis then is not a simple property of inversion heterozygosity, intrinsic to the zygotic combination *per se*, but must have been acquired and perfected under specific local ecological conditions through natural selection. Each complex from a local population differs in gene contents from every other so that the response from mixing complexes is indeterminate, or unpredictable. Such historically determined heterotic effects have been termed "euheterosis" in contrast with the well known superiority phenomenon often associated with crossing inbred strains and resulting in fitness loss following inbreeding of the F_1, termed "luxuriance" by Dobzhansky (5, 97). Whether the two phenomena have the same genetic basis is a current problem.

It is difficult to see how balanced chromosomal polymorphism can originate in a population without initial heterozygote advantage accompanying the introduction of a new inverted sequence (or new "mutation"). This problem has been discussed in mathematical terms by Haldane (162) and Bodmer and Parsons (40). Apparently some heterozygote advantage is essential for a new allele to become established in a population unless inbreeding or small breeding size raises the frequency sufficiently. In large populations heterosis must accompany the origin of the inversion or allele to insure its survival, increase, and subsequent adaptive improvement. In other words, selection may capitalize on natural "luxuriance" when it occurs and thereby tend to increase the amount of heterozygosity still more.

Further properties of balanced polymorphism with multiple alleles have been examined by Levene (207), who simplified Wright's equations (384), by Li (225), Mandel (228), and Owen (270).

Finally the question of stability of polymorphism arises. Two aspects have been argued in the literature: 1) if high net fitness of HTK's is the result of selection in which cyclic environmental fluctuation is common, or numerous environments are available to the species, so that homozygotes are favored at different times or places, then in a constant uniform environment heterozygosity should tend to be lost (Lewontin, 219, 221); 2) if "mutation" can produce an allele (or inversion) such that fitness of the new allele in homozygous condition equals or exceeds that of the old heterozygote, the polymorphism should be lost in favor of monomorphism with the new allele fixed (Muller, 260). In the first case inversion polymorphism may not be the result of cryptic disruptive selection since many fitness property studies have shown HTK's superior to HOK's (321, 326, 253, 339). Superior HTK's are often homeostatic; if homeostasis is an essential component of fitness in fluctuating environments, the first case may be quite valid. Long term population cage studies have indicated that polymorphism is stable (116, 210, 324), illustrating that "ample genetic variance and constant environmental conditions do not of themselves produce monomorphism from polymorphism" (210). Heterozygote superiority may be conferred upon many phenotypic fitness qualities only one of which is the homeostatic quality. There is no doubt that homeostasis would be advantageous to a population trying to survive in a variable or oscillating environment. Of course, in spite of the investigator's attempts to keep laboratory conditions "constant", there is much evidence that a variety of niches does exist in experimental population cages. Attainment of adaptive polymorphism may be a response to such variation within the closed system.

The second case proposed by Muller is more difficult to verify. Dobzhansky and Pavlovsky (116) report several instances in which long term polymorphisms have remained stable and suggest that greater adaptational plasticity derived from their *genetic* homeostasis (Lerner's self-regulation of populations) may be their secret to success. All these considerations for chromosomal adaptive polymorphism may apply equally to single loci (258, 259, 308) or greater genetic complexes which show heterozygote superior fitness. It may be that the fitness conferred upon their carriers by heterozygosis for such single loci or for balanced "supergenes" is not often equalled in homozygotes.

A single gene balanced polymorphism in man is well documented in the extensive analysis of Allison, especially with sickle cell trait and its resistance to malaria among the Negro tribes of Africa (26–29). The short paper included in this collection summarizes the frequency data on the H^s and H^c genes in the regions of subtertian endemic malaria. Maintenance of the polymorphism by selection is abundantly clear by the high frequency (up to 20% for the H^s allele) in only those regions plus the reduction in frequency among Negros of West African descent living in the United States. While the physiological cause of resistance among H^s/H^+ individuals is still uncertain, Allison has demonstrated that children under 1 year of both normal and sickle cell trait types have equal parasite counts while children between age 1 and 4 differ markedly, the H^s/H^+ children showing a much lower parasite count, so that most protection against malaria probably comes between birth and reproductive age. The third common allele (H^c) occurs in high frequency in some tribes also (13.5% in the Dagomba tribe); though it never attains the high frequency of H^s, it is negatively correlated with H^s: the interpretation most likely is that H^s and H^c are allelic with a heterozygote producing almost as severe an anemia as the H^s/H^s individual. Allison proposes that H^c is an allele of recent origin. His data fit fairly well a regression equation worked out by Penrose et al., but suggest that the fitness values may need slight adjustment. Another interesting polymorphism recently described (29) is that of glucose-6-phosphate dehydogenase deficiency, which is similar to H^s in that heterozygous children have lower parasite counts than normal children, but the factor is sex-linked so that it is disadvantageous for males. It is positively correlated with H^s and thalassemia which may indicate increased advantage to double heterozygotes in malarial regions.

Genetic and developmental homeostasis

In spite of "cryptomorphism" and genetic diversity within natural populations of many animals, the wild type presents a sufficiently uniform phenotype
to merit naming as a species.   If the genotypes of wild populations are revealed
by inbreeding or special techniques, the phenotypic uniformity is found to be a
façade, an end product of development arrived at presumably through diverse
genetic pathways.   Individuals of most populations present to the observer
what has been called the "adaptive norm" (20) and is reflected in taxonomic keys.
The adaptive norm, however, is a well-adapted more or less stable complex of
genetic diversity within the population.   As pointed out by Mather (230) and
Thoday (344) developmental flexibility is the capacity of the individual during
ontogeny to develop a phenotype specifically adapted to the local conditions
buffered internally to counteract the upsetting tendencies of environmental
stresses.   It is important to note that the implication is not that homeostasis
brings rigid stability to development; on the contrary as stressed by Dobzhansky
in the discussion of Thoday (344): "homeostatic changes enable the body to
follow its normal developmental paths, but they do not necessarily result in
morphological stability . . . one of the most important kinds of homeostatic
reactions is that which makes the organism react to environmental change by
switching from one historically determined developmental path to an alternative
path . . . " permitting life and development of the organism to proceed unimpeded by environmental disturbances.

Dobzhansky and Wallace (125) followed by Cordeiro and Dobzhansky (79)
demonstrated that the combining abilities of random pairs of different chromosomes ("heterozygotes") within various species of Drosophila gave uniform
survival despite environmental variation compared with significantly variable
survival of homozygotes.   They proposed as an extension of the coadaptation
hypothesis that homeostatic adjustments are common to heterozygotes more
than to homozygotes, and since homeostasis must be an important component
of fitness in nature, the genotypes of Mendelian populations are further integrated by the auto-regulation of development in heterozygotes.   Lerner (9)
amassed much evidence in favor of that view (developmental homeostasis and
Waddington's canalization) and in addition extended the concept of integrated
gene pools to include the phenomenon of populational self-regulation (genetic
homeostasis) which is observed in the familiar outcome of linear selection when
attempts to shift the genetic balance by selection are resisted until new genetic
combinations can be released from the "potential" state into a "free" state by
recombination.

Thoday (344, 345) has called attention to the numerous terms used by various
authors for this effect and tested the proposition that heterozygosity alone is
responsible for improved buffering.   One view states that "there is some special
virtue of the heterozygous state that permits versatility of development of the
individual not open to homozygotes . . . The alternative view involves no special
virtue of the heterozygous state except its classic virtue, that it permits genetic

flexibility because it permits segregation, and would make contemporary, demonstrably superior heterozygotes superior because the species involved have a past history of outbreeding and hence an evolved heterozygous balance." (cf. *relational balance* of Mather and *coadaptation* of Dobzhansky and Wallace.) Thoday relies on sternopleural asymmetry as a measure of developmental homeostasis since Mather found F_1's between inbred lines were less asymmetrical than their parents. He finds for the X chromosome interpopulational heterozygotes to have greater asymmetry than intrapopulational even though they are presumably equal and possibly greater in total heterozygosity. In discussing Beardmore's data and further experiments which are included in this collection (345), Thoday showed that selection for bristle number not only brought about decline in homeostasis as measured by asymmetry within selected lines but also in their F_1's. Heterozygosity did not by itself bring about homeostasis, therefore, if bristle asymmetry is accepted as a measure of homeostasis. Either selection was direct for "asymmetry" genes in both lines or the balance of linked genic complexes deteriorated. The weight of evidence was in favor of the latter, which again reinforces the coadaptation hypothesis.

Further evidence that asymmetry of bristles is of some importance as a measure of coadaptive homeostasis and consequently to fitness, comes from Beardmore's experiments (35) in constant and fluctuating temperatures. F_1 hybrids between inbred lines which had been kept at constant temperature for generations showed less asymmetry in constant than in fluctuating temperatures. Second generation descendents of wild-captured flies and F_1 hybrids between them, however, displayed less asymmetry in fluctuating than in constant temperatures, but after fifteen generations in the laboratory this difference reversed. Populations containing complexes buffering development under fluctuating conditions then may lose them when the populations are maintained under constant conditions. Free recombination and selection for balanced complexes beneficial to a constant environment effected the alteration rather rapidly.

Lewontin (218) has attempted to develop the homeostasis concept more broadly, almost equating it with "adaptive value" (see Dempster's comments, 93). Whether or not we agree with the broader definition, Lewontin's data are very pertinent to the problem of bristle number symmetry (correlation between two parts of the same organism) as a measure of developmental stability. Using bristle numbers on two abdominal sternites, Lewontin obtained the reverse of expectation if morphological uniformity between individuals is a measure of buffering ability: variance in homozygotes which are undoubtedly not as homeostatic as heterozygotes was less than that in F_1 hybrids between lines or F_2 populations. However, the difference between sternal segments was consistently less in heterozygotes. As in the case of Mather and Thoday's right-left bristle symmetry, correlation between two parts of the same organism might be a concomitant of superior homeostatic adjustment.

The problem of finding an easily observed character with which to measure developmental homeostasis is very difficult. Reeve (285, 286) has objected to the use of bristle asymmetry on the grounds that the level of asymmetry can be reduced by selection well below that of typical wild stocks; and in selection for twenty generations to modify the ventral-dorsal bristle difference, the left-right side asymmetry was not affected. Certainly in both cases long selection should reduce the homeostatic balance. Reeve states, "It still remains an open question, then, whether the number of sternopleurals is an adaptive character in the sense that it matters to the individual or population whether it has one or two bristles more or less on each side, or in the sense that the optimum number of bristles is different in different environments."

Perhaps the more difficult but more direct measures of fitness give the best indications of homeostasis, namely those illustrated by Dobzhansky and Levene's data (110, 117) on viability in several different macro- and micro-environments. There is no question of viability's being an essential component of fitness, and the variance comparisons between homozygotes and heterozygotes were very clearly demonstrative that heterozygotes are better buffered, having higher viability more consistently than homozygotes even when homozygotes are chosen for normal or supervitality. Coadapted chromosomes "are more often many-sided and versatile in their adaptedness, hence able to live successfully in a broader range of environments" than homozygotes which are "narrow specialists" doing well in a restricted range of environments. In the question of polymorphism stability, this is perhaps why a homozygote will never profit under the genetic architecture available to these diploid outcrossing species: for such a species in a diversity of environments, a valuable component of fitness is homeostasis.

Fitness and genetic architecture of populations

General fitness considerations. Darwin's concept of relative fitness, or ability to survive and produce progeny which survive and reproduce (see Fisher's Malthusian parameter) is a concept easily accepted but very difficult to comprehend. Thoday (343) has discussed its biological significance in broad generalization which can serve well as a framework within which to model future definitions: according to Thoday, a fitness definition should not be restricted to the contemporary environment since the fitness of each generation depends on the fitness of its descendants. While in short term survival, selection acts to stabilize the genotype as an adaptation to contemporary conditions, in longer term the population with well stabilized genotypes must be capable of variation, that is, fitness should include genetic and phenotypic flexibility (including developmental buffering against environmental variation). An improvement in fitness can be regarded as a compromise in the antagonism between stability and variability, and highest fitness would include maximization of both: 1) "diploidy resolves some of the conflict because much genetic variation is stored by heterozygosity, 2) a balanced polygenic system provides relative phenotypic uniformity and maintenance of adaptation with loss of genetic flexibility."

Under natural selection a population containing some genetic variance in fitness will improve until that fitness is maximized, or the variance in fitness is minimized (Fisher's fundamental theorem). Buzzati-Traverso's extensive analysis (52) of fitness changes in very densely crowded populations of Drosophila indicated an improvement of about 800% over eighty generations owing to the evolution of new polygenic systems from just two original strains (a wild inbred and an X chromosome double mutant). Even after both mutants were eliminated from the population several fitness components continued to improve. Remarkably enough, F_1 hybrids between the original strains showed considerable heterosis, in fact higher fertility values than for the populational flies at the end of selection. The question as to whether the populational improvement simply resulted from partial retention of the F_1 hybrid genotype or from a stepwise selection of the most favorable polygenic combinations in stages was answered in favor of the latter from several bits of evidence: 1) fecundity changes were progressive in the population; 2) the rate of elimination of the mutants was much faster when flies derived from the experimental populations were put in competition with those mutants; and 3) the biotic potential as shown by comparison with the calculated logistic curve of population growth improved. The conclusion was that natural selection had "produced from the combination of the two original genotypes new polygenic constellations which ensured a better viability to their carriers and thereby made the populations progressively better adapted to their environments." High adaptedness, while it had some heterotic basis, most probably was due to selection for properly adjusted combinations both intra- and interchromosomal.

That simple "luxuriance," or hybrid vigor, as seen in crossbred F_1's can contribute to the continued biological success of a group has been demonstrated by Carson and his students (63, 66, 67, 336, 388): "Thus a population of mutant individuals held under strictly uniform environmental conditions was maintained by natural selection at an equilibrated size. Following introduction of one haploid set of wild type autosomes, the size of the population trebled in three generations and has remained essentially so since, simultaneously retaining all five mutants at substantial frequencies in the experimental populations." The biomass of the experimental populations exceeded the level of the wild type control population which was used as a donor. Simple hybrid vigor, then, may well be immediately exploited in a population, be retained without breakdown, and become an ingredient of coadapted complexes. Ultimately it may serve as a basis for further improvement. Final coadaptation must take advantage of favorable non-allelic interactions as well and accommodate the population for a compromise between genetic flexibility and stability.

Lewontin's (217) study of the relative fitness of genotypes in mixed and pure cultures concluded that viability was a function of the relative frequency of other genotypes coexisting in any culture, the viability of any particular combination not being predictable on the basis of the viability of the coexisting genotypes when tested in isolation. His discussion of the evolutionary implications of this "symbiotic" effect includes a change in fitness as the genetic structure of the population is altered. Lewontin shows that if fitness is a function of genotype frequency, a stable polymorphism may result. The situation is similar if each of the genotypes occupies particular subniches in the culture with each genotype differing in fitness from one subniche to another. Levene (203) and Li (225) have discussed the dynamics of such situations, all of which represent cases of disruptive selection.

How much improved fitness is due to primary genetic causes (balanced heterozygous complexes) and how much to ecological (secondary, or "symbiotic" relations between members of the population) is an open question. Apparently both may be important in total fitness.

Linkage, recombination, and non-allelic interaction. Evidence is overwhelming that coadaptation depends to a considerable extent on specific linkage relations and epistatic interactions selected for high fitness, that is to primary genetic causes. Carson (in 13) has emphasized the significance of genetic flexibility in the following: "The amount of recombination permitted . . . is best looked upon as an adaptive property which is under the control of natural selection. Too much recombination is inadaptive because it tends to break up adaptive complexes of genes which have been welded together by natural selection. This [process] reduces the immediate fitness of the organism. In order to survive, a species must maintain high immediate fitness, and it is not surprising that devices limiting or preventing recombination are common in species populations. (cf. chromosomal balanced polymorphism) . . . it appears that too little recombination jeopardizes the ability of the species to meet drastic changes in environmental conditions over very long periods of time. Most organisms which have survived to the present day display a balance between these two forces."

To compare relative recombination potential of populations, Carson (62) introduced a measure (index of free crossing over) suitable in theory to any organism in which crossing-over blockage regions could be described. With salivary gland analysis of chromosomal arrangement heterogeneity, this index (cf. also Darlington's 1937 recombination index and White's comments, 376) becomes a more accurate tool than for non-Dipteran organisms. The correlation between geographic distribution and free crossing-over index (marginal populations with greatest free recombination contrast with central populations of least free recombination) draws attention to the adaptive significance of genetic flexibility. The same considerations apply to many other species of Drosophila (*willistoni*, *pseudoobscura*, and *persimilis*, 90–92). According to White (376), however, this correlation is not true for several species of grasshoppers; that is, populations which are clearly peripheral in the distribution area are highly polymorphic cytologically. In several species of Drosophila little or no cytological polymorphism is displayed except in restricted localities (*melanogaster*, *repleta*, and *virilis*, for example). Among those species which do, only one or two chromosomes out of the complement may exhibit polymorphism to any extent (as the III and X in the *D. pseudoobscura* complex). Chromosomes not displaying polymorphism nevertheless are highly variable genetically. The devices of chromosomal arrangement polymorphism serve to "capture" separate heteroses in large blocks, or complexes, thereby reducing the number of relatively unfit homozygotes resulting from recombination. The more expensive free recombination can be borne more easily 1) in large populations (such as in cosmopolitan species) or 2) in marginal situations where extra genetic flexibility is advantageous for rapid adjustment. From the genetic standpoint it may be that in some chromosomes of average species there are favored linked complexes which can resist recombination or more commonly, such a highly heterozygous milieu may exist that genic homozygotes will have extremely low probability of formation even where recombination is completely free, heterozygosity and general relational balance within and between chromosomes being favored by selection. The studies of Carson (65, 66, 67) are highly instructive: In response to selection and total production (biomass) among laboratory populations derived from marginal or central range wild populations of *D. robusta*, it was the marginal populations which displayed greater genetic variability by responding to selection for rate of activity, but the central range populations showed the higher degree of biomass productivity and retained a chromosomal polymorphism tenaciously. Fitness at the periphery of this species' range may be said to be concerned principally with providing genetic flexibility in exploiting numerous specialized environments while at the center of its distribution fitness is maximized by stabilizing the phenotype through "heterotic buffering."

A summary of the extensive experiments of Dobzhansky and his colleagues (111, 123, 204, 323, 318, 369), on the release of variability from recombination between "good viability" chromosomes is given by Spiess (322). While homozygous recombinants such as those observed in these studies are probably never produced in wild populations of these species, the array of such homozygotes measures the relative diversity in terms of their ability to engender new linked combinations and the resulting non-allelic interactions of those combinations. There is no doubt that a substantial portion of the genetic variation controlling viability in wild populations arises from intrachromosomal recombination even when the chromosomes before recombination are selected for their normal effects. In all species tested average viabilities were lower following recombination, and the non-additive component of variance was consistently significant, facts which indicate considerable epistatic interaction between linked loci controlling viability. Several isoallelic differences must exist between these samples of chromosomes and consequently the populations from which they were extracted are likely to have been highly heterozygous and probably "balanced" (97, 369), though in cases where much less genetic variance was engendered the populations may have tended toward the "classical" structure.

The magnitude of change after recombination depends on 1) the number of loci recombined; 2) ability of those loci to recombine; 3) additive effects of those loci; 4) their dominant effects (not measured in the above experiments with homozygous viability only); and 5) their epistatic interaction effects both intrachromosomal and interchromosomal. The hope of ascertaining the number of loci recombined and their ability to recombine seems remote, although the approach of Breese and Mather (42, 43) gives some assurance of ultimate solution.

In *D. pseudoobscura* the range of variation produced following recombination was great enough to include extremes of viability such as lethality ("synthetic lethals"). Some lethals so produced were tested for linkage position with markers on chromosome II and shown to be "synthetic" rather than positional (123). Wallace and others (369) reported statistical evidence for synthetic lethals on chromosome II of *D. melanogaster*, but considerable doubt was cast on the existence of synthetic lethals by Hildreth when he was unable to demonstrate them on the X and III chromosomes of that species. Spiess (322) suggested that the Wallace results for chromosome II vs. Hildreth's results for chromosome X and III might be reconciled if these chromosomes were in fact different in their abilities to release extreme recombinants. Breese and Mather (43) drew attention to the highly significant interactions for viability on chromosome III which they observed, and they quite correctly pointed out that their earlier results with the morphological character (chaeta number) which had shown very low interaction on chromosome III was a feature of the character, not of the chromosome. Fitness characters like viability could well be expected to depend on considerable non-allelic interaction.

Subsequently Gibson and Thoday (150) have reported recombinational lethals on chromosome II derived from their disruptive selection population.

Therefore if heterozygosity of heterotic loci is to be maintained in nature, a high order multiple allelic system and consequently a vast number of linkages must exist, any one of which would be selected against in homozygous condition unless it were preadapted for its environment by chance. For inversion systems heterozygosity could be maintained at fewer loci and/or with fewer alternative alleles than for systems lacking crossover suppressors within which linkage equilibrium has to be postulated.

The importance of non-allelic interaction on fitness has been well documented; the selective favoring of particular linkages (intrachromosomal) and of independently assorting compounds (interchromosomal) have been found: Fisher (143) calculated that compounds of certain non-allelic dominant factors in populations of grouse locusts were selectively eliminated at a rate estimated at 40% per generation; Levitan (213–216) has found compounds of linked inversions selected for in *D. robusta*, Brncic has found the same phenomenon in *D. pavani* (46) and Stalker in *D. paramelanica* (329). The dynamics of systems guided by epistatic interactions have been examined and reviewed by Kimura (188) and Lewontin and Kojima (223), who conclude that when "epistasis is present, linkage must be fairly tight in order for there to be any effect on the final equilibrium. If linkage is tighter than the value demanded by the magnitude of epistatic deviations there may be *permanent linkage disequilibrium* of considerable magnitude, and the gene frequencies may also be affected." The dynamics analysis of this higher order of complexity (simultaneously segregating systems of inversions) is examined by Lewontin and White (224) for certain grasshopper populations (*Moraba scurra*) from New South Wales. The paper illustrates the "topographic" method of analysis (cf. Wright's metaphorical "adaptive peaks and valleys"). The unexpected outcome was that each population sampled was at a minimax point of the adaptive "surface"— that is, not at highest net fitness. Possible reasons for apparent equilibrium at such an unstable point may well be that the equilibrium is maintained by a combination of gene-frequency dependent selection and yearly fluctuation in environmental factors. The basis for populational fitness then may be a response to disruptive selection, that is, several optima or "symbiotic" relations between members of the population.

Integration of gene pools and hybrid breakdown

If coadaptation is a local population's acquisition, or a balance of genic complexes leading to high fitness under selection, when such complexes are mixed the balance should be easily upset with a lowering of fitness. Dobzhansky and Pavlovsky (96, 112) demonstrated a loss in chromosomal balanced polymorphism when arrangements from widely separated localities are mixed in population cages. An extension of those experiments was devised by Brncic (44) in order to describe the effects on viability of mixing identical chromosomal arrangements of *D. pseudoobscura* from widely separated geographic localities. Although the F_1 hybrids between populations were luxuriant, the F_2 and F_3 viabilities were much lower than either parental viability average. Brncic further demonstrated that this breakdown of high viability was an effect of recombination by crossing-over between the chromosomes of diverse origin, the lowest viability being found in the individuals in which both chromosomes of a pair were crossover products. It seems evident that the internal balance of genic complexes selected within the respective localities for high fitness was thereby broken down.

Wallace and Vetukhiv (371) have proposed that in addition to integration levels of allelic (heterotic and homeostatic) and non-allelic epistatic interactions, a third level of coadaptation may exist: the entire gene pool through selection based on the action of genes in the heterozygous condition. Such a proposition amounts to a very high order integration derived from the lower orders of integration upon which it depends. Vetukhiv's experiments (351–354) extended those of Brncic with measurement of many fitness properties, all of which displayed the same hybrid breakdown following recombination of diverse gene pools.

Wallace (362) working with *D. melanogaster* developed further the gene pool coadaptation hypothesis. Three levels of recombination were designed with varying amounts of "heterozygosity" (defined as proportional amounts of loci from diverse populations). Three important facts emerge: 1) inter-populational F_1 hybrids had higher viabilities than did flies obtained by crossing different lines of the same population; 2) among the classes which were 100% heterozygous are found the highest and the lowest viabilities of the entire experiment, so that again it was demonstrated that heterozygosity alone does not confer highest viability; and 3) with increased "derivation" (recombination) between population sets of chromosomes viability tended to decrease, as would be expected if balanced complexes were breaking down in the process.

The luxuriance of the F_1 is not always a feature of an interpopulational cross. King (191, 192) has hybridized populations selected for DDT resistance without obtaining an increased resistance in the F_1, though F_2's had lower mean tolerance and increased variance, facts which were interpreted as evidence of integrated gene pools. Merrell (242), by contrast, did find superior fecundity both in control and in resistant line cross F_1's and increased resistance in the resistant line F_1's; but he interprets these maxima as evidence against coadaptation hypothesis. He states there is "no evidence of hybrid breakdown in the F_2," although his data show a lowering of resistance in both control and resistant F_2's as well as a lowering of fecundity in the resistant F_2's. The lowering is not drastic but it appears significant.

A clear distinction should be made between superiority in the characters which have been selected and characters of general fitness. There seems to be little doubt that increased heterozygosity is luxuriant in that numerous cases of specific traits' being maximized are recorded, but fitness is another matter: while some components of fitness can be amplified by outcrossing, the total net fitness has to be a matter of long term adjustment and the coadapted system probably does not incorporate more than a compromise of fitness traits for the conditions under which the population exists. An absolute measure of heterozygosity is needed in order to make certain of these phenomena. The experiments described by Wallace indicate strongly that a distinction must be made between heterozygosity attained by "accident" and that attained by selection, or "relational balance." The former can be heterotic for a number of traits and may be utilized to some extent in attaining adaptation in a hybrid population. However, the outcome of selection may be indeterminate; in contrast, the latter heterozygosity with a selective history should bring about a determinate outcome under selection. A finding that "accidental" heterosis occurs after crossing two diverse populations does not by itself rule out the possibility that the two populations were internally coadapted. The finding that heterozygotes with mixed interpopulational linkages are lower in fitness than random intrapopulational combinations seems to favor the hypothesis of high level integration of each gene pool provided that the total number of heterozygous loci are about equal in the two cases.

The viability tests of Wallace would indicate that two coadapted systems may when crossed produce improved viability, but no experiments were devised to discover whether such heterosis is retained in subsequent generations. As in Buzzati-Traverso's (52) experiments, it is clear that luxuriant heterosis is not retained at least for the viability trait. Quite probably under natural selection the population must compromise and obtain maximum fitness for the net effects of all it physiological capabilities. Too high an attainment in one fitness property may easily bring about negative correlations in other fitness traits, as Robertson pointed out (289).

While absolute heterozygosity cannot yet be measured, Wallace has attempted to find out whether heterozygosity alone has any heterotic effect on viability. Owing to the results of his irradiation experiments (referred to in the section on irradiation), and the known high heterozygosity of coadapted systems, experiments were designed (365, 366) for measuring viability changes following acquisition of new mutants. The small but positive increment in viability among flies heterozygous for an unirradiated chromosome and a chromosome which had been exposed to 500 r of X rays was consistent and significant. These observations which tend to indicate that heterozygosity does in general increase viability, Wallace has interpreted as meaning that heterozygosis among gene loci of most individuals of a crossmating population may reach an extremely high figure. These results are at variance with those obtained by Muller and Falk (263, 141) who used different radiation techniques; also they contrast with the common observation that most mutations produced by radiation are deleterious often by about 1 or 2% in heterozygous condition (331) though occasional heterotic mutants occur. Clearly the entire matter is still open, and the resolving of such differences can only be effected by careful reexamination. The student should realize that discrepancies over such issues and their resolution by careful experiment are the most vital part of population genetics.

Populational fitness concepts

In the field studies of daCunha, Dobzhansky, and co-workers (91, 92) on neotropical Drosophila species (*D. willistoni* and its relatives), a correlation between levels of chromosomal polymorphism and distribution range, or availability of adaptive niches, was found. Their working hypothesis was stated as follows: "One of the methods whereby a living population may achieve a mastery of its environment is by means of adaptive polymorphism. This hypothesis is a corollary to the simple consideration that no one genotype is likely to be superior to all others in all ecological niches which are potentially accessible to a Mendelian population in a given geographic region. Successful settlement of these niches and exploitation of their adaptive opportunities may, therefore, be facilitated by genetic diversification." Consequently a multiplicity of chromosomal arrangements might enable a species to exploit a variety of habitats more efficiently than a monomorphic species.

Numerous exceptions to this hypothesis have been recorded including a few anomalous populations of *D. willistoni*, the species upon which these authors based their hypothesis, populations of *D. subobscura* (151, 335), and White's grasshopper populations (cf. Carson's index of free recombination). White (375) calls attention to the fact that such exceptions may be due to differences in contraction or expansion of the species range. Of course, chromosomal monomorphism does not mean necessarily genic monomorphism (cf. *D. melanogaster*, above). In Carson's words (65), highly polymorphic populations may be regarded as having reached a relatively stable state of adaptedness but at the same time of specialization adapting to the varied ecological niches which they have mastered in a long-occupied territory (implying response to disruptive selection).

Dobzhansky (3) was careful not to imply that one could compare total populations as to relative fitness, or adaptedness. His statements did signify that he recognized genic and cytological diversity as a reflection of ecological diversity, a response of genetic mechanisms within populations to numerous selective demands. Cain and Sheppard (56, 58) took exception to what they felt was a populational fitness comparison, and while their objection was not initially well-founded, the ideas they propounded are essential to the discussion of evolutionary mechanisms since they uncover a concept which had not been dealt with experimentally before: namely how populations can be compared for relative fitness. In interpopulational selection (see Wright, 380, 381, 382) especially such a value becomes important. Li (225) emphasized that selection dynamics has been entirely modelled on intrapopulational phenomena and that comparisons between populations cannot be made on the basis of net fitness values of genotypes competing within a population. As to the problem of which came first, polymorphism or numerous niches, some remarks by Fisher (145) indicate that polymorphism may have arisen to randomize the attack of predators, or antagonists.

Experimental comparisons of total population relative fitness has only recently been undertaken: for example, the studies of Wallace (368) and Beardmore et al. (36). Wallace states: "The measure one really wants to make when describing a population is that which refers to its ability to perpetuate itself through time under a certain set or sequence of environmental conditions . . . It would be informative to observe a population for a number of generations in a variable environment and attempt to estimate the probability that, faced with an array of environmental conditions of which the several observed ones represent a random sample, the population will continue to exist for a specified number of generations" (see Thoday, 343).

Wallace's technique combined the total production of offspring from single pair matings with the proportion of fertile cultures per population for eight different populations over a period of ten generations; thus he incorporated more components of fitness than in his previous work which was primarily limited to viability of larvae and pupae (363). By running populations in pairs, populational fitness comparisons were obtained by comparing the total outputs of each population with respect to a standard (each population in turn served as a standard). Differences between populations, were often difficult to discern because of fluctuations in fitness, which made the picture a bit disappointing for those who expected the fitness of a population to represent a biological constant. Nevertheless, in some generations populations were clearly distinct enough to say that flies derived from large irradiated populations showed a decline in fertility (offspring per mating relative to the standard) while the others did not decline.

The attempt to compare populations in fitness by Beardmore, Dobzhansky, and Pavlovsky (36) has been somewhat more successful in obtaining clear differences between populations in total output. Using laboratory populations already at equilibrium they measured both fitness properties and morphological traits in single gene arrangement (monomorphic) and two gene arrangement (polymorphic) populations derived from Pinon Flats, California. Under most natural conditions fitness must be an expression in terms of total output. A high fitness may for most insects be expressed as high biomass potential. It is conceivable, however, that there must be a limit to the advantage of high biomass output, for example in an overcrowded population a still greater biomass production might be detrimental. High fitness may include by definition some mechanism for compensation against overproduction in a situation of that sort. Under the conditions of this experiment, the polymorphic populations have superior capability in being able to utilize the conditions available to increase their numbers. For such a short term, fitness is in favor of the polymorphic population. In addition, homeostatic mechanisms both as to fitness properties and to morphological traits are greater in the polymorphic populations. Whether these facts will insure such a population in nature to the extent it can be said to have greater "adaptedness" is another question; though it can only be proposed that even with the gap in our knowledge of wild habitat ecology, the well adapted wild population might be expected to transfer into the laboratory environment just such fitness qualities and conversely in nature such qualities must have high fitness value.

MUTATION IN POPULATIONS

Mutational and balanced loads

The genetic load of a population has been defined in the section on intensity of selection. Another way of expressing the concept is by considering that many detrimental genotypes damage the population by their presence. Until such variants are completely eliminated, as long as the population suffers to the extent that selection is regularly eliminating them, it carries a load (Muller, 260) which would be reduced to zero only if the population consisted entirely of a single optimal genotype. (Note, in view of the section on populational fitness, that such a statement has no relevant connection with the probability of the whole population's survival or extinction under "competition" with other populations.)

Depending on its genetic origin or mechanism of maintenance, different loads have been distinguished. Crow (in 23) defines and illustrates three such loads: 1) mutational, 2) segregational, and 3) incompatibility. Haldane (163) and Kimura (189) discuss the substitutional load. Crow's use of the term "segregational" in preference to Dobzhansky's term "balanced" (for selective favoring of heterozygotes which segregate constantly inferior homozygotes), while it emphasizes the genetic mechanism operating, is not necessary: Crow conceives of the "balanced" load as including polymorphism maintained by disruptive selection (adaptation to several niches, or multiple optima without heterozygote superiority). However, polymorphism of that sort may be the net outcome of having multiple and quite different loads under the various niches, or optima, into which the population penetrates; for example (203, 225) a stable equilibrium is possible in which two niches are occupied with the heterozygote intermediate in each or possibly quite inferior in one niche but superior in the other. Such a population experiences more than one kind of load. Perhaps it should also be made clear that each genic locus or genetic complex may have a different load, although the population may be considered to possess a net load if all loci and complexes are taken into account. It is this total load which is of primary interest in generalizations concerning the basic genetic architecture of any population. In this discussion the term "balanced" will be used in the narrower sense of Crow's term "segregational." It may often be difficult in practice to distinguish between multiple loads with diverse components and a net load of preponderantly similar components with the result that opinions will vary until careful genetic examination has been made.

Formalized description and expectation from the two principle types of load have been made by Dobzhansky (his "classical and balanced hypotheses of the adaptive norm," 97, 105, 108, 319) and by Wallace et al. (369). The evidence from large natural populations of Drosophila favor a coadapted, relationally balanced genetic architecture. On the other hand, it is well known that newly arising mutations are often detrimental in heterozygotes (260, 331). Often naturally occurring deleterious genes lower some fitness components of heterozygotes (279, 167). But genes may be deleterious on some backgrounds and not on others; some mutants may be heterotic in heterozygotes (49, 258, 259, 365, 366). Dobzhansky and the Krimbas's (108) present data showing no significant difference between the viabilities of lethal free and lethal-carrying heterozygotes from wild populations and no significant correlation between the performance of a homozygote and its heterozygote with a marker chromosome.

The classical hypothesis implies that nearly all new mutants are deleterious. When an unusual mutant has higher fitness than the remaining genes, it will eventually replace the ancestral genotypes. Muller points out (260) that new mutants in general have slightly detrimental effects in heterozygotes; and since rare mutants will occur almost exclusively in heterozygotes, the aggregate will add up to a substantial load by slight incapacitations in many heterozygous individuals. With the variance of views and observations concerning whether or not heterozygotes tend to be heterotic, neutral, or slightly detrimental, it may seem quite difficult to reach a decision concerning which is the more likely load in natural populations.

Morton, Crow, and Muller (256) have made estimates from human populations by comparing the amount of deleterious effect from inbred families vs. non-inbred families. They tried to distinguish the loads by the method given by Crow (23): using the ratio of genetic load in an inbred homozygous population to the load of a randomly mating population from which it was derived, the expectation will be a much greater ratio (about 25:1) if, with a single pair of alleles, the "mutant" acts as a fitness depressor in heterozygous condition than if the heterozygote has superior fitness (about 2:1). This latter ratio will increase in a multiple allelic system where all heterozygotes are superior to all homozygotes (in fact, k : 1, where k = the number of alleles at the locus). Since the genetic basis for the deleterious effects observed was unknown, the results of these authors (their ratio was estimated from 15:1 up to 25:1) remain ambiguous, though they are certainly useful in principle. Undoubtedly the assumption of a single pair of alleles without epistatic interactions is too simple in view of what is known about relationally balanced genetic systems. Multiple allelic systems may be very common at loci determining fitness traits. The complication of epistasis's effect on fitness has not yet been sufficiently worked out mathematically to apply to this ratio.

Selection, irradiation, and polygenic mutation

Unfortunately there is too little known of the mutability of polygenic systems, yet both evolutionary theory and breeding theory are dependent on a detailed account of the origin of quantitative variability under irradiation. Clayton and Robertson (75) discuss many of the earlier experiments, some of which showed response to selection after irradiation (Lewis) with 4000 r and others with rather little response (Rokizky). Scossiroli's (309) irradiation of a plateaued population with 3000 r exhibited marked increase in variability and considerable upward response though little downward. Scossiroli interprets his results as evidence for polygenic mutation. While in the light of later experiments there was undoubtedly mutation providing a portion of the total variability for use by selection, Clayton and Robertson point out that Scossiroli may well have had remaining some unfixable genetic variation in the plateaued base population which was released by the radiation. Their own experiments given in this collection show a slow but significant response of inbred strains in the irradiated lines within seventeen generations. Perhaps their response was slower because of lower dosage of irradiation, a much less stringent selection differential (10 selected out of 25 measured of each sex compared with Scossiroli's family selection method of taking 5 out of 30 families), and less opportunity for proper genetic combinations to be produced (since Scossiroli used a cyclic scheme in which artificial selection was applied in alternating generations with natural selection).

The later experiments of Buzzati-Traverso and the Scossirolis (55, 310) leave little doubt that polygenic mutation is highly significant to a population in response to selection. The first of these experiments employed a set of six isogenic populations homozygous for the spineless (ss) mutant. After about 24 generations longer bristles began to appear in the irradiated populations (given 2000 and 4000 r per generation). Frequencies of longer bristles increased by natural selection rapidly in the 4000 r populations and less so in the 2000 r populations. Several months later long bristle flies appeared in the controls as well, and by the time two years had passed all six populations had more than 90% long bristle flies. Genetic analysis showed the flies to be all genetically ss/ss. In each of the six populations then a different modifier system had been selected, as revealed by statistical analysis of the six strains and crosses between strains.

The second Scossiroli experiments (310) are included in this collection to illustrate the response of isogenic lines to selection under irradiation and also the increased effectiveness of selection after crossing two lines to gain new recombination groups. The differences between regression coefficients of irradiated and non-irradiated regression coefficients (Table 2) are nearly the same for isogenic and hybrid populations. That is to say, while the response from hybrid populations is greater than that of isogenic populations as expected because of the greater additive genetic variance available in the hybrids (see heritability estimates in Table 4), the new mutations produced are measured by the small difference between 'irradiated and non-irradiated. Spontaneous polygenic mutation creates enough variation to allow a significant though slight response when selection is performed every generation (isogenic control D).

The response of populations to polygenic mutation improving fitness was examined by Dobzhansky and Spassky in a long term series of experiments (118) with the following design: beneficial fitness mutation could be detected if strains of reduced fitness were used initially within which rate of improvement could be measured. Since the majority of new mutations are detrimental, it was of interest to find out if beneficial mutations occur often enough to bring about improvement through natural selection. Seven strains of *D. pseudoobscura* made homozygous for II and IV chromosomes which were known to lower either viability, rate of development, fertility, or other fitness characters were each divided four ways: 1) kept homozygous control, 2) homozygous irradiated, 3) balanced in heterozygotes over markers in II and IV chromosomes, 4) balanced over markers irradiated. Irradiation of 1000 r X rays was given males in each generation. Homozygous populations were maintained in overcrowded cultures (25 pairs of parents per culture) while heterozygous balanced cultures were less crowded (5 pairs of parents per culture). Viability, developmental rate, and other characteristics were tested at intervals of several generations by measuring fitness properties of homozygotes either by inbreeding balanced heterozygotes or by outcrossing "homozygotes" to the marker stocks and inbreeding their progeny. Improvements of viability occurred in five out of seven homozygote control and six out of seven homozygote irradiated populations, the others being not significantly changed. Among the balanced populations, however, three of the untreated developed lethals, three were unchanged, and one improved slightly, while in the X-rayed five had gained lethals, two were not significantly changed. The contrast was striking: most of the homozygous populations improved while most of the balanced ones degenerated as far as their fitness effects in tested homozygotes was concerned. Polygenic mutation producing improved fitness traits does occur and can be utilized in a population's adaptation; however it is very informative to notice the similarity between natural population homozygotes and those from the balanced cultures. The genetic load of naturally occurring detrimental genes has been well documented. Unfortunately random heterozygotes' fitness properties were not recorded in that experiment, and there can be no comparison between populations for total fitness. Nevertheless, it is obvious that in those populations which might be

termed "classical," initially homozygous, improvement was effected by polygenic mutation for higher fitness, while in the "balanced" ones individual
chromosomes could degenerate without disturbing the perpetuation of those
populations.

The adaptation of random mating populations to such a detrimental environmental agent as chronic irradiation has been investigated by Wallace (363)
over several years. The observations of Gregg (156) and Stone and Wilson
(333, 334) give similar results for populations of Drosophila existing at the
South Pacific atomic bomb testing grounds. Wallace's measurement of viability
effects mutant changes given in this collection are most informative: beginning
with lethal-free second chromosome stocks of low mutation rate Oregon-R
derivation, the changes in lethal frequencies and viability determinations of
heterozygotes within the seven respective populations indicate many important
phenomena. Spontaneous lethal mutations arise in the control so that the
population is supporting an equilibrium value of 20–25% lethals after about
50 generations. The population with an initial high dose of radiation (1) and
the population with low chronic dose (7) maintain about the same levels. These
can be considered levels preserved by a balance between mutation and selection
with negligible irradiation. A much more substantial amount of lethality arises
and is supported in the high dosage chronically irradiated populations (both
"large" and "small" size retain about the same average though fluctuations in
the "small" are greater). Random heterozygotes from the chronically irradiated
populations show no less viability than those from the unirradiated control
population, and may actually be slightly superior (Table 5). (Haldane's correction [160] for measuring relative viabilities could reduce the difference
slightly making the apparent superiority less.) It is evident from Table 6 that
detrimental (lethal and semi-lethal) chromosomes have no average lowering
effect on viability when in heterozygous condition with normal viability chromosomes though they may have about 2% reductional effect when coupled together.
Certainly the populations under chronic irradiation have adapted to a high
mutation rate: favored heterozygous effects will be most common and therefore
most available for natural selection to utilize. Retention of a mutant in such
populations then depends upon its action in heterozygotes, and Wallace interprets his results as evidence for a primarily balanced load under environmental
stress as drastic as chronic irradiation.

RANDOM GENETIC DRIFT AND EVOLUTIONARY CHANGE

Role of random changes in natural populations

The relative effectiveness of random, or stochastic, processes on determination
of gene and zygote frequencies either in small breeding sized populations or in

larger populations in which the directed pressures are considerably reduced has been examined chiefly by Wright (379, 380, 382) and Kimura (187). The importance. of random genetic drift to evolutionary situations has been variously interpreted or misinterpreted by countless biologists when "needed" to help explain or argue against the possible mechanisms at work in populations. Wright has repeatedly insisted that drift in small isolated populations will be non-adaptive and will lead to extinction; but that drift has two highly important aspects: 1) preventing too strict adherence to the influence of the directed pressures, which can reduce genetic plasticity, and 2) the condition for most rapid evolution requires the total population to consist of partially discontinuous subpopulations. "The most general conclusion is that evolution depends on a certain balance among its factors. There must be gene mutation, but an excessive rate gives an array of freaks, not evolution; there must be selection but too severe a process destroys the field of variability . . . too close inbreeding leads to extinction. . . . In this dependence on balance the species is like a living organism. At all levels of organization, life depends on the maintenance of a certain balance among its factors." ". . . The most effective mechanism [of evolution] was that of subdivision into many partially isolated local populations, the differentiation of these under joint action of random processes and local selection, and finally, interdeme selection through differential growth and dispersion, in accordance with degree of success in meeting the challenge of the common aspects of the environment."

To what extent the effects of sampling are responsible for observed changes in natural or experimental populations is exceedingly difficult to determine. In the absence of knowledge about selective differences between genotypes, their frequencies were often interpreted as due to random sampling (*e.g.* human blood types) twenty years ago, but now are being shown to possess significant differences of adaptive value (14, 15, 18, 23, 107, 149, 257). There is no doubt however, that the population genetic structure of large and small populations differ because of sampling effects (Carson, 60; Dobzhansky and Pavlovsky, 114). Where small changes in gene frequencies are observed, it is certainly difficult indeed to distinguish the cause of those changes as being due to selection or random effects. Wright (379) has reexamined data by Fisher and Ford (142) to emphasize caution in the interpretation of data and consideration of all factors possible in population structure. His diagrams impress us with the fact that some drift is influential even in fairly large populations, especially if the directed processes themselves are fluctuating randomly.

Characteristically marginal populations fulfill the requirements for small semi-isolated populations to which Wright attributed the greatest potential for progressive change (Carson, 66); "Marginal populations tend to be isolated and inbred. They usually exist in areas which offer to the species a limited series of environmental niches to be conquered. It seems inescapable that, when a subspecies becomes progressively adapted to these niches as the margin is approached, homoselection should play the dominant role."

Laboratory determination

Measurement of the magnitude of random sampling effects can best be done in the laboratory, the most successful experimental measurements being made by Kerr and Wright (178, 179, 386), Merrell (239), Prout (280), Crow and Morton (87), and Buri (50). The first two are included in this collection since they illustrate the diverse outcomes for two quite different modes of genic action (recessive sex-linked and autosomal with overdominant heterozygote). From the constant rate of fixation an effective breeding size of these populations can be calculated: about 83% in the first case and about 67% in the second. The experiments with Bar-eye give a model in which even though it is very strongly selected against is nevertheless fixed in a small proportion of the cases; the forked experiments are a model of inbreeding in almost pure form; while the spineless vs. aristapedia illustrate a balance between selection pressures and random drift.

Prout's study of lethal allelism frequencies in three of the Wallace populations is of interest for methodology and his population size estimates. Allelism frequencies for studying genetic drift were used which did not seem to include any heterotic lethals. (One definitely heterotic lethal in population 5 which had persisted at high frequency for several generations was omitted.) With the low allelism in the large populations and the relatively high frequency in the small population, Prout estimated the large populations to have an effectively infinite size but the small one to have about 26% of the actual size. Still the latter figure could be subject to large error if any overdominant loci were included.

Crow and Morton's (87) experiments are more inclusive. In three kinds of experiments, using an "index of variability" in progeny number, their data suggest that the effective population size to be about 75% of the actual size for progeny of females, while between 33% and 50% of actual size for progeny of males. These are the same orders of magnitude as found by Kerr and Wright. Buri's experiments describe the dispersion of variability for a nearly neutral pair of alleles in some detail. With a sample size of sixteen individuals the effective breeding size was between 56% and 72%. As suggested by Falconer (4) in discussion of these results, a reasonable estimate of effective size might be 75% of the actual number. Buri estimates about 60% if both sexes share equally in effective production of offspring.

ANOMALOUS MECHANISMS

Meiotic drive and transmission ratios

Unquestionably the segregation principle is the most fundamental of classic genetics. The constancy of allelic frequencies with generation regularity in large populations depends on a meiotic mechanism which permits gametes to carry half the heredity of the parent individual. An increasing number of observations indicate that a wide distribution of phenomena occur in natural populations which drastically alter the famous equality ratio in heterozygotes. At least two mechanisms could bring about such distortion: 1) selective differences between gametes, and 2) mechanical alteration in meiotic division. These may be difficult to distinguish in practice.

Instances of aberrant ratios induced by the latter mechanism were reviewed and termed "meiotic drive" by Sandler and Novitski in 1957 (see 168, 299–303). Familiar examples of the "sex ratio" condition in the obscura group of Drosophila and more recently discovered cases in *D. paramelanica* by Stalker (330) are generally associated with inversion systems on the X chromosome and operate on the elimination of the Y chromosome in males so that such males produce no sons. Cytoplasmically transmitted sex ratio conditions have been reviewed by Malagolowkin and others (227) and have found the mechanism to be sensitivity to a transmitted infective microorganism. Also well known is the non-random disjunction of heteromorphic homologues in which one member of a chromosome pair has one or more aberrations, but such non-random events are not usually dependent on a specific genetic constitution as in the sex ratio condition.

The extensively studied "segregation-distorter" locus on chromosome II of *D. melanogaster* is associated in natural populations with an inversion complex which interacts with the SD locus to boost and stabilize the amount of distortion. SD is linked with a recessive lethal and is operative only in heterozygous males. It brings about its distorted ratio effect from some sort of misreplication of the homologous (SD^+) chromosome so that functional SD^+ sperm are not produced. Synapsis of the two chromosomes at the SD region near the centromere is essential for distortion. Cytogenetic complexity is increased by a stability modifier at the extreme right end of the chromosome, a conditional distortion obtained by passing the SD chromosome through certain female lines, different sensitivity of the SD^+ chromosomes to distorting action, and the presence of a specific activator closely linked to SD.

Dunn and his colleagues (132–136, 222) have found at least sixteen different "zero tail" (t^w) alleles which produce very high transmission ratios in heterozygous male mice such that 90%–99% of their sperm carry the lethal t^w preferentially to the wild type allele or to the T (Brachy) allele. Without cytogenetic evidence it is still not certain whether the mechanism is due to meiotic drive or gamete selection, though intrauterine selection against non-zero-tail zygotes has been ruled out. Some experiments of Braden on time of mating and egg penetration (134) suggest that the t-bearing sperm has a physiological advantage in egg penetration, in which case the mechanism would be an exception to the principle of random gamete union at fertilization rather than a segregational exception.

The population dynamics of sex ratio, SD, and transmission ratios have been examined by Shaw (311, 312), Watson (372), Bruck (48), Hiraizumi et al. (168), and Lewontin and Dunn (222). The last two references included in this collection present data from natural populations, laboratory, and simulated digital computer populations. It is clear that any genetic element favored by meiotic drive or aberrant ratio will increase in a population, and even though conferring lethality in double dose may be preserved at high frequency if the ratio is distorted sufficiently in its favor. If the "driven element" has selective advantage (overdominance) in the heterozygote in addition, then the population may benefit; however, as Hiraizumi et al. discuss, all the known cases are associated with homozygote reduction in fitness. If completely neutral or slightly disadvantageous in the heterozygote, the driven element may increase bringing about overall lowering of populational fitness ultimately, or non-adaptive change. Natural selection may when confronted with such a situation bring about counteracting measures: 1) tighten linkage with a beneficial gene or complex; 2) present balanced lethal systems or numerous deleterious alleles on other chromosomes, favoring an excess of one chromosome in the gametes of one sex and the other chromosome in the gametes of the other; or 3) bring about evolution of suppressor systems nullifying the effect of drive (as in SD insensitivity or sex ratio suppression in Y chromosomes or autosomes, see 301, 330).

WIDESPREAD SECULAR CHANGES IN NATURAL POPULATIONS

Seldom indeed have widespread evolutionary changes been recorded in recent history, and even less often have they been studied in enough detail to analyze the forces at work. Two examples of such widespread changes in natural populations which are currently under surveillance are the increase in melanic forms of Lepidoptera following the Industrial Revolution in Great Britain studied by Kettlewell and others (181–186) and the changes in frequencies of certain chromosomal arrangements in populations of *D. pseudoobscura* throughout Southwestern United States studied by Dobzhansky (98, 103). The first instance has been brought about by human interference in the natural habitats of moths over the last century; but the second was recognized over a period of only seventeen years and seems independent of human factors.

Kettlewell has demonstrated beyond doubt that selective predation especially by birds in a major factor in affecting frequencies of melanism of the Peppered Moth, *Biston betularia;* that the melanics are favored by being inconspicuous in heavily industrialized and polluted areas, while the light forms are favored in unpolluted countryside as they were everywhere before 1850. (See Figures 1 and 1a in 183). The whitish gray with sprinkling of black dots is the ancestral color pattern which conceals the moth when resting on light bark or lichens. Two melanic forms are *carbonaria*, the common simple dominant and *insularia*, much less common and due to a non-linked set of alleles. Evidence for selective elimination has been acquired through experiments of release and recapture coupled with direct observations of bird predators capturing selectively one or the other form.   The complementary series of experiments in contrasting habitats is especially impressive.

Haldane in 1924 estimated that if the melanic frequency were no higher than 1% in 1848 that the rate of increase has reflected an approximate 30% advantage of the black form over the light.   Such a large selective advantage had not been recorded before, but considering recent drosophila population studies this advantage in fitness does not seem unusually great.   There has undoubtedly been a selection of modifying genes which improve dominance as well as darkening both homozygous and heterozygous carbonaria (Haldane, 159).   Evidence for such modifiers has been demonstrated by outcrossing between widely separated populations and obtaining heterozygous backcross *carbonaria* with increased white markings or a dusting of white scales unlike any naturally occurring *carbonaria*.

It is important to realize that while selective predation may be the major influence, fitness has been regulated in this moth to reinforce the primary adaptation: 1) viability of backcross larvae on polluted leaves was superior for melanic heterozygotes, though *typica* developed faster than *carbonaria*; 2) mating preferences differ; and 3) background recognition exists significantly in both forms, a fact which would increase the polymorphism by disruptive selection (185, 186).

In contrast, the adaptive nature of the long term changes in chromosomal arrangement frequencies of *D. pseudoobscura* is a matter for conjecture.   Widespread changes of the same kind would suggest a common environmental factor in all localities concerned and at the same time a common fitness function on the part of the arrangements undergoing the change.   The reconstruction of a great many gene pools is necessary.   Mass migration is ruled out by the evidence.   On the basis of known migration rates even a "lucky" mutational change within the rare arrangement (PP) could not possibly spread so fast as observed in the California populations.   Accidental transfer by man or by passage of large air masses from the Rockies to California might have introduced enough pseudoobscura to bring about a luxuriance in hybrids between local and introduced flies.   If this surge in frequency is not due to mass introduction of forms, the emergence of entirely·new genetic complexes in these populations must be invoked.   Final proof can only come after some understanding is achieved concerning the common selective agents involved and the relation of the chromosomal polymorphism to those agents.

ORIGIN OF REPRODUCTIVE ISOLATING MECHANISMS

Genetically conditioned mechanisms which restrict, or limit, the amount of genic exchange between distinctive populations of organisms are essential for the preservation of organic diversity.   (See 3, 7, 13, 16, 17, 20, 21, 22, and 24).   Species have been defined somewhat statically as "groups of actually or potentially interbreeding natural populations that are reproductively isolated from other such groups" (Mayr, 7); they have been defined with more emphasis on the dynamics of evolution as a stage in the process of divergence in Mendelian populations at which the process becomes irreversible and the differences become permanent (Dobzhansky): "The process of speciation must, then be regarded as an evolutionary adaptation which permits the development of an immense organic diversity. . . . [It] is a device which enables life to exploit the multiform opportunities offered by the environment. Speciation is accordingly a form of integration of Mendelian populations engendered by natural selection in response to the challenge of the diversity of sympatric environments."

Laboratory determination and natural populations

Speciation is one of the critical processes in nature, yet experimental population genetics has produced very little positive evidence to describe the origin of mechanisms which promote species formation. The rise of isolation is conditional upon persistent differences in environment for diverging populations and separation of those populations. Isolation and divergence then will continue as the outcome of disruptive selection (Mather, 232).

For a majority of animal species, a primary factor in keeping species delimited depends on the mutual attraction and behavior of the sexes in the diverging populations. It has been proposed by Muller (see 197, 200) that genes controlling behavior and interbreeding are incorporated as by-products of genetic divergence in the course of building up adaptive complexes. Dobzhansky has stressed the role of natural selection in reinforcing divergence already attained by eliminating hybrids between those populations and consequently increasing any genotypes which favor or insure intrapopulational breeding. Such a response to selection might be termed the reduction in genotypes which foster promiscuity. As a corollary to the coadaptation hypothesis of integrated gene pools, the phenomenon of hybrid breakdown, lowered fitness of backcross or F_2 hybrids compared with parent populations, could serve as an important mechanism in such a process, because genotypes would be favored which insure intrapopulational breeding.

In order to test these two possibilities Koopman (200) selected against hybrids between two already well delimited species which do not interbreed in nature but do in the laboratory (*D. pseudoobscura* and *D. persimilis*). Intensification of a partial sexual isolation was effective in reducing hybrids with a few generations and also in reducing the number of interspecific matings occurring. More recently Wallace (361) was able to effect sexual preference and isolation between two genetic strains of *D. melanogaster* (straw and sepia). By simply destroying hybrids between these strains for about 73 generations, he found a marked preference for intra-sepia matings; mating behavior then had been altered. In another pair of populations which had diverged morphologically (his #3 and #6 populations of the irradiation experiments), a test for sexual preferences between individuals of the different populations brought negative results: no evidence of sexual preferences were found.   Random divergence had not produced isolation as a by-product.

In this collection Knight, Robertson, and Waddington (197) describe successful experiments bringing about partial sexual isolation comparable to Wallace's work.   Their large population box experiments indicated that, when hybrids between two mutants (ebony and vestigial) are selected against, hybrid frequency declined.   The sexual isolation has been achieved apparently by an increase in homogamic matings among vestigial flies (Figure 2).   Progeny tests of individual parent females taken from the 20th to 30th generations, however, indicated that both mutants showed a strong tendency for homogamic mating. In view of the fact that light intensity is known to affect mating behavior of ebony flies, when a different container was used which distributed the light more uniformly than in the population box, ebony became as successful in mating as vestigial.   Such microenvironmental differences may then assist in the population's response to disruptive selection.

These experiments lend support to the view that a population can respond to selection for homogamic behavior, and sexual isolation may be increased thereby.   While both the Wallace and Knight et al. experiments also included tests for chance origin of isolation with negative results, other workers have had some success (Santibanez and Waddington, 307) in finding mating preferences within genetically isolated strains of *D. melanogaster* which had had no artificial selective history expected to influence inter-strain mating.   In four out of six inbred lines there was a significant tendency in "male choice" tests for homogamic matings, and two of the four were likewise significant in "female choice" tests.   Among lines selected for bristle numbers, however, mating was at random. The possibility for inbred lines to adopt incipient sexual isolation by chance, then, is supported.

Facts such as these have brought about a search for intrapopulational variability in mating propensity and behavior in the hope of finding further evidence for the existence of incipient sexual isolation.   Studies of Bastock (31) and Petit (277) are especially explicit in disclosing the variation of behavior brought about in single mutant stocks: it is clear that selection can act on the courtship pattern to "gear" the sexes for highest efficiency of mating.   The mechanism may be very dependent on frequency of competing genotypes as shown by Petit.   "Gearing" of the sexes may be brought about by intra-male selection for frequency of insemination as shown by Bateman (32).   It may also be that the role of chromosomal polymorphism is of considerable importance to the evolution of mating behavior within populations (Spiess and Langer, 325).

A stronger argument for the doctrine of biological evolution and the gradual divergence and gain in sexual isolation of subspecies, or races, cannot be found than the "borderline cases" such as circular chains of subspecies.   While such cases are "difficult" for the taxonomist, they represent important evidence which demonstrates the continual process of origin of species.   The rates of this process in nature, the forces that bring it about, and all the conditions upon which it depends can be ascertained only after several such cases are described and understood. To watch species come into being within a human lifetime is commonly supposed to be a fruitless hope. Studies of incipient isolation between "races" within a "species" as illustrated by the paper of Dobzhansky and Spassky (122) in this collection document the process conclusively and bring that hope closer to reality.

BIBLIOGRAPHY

Over the past two decades the number of papers in the genetics of animal populations has increased to more than two thousand. The list of references below represents therefore an arbitrary selection within the limitations of the introduction. Preference has been given to recent papers and representative works with comprehensive bibliographies from which the student can proceed into a detailed search of the literature. In most cases articles published in books are not listed separately. References given in book bibliographies are not included unless specifically cited in the introduction.

I. Books and monographs

1. Andrewartha, H. G. and Birch, L. C. "The Distribution and Abundance of Animals." Univ. Chicago Press, Chicago, 1954.

2. Buzzati-Traverso, A. A., (Ed.). Symposium on Genetics of Population Structure held at Pavia, Italy, 1953. Intern. Union of Biol. Sciences Series B, No. 15. 1954.

3. Dobzhansky, Th. "Genetics and the Origin of Species." Columbia Univ. Press, New York, 1951. (3rd edition).

4. Falconer, D. S. "Introduction to Quantitative Genetics." Ronald Press, New York, 1960.

5. Gowen, J. W., (Ed.). "Heterosis." Iowa State College Press, Ames, 1952.

6. Huxley, J., Hardy, A. C., and Ford, E. B., (Eds.). "Evolution as a Process." Allen and Unwin, London, 1954.

7. Jepsen, G. L., Mayr, E., and Simpson, G. G., (Eds.). "Genetics, Paleontology, and Evolution." Princeton Univ. Press, Princeton, 1949.

8. Kempthorne, O., (Ed.). International Symposium held at Ottawa, 1958, "Biometrical Genetics." Pergamon Press, Inc., New York, 1960.

9. Lerner, I. Michael. "Genetic Homeostasis." John Wiley and Sons, Inc., New York, 1954.

10. Lerner, I. Michael. "The Genetic Basis of Selection." John Wiley and Sons, Inc., New York, 1958.

11. Li, C. C. "Population Genetics." Univ. Chicago Press, Chicago, 1955.

12. Lush, J. L. "Animal Breeding Plans." Iowa State College Press, Ames, 1945 (3rd edition).

13. Mayr, E., (Ed.). "The Species Problem." Symposium presented at the Atlanta meeting (AAAS). Am. Assoc. Adv. Sci., publ. 50 (Washington, D.C.), 1957.

14. Neel, J. V. and Schull, W. J. "Human Heredity." Univ. Chicago Press, Chicago, 1954.

15. Osborne, R. H., (Ed.). "Genetic Perspectives in Disease Resistance and Susceptibility." *Annals New York Acad. Sci., 91*, 595–818 (1961).

16. Patterson, J. T. and Stone, W. S. "Evolution in the Genus Drosophila." The Macmillan Co., New York, 1952.

17. Rensch, B. "Evolution Above the Species Level." Columbia Univ. Press, New York, 1960.

18. Roberts, D. F. and Harrison, G. A., (Eds.). "Natural Selection in Human Populations." Symposia of the Soc. for the Study of Human Biology, 2. Pergamon Press, London, 1959.

19. Roe, A. and Simpson, G. G. "Behavior and Evolution." Yale Univ. Press, New Haven, 1958.

20. Schmalhausen, I. I. "Factors of Evolution." Blackiston Co., Philadelphia, 1949.

21. Sheppard, P. M. "Natural Selection and Heredity." Hutchinson and Co., Ltd., London, 1958.

22. Simpson, G. G. "The Major Features of Evolution." Columbia Univ. Press, New York, 1953.

23. Spuhler, J. N., (Ed.) "Natural Selection in Man." Wayne State Univ. Press, Detroit, Michigan, 1958.

24. Tax, Sol. (Ed.). "Evolution After Darwin, Vol. 1., The Evolution of Life, Vol. 2, The Evolution of Man, Vol. 3, Issues in Evolution." Univ. of Chicago Press, Chicago, 1960.

25. Waddington, C. H. "The Strategy of the Genes." Allen and Unwin, London, 1957.

25a. Wallace, B. and Dobzhansky, Th. "Radiation, Genes, and Man." Henry Holt and Co., New York, 1959.

II. Papers (a number in **boldface** type indicates that the paper is reprinted in this collection)

26. Allison, A. C. Aspects of polymorphism in man. *Cold Spring Harbor Symp. Quant. Biol., 20*, 239–255 –1955—.

27. Allison, A. C. Population genetics of abnormal human haemoglobins. *Acta Genetica 6*, 430–434, (1956.).

28. Allison, A. C. The sickle-cell and haemoglobin *C* genes in some African populations. *Annals of Human Genetics 21*, 67–89. (1956.).

29. Allison, A. C. Genetic factors in resistance to malaria. *Annals New York Acad. Sci., 91*, 710–729 (1961).

30. Barker, J. S. F. Simulation of genetic systems by automatic digital computers. III. Selection between alleles at an autosomal locus. *Austral. J. Biol. Sci., 2*, 603–612 (1958).

31. Bastock, M. A gene mutation which changes a behavior pattern. *Evolution, 10*, 421–439 (1956).

32. Bateman, A. J., Intrasexual selection in Drosophila. *Heredity, 2,* 349–368 (1948).

33. Bateman, K. G. The genetic assimilation of the dumpy phenocopy. *J. Genetics, 56,* 1–10 (1959).

34. Bateman, K. G. The genetic assimilation of four venation phenocopies. *J. Genetics, 56,* 443–474 (1959).

35. Beardmore, J. A. Developmental stability in constant and fluctuating temperatures. *Heredity, 14,* 411–422 (1960).

36. Beardmore, J. A., Dobzhansky, Th., and Pavlovsky, O. A. An attempt to compare the fitness of polymorphic and monomorphic experimental populations of *D. pseudoobscura. Heredity, 14,* 19–33 (1960).

37. Bennett, Jack. A comparison of selective methods and a test of the pre-adaptation hypothesis. *Heredity, 15,* 65–77 (1960).

38. Birch, L. C. The meanings of competition. *The American Naturalist, 91,* 5–18 (1957).

39. Birch, L. C. Selection in *D. pseudoobscura* in relation to crowding. *Evolution, 9,* 389–399 (1955).

40. Bodmer, W. F., and Parsons, P. A. The initial progress of new genes with various genetic systems. *Heredity, 15,* 283–299 (1960).

41. Bonnier, G., Jonsson, U. B., and Ramel, C. Experiments on the influence of selection pressure on irradiated populations of *D. melanogaster. Proc. 2nd U.N. Intern. Conf. on the Peaceful Uses of Atomic Energy, 22,* 322–324 (1958).

42. Breese, E. L., and Mather, K. The organization of polygenic activity within a chromosome in Drosophila. I. Hair characters. *Heredity, 11,* 373–395 (1957).

43. Breese, E. L., and Mather, K. The organization of polygenic activity within a chromosome in Drosophila. II. Viability. *Heredity, 14,* 375–399 (1960).

44. Brncic, D. Heterosis and the integration of the genotype in geographic populations of *D. pseudoobscura. Genetics, 39,* 77–88 (1954).

45. Brncic, D. Integration of the genotype in geographic populations of *D. pavani. Evolution, 15,* 92–97 (1961).

46. Brncic, D. Non random association of inversions in *D. pavani. Genetics, 46,* 401–406 (1961).

47. Brown, W. P., and Bell, A. E. Genetic analysis of a "plateaued" population of *D. melanogaster. Genetics, 46,* 407–425 (1961).

48. Bruck, David. Male segregation ratio advantage as a factor in maintaining lethal alleles in wild populations of house mice. *Proc. Natl. Acad. Sci. U.S., 43,* 152–158 (1956).

49. Burdick, A. B., and Mukai, A. Experimental consideration of the genetic effect of low doses of irradiation on viability in *D. melanogaster. Proc. Second U.N. Intern. Conf. on the Peaceful Uses of Atomic Energy, 22,* 325–329 (1958).

50. Buri, P. Gene frequency in small populations of mutant Drosophila. *Evolution, 10,* 367–402 (1956).

51. Buzzati-Traverso, A. A. On the role of mutation in evolution. *Caryologia (Vol. 6 Suppl.),* 450–462 (1954).

52. Buzzati-Traverso, A. A. Evolutionary changes in components of fitness and other polygenic traits in *D. melanogaster* populations. *Heredity, 9,* 153–186 (1955).

53. Buzzati-Traverso, A. A. On the growth of populations. *Proc. 14th Int. Cong. Zoology, Copenhagen, 1953,* 66–75 (1956).

54. Buzzati-Traverso, A. A. Quantitative traits and polygenic systems in evolution. *Cold Spring Harbor Symp. Quant. Biol., 24,* 41–46 (1959).

55. Buzzati-Traverso, A. A., and Scossiroli, R. E. X Ray-induced mutations in polygenic systems. *Proc. Second U.N. Intern. Conf. on the Peaceful Uses of Atomic Energy, 22,* 293–297 (1958).

56. Cain, A. J., and Sheppard, P. M. The theory of adaptive polymorphism. *The American Naturalist, 88,* 321–326 (1954).

57. Cain, A. J., and Sheppard, P. M. Natural selection in Cepaea. *Genetics, 39,* 89–116 (1954).

58. Cain, A. J., and Sheppard, P. M. Adaptive and selective value. *The American Naturalist, 90,* 202–203 (1956).

59. Cain, A. J., King, J. M. B., and Sheppard, P. M. New data on the genetics of polymorphism in the snail *Cepaea nemoralis* L. *Genetics, 45,* 393–411 (1960).

60. Carson, H. L. Contrasting types of population structure in Drosophila. *The American Naturalist, 86,* 239–248 (1952).

61. Carson, H. L. The genetic characteristics of marginal populations of Drosophila. *Cold Spring Harbor Symp. Quant. Biol., 20,* 276–287 (1955).

62. Carson, H. L. Variation in genetic recombination in natural populations. *J. Cell and Comp. Physiol., 45,* 221–236 (1955).

63. Carson, H. L. Increase in fitness in experimental populations resulting from heterosis. *Proc. Natl. Acad. Sci. U.S., 44,* 1136–1141 (1958).

64. Carson, H. L. The population genetics of *D. robusta. Advances in Genetics, 9,* 1–40 (1958).

65. Carson, H. L. Response to selection under different conditions of recombination in Drosophila. *Cold Spring Harbor Symp. Quant. Biol., 23,* 291–306 (1958).

66. Carson, H. L. Genetic conditions which promote or retard the formation of species. *Cold Spring Harbor Symp. Quant. Biol., 24,* 87–105 (1960).

67. Carson, H. L. Relative fitness of gentically open and closed experimental populations of *D. robusta. Genetics, 46,* 553–567 (1961).

68. Chetverikov, S. S. New translation by Malina Barker (Ed., I. M. Lerner) of "Concerning certain aspects of the evolutionary process from the standpoint of modern genetics". *Proc. Am. Philos. Soc., 105,* 167–195 (1961).

69. Clarke, Bryan. Divergent effects of natural selection on two closely-related polymorphic snails. *Heredity, 14,* 423–443 (1960).

70. Clarke, C. A., and Sheppard, P. M. The evolution of dominance under disruptive selection. *Heredity, 14,* 73–87 (1960).

71. Clarke, C. A., and Sheppard, P. M. The evolution of mimicry in the butterfly *Papilio dardanus. Heredity, 14,* 163–173 (1960).

72. Clarke, C. A., and Sheppard, P. M. Super-genes and mimicry. *Heredity, 14,* 175–185 (1960).

73. Clarke, Jean M., and Smith, J. Maynard. The genetics and cytology of *D. subobscura*. XI. Hybrid vigour and longevity. *J. Genetics, 53,* 172–180 (1955).

74. Clarke, Jean M., and Smith, J. Maynard. Asymmetrical response to selection for rate of development in *D. subobscura*. *Genetical Research, 2,* 70–81 (1961).

75. Clayton, G. A., and Robertson, A. Mutation and quantitative variation. *The American Naturalist, 89,* 151–158 (1955).

76. Clayton, G. A., Knight, G. R., Morris, J. A., and Robertson, A. An experimental check on quantitative genetical theory. III. Correlated responses. *J. Genetics, 55,* 171–180 (1957).

77. Clayton, G. A., Morris, J. A., and Robertson, A. An experimental check on quantitative genetical theory. I. Short-term responses to selection. *J. Genetics, 55,* 131–151 (1957).

78. Clayton, G. A., and Robertson, A. An experimental check on quantitative genetical theory. II. The long-term effects of selection. *J. Genetics, 55,* 152–170 (1957).

79. Cordeiro, A. R., and Dobzhansky, Th. Combining ability of certain chromosomes in *D. willistoni* and invalidation of the wild type concept. *The American Naturalist, 88,* 75–86 (1954).

80. Cordeiro, A. R., Salzano, F. M., and Marques, V. B. An interracial hybridization experiment in natural populations of *D. willistoni*. *Heredity, 15,* 35–45 (1960).

81. Crow, James F. General theory of population genetics synthesis. *Cold Spring Harbor Symp. Quant. Biol., 20,* 55–59 (1955).

82. Crow, James F. Genetics of insect resistance to chemicals. *Ann. Rev. Entomology, 2,* 227–246 (1957).

83. Crow, James F. Genetics of insecticide resistance: General considerations. *Miscellaneous Publications of Entomological Soc. of America, 2,* 69–74 (1960).

84. Crow, James F. "Radiation, Genes and Man" by Wallace and Dobzhansky — Book Review. *Am. J. Human Genetics, 12,* 374–377 (1960).

85. Crow, James F. Population genetics. *Am. J. Human Genetics, 13,* 137–150 (1961).

86. Crow, James F., and Kimura, Motoo. Some genetic problems in natural populations. *Proc. 3rd Berkeley Symp. Math. Statistics and Probability, Univ. California Press, 4,* 1–22 (1955).

87. Crow, James F., and Morton, Newton E. Measurement of gene frequency drift in small populations. *Evolution, 9,* 202–214 (1955).

88. da Cunha, A. B. Adaptation of carriers of different chromosomal types in *D. willistoni* to a variety of environments. *Rev. Brasil. Biol., 16,* 263–272 (1956).

89. da Cunha, A. B. Chromosomal polymorphism in the Diptera. *Advances in Genetics, 7,* 93–138 (1955).

90. da Cunha, A. B. Chromosomal variation and adaptation in insects. *Ann. Rev. Entomology, 5,* 85–110 (1960).

91. da Cunha, A. B., and Dobzhansky, Th. A further study of chromosomal polymorphism in *D. willistoni* in its relation to the environment. *Evolution, 8,* 119–134 (1954).

92. da Cunha, A. B., Dobzhansky, Th., Pavlovsky, O., and Spassky, B.   Genetics of natural populations. XXVIII. Supplementary data on the chromosomal polymorphism in *D. willistoni* in its relation to the environment. *Evolution, 13,* 389–404 (1959).

93. Dempster, E. R.   A letter to the editor on Lewontin's article on "Homeostasis" *The American Naturalist, 90,* 385–386 (1956).

94. Dempster, E. R.   Maintenance of genetic heterogeneity. *Cold Spring Harbor Symp. Quant. Biol., 20,* 25–32 (1955).

95. Dobzhansky, Th.   Experiments on sexual isolation in Drosophila. X. Reproductive isolation between *D. pseudoobscura* and *D. persimilis* under natural and under laboratory conditions. *Proc. Nat. Acad. Sci., 37,* 792–796 (1951).

96. Dobzhansky, Th.   Evolution as a creative process. *Caryologia (Vol. suppl.),* 435–449 (1954).

97. Dobzhansky, Th.   A review of some fundamental concepts and problems of population genetics. *Cold Spring Harbor Symp. Quant. Biol., 20,* 1–15 (1955).

98. Dobzhansky, Th.   Genetics of natural populations. XXV. Genetic changes in populations of *D. pseudoobscura* and *D. persimilis* in some localities in California. *Evolution, 10,* 82–92 (1956).

99. Dobzhansky, Th.   What is an adaptive trait? *Am. Naturalist, 90,* 337–347 (1956).

100. Dobzhansky, Th.   Genetic loads in natural populations. *Science, 126,* 191–194 (1957).

101. Dobzhansky, Th.   Genetics of natural populations. XXVI. Chromosomal variability in island and continental populations of *D. willistoni* from Central America and the West Indies. *Evolution, 11,* 280–293 (1957).

102. Dobzhansky, Th.   Mendelian populations as genetic systems. *Cold Spring Harbor Symp. Quant. Biol., 22,* 385–394 (1957).

103. Dobzhansky, Th.   Genetics of natural populations. XXVII. The genetic changes in populations of *D. pseudoobscura* in the American southwest. *Evolution, 12,* 385–401 (1958).

104. Dobzhansky, Th.   Evolution of genes and genes in evolution. *Cold Spring Harbor Symp. Quant. Biol., 24,* 15–30 (1959).

105. Dobzhansky, Th.   Variation and evolution. *Proc. Am. Philos. Soc., 103,* 252–263 (1959).

106. Dobzhansky, Th.   Man and natural selection. *Am. Scientist, 49,* 285–299 (1961).

107. Dobzhansky, Th., and Allen, G.   Does natural selection continue to operate in modern mankind? *Am. Anthropologist, 58,* 591–604 (1956).

108. Dobzhansky, Th., Krimbas, C., and Krimbas, M. G.   Genetics of natural populations. XXX. Is the genetic load in *D. pseudoobscura* a mutational or a balanced load? *Genetics, 45,* 741–753 (1960).

109. Dobzhansky, Th., and Levene, H.   Development of heterosis through natural selection in experimental populations of *D. pseudoobscura*. *Am. Naturalist, 85,* 247–264 (1951).

110. Dobzhansky, Th., and Levene, H. Genetics of natural populations. XXIV. Developmental homeostasis in natural populations of *D. pseudoobscura*. *Genetics, 40,* 797–808 (1955).

111. Dobzhansky, Th., Levene, H., Spassky, B., and Spassky, N. Release of genetic variability through recombination. III. *D. prosaltans*. *Genetics, 44,* 75–92 (1959).

112. Dobzhansky, Th., and Pavlovsky, O. Indeterminate outcome of certain experiments on Drosophila populations. *Evolution, 7,* 198–210 (1953).

113. Dobzhansky, Th., and Pavlovsky, O. An extreme case of heterosis in a Central American population of *D. tropicalis*. *Proc. Nat. Acad. Sci., 41,* 289–295 (1955).

114. Dobzhansky, Th., and Pavlovsky, O. An experimental study of interaction between genetic drift and natural selection. *Evolution, 11,* 311–319 (1957).

115. Dobzhansky, Th., and Pavlovsky, O. Interracial hybridization and breakdown of coadapted gene complexes in *D. paulistorum* and *D. willistoni*. *Proc. Nat. Acad. Sci., 44,* 622–629 (1958).

116. Dobzhansky, Th., and Pavlovsky, O. How stable is balanced polymorphism? *Proc. Nat. Acad. Sci., 46,* 41–47 (1959).

117. Dobzhansky, Th., Pavlovsky, O., Spassky, B., and Spassky, N. Genetics of natural populations. XXII. Biological role of deleterious recessives in populations of *D. pseudoobscura*. *Genetics, 40,* 781–796 (1955).

118. Dobzhansky, Th., and Spassky, B. Evolutionary changes in laboratory cultures of *D. pseudoobscura*. *Evolution, 1,* 191–216 (1947).

119. Dobzhansky, Th., and Spassky, B. Genetics of natural populations. XXI. Concealed variability in two sympatric species of Drosophila. *Genetics, 38,* 471–484 (1953).

120. Dobzhansky, Th., and Spasskey, B. Genetics of natural populations. XXII. A comparison of the concealed variability in *D. prosaltans* with that in other species. *Genetics, 39,* 472–487 (1954).

121. Dobzhansky, Th., Spassky, N., and Spassky, B. Rates of spontaneous mutation in the second chromosomes of the sibling species *D. pseudoobscura* and *D. persimilis*. *Genetics, 39,* 899–907 (1954).

122. Dobzhansky, Th., and Spassky, B. *D. paulistorum*, a cluster of species in statu nascendi. *Proc. Nat. Acad. Sci., 45,* 419–428 (1959).

123. Dobzhansky, Th., and Spassky, B. Release of genetic variability through recombination. V. Break up of synthetic lethals by crossing over in *D. pseudoobscura*. *Zoölogische Jahrbücher, 88,* 57–66 (1960).

124. Dobzhansky, Th., Spassky, B., and Spassky, N. A comparative study of mutation rates in two ecologically diverse species of Drosophila. *Genetics, 37,* 650–664 (1952).

125. Dobzhansky, Th., and Wallace, B. The genetics of homeostasis in Drosophila. *Proc. Nat. Acad. Sci., 39,* 162–171 (1953).

126. Dobzhansky, Th., and Wallace, B. The problem of adaptive differences in human populations. *Am. J. Human Genetics, 6,* 199–207 (1954).

127. Dobzhansky, Th., and Wright, S. Genetics of natural populations. V. Relations between mutation rate and accumulation of lethals in populations of *D. pseudoobscura*. *Genetics, 26,* 23–51 (1941).

128. Dobzhansky, Th., and Wright, S. Genetics of natural populations. X. Dispersion rates in *D. pseudoobscura*. *Genetics, 28*, 304–340 (1943).

129. Dowdeswell, W. H. Experimental studies on natural selection in the butterfly, *Mamiola jurtina*. *Heredity, 16*, 39–52 (1961).

130. Dowdeswell, W. H., Fisher, R. A., and Ford, E. B. The quantitative study of populations in the Lepidoptera. *Heredity, 3*, 67–84 (1949).

131. Dowdeswell, W. H., Ford, E. B., and McWhirter, K. G. Further studies on the evolution of *Mamiola jurtina* in the Isles of Scilly. *Heredity, 14*, 333–364 (1960).

132. Dunn, L. C. Variations in the segregation ratio as causes of variations in gene frequency. *Acta Genetica et Statistica Medica, 4*, 139–151 (1953).

133. Dunn, L. C. Studies of the genetic variability in populations of wild house mice. II. Analysis of eight additional alleles at locus T. *Genetics, 42*, 299–311 (1957).

134. Dunn, L. C., Variations in the transmission ratios of alleles through egg and sperm in *Mus musculus*. *Am. Naturalist, 94*, 385–393 (1960).

135. Dunn, L. C., Beasley, A. B., and Tinker, H. Relative fitness of wild house mice heterozygous for a lethal allele. *Am. Naturalist, 92*, 215–220 (1958).

136. Dunn, L. C., Beasley, A. B., and Tinker, H. Polymorphisms in populations of wild house mice. *J. Mammology, 41*, 220–229 (1960).

137. Ehrmann, L. The genetics of hybrid sterility in *D. paulistorum*. *Evolution, 14*, 212–223 (1960).

138. Ehrmann, L. The genetics of sexual isolation in *D. paulistorum*. *Genetics, 46*, 1025–1038 (1961).

139. Falconer, D. S. Selection for phenotypic intermediates in Drosophila. *J. Genetics, 55*, 551–561 (1957).

140. Falconer, D. S., and Robertson, A. Selection for environmental variability of body size in mice. *Z. indukt. Abstamm.-u. Vererbungslehre, 87*, 385–391 (1956).

141. Falk, R. Are induced mutations in Drosophila overdominant? II. Experimental results. *Genetics, 46*, 737–758 (1961).

142. Fisher, R. A., and Ford, E. B. The spread of a gene in natural conditions in a colony of the moth, *Panaxia dominula* L. *Heredity, 1*, 143–174 (1947).

143. Fisher, R. A. Selective forces in wild populations of *Paratettix texanus*. *Ann. Eugen., London, 9*, 109–122 (1939).

144. Fisher, R. A. Population genetics. *Proc. Roy. Soc., 141B*, 510–523 (1953).

145. Fisher, R. A. Polymorphism and natural selection. *J. Ecology, 46*, 289–293 (1958).

146. Ford, E. B. The genetics of polymorphism in the Lepidoptera. *Adv. in Genetics, 5*, 43–88 (1953).

147. Ford, E. B. Rapid evolution and the conditions which make it possible. *Cold Spring Harbor Symp. Quant. Biol., 20*, 230–238 (1955).

148. Ford, E. B. A discussion on the dynamics of natural populations. *Proc. Roy. Soc., 145*, 291–364 (1956).

149. Glass, B. Genetic changes in human populations, especially those due to gene flow and genetic drift. *Adv. in Genetics, 6*, 95–140 (1954).

150. Gibson, J. B., and Thoday, J. M. Recombinational lethals in a polymorphic population. *Nature, 184,* 1593–1594 (1959).

151. Goldschmidt, Elisabeth. Polymorphism and coadaptation in natural populations of D. *subobscura. Proc. 10th Intl. Cong. Entomology, 2,* 821–828 (1956).

152. Goldschmidt, E., Wahrman, J., Ledermanklein, A., and Weiss, R. A two years survey of population dynamics in D. *melanogaster. Evolution, 9,* 353–366 (1955).

153. Goldschmidt, E., and Falk, R. On the dominance of "recessive" lethals. *Bull. Res. Counc. of Israel, 8B,* 1–8 (1959).

154. Greenberg, Rayla, and Crow, J. F. A comparison of the effect of lethal and detrimental chromosomes from Drosophila populations. *Genetics, 45,* 1154–1168 (1960).

155. Gordon, Hugh and Gordon, M. Maintenance of polymorphism by potentially injurious genes in 8 natural populations of the platyfish, *Xiphophorus maculatus. J. Genetics, 55,* 1–44 (1957).

156. Gregg, T. G. Genetic studies of irradiated natural populations of Drosophila. III. Experimental populations of D. *ananassae* derived from irradiated natural populations. *Univ. Texas Publ., 5914,* 207–222 (1959).

157. Haldane, J. B. S. The measurement of natural selection. *Proc. 9th Intern. Cong. Genetics,* 480–487 (1954).

158. Haldane, J. B. S. An exact test for randomness of mating. *J. Genetics, 52,* 631–635 (1954).

159. Haldane, J. B. S. The theory of selection for melanism in Lepidoptera. *Proc. Roy. Soc., B., 145,* 303–306 (1956).

160. Haldane, J. B. S. Estimation of viability. *J. Genetics, 54,* 294–296 (1956).

161. Haldane, J. B. S. The relation between density regulation and natural selection. *Proc. Roy. Soc. B., 145,* 306–308 (1956).

162. Haldane, J. B. S. Conditions for co-adaptation in polymorphism for inversions. *J. Genetics, 55,* 218–225 (1957).

163. Haldane, J. B. S. Cost of natural selection. *J. Genetics, 55,* 511–524 (1957).

164. Haldane, J. B. S. The theory of evolution before and after Bateson. *J. Genetics, 56,* 11–27 (1958).

165. Haldane, J. B. S. More precise expressions for the cost of natural selection. *J. Genetics, 57,* 351–360 (1961).

166. Hiraizumi, Y. Negative correlation between rate of development and female fertility in D. *melanogaster. Genetics, 46,* 615–624 (1961).

167. Hiraizumi, Y., and Crow, J. F. Heterozygous effects on viability, fertility, rate of development, and longevity of Drosophila chromosomes that are lethal when homozygous. *Genetics, 45,* 1071–1083 (1960).

168. Hiraizumi, Y., Sandler, L., and Crow, J. Meiotic drive in natural populations of D. *melanogaster.* III. Populational implications of the segregation-distorter locus. *Evolution, 14,* 433–444 (1960).

169. Hochman, B. Competition between wild type isoalleles in experimental populations of D. *melanogaster. Genetics, 43,* 101–121 (1958).

170. Hochman, B. Isoallelic competition in populations of *D. melanogaster* containing a genetically heterogeneous background. *Evolution, 15,* 239–246 (1961).

171. Hoenigsberg, H. F. Sexual behavior: a discussion. *Evolution, 14,* 527 (1960).

172. Hoenigsberg, H. F., and Santibanez, S. K. Courtship and sensory preferences in inbred lines of *D. melanogaster. Evolution, 14,* 1–7 (1960).

173. Hollingsworth, M. J., and Smith, J. M. The effects of inbreeding on rate of development and on fertility in *D. subobscura. J. Genetics, 53,* 295 (1955).

174. Huxley, J. S. Morphism and evolution. *Heredity, 9,* 1–52 (1955).

175. Ives, P. T. The genetic structure of American populations of *D. melanogaster. Genetics, 30,* 167–196 (1945).

176. Ives, P. T. Genetic changes in American populations of *D. melanogaster. Proc. Nat. Acad. Sci., 40,* 87–92 (1954).

177. Ives, P. T. Chromosomal distribution of mutator- and radiation-induced mutations in *D. melanogaster. Evolution, 13,* 526–531 (1959).

178. Kerr, W. E., and Wright, S. Experimental studies of the distribution of gene frequencies in very small populations of *D. melanogaster.* I. Forked. *Evolution, 8,* 172–177 (1954).

179. Kerr, W. E., and Wright, S. Experimental studies of the distribution of gene frequencies in very small populations of *D. melanogaster.* III. Aristapedia and spineless. *Evolution, 8,* 293–302 (1954).

180. Kerr, W. E., and Kerr, L. S. Concealed variability in the X-chromosome of *D. melanogaster. Am. Naturalist, 86,* 405–408 (1952).

181. Kettlewell, H. B. D. Selection experiments on industrial melanism in the Lepidoptera. *Heredity, 9,* 323–342 (1955).

182. Kettlewell, H. B. D. A resumé of investigations on the evolution of melanism in the Lepidoptera. *Proc. Roy. Soc. B., 145,* 297–303 (1956).

183. Kettlewell, H. B. D. Further selection experiments on industrial melanism in the Lepidoptera. *Heredity, 10,* 287–303 (1956).

184. Kettlewell, H. B. D. A survey of the frequencies of *Biston betularia* L. (Lep.), and its melanic forms in Great Britain. *Heredity, 12,* 51–72 (1958).

185. Kettlewell, H. B. D. Industrial melanism in the Lepidoptera and its contribution to our knowledge of evolution. *Proc. 10th Intern. Cong. Entomology, 2,* 831–841 (1958).

186. Kettlewell, H. B. D. The phenomenon of industrial melanism in Lepidoptera. *Ann. Rev. Entomology, 6,* 245–262 (1961).

187. Kimura, Motoo. Stochastic processes and distribution of gene frequencies under natural selection. *Cold Spring Harbor Symp. Quant. Biol., 20,* 33–53 (1955).

188. Kimura, Motoo. A model of a genetic system which leads to closer linkage by natural selection. *Evolution, 10,* 278–287 (1956).

189. Kimura, Motoo. Optimum mutation rate and degree of dominance as determined by the principle of minimum genetic load. *J. Genetics, 57,* 21–34 (1960).

190. Kimura, Motoo. Natural selection as the process of accumulating genetic information in adaptive evolution. *Genetical Research, 2,* 127–140 (1961).

191. King, James C. Evidence for the integration of the gene pool from studios of DDT resistance in Drosophila. *Cold Spring Harbor Symp. Quant. Biol., 20,* 311–317 (1955).

192. King, James C. Integration of the gene pool as demonstrated by resistance to DDT. *Am Naturalist, 89,* 39–46 (1955).

193. King, James C. Some light on population dynamics provided by lines of *D. melanogaster* selected for resistance to DDT. *Proc. 10th Intern. Cong. Entomology, 2,* 811–820 (1958).

194. King, James C., and Somme, L. Chromosomal analyses of the genetic factors for resistance to DDT in two resistant lines of *D. melanogaster. Genetics, 43,* 577–593 (1958).

195. Kitsmiller, J. B., and Lawen, H. Speciation in mosquitoes. *Cold Spring Harbor Symp. Quant. Biol., 24,* 161–175 (1959).

196. Knight, G. R., and Robertson, A. Fitness as a measurable character in Drosophila. *Genetics, 42,* 524–530 (1957).

197. Knight, G. R., Robertson, Alan, and Waddington, C. H. Selection for sexual isolation within a species. *Evolution, 10,* 14–22 (1956).

198. Komai, T. Comparison of wild populations in the lycaenid butterfly, *Neozephyrus taxila. Am. Naturalist, 87,* 87–95 (1953).

199. Komai, T. Genetics in ladybeetles. *Adv. in Genetics, 8,* 155–189 (1956).

200. Koopman, Karl F. Natural selection for reproductive isolation between *D. pseudoobscura* and *D. persimilis. Evolution, 4,* 135–148 (1950).

201. Krimbas, Costas. Comparison of concealed variability in *D. willistoni* with that in *D. prosaltans. Genetics, 44,* 1359–1369 (1959).

202. Lamotte, M. Polymorphism of natural populations of *Cepaea nemoralis. Cold Spring Harbor Symp. Quant. Biol., 24,* 65–86 (1959).

203. Levene, H. Genetic equilibrium when more than one ecological niche is available. *Am. Naturalist, 87,* 311 (1953).

204. Levene, H. Release of genetic variability through recombination. IV. Statistical theory. *Genetics, 44,* 93–104 (1959).

205. Levene, H. and Dobzhansky, Th. New evidence of heterosis in naturally occurring inversion heterozygotes in *D. pseudoobscura. Heredity, 12,* 37–49 (1958).

206. Levene, H. and Dobzhansky, Th. Possible genetic difference between the head louse and the body louse (*Pediculus humanus* L.). *Am. Naturalist, 93,* 347–353 (1959).

207. Levene, H., Pavlovsky, O., and Dobzhansky, Th. Interaction of the adaptive values in polymorphic experimental populations of *D. pseudoobscura. Evolution, 8,* 335–349 (1954).

208. Levene, H., Pavolvsky, O., and Dobzhansky, Th. Dependence on the adaptive values of certain genotypes in *D. pseudoobscura* on composition of gene pool. *Evolution, 12,* 18–23 (1958).

209. Levine, Louis. Studies on sexual selection in mice. I. Reproductive competition between albino and black-agouti males. *Am. Naturalist, 92,* 21–26 (1958).

210. Levine, Louis, and Beardmore, J. A. A study of an experimental population in equilibrium. *Am. Naturalist, 93,* 35–40 (1959).

211. Levine, Louis, and Dunn, L. C. Frequency of t^w alleles in a confined population of wild house mice. *Proc. Soc. Exp. Biol. & Medicine, 92,* 308–310 (1956).

212. Levine, R. P., and Ives, P. T. Mutation rates and lethal gene frequencies in populations of *D. melanogaster. Proc. Nat. Acad. Sci., 39,* 817–823 (1953).

213. Levitan, Max. Studies of linkage in populations. I. Associations of second chromosome inversions in *D. robusta. Evolution, 9,* 62–74 (1955).

214. Levitan, Max. Non-random associations of inversions. *Cold Spring Harbor Symp. Quant. Biol., 23,* 251–268 (1958).

215. Levitan, Max. Studies of linkage in populations. II. Recombination between linked inversions of *D. robusta. Genetics, 43,* 620–633 (1958).

216. Levitan, Max, and Salzano, F. M. Studies of linkage in populations. III. An association of linked inversions in *D. guaramanu. Heredity, 13,* 243–248 (1959).

217. Lewontin, R. C. The effects of population density and composition on viability in *D. melanogaster. Evolution, 9,* 27–41 (1955).

218. Lewontin, R. C. Studies on homeostasis and heterozygosity. I. General considerations abdominal bristle number in second chromosome homozygotes of *D. melanogaster. Am. Naturalist, 90,* 237–255 (1956).

219. Lewontin, R. C. The adaptations of populations to varying environments. *Cold Spring Harbor Symp. Quant. Biol., 22,* 395–408 (1957).

220. Lewontin, R. C. A general method for investigating the equilibrium of gene frequency in a population. *Genetics, 43,* 419–434 (1958).

221. Lewontin, R. C. Studies on heterozygosity and homeostasis. II. Loss of heterosis in a constant environment. *Evolution, 12,* 494–503 (1958).

222. Lewontin, R. C., and Dunn, L. C. The evolutionary dynamics of a polymorphism in the house mouse. *Genetics, 45,* 705-722 (1960).

223. Lewontin, R. C., and Kojima, Ken-ichi. The evolutionary dynamics of complex polymorphisms. *Evolution, 14,* 458–472 (1960).

224. Lewontin, R. C., and White, M. J. D. Interaction between inversion polymorphisms of two chromosome pairs in the grasshopper, *Moraba scurra. Evolution, 14,* 116–129 (1960).

225. Li, C. C. The stability of an equilibrium and the average fitness of a population. *Am. Naturalist, 89,* 281–295 (1955).

226. Lints, F. A. Nucleo-cytoplasmic interactions in *D. melanogaster. Genetica, 31,* 188–239 (1960).

227. Malagolowkin, C., and Carvalho, G. Direct and indirect transfer of the "sex ratio" condition in different species of Drosophila. *Genetics, 46,* 1009–1013 (1961).

228. Mandel, S. P. H. Stability of a multiple allelic system. *Heredity, 13,* 289–302 (1959).

229. Marien, Daniel. Selection for developmental rate in *D. pseudoobscura*. *Genetics, 43,* 3–15 (1958).

230. Mather, K. Genetical control of stability in development. *Heredity, 7,* 297–336 (1953).

231. Mather, K. The genetical structure of populations. *Symp. Soc. Exp. Biol., 7,* 66–95 (1953).

232. Mather, K. Polymorphism as an outcome of disruptive selection. *Evolution, 9,* 52–61 (1955).

233. Mather, K. Response to selection. *Cold Spring Harbor Symp. Quant. Biol., 20,* 158–165 (1955).

234. Mather, K., and Harrison, B. J. The manifold effect of selection. *Heredity, 3,* 1–52, 131–162 (1949).

235. Mayr, Ernst. Integration of genotypes: synthesis. *Cold Spring Harbor Symp. Quant. Biol., 20,* 327–333 (1955).

236. Mayr, Ernst. Where are we? *Cold Spring Harbor Symp. Quant. Biol., 24,* 1–14 (1959).

237. McDonald, Daniel J., and Peer, N. J. Natural selection in experimental populations of Tribolium. I. Preliminary experiments with population cages. *Genetics, 45,* 1317–1333 (1960).

238. Merrell, D. J. Measurement of sexual isolation and selective mating. *Evolution, 4,* 326–331 (1950).

239. Merrell, D. J. Gene frequency changes in small laboratory populations of *D. melanogaster*. *Evolution, 7,* 95–101 (1953).

240. Merrell, D. J. Selective mating as a cause of gene frequency changes in laboratory populations of *D. melanogaster*. *Evolution, 7,* 287–296 (1953).

241. Merrell, D. J. Sexual isolation between *D. persimilis* and *D. pseudoobscura*. *Am. Naturalist, 88,* 93–99 (1954).

242. Merrell, D. J. Heterosis in DDT resistant and susceptible populations of *D. melanogaster*. *Genetics, 45,* 573–581 (1960).

243. Merrell, D. J. Mating preferences in Drosophila. *Evolution, 14,* 525–526 (1960).

244. Merrell, D. J., and Underhill, J. C. Selection for DDT resistance in inbred, laboratory and wild stocks of *D. melanogaster*. *J. Econ. Entomology, 49,* 300–306 (1955).

245. Merrell, D. J., and Underhill, J. C. Competition between mutants in experimental populations of *D. melanogaster, Genetics, 41,* 469–485 (1956).

246. Mettler, L. E. XII. Studies on experimental populations of *D. arizonensis* and *D. mojavensis*. *Genetics of Drosophila (Univ. Texas Publ.), 5721,* 157–181 (1957).

247. Milkman, R. D. The genetic basis of natural variation. I. Crossveins in *D. melanogaster*. *Genetics, 45,* 35–48 (1960).

248. Milkman, R. D. The genetic basis of natural variation. II. Analysis of a polygenic system in *D. melanogaster*. *Genetics, 45,* 377–391 (1960).

249. Milkman, R. D. The genetic basis of natural variation. III. Developmental lability and evolutionary potential. *Genetics, 46,* 25–38 (1961).

250. Miller, Dwight D. Sexual isolation and variation in mating behavior within *D. athabasca. Evolution, 12,* 72–81 (1958).

251. Millicent, E., and Thoday, J. M. Gene flow and divergence under disruptive selection. *Science, 131,* 1311–1312 (1960).

252. Moore, J. A. Abnormal combinations of nuclear and cytoplasmic systems in frogs and toads. *Adv. in Genetics, 7,* 139–182 (1955).

253. Moos, Joan R. Comparative physiology of some chromosomal types in *D. pseudo-obscura. Evolution, 9,* 141–151 (1954).

254. Moriwaki, D., Ohnishi, M., and Nakajima, Y. Analysis of heterosis in populations of *D. ananassae. Cytologia (Vol. Suppl. 22),* 370–379 (1957).

255. Morton, N. E., and Chung, C. S. Are the MN blood groups maintained by selection? *Am. J. Human Genetics, 11,* 237–251 (1959).

256. Morton, N. E., Crow, J. F., and Muller, H. J. An estimate of the mutational damage in man from data on consanguineous marriages. *Proc. Natl. Acad. Sci. U.S., 42,* (1956).

257. Mourant, A. E. Human blood groups and natural selection. *Cold Spring Harbor Symp. Quant. Biol., 24,* 57–63 (1959).

258. Mukai, T., and Burdick, A. B. Single gene heterosis associated with a second chromosome recessive lethal in *D. melanogaster. Genetics, 44,* 211–232 (1959).

259. Mukai, T., and Burdick, A. B. Concerning equilibria of heterotic lethals in random mating populations with particular reference to 1(2)55i— in *D. melanogaster. Genetics, 45,* 1581–1594 (1960).

260. Muller, H. J. Our load of mutations. *Am. J. Human Genetics, 2,* 111–176 (1950).

261. Muller, H. J. Partial dominance in relation to the need for studying induced mutations individually. *J. Cell. Comp. Physiol., 35, Suppl. 1,* 205–210 (1950).

262. Muller, H. J. Further studies bearing on the load of mutations in man. *Acta Genetica, 6,* 157–168 (1956).

263. Muller, H. J., and Falk, R. Are induced mutations in Drosophila overdominant? I. Experimental design. *Genetics, 46,* 727–736 (1961).

264. Neel, James V. Some problems in the estimation of spontaneous mutation rates in animals and man. *Effect of Radiation on Human Heredity World Health Organization Geneva,* 139–150 (1957).

265. Novitski, E., and Dempster, E. R. An analysis of data from laboratory populations of *D. melanogaster. Genetics, 43,* 470–479 (1958).

266. Oshima, C. Studies on the laboratory populations of *D. virilis. Evolution, 7,* 187–197 (1953).

267. Oshima, C. Studies on DDT-resistance in *D. melanogaster. J. Heredity, 49,* 22–31 (1958).

268. Oshima, C., and Kitagawa, O. The persistence of deleterious genes in natural populations of *D. melanogaster. Proc. Japan Acad., 37,* 158–162 (1961).

269. Owen, A. R. G. Genetical system admitting of two distinct stable equilibria under natural selection. *Heredity, 7,* 97–102 (1953).

270. Owen, A. R. G. Balanced polymorphism of a multiple allelic series. *Proc. 9th Intern. Cong. Genetics*, 1240–1241 (1954).

271. Paik, Y. K. Genetic variability in Korean populations of *D. melanogaster*. *Evolution, 14*, 293–303 (1960).

272. Pavan, C., Cordeiro, A. R., Dobzhansky, N., Dobzhansky, Th., Malogolowkin, C., Spassky, B., and Wedel, M. Concealed genic variability in Brazilian populations of *D. willistoni*. *Genetics, 36*, 13–30 (1951).

273. Pavan, C., Dobzhansky, Th., and da Cunha, A. B. Heterosis and elimination of weak homozygotes in natural populations of 3 related species of Drosophila. *Proc. Natl. Acad. Sci., 43*, 226–234 (1957).

274. Pavan, C., Knapp, E. N. The genetic population structure of Brazilian *D. willistoni*. *Evolution, 8*, 303–313 (1954).

275. Penrose, L. S. Mutation in man. *Acta Genetica, 6*, 169–182 (1956).

276. Penrose, L. S., Smith, S. M., and Sprott, D. A. On the stability of allelic systems, with special reference to haemoglobins A, S and C. *Annals Human Genetics, 21*, 90–93 (1956).

277. Petit, C. Le déterminisme génétique et psycho-physiologique de la compétition sexuelle chez *D. melanogaster*. *Bull. Biol. de France et Belgique, 92*, 248–329 (1958).

278. Prevosti, Antonio. Geographic variability in quantitative traits in populations of *D. subobscura*. *Cold Spring Harbor Symp. Quant. Biol., 20*, 294–299 (1955).

279. Prout, T. Selection against heterozygotes for autosomal lethals in natural populations of *D. willistoni*. *Proc. Nat. Acad. Sci., 38*, 478–481 (1952).

280. Prout, T. Genetic drift in irradiated experimental populations of *D. melanogaster*. *Genetics, 39*, 529–545 (1954).

281. Rasmuson, M. Selection for bristle numbers in some unrelated strains of *D. melanogaster*. *Acta Zool. (Stockholm), 36*, 1–49 (1955).

282. Rasmuson, M. Recurrent reciprocal selection. Results of three model experiments on Drosophila for improvement of quantitative characters. *Hereditas, 42*, 397–414 (1956).

283. Reed, S. C., and Reed, E. W. Natural selection in laboratory populations of Drosophila. II. Competition between a white-eye gene and its wild type allele. *Evolution, 4*, 34–42 (1950).

284. Reed, T. E. The definition of relative fitness of individuals with specific genetic traits. *Am. J. Human Genetics, 11*, 137–155 (1959).

285. Reeve, E. C. R. Some genetic tests on asymmetry of sternopleural chaeta number in Drosophila. *Genetical Research, 1*, 151–172 (1959).

286. Reeve, E. C. R. Modifying the sternopleural hair pattern in Drosophila by selection. *Genetical Research, 2*, 158–160 (1961).

287. Reeve, E. C. R., and Robertson, F. W. Studies in quantitative inheritance. II. Analysis of a strain of *D. melanogaster* selected for long wings. *J. Genetics, 51*, 276–316 (1953).

288. Remington, C. L. The genetics of *Colias* (Lepidoptera). *Adv. in Genetics, 6*, 403–451 (1954).

289. Robertson, Alan. Selection in animals: synthesis. *Cold Spring Harbor Symp. Quant. Biol., 20*, 225–229 (1955).

290. Robertson, Alan. The effect of selection against extreme deviants based on deviation or on homozygosis. *J. Genetics, 54*, 236–248 (1956).

291. Robertson, F. W. Selection response and the properties of genetic variation. *Cold Spring Harbor Symp. Quant. Biol., 20*, 166–177 (1955).

292. Robertson, F. W. Studies in quantitative inheritance. XI. Genetic and environmental correlation between body size and egg production in *D. melanogaster. J. Genetics, 55*, 428–443 (1957).

293. Robertson, F. W. Studies in quantitative inheritance. XII. Cell size and number in relation to genetic and environmental variation of body size in Drosophila. 869–896 (1959).

294. Robertson, F. W. Gene-environment interaction in relation to the nutrition and growth of Drosophila. *Univ. of Texas Publ., 5914*, 88–98 (1959).

295. Robertson, F. W. Ecological genetics of growth in Drosophila. I. Body size and developmental time on different diets. *Genetical Research, 1*, 288–304 (1960).

296. Robertson, F. W. Ecological genetics of growth in Drosophila. II. Selection for large body size on different diets. *Genetical Research, 1*, 305–318 (1960).

297. Robertson, F. W. Ecological genetics in growth in Drosophila. III. Growth and competitive ability of strains selected on different diets. *Genetical Research, 1*, 333–350 (1960)

298. Robertson, F. W., and Reeve, E. Studies in quantitative inheritance. I. The effects of selection of wing and thorax length in *D. melanogaster. J. Genetics, 50*, 414–448 (1952).

299. Sandler, L., Hiraizumi, Y., and Sandler, S. Meiotic drive in natural populations of *D. melanogaster*. I. Cytogenetic basis of segregation-distortion. *Genetics, 44*, 233–250 (1959).

300. Sandler, L., and Hiraizumi, Y. Meiotic drive in natural populations of *D. melanogaster*. II. Genetic variation at the segregation-distorter locus. *Proc. Nat. Acad. Sci., 45*, 1412–1422 (1959).

301. Sandler, L., and Hiraizumi, Y. Meiotic drive in natural populations of *D. melanogaster*. IV. Instability at the segregation-distorter locus. *Genetics, 45*, 1269–1287 (1960).

302. Sandler, L., and Hiraizumi, Y. Meiotic drive in natural populations of *D. melanogaster*. V. On the nature of the SD region. *Genetics, 45*, 1671–1689 (1960).

303. Sandler, L., and Hiraizumi, Y. Meiotic drive in natural populations of *D. melanogaster*. VII. Conditional segregation distortion: a possible nonallelic conversion. *Genetics, 46*, 585–604 (1961).

304. Sang, J. H. Populational growth in Drosophila cultures. *Biological Review, 25*, 188–219 (1950).

305. Sang, J. H., and Clayton, G. A. Selection for larval development time in Drosophila. *Jour. Heredity, 48*, 265–270 (1957).

306. Santibanez, S. K., Casanova, A., and Brncic, D. Experiments on sexual isolation in species of the *mesophragmatica* group of Drosophila (Diptera). *Proc. Roy. Entomology Soc. London, 33,* 179–185 (1958).

307. Santibanez, S. K., and Waddington, C. H. The origin of sexual isolation between different lines within a species. *Evolution, 12,* 485–493 (1958).

308. Schnick, S. M., Mukai, T., and Burdick, A. B. Heterozygote viability of a second chromosome recessive lethal in *D. melanogaster. Genetics, 45,* 315–330 (1960).

309. Scossiroli, R. E. Effectiveness of artificial selection under irradiation of plateaued populations of *D. melanogaster. Symp. Genetics of Population Structure Intern. Union Biol. Sci., Series B, 15,* 42–66 (1954).

310. Scossiroli, R. E., and Scossiroli, S. On the relative role of mutation and recombination in responses to selection for polygenic traits in irradiated populations of *D. melanogaster. Intern. J. Rad. Biol., 1,* 61–69 (1959).

311. Shaw, Richard. The theoretical genetics of the sex ratio. *Genetics, 43,* 149–163 (1958).

312. Shaw, R. F., and Mahler, J. D. The selective significance of the sex ratio. *Am. Naturalist, 87,* 337–342 (1953).

313. Sheppard, P. M. Polymorphism and population studies. *Symp. Soc. Exp. Biol., 7,* 274–289 (1953).

314. Sheppard, P. M. Genetic variability and polymorphism: synthesis. *Cold Spring . Harbor Symp. Quant. Biol., 20,* 271–275 (1955).

315. Smith, J. M. Acclimatization to high temperatures in inbred and outbred *D. subobscura. J. Genetics, 54,* 497–505 (1956).

316. Smith, J. M. Fertility, mating behaviour, and sexual selection in *D. subobscura. J. Genetics, 54,* 261–279 (1956).

317. Smith, J. M., and Smith, S. M. Genetics and cytology of *D. subobscura.* VIII. Heterozygosity, viability, and rate of development. *J. Genetics, 52,* 152–164 (1954).

318. Spassky, B., Spassky, N., Levene, H., and Dobzhansky, Th. Release of genetic variability through recombination. I. *Drosophila pseudoobscura. Genetics, 43,* 844–867 (1959).

319. Spassky, B., Spassky, N., Pavlovsky, D., Krimbas, M. G., Krimbas, C., and Dobzhansky, Th. Genetics of natural populations. XXIX. The magnitude of the genetic load in populations of *D. pseudoobscura. Genetics, 45,* 741–754 (1960).

320. Spiess, E. B. Relation between frequencies and adaptive values of chromosomal arrangements in *D. persimilis. Evolution, 11,* 84–93 (1957).

321. Spiess, E. B. Chromosomal adaptive polymorphism in *D. persimilis.* II. Effects of population cage conditions on life cycle components. *Evolution, 12,* 234–245 (1958).

322. Spiess, E. B. Effects of recombination on viability in Drosophila. *Cold Spring Harbor Symp. Quant. Biol., 23,* 239–250 (1958).

323. Spiess, E. B. Release of genetic variability through recombination. II. *D. persimilis. Genetics, 44,* 43–58 (1959).

324. Spiess, E. B. Chromosomal fitness changes in experimental populations of *D. persimilis* from Timberline in the Sierra Nevada. *Evolution, 15,* 340–351 (1961).

325. Spiess, E. B., and Langer, B., with appendix by Li, C. C. Chromosomal adaptive polymorphism in *D. persimilis*. III. Mating propensity of homokaryotypes. *Evolution, 15,* 535-544.

326. Spiess, E. B., and Schuellein, R. J. Chromosomal adaptive polymorphism in *D. persimilis*. I. Life cycle components under near optimal conditions. *Genetics, 41,* 501–516 (1956).

327. Spieth, H. T. Mating behavior within the genus D. (Diptera). *Bull. Am. Museum Nat. Hist., 99,* 399–474 (1952).

328. Spofford, J. B. The relation between expressivity and selection against eyeless in *D. melanogaster*. *Genetics, 41,* 938–959 (1956).

329. Stalker, H. D. Chromosomal polymorphism in *D. paramelanica* Patterson. *Genetics, 45,* 95–114 (1960).

330. Stalker, H. D. The genetic systems modifying meiotic drive in *D. paramelanica*. *Genetics, 46,* 177–202 (1961).

331. Stern, C., Carson, G., Kinst, M., Novitski, E., and Uphoff, D. The viability of heterozygotes for lethals. *Genetics, 37,* 413–449 (1952).

332. Stone, W. S., Alexander, M. L., Clayton, F. E. Heterosis studies with species of Drosophila living in small populations. *Univ. Texas Publ., 5422,* 272–307 (1954).

333. Stone, W. S., and Wilson, Florence D. Genetic studies of irradiated natural populations of Drosophila. II. 1957 tests. *Proc. Nat. Acad. Sci., 44.* 565–575 (1958).

334. Stone, W. S., and Wilson, F. D. Genetic studies of irradiated natural populations of Drosophila. IV. 1958 tests. *Univ. Texas Publ., 5914,* 223–233 (1959).

335. Stumm-Zollinger, E., and Goldschmidt, E. Geographical differentiation of inversion systems in *D. subobscura*. *Evolution, 13,* 89–98 (1959).

336. Susman, M., and Carson, H. L. Development of balanced polymorphism in laboratory populations of *D. melanogaster*. *Am. Naturalist, 92,* 359–364 (1958).

337. Tantawy, A. O. Selection limits with sibmatings in *D. melanogaster*. *Genetics, 44,* 287–295 (1959).

338. Tantawy, A. O. Effects of temperature on productivity and genetic variance of body size in populations of *D. pseudoobscura*. *Genetics, 46,* 227–238 (1961).

339. Tantawy, A. O. Developmental homeostasis in populations of *D. pseudoobscura*. *Evolution, 15,* 132–144 (1961).

340. Tantawy, A. O., and Mallah, G. S. Studies on natural populations of Drosophila. I. Heat resistance and geographical variations in *D. melanogaster* and *D. simulans*. *Evolution, 15,* 1–14 (1961).

341. Tantawy, A. O., and Vetukhiv, M. O. Effects of size on fecundity, longevity and viability in populations of *D. pseudoobscura*. *Am. Naturalist, 94,* 395–404 (1960).

342. Tebb, G., and Thoday, J. M. Stability in development and relational balance of X-chromosomes in *D. melanogaster*. *Nature, 174,* 1109–1110 (1954).

343. Thoday, J. M. Components of fitness. *Symp. Soc. Exp. Biol., 7,* 96–113 (1953).

344. Thoday, J. M. Balance, heterozygosity and developmental stability. *Cold Spring Harbor Symp. Quant. Biol., 20,* 318–326 (1955).

345. Thoday, J. M. Homeostasis in a selection experiment. *Heredity, 12,* 401–416 (1958).

346. Thoday, J. M. Effects of disruptive selection. I. Genetic flexibility. *Heredity, 13,* 187–204 (1959).

347. Thoday, J. M. Effects of disruptive selection. III. Coupling and repulsion. *Heredity, 14,* 35–49 (1960).

348. Thoday, J. M., and Boam, T. B. Effects of disruptive selection. II. Polymorphism and divergence without isolation. *Heredity, 13,* 205–218 (1959).

349. Thorpe, W. H. The evolutionary significance of habitat selection. *J. Animal Ecol., 14,* 67–70 (1945).

350. Townsend, J. I. Chromosomal polymorphism is Caribbean Island populations of *D. willistoni. Proc. Nat. Acad. Sci., 44,* 38–42 (1958).

351. Vetukhiv, M., Viability of hybrids between local populations of *D. pseudoobscura. Proc. Nat. Acad. Sci., 39,* 30–34 (1953).

352. Vetukhiv, M. Integration of the genotype in local populations of three species of Drosophila. *Evolution, 8,* 241–251 (1954).

353. Vetukhiv, M. Fecundity of hybrids between geographic populations of *D. pseudoobscura. Evolution, 10,* 139–146 (1956).

354. Vetukhiv, M. Longevity of hybrids between geographic populations of *D. pseudoobscura. Evolution, 11,* 348–360 (1957).

355. Waddington, C. H. Genetic assimilation of an acquired character. *Evolution, 7,* 118–126 (1953).

356. Waddington, C. H. Environmental selection by Drosophila mutants. *Evolution, 8,* 89–96 (1954).

357. Waddington, C. H. Genetic assimilation of the bithorax phenotype. *Evolution, 10,* 1–13 (1956).

358. Waddington, C. H. The genetic basis of the "assimilated bithorax" stock. *J. Genetics, 55,* 241–245 (1957).

359. Waddington, C. H. Experiments on canalizing selection. *Genetical Research, 1,* 140–150 (1960).

360. Waddington, C. H., Graber, H., and Woolf, B. Iso-alleles and the response to selection. *J. Genetics, 55,* 246–250 (1957).

361. Wallace, B. Genetic divergence of isolated populations of *D. melanogaster. Caryologia,* 761–764 (1954).

362. Wallace, B. Inter-population hybrids in *D. melanogaster. Evolution, 9,* 302–316 (1955).

363. Wallace, B. Studies on irradiated populations of *D. melanogaster. J. Genetics, 54,* 280–293 (1956).

364. Wallace, B. Some of the problems accompanying an increase of mutation rates in Mendelian populations. Reprinted from "Effect of Radiation on Human Heredity", *World Health Organization, Geneva,* 57–62 (1957).

365. Wallace, B. The average effect of radiation-induced mutations on viability in *D. melanogaster. Evolution, 12,* 532–556 (1958).

366. Wallace, B. The role of heterozygosity in Drosophila populations. *Proc. 10th Int. Cong. Genetics, 1*, 408–419 (1958).

367. Wallace, B. Influence of genetic systems on geographical distribution. *Cold Spring Harbor Symp. Quant. Biol., 24*, 193–204 (1959).

368. Wallace, B. Studies of the relative fitnesses of experimental populations of *D. melanogaster. Am. Naturalist, 93*, 295–314 (1959).

369. Wallace, B., King, J. C., Madden, C. V., Kaufmann, B., and McGunnigle, E. C. An analysis of variability arising through recombination. *Genetics, 38*, 272–307 (1953).

370. Wallace, B., and Madden, C. The frequencies of sub- and supervitals in experimental populations of *D. melanogaster. Genetics, 38*, 456–470 (1953).

371. Wallace, B., and Vetukhiv, M. Adaptive organization of the gene pools of Drosophila populations. *Cold Spring Harbor Symp. Quant. Biol., 20*, 303–310 (1955).

372. Watson, G. S. The cytoplasmic "sex-ratio" condition in Drosophila. *Evolution, 14*, 256–265 (1960).

373. White, M. J. D. Cytogenetics of orthopteroid insects. *Adv. in Genetics, 4*, 268–330 (1951).

374. White, M. J. D. Adaptive chromosomal polymorphism in an Australian grasshopper. *Evolution, 10*, 298–313 (1956).

375. White, M. J. D. Some general problems of chromosomal evolution and speciation in animals. *Survey of Bio. Progress, 3*, 109–147 (1957).

376. White, M. J. D. Restrictions on recombination in grasshopper populations and species. *Cold Spring Harbor Symp. Quant. Biol., 23*, 307–317 (1958).

377. White, M. J. D., and Andrew, L. E. Cytogenetics of the grasshopper *Moraba scurra.* V. Biometric effects of chromosomal inversions. *Evolution, 14*, 284–292 (1960).

378. Woolf, Barnet. Estimation of mutation rates. I. Visible recessive characters detected in inbred lines maintained by single sib-matings. *J. Genetics, 52*, 332–353 (1954).

379. Wright, S. On the roles of directed and random changes in gene frequency in the genetics of populations. *Evolution, 2*, 279–294 (1948).

380. Wright, S. Classification of the factors of evolution. *Cold Spring Harbor Symp. Quant. Biol., 20*, 16–24 (1955).

381. Wright, S. Modes of selection. *Am. Naturalist, 90*, 5–24 (1956).

382. Wright, S. Physiological genetics, ecology of populations, and natural selection. *Prespectives in Biol. and Medicine, 3*, 107–151 (1959).

383. Wright, S. "Genetics and Twentieth Century Darwinism". A review and discussion. *Am. J. Human Gen., 12*, 365–372 (1960).

384. Wright, S., and Dobzhansky, Th. Genetics of natural populations. XII. Experimental reproduction of some of the changes caused by natural selections in certain populations of *D. pseudoobscura. Genetics, 31*, 125–156 (1946).

385. Wright, S., Dobzhansky, Th., and Hovanitz, W. Genetics of natural populations. VII. The allelism of lethals in the third chromosome of *D. pseudoobscura. Genetics, 27*, 363–394 (1942).

386. Wright, S., and Kerr, W. E. Experimental studies of the distribution of gene frequencies in very small populations of *D. melanogaster*. II. Bar. *Evolution, 8*, 225–240 (1954).

III. Supplementary papers

387. Birch, L. C. The genetic factor in population ecology. *Am. Nat., 94*, 5–24 (1960).

388. Carson, H. L. Heterosis and fitness in experimental populations of *D. melanogaster. Evolution, 15*, 496–509 (1961).

389. Clarke, J. M., Smith, J. M., and Sondhi, K. C. Asymmetrical response to selection for rate of development in *D. subobscura. Gen. Res., 2*, 70–81 (1961).

390. Hirsch, J. and Erlenmeyer-Kimling, L. Sign of taxis as a property of the genotype. *Science, 134*, 835–836 (1961).

391. Kimura, M. On the change of population fitness by natural selection. *Heredity, 12*, 145–167 (1958).

392. King, J. C. Inbreeding, heterosis and information theory. *Am. Nat., 95*, 345–364 (1961).

393. Kojima, K. and Kelleher, T. M. Changes of mean fitness in random mating populations when epistasis and linkage are present. *Genetics, 46*, 527–540 (1961).

394. McDonald, D. J. and Peer, N. J. Natural selection in experimental populations of Tribolium II. Factors affecting the fitness of the mutant "split" of *T. confusum. Heredity, 16*, 317–330 (1961).

395. Parsons, P. A. Dependence of genotypic viabilities on coexisting genotypes in Drosophila. *Heredity, 13*, 393–402 (1959).

396. Parsons, P. A. and Bodmer, W. F. The evolution of overdominance: natural selection and heterozygote advantage. *Nature, 190*, 7–12 (1961).

397. Rasmuson, M. Frequency of morphological deviants as a criterion of developmental stability. *Hereditas, 46*, 511–535 (1960).

398. Sondhi, K. C. Selection for a character with a bounded distribution of phenotypes in *D. subobscura. J. Genetics, 57*, 193–221 (1961).

399. Thoday, J. M. Location of polygenes. *Nature, 191*, 368–370 (1961).

400. Thoday, J. M., and Boam, T. B. Effects of disruptive selection. V. Quasi-random mating. *Heredity, 16*, 219–223 (1961).

PAPERS ON ANIMAL POPULATION GENETICS

THE MEASUREMENT OF NATURAL SELECTION

by

J. B. S. HALDANE

Although nearly a century has elapsed since DARWIN and WALLACE formulated the theory of evolution by natural selection, it is remarkable that no agreement exists as to how it should be measured. Ideally we should wish to follow a sufficient number of members of every genotype (including gametes) of a species through a life cycle, and discover what advantages or disadvantages each possesses at every stage. This is clearly impossible. But it would also be insufficient. For natural or artificial selection acts on phenotypes. It is ineffective unless it favours one genotype at the expense of another. But it may occur without doing so. If we only breed from the heaviest 1% of members of a pure line, this intense artificial selection has no effect on the distribution of weights in the next generation. Nor would natural selection of comparable intensity have any effect. This is indeed the usual criterion for a pure line, though it may break down if there are strong maternal influences.

We must not judge the intensity of natural selection by its effect on the next generation, but by a comparison of the actual parents of the next generation with the population of which they are a sample, biassed by the very fact of selection. In this communication I shall only consider selection by differential mortality over a certain part of the life cycle, and I shall mainly be concerned with continuously variable metrical characters such as weight. How shall we measure the intensity of selection?

If, over the period considered, 10% of the population die, it is reasonable to assume that the intensity of natural selection cannot exceed 10%, or, if a logarithmic scale is used, $-\log_e$ (.9) or .1054. If all phenotypes and genotypes have the same mortality, we say that the

Reprinted by permission of CARYOLOGIA from Proceedings of the
9th International Congress of Genetics: 480–487 (1954).

deaths are entirely accidental, and there is no natural selection. If one phenotype has no mortality at all, but all the deaths occur in others, we say that the intensity of selection is .1054. If we can distinguish several phenotypes, there is an optimal phenotype, or set of phenotypes, of which a fraction s_o survives, while of the total population a smaller fraction S survives. If all the population had belonged to the optimal phenotype, then a fraction s_o of it would have survived. The extra mortality due to natural selection is $s_o - S$. I define the intensity of natural selection as $I = \log_e s_o - \log_e S$. For example if $S = .9$ and $s_o = .95$, that is to say 10% of the whole population dies, but only 5% of the optimal phenotype, then $s_o - S = .05$, and $I = .0541$. The two measures are nearly the same when death rates are small.

In practice we generally consider only one measurable character x, say weight at birth, at a time. We can then roughly determine the value of x for which the mortality is a minimum. This is not usually, if ever, an extreme value, and is often close to the mean. Within this optimal phenotype we could doubtless pick out a still more « favoured » phenotype, to use DARWIN'S word, by other criteria. For example ducks' eggs have an optimal weight, but within the group of optimal weight there is presumably a group with optimal water content, if this could be determined without killing the eggs, and so on. Similarly there is an optimal genotype.

This measure of the intensity of selection for a metrical character is quite different from that of LUSH (1953). If the mean value of x is the same in the survivors as in the original population. LUSH puts the intensity of selection as zero. This may be justifiable when artificial selection is being measured. It is not so in the case of natural selection, which may have no effect on the mean, while considerably reducing the variance.

In some cases full data are available which enable us to measure S and s_0. Thus KARN and PENROSE (1951) recorded the birth weights of 13,730 babies, and the fractions in various weight groups which survived the hazards of birth and of the first 28 days of life. I shall only consider their data on the 6693 females. The mortality rates for males were slightly higher. The overall survival S was .959 ± .002. The survival for weights between 7.5 and 8.5 pounds was .985 ± .003. It fell to .414 ± .037 for babies weighing under 4.5 pounds, and to .905 ± .064 for weights over 10 pounds. Although the latter figure does not differ significantly from the optimal survival, there is no doubt of the lower viability of heavy babies. Although the distribution of birth-weights is decidedly negatively skew, and that of the weights of the dead babies is even bimodal, the ratio of survivors to dead, when plotted against weight at birth, has a very nearly normal (Gaussian) distribution. For KARN and PENROSE'S Fig. 3 shows that its logarithm, when plotted against birth weight, is well fitted by a parabola. That is to say if s_x is the fraction of babies of birth weight x which survives, $\dfrac{s_x}{1-s_x}$ gives a parabolic graph; and in the neighbourhood of the maximum value s_o, s_x gives a parabolic graph. The optimal survival s_o can be calculated with considerable accuracy, though the optimal birth-weight x_o is less precisely known. We find $s_o = .9828$, or very close to the survival frequency of the optimal group. That is to say only 1.7% of the babies would have died if all had been of the optimal weight, while, in fact 4.1% did so. Thus 58% of all the deaths were selective, on the sole criterion of weight, and the intensity of natural selection for weight was:

$$I = .0240 \pm .004.$$

These data do not, of course, show that any of the differences in weight were genetically determined. PENROSE (1953) has produced evidence that they depend to a considerable extent on the mother's genotype.

The effect of this natural selection on the population was to increase the mean birth weight from 7.06 to 7.13 pounds, that is to say by 1%, but to decrease the standard deviation of birth weights from 1.22 to 1.10, that is to say by 10%. Its effect in reducing the variance was therefore far greater than its effect in increasing the mean.

This appears to be true in every case where natural selection for a metrical character has been observed. A little of this selection against extremes may be due to the elimination of mutants. Thus the majority of human achondroplasic dwarfs result from recent mutation, and a large fraction of these die at birth or in the first month of life. But the intensity of natural selection on such a gene throughout the whole life cycle is less than the frequency in the population, and about equal to the mutation rate. Natural selection against achondroplasics contributes about 2×10^{-5} to KARN and PENROSE'S value of .024, that is to say about one thousandth. I believe that a large fraction of the selection is of homozygotes for pairs of genes at loci where the heterozygous genotype is fitter than either homozygote. That is to say selection is not mainly counterbalancing the effects of mutation, but those of segregation.

It is possible to calculate the intensity I of natural selection even when the fraction S of survivors is unknown, provided that the distributions of x among the population originally at risk, and among the survi-

vors, is known. For if the distribution fuction for the original popul·
ation is $dF = f_1 (x)dx$,

and that for the survivors is

$$dF = f_2 (x)dx,$$

then the fraction surviving for any given value of x is

$$s_x = \frac{Sf_2 (x)}{f_1 (x)}.$$

Hence if x_0 is the optimal value of x, for which s_x is greatest,

$$I = \log_e f_2 (x_0) - \log_e f_1 (x_0).$$

In particular if x has a normal distribution among the original population and among the survivors, and their means are m_1, m_2, their
standard deviations σ_1 and σ_2, then

$$I = \log_e \left(\frac{\sigma_1}{\sigma_2} \right) + \frac{(m_1 - m_2)^2}{2 (\sigma_1^2 - \sigma_2^2)}.$$

If m_1 and m_2 do not differ significantly, the last term may be neglected. And where it is not negligible it may often be made so by a change
in the scale of x, for example by taking logarithms.

RENDEL (1943) weighed 960 ducks' eggs of the N.P.I. breed. Of these
619 hatched, so $S = .6448$. The mean weight of the original population
was 73.92 ± 0.23 gms., that of those which hatched was 73.78 ± 0.27 gms.
The difference is insignificant. On the other hand the variance of weights
was reduced from 52.72 ± 2.18 to 43.87 ± 3.02, which was highly significant. This gives $I = .094$. However, the distributions were both rather
positively skew and leptokurtic. The distributions of the logarithms of
the weights were much more nearly normal, and give $I = .100 \pm .032$.
In this case about 30% of the total deaths during the period considered
were selective for weight. Many of the rest may have been selective for
other measurable characters.

However RENDEL made similar observations at the same time on 930
eggs of the Allport breed. Here S was $.6269$, but s_0 was only $.6445$, and
I only $.0276$, which is not significantly positive, though probably so. The
variance was in fact reduced from 44.62 to 41.32, but the reduction was
not significant at the 5% level.

WELDON (1901, 1904) and his pupil DI CESNOLA (1907) worked on
snails as follows. The earliest formed whorls of a snail's shell are preserved in the adult. So if we make measurements on the shells of young
snails, and on the early formed whorls of those adult snails, we can see
whether natural selection has been occurring. WELDON proved that this

had occurred, but could not measure its intensity. In *Clausilia laminata* he measured the distance from the apex to the external groove between two whorls at various angular distances measured backwards towards the apex from the point where the columellar distance from the apex was 5 millimetres. This gave him a shape parameter for the shell, measuring the increase in size with each successive coil.

He found that the mean values differed by less than 1% in 100 young snails and in the juvenile parts of 100 old ones. But the standard deviations were always less in the adults, on the average less by 11.4%. It follows that the intensity of natural selection for this character was about .12. DI CESNOLA'S somewhat less consistent data for *Helix arbustorum* give a value of about .10 for I.

WELDON'S sample of *Clausilia laminata* came from a fairly ancient German forest. When he repeated the work on a population of *Clausilia itala* from the citadel of Brescia, he found no evidence of natural selec-tion. We now see that this could be explained if this population were very homogeneous genetically, being derived from one or a few indivi-duals which had colonized the citadel. It would clearly be of great interest if an Italian biologist repeated this work, comparing the Brescia population with one less isolated.

A number of results of other workers are concordant with those here cited. We can, of course, apply the same methods to populations studied over the whole life cycle. Thus DOBZHANSKY (1953) described a population of *Drosophila pseudoobscura* which had reached equilibrium under labor-atory conditions, and which was polymorphic for two chromosomal configurations, ST and CH. The relative fitnesses, or adaptive values, of $\frac{ST}{ST}$, $\frac{ST}{CH}$ and $\frac{CH}{CH}$ were as $0.90 : 1.00 : 0.41$. If these fitnesses are as $1-h : 1 : 1-k$, it can easily be shown that under random mating the frequencies of the three genotypes at fertilization are : $\frac{k^2}{(h+k)^2}$, $\frac{2hk}{(h+k)^2}$, and $\frac{h^2}{(h+k)^2}$. If selection were entirely by mortality before maturity, the extra deaths of homozygotes would be $\frac{hk^2}{(h+k)^2} + \frac{kh^2}{(h+k)^2}$ or $\frac{hk}{h+k}$. Since $h = 0.1$, $k = 0.59$, $\frac{hk}{h+k} = .0855$, and $I = .089$, a value close to those found above.

In fact much of the selection was for fertility rather than for via-bility. This makes no difference to the value of I arrived at. The fact that the value found is close to those found above by quite different methods suggests that DOBZHANSKY'S results do not refer to a special case, but to a phenomenon which is occurring in many or most outbred populations.

It is entirely possible to apply WELDON'S method, with suitable modifications, to populations of shells of fossil molluscs, such as ammonites, and thus perhaps to discover that natural selection was occurring in Palaeozoic times.

The interpretation of such data must vary in different cases. If, for example, as with some of SALISBURY'S (1943) data on plants, the larger individuals contribute up to 800 times more seeds than the smaller, this may well be (as he showed to be the case for *Dianthus prolifer*) because the differences in growth were mainly determined by soil differences. There is no reason to assume selection for genotypes making for large sized plants. On the other hand when tne mean of parents, or of survivors, differs little from that of the original population, this kind of explanation is much less probable. It is difficult to suppose that the heavy babies or eggs, which had a higher death rate than those of the mean weight, were due to unfavourable environmental conditions, and it is reasonable to suppose that they were due to unfavourable genotypes, in these two cases maternal rather than individual. It is further reasonable to suppose that a good deal of the selection was not for weight as such, but for heterozygosity for genes at a number of loci which, among other things, control weight.

In all the cases considered selection reduced the variance, that is to say it was of the type described as stabilizing or normalizing. Probably almost all natural selection for a quantitative character is of this type. Even when the mean of x is appreciably higher in the parents of the next generation it is probable that selection occurs against very high values of x. This seems to be so in a good many cases of artificial selection. The individuals showing the selected character with the highest intensity are often weak or sterile. If this is so, natural selection, even when it is altering the genetic composition of a population, is probably usually weeding out homozygotes at a number of loci.

If a population is in equilibrium under selection for heterozygosis for genes at a number of loci, the mean value of a metrical character determinable in early life will not, in general, be quite the same in the parents of the next generation as in the population of which they are a sample biassed by natural selection, though it may not be very different. But this selective differential will not alter the genetical composition of the next generation.

8

The examples which I have discussed, apart from DOBZHANSKY'S data, all refer to natural selection by differential survival over a fraction of the life cycle. It is theoretically possible that this selection could be reversed over another part of the life cycle. But this is improbable, as it would usually involve a bimodal distribution of fitness, such as could occur if, for example, a structural heterozygote were viable but infertile. But even among these few examples there were very great differences in the intensities of selection. In RENDEL'S case the difference was certainly due to genetical differences between the two populations. In WELDON'S it may have been.

Similar work could and should be done on a number of different human, animal, and plant populations, for example by following up the survival and fertility of some thousands of men measured at school or in the army, by measurements on fossil populations, by following the birds which hatched from eggs of different weights through a life cycle, and so on. Only when this has been done shall we have a satisfactory knowledge concerning phenotypic natural selection. Genotypic natural selection will, of course, be still harder to follow. At present we merely know that both of them occur. We know very little about their intensity.

SUMMARY

When any phenotypic character is measured or otherwise determined, there is usually an optimal phenotype, whose fitness, either over the whole life cycle or a portion of it, exceeds that of other phenotypes. The intensity of natural selection for the character in question is defined as the logarithm of the ratio of the fitness of the optimal phenotype to that of the whole population. This can sometimes be determined from frequency distributions, even when the actual fitnesses are unknown. The values found for the intensity of natural selection range from near zero to about 12%. In all cases natural selection reduces variance by weeding out extreme forms.

BIBLIOGRAPHY

DI CESNOLA A. P., 1907. — *A first study of natural selection in* « Helix arbustorum » (Helicogena). Biometrika, *5:* 387-399.

DOBZHANSKY T., 1953. — *Evolution as a creative process.* Proc. IXth Int. Gen. Congress (in press).

KARN M. N. & PENROSE L. S., 1951. — *Birth weight and gestation time in relation to maternal age, parity, and infant survival.* Ann. Eugen, *16:* 147-164.

LUSH J. L., 1953. — *Rates of genetic change in populations of farm animals.* Proc. IXth Int. Cong. Genetics (in press).

PENROSE L. S. 1953. — *Some recent trends in human genetics.* Proc. IXth Int. Cong. Genetics (in press).

RENDEL J. M., 1943. — *Variations in the weights of hatched and unhatched ducks' eggs.* Biometrika, *33:* 48-58.

SALISBURY E. J., 1943. — *The reproductive capacity of plants.* [Bell, London].

WELDON W. F. R., 1901. — *A first study of natural selection in* Clausilia laminata (*Montagu*). Biometrika, *1:* 109-124.

—, 1904. — *Note on a Race of* Clausilia itala (*von Martens*). Biometrika, *3:* 299-307.

10

THE COST OF NATURAL SELECTION

By J. B. S. HALDANE

University College, London, and Indian Statistical Institute, Calcutta

(*Received* 10 *January*, 1957)

INTRODUCTION

It is well known that breeders find difficulty in selecting simultaneously for all the qualities desired in a stock of animals or plants. This is partly due to the fact that it may be impossible to secure the desired phenotype with the genes available. But, in addition, especially in slowly breeding animals such as cattle, one cannot cull even half the females, even though only one in a hundred of them combines the various qualities desired.

The situation with respect to natural selection is comparable. Kermack (1954) showed that characters which are positively correlated in time may be negatively correlated at any particular horizon. The genes available do not allow the production of organisms which are advanced in respect of both characters. In this paper I shall try to make quantitative the fairly obvious statement that natural selection cannot occur with great intensity for a number of characters at once unless they happen to be controlled by the same genes.

Consider a well-investigated example of natural selection, the spread of the dominant *carbonaria* gene through the population of *Biston betularia* in a large area of England (Kettlewell, 1956 *a*, *b*). Until about 1800 the original light type, which is inconspicuous against a background of pale lichens, was fitter than the mutant *carbonaria* due to a gene C. Then, as a result of smoke pollution, lichens were killed in industrial regions, and the tree trunks on which the moths rest during the day were more or less completely blackened. The cc moths became more conspicuous than Cc or CC and the frequency of the gene C increased, so that cc moths are now rare in polluted areas. During the process of selection a great many cc moths were eaten by birds. Kettlewell (1956 *b*) showed that the frequency of the more conspicuous phenotype may be halved in a single day.

Now if the change of environment had been so radical that ten other independently inherited characters had been subject to selection of the same intensity as that for colour, only $(\frac{1}{2})^{10}$, or one in 1024, of the original genotype would have survived. The species would presumably have become extinct. On the other hand, it could well have survived ten selective episodes of comparable intensity occurring in different centuries. We see, then, that natural selection must not be too intense. In what follows I shall try to estimate the effect of natural selection in depressing the fitness of a species.

The principal unit process in evolution is the substitution of one gene for another at the same locus. The substitution of a new gene order, a duplication, a deficiency, and so on, is a formally similar process. For the new order behaves as a unit like a gene in inheritance. The substitution of a maternally inherited self-reproducing cytoplasmic factor by a different such factor is formally similar to the substitution of a gene by another gene in a haploid or of a gene pair by another gene pair in a self-fertilized diploid. I shall show that the number of deaths needed to carry out this unit process by selective survival is independent of the intensity of selection over a wide range.

Reprinted by permission of A. K. Bhattacharyya from JOURNAL OF
GENETICS, **55**, 511–524 (1957).

11

Natural selection may be defined as follows in a population where generations are separate. The animals in a population are classified as early as possible in their life cycle for phenotypic characters or for genotypes. Some of them become parents of the next generation. A fictitious population of parents is then constituted, in which a parent of n progeny (counted at the same age as the previous generation) is counted n times. If the sex ratio is not unity a suitable correction must be made. If generations overlap Fisher's (1930) reproductive value can be used instead of a count of offspring. Natural selection is a statement of the fact that the fictitious parental population differs significantly from the population from which it was drawn. For example, with respect to any particular metrical character it may differ as regards the mean, variance, and other moments. A difference in means is called a selective differential (Lush, 1954).

Selection may be genotypic or phenotypic. Phenotypic selection may or may not result in genotypic selection. By definition it does not do so in a pure line. Nor need it do so in a genetically heterogeneous population. If underfed individuals are smaller than the mean, and also on an average yield less progeny as a result of premature death or infertility, there is phenotypic selection against small size. But this could be associated with genotypic selection for small size, if organisms whose genotypes disposed them to small size were less damaged by hunger.

In what follows I shall consider genotypic selection; that is to say, selection in which some genotypes are more frequent in the parental population than in the population from which it was drawn.

We can measure the intensity of natural selection as follows. First let us consider selection by juvenile survival. For any range of phenotypes there is a phenotype with optimal survival, s_0, compared with S in the whole population, and similarly for a range of genotypes which includes the whole population. The intensity of selection is defined (Haldane, 1954) as $I = \ln(s_0/S)$. Thus Karn & Penrose (1951) found that about 95·5% of all babies born in a London district and 98·5% of those weighing 7·5–8·5 lb. survived birth and the first month of life: $s_0 = 0.985$, $S = 0.955$, $I = 0.03$. The notion is even simpler for genotypes where they can in fact be distinguished. If all genotypes had survived as well as the optimal genotype, s_0 individuals would have survived for every S which did so. That is to say, of the $1 - S$ deaths, $s_0 - S$ were selective. When s_0 and S are nearly equal, $I = s_0 - S$ approximately.

If selection is measured by comparing the parental population with the one from which it is derived, suppose that a number of genotypes are distinguished. Let f_r be the frequency of the rth genotype in the original population, F_r its frequency in the parental population:

$$\Sigma f_r = \Sigma F_r = 1.$$

Let $F_r f_r^{-1}$ be maximal when $r = 0$. The 0th genotype is called the optimal. If all genotypes had been as well represented in the parental population it would have contained $F_0 f_0^{-1}$ individuals for every one which it contained in fact. Thus the intensity of selection is $I = \ln(F_0/f_0)$.

It is convenient to think of natural selection provisionally in terms of juvenile deaths. If it acts in this way, by killing off the less fit genotypes, we shall calculate how many must be killed while a new gene is spreading through a population. This supplements my earlier calculation (Haldane, 1937) as to the effect of variation on fitness. I pointed out that, in a stable population, genetic variation was mainly due to mutation and to the

12

lesser fitness of homozygotes at certain loci. I calculated that each of these agencies might lower the mean fitness of a species by about 5–10 %. In fact the effect of sublethal homozygotes is much greater than this in such organisms as *Drosophila subobscura* and *D. pseudo-obscura*. I did not deal with the dynamic effect of Darwinian natural selection in lowering fitness.

Loss of fitness in genotypes whose frequency is being lowered by natural selection will have different effects on the population according to the stage of the life cycle at which it occurs, and the ecology of the species concerned. In some species the failure of a few eggs or seeds to develop will have little effect on the capacity of the species for increase. This is perhaps most obvious in such polytokous animals as mice, where a considerable prenatal elimination occurs even when no lethal or sublethal genes are segregating. But we can judge of the effect of elimination of a fraction of seeds from Salisbury's (1942, p. 231) conclusion that 'for ecologically comparable species, the magnitude of the reproductive capacity is associated with the frequency and abundance of which it is probably one of the determining factors'. Failure to germinate lowers the reproductive capacity. But death or sterility at a later stage is probably more serious in species whose members compete with one another for food, space, light and so on, or where overcrowding favours the prevalence of disease.

Natural selection, or any other agency which lowers viability or fertility, lowers the reproductive capacity of a species. This is sometimes called its 'natural rate of increase', but this expression is unfortunate, since in nature a population very rarely increases at this rate. Haldane (1956a) pointed out that in those parts of its habitat where climate, food, and so on are optimal, the density of a species is usually controlled by negative density-dependent factors, such as disease promoted by overcrowding, competition for food, and space, and so on. In such areas a moderate fall in reproductive capacity has little effect on the density. In exceptional cases, such as control by a parasite affecting no other species, it can even increase the density (Nicholson & Bailey, 1935). But in the parts of the habitat where the population is mainly regulated by density-independent factors such as temperature and salinity, the species can only maintain its numbers by utilizing its reproductive capacity to the full. A fall in reproductive capacity will lead to the disappearance of a species in these marginal areas, except in so far as it is kept up by migration from crowded areas. Birch (1954) showed very clearly that in some cases species with a similar ecology compete on the basis of their reproductive capacities.

It must, however, be emphasized that natural selection against density-independent factors is quite efficient in populations controlled by density-dependent factors. If in some parts of its range *Biston betularia* is so common as to be controlled mainly by parasites favoured by overcrowding, selective predation is not abolished. If 90 % of the larvae die of disease, the 10 % of imagines which emerge are still liable to be eaten by birds. Negative density-dependent factors must, however, slightly lower the overall efficiency of natural selectiòn in a heterogeneous environment. If as the result of larval disease due to overcrowding the density is not appreciably higher in a wood containing mainly *carbonaria* than in a wood containing the original type, the spread of the gene C by migration is somewhat diminished.

A serious complication arises in bisexual organisms if the selective killing or stėrilization is of different intensity in the two sexes. In any particular species and environment there is presumably an optimal sex ratio which would give the most rapid possible rate of increase. This would be near equality for monogamous animals, whereas an excess of females might be optimal where a male can mate with many females. But if males are smaller than females or have to search for them intensively an excess of males might be optimal. There is little reason to think that the sex ratio found in nature is closely adjusted to the optimum.

In a species with considerable embryonic or larval competition, and an excess of males above the optimum, the early death of some males might be advantageous. But even in this case an increased death-rate of males soon before maturity or during maturity would be of no advantage. Before dying they would have eaten the food which might have nourished other members of the species, and would have infected them, and so on. There seems no good reason why natural selection should fall more heavily on males than on females except in so far as males are haploid or hemizygous. But even if it fell wholly on males, it would not in general be harmless to the species.

I shall investigate the following case mathematically. A population is in equilibrium under selection and mutation. One or more genes are rare because their appearance by mutation is balanced by natural selection. A sudden change occurs in the environment, for example, pollution by smoke, a change of climate, the introduction of a new food source, predator, or pathogen, and above all migration to a new habitat. It will be shown later that the general conclusions are not affected if the change is slow. The species is less adapted to the new environment, and its reproductive capacity is lowered. It is gradually improved as the result of natural selection. But meanwhile a number of deaths, or their equivalents in lowered fertility, have occurred. If selection at the ith selected locus is responsible for d_i of these deaths in any generation the reproductive capacity of the species will be $\Pi(1-d_i)$ of that of the optimal genotype, or $\exp(-\Sigma d_i)$ nearly, if every d_i is small. Thus the intensity of selection approximates to Σd_i.

Let D_i be the sum of the values of d_i over all generations of selection, neglecting the very small values when the eliminated gene is only kept in being by mutation. I shall show that D_i depends mainly on p_0, the small frequency, at the time when selection begins, of the gene subsequently favoured by natural selection. I shall assume that the frequency of the phenotype first kept rare, and later favoured, by natural selection is about 10^{-4}, a value typical for disadvantageous but not lethal human phenotypes. If so p_0 would be about 5×10^{-5} for a partially or wholly dominant gene, and about $0 \cdot 01$ for a fully recessive one. The former are probably the more important in evolution. All the known genes responsible for industrial melanism are at least partially dominant, and most gene pairs which are responsible for variation of metrical characters in natural populations (as opposed to laboratory or 'fancy' mutants) seem to give heterozygotes intermediate between the homozygotes.

SELECTION IN HAPLOID, CLONAL, OR SELF-FERTILIZING ORGANISMS, OR FOR MATERNALLY INHERITED CYTOPLASMIC CHARACTERS

Let the nth generation, before selection, occur in the frequencies

$$p_n \mathbf{A}, q_n \mathbf{a}, \quad \text{where} \quad p_n + q_n = 1.$$

Here $\mathbf{A}$ and $\mathbf{a}$ are allelomorphic genes in a haploid, genotypes in clonal or self-fertilizing organisms, or different types of cytoplasm. If $1-k$ of **a** survive for every one of **A**, then the fraction of selective deaths in the nth generation is

$$d_n = kq_n. \tag{1}$$

Also

$$q_{n+1} = \frac{(1-k)q_n}{1-kq_n}.$$

So

$$\Delta q_n = \frac{-kp_n q_n}{1-kq_n}. \tag{2}$$

Hence $q_n = [1+(1-k)^{-n}(q_0^{-1}-1)]^{-1}$, which tends to zero with $(1-k)^n$. So the total of the fractions of selective deaths is

$$D = k \sum_{n=0}^{\infty} q_n,$$

which is finite. When k is small, taking a generation as a unit of time,

$$\frac{dq}{dt} = -kq(1-q),$$

approximately. This is also true if generations overlap. So, approximately,

$$
\begin{aligned}
D &= k \int_0^{\infty} q\, dt \\
&= \int_0^{q_0} -q \frac{dt}{dq}\, dq \\
&= \int_0^{q_0} \frac{dq}{1-q} \\
&= -\ln p_0 + O(k). \tag{3}
\end{aligned}
$$

If greater accuracy is required, we note that

$$
\begin{aligned}
\int_{q_{n+1}}^{q_n} \frac{dq}{1-q} &= \ln\left(\frac{1-q_{n+1}}{1-q_n}\right) \\
&= -\ln(1-kq_n) \\
&= kq_n + \tfrac{1}{2}k^2 q_n^2 + \tfrac{1}{3}k^3 q_n^3 + \cdots.
\end{aligned}
$$

We require the sum of the first term of this series, namely,

$$D = \sum_{n=0}^{\infty} kq_n.$$

We must subtract suitable terms from the integrand.

$$
\begin{aligned}
\int_{q_{n+1}}^{q_n} q^r\, dq &= (r+1)^{-1}(q_n^{r+1} - q_{n+1}^{r+1}) \\
&= (r+1)^{-1} q_n^{r+1}(1-kq_n)^{-r-1}[(1-kq_n)^{r+1} - (1-k)^{r+1}] \\
&= kq_n^{r+1}(1-q_n)(1-kq_n)^{-r-1}[1 - \tfrac{1}{2}kr(1+q_n) + \tfrac{1}{6}k^2 r(r-1)(1+q_n+q_n^2) + \cdots].
\end{aligned}
$$

Hence we find

$$\int_{q_{n+1}}^{q_n} [(1-\tfrac{1}{2}k-\tfrac{1}{12}k^2)(1-q)^{-1} + \tfrac{1}{2}k + \tfrac{1}{12}k^2 - \tfrac{1}{6}k^2 q]\, dq = kq_n + O(k^4).$$

So
$$D = \int_0^{q_0} [(1 - \tfrac{1}{2}k - \tfrac{1}{12}k^2)(1-q)^{-1} + \tfrac{1}{2}k + \tfrac{1}{12}k^2 - \tfrac{1}{6}k^2 q]\, dq$$
$$= -(1 - \tfrac{1}{2}k - \tfrac{1}{12}k^2)\ln(1-q_0) + (\tfrac{1}{2}k + \tfrac{1}{12}k^2)\, q_0 - \tfrac{1}{12}k^2 q_0^2 + O(k^3)$$
$$= (1 - \tfrac{1}{2}k - \tfrac{1}{12}k^2)\ln(p_0^{-1}) + \tfrac{1}{2}k - (\tfrac{1}{2}k - \tfrac{1}{12}k^2)\, p_0 + O(k^3) + O(k^2 p_0^2). \tag{4}$$

To obtain the coefficient of k^3 we have only to use the method of undetermined coefficients, adding $k^3[\alpha(1-q)^{-1} + \beta + \gamma q + \delta q^2]$ to the integrand, and equating the coefficient of k^4 to zero.

Clearly if k is small, D is almost independent of k, while if k is large, D is less than $-\ln p_0$. When $k=1$, that is to say, the fitness of **a** is zero, $D = q_0$, for selection is complete after one generation; that is to say, $D=1$, very nearly. If $p_0 = 10^{-4}$, as suggested, $D = 9 \cdot 2$, provided selection is slow. If p_0 were as high as $0 \cdot 01$, or 1 %, D would still be $4 \cdot 6$, while if it were as low as 10^{-6}, D would only be $13 \cdot 8$.

The correction to be made for the fact that q_n does not become zero, but reaches a small value set by the rate of back mutation, is negligible. If the final small value is Q, (3) becomes
$$D = -\ln p_0 + \ln(1-Q)$$
$$= -\ln p_0 - Q,$$

very nearly. If Q is about 10^{-4} the error is of this order, though, of course, a slight loss of fitness equal to the back mutation rate will go on indefinitely. The same is true for other expressions such as (7).

We may, therefore, take it that when selection is fairly slow, the total number of selective deaths over all generations is usually 5–15 times the total number in the population in each generation, 10 times this number being a representative value. When k exceeds $\tfrac{1}{3}$, this number is appreciably reduced.

During the course of selection the value of k may vary. If the environment is changing progressively it will, on the whole, increase. But provided it is small this makes no difference to the result. The cost of changing q from q_1 to q_2 is
$$\int_{q_2}^{q_1} \frac{dq}{1-q} + O(k) = \ln\left(\frac{1-q_2}{1-q_1}\right) + O(k),$$

which is nearly independent of the value of k.

SELECTION AT AN AUTOSOMAL LOCUS IN A DIPLOID

Consider an autosomal pair of allels **A** and **a** in a large random mating population, with frequencies p_n and q_n in the nth generation. Let their relative fitnesses be as below:

Genotype	**AA**	**Aa**	**aa**
Frequency	p_n^2	$2p_n q_n$	q_n^2
Fitness	1	$1-k$	$1-K$

where $K \geqslant k \geqslant 0$. Let $k = \lambda K$. If $\lambda = 1$, **a** is dominant as regards fitness. If $\lambda = 0$, $k = 0$, and **a** is recessive as regards fitness. λ is usually between 1 and 0. I assume $\lambda \leqslant 1$, for if $k < 0$, the gene **A** will not displace **a** completely, but an equilibrium will be reached, while if $k > K$ selection will not occur. For the reasons given above I assume $p_0 = 5 \times 10^{-5}$ unless λ is very small or zero, in which case p_0 may be about $0 \cdot 01$.

The fraction of selective deaths in the nth generation is

$$d_n = 2kp_nq_n + Kq_n^2$$
$$= Kq_n[2\lambda + (1-2\lambda)q_n]. \qquad (5)$$

So the total deaths are the population number multiplied by

$$D = K \sum_{n=0}^{\infty} [2\lambda q_n + (1-2\lambda)q_n^2].$$

Also

$$\Delta q_n = \frac{-p_nq_n[k(p_n-q_n) + Kq_n]}{1 - 2kp_nq_n - Kq_n^2}$$
$$= -Kp_nq_n[\lambda + (1-2\lambda)q_n], \qquad (6)$$

approximately. Using the same approximation as before,

$$D = \int_0^{q_0} \frac{[2\lambda + (1-2\lambda)q]\,dq}{(1-q)[\lambda + (1-2\lambda)q]}$$
$$= \frac{1}{1-\lambda} \int_0^{q_0} \left[\frac{1}{1-q} + \frac{\lambda(1-2\lambda)}{\lambda + (1-2\lambda)q} \right] dq$$

(provided $\lambda < 1$)

$$= \frac{1}{1-\lambda} \left[-\ln p_0 + \lambda \ln \left(\frac{1-\lambda-p_0}{\lambda} \right) \right]$$
$$= \frac{1}{1-\lambda} \left[-\ln p_0 + \lambda \ln \left(\frac{1-\lambda}{\lambda} \right) \right], \qquad (7)$$

nearly. If, however, $\lambda = 1$,

$$D = \int_0^{q_0} \frac{(2-q)\,dq}{(1-q)^2}$$
$$= \int_0^{q_0} \left[\frac{1}{1-q} + \frac{1}{(1-q)^2} \right] dq$$
$$= p_0^{-1} - \ln p_0 + O(k). \qquad (8)$$

If $\lambda = 0$ (**A** dominant), then from (7), $D = -\ln p_0$, if $\lambda = \frac{1}{2}$, $D = -2 \ln p_0$, if $\lambda = \frac{3}{4}$, $D = -4 \ln p_0 - 3 \cdot 3$, and if $\lambda = 0 \cdot 9$, $D = -10 \ln p_0 - 19 \cdot 8$. Thus if $p_0 = 5 \times 10^{-5}$, $\ln p_0 = 9 \cdot 9$, and D ranges from 9·9 to about 79. However, when **A** is nearly recessive, p_0 is probably somewhat larger than 5×10^{-5}, and when it is fully recessive p_0 is more probably about 0·01, giving $D = 105$ approximately, from (8). Thus D usually lies between 10 and 100, with 30 as a representative value.

We can find corrections to be made when K is not small. They are analogous to (4). In the limiting cases when $K = 1$, $k = 0$, $D = 1$ approximately. While if $K = k = 1$,

$$D = 1 + \frac{1}{2^2} + \frac{1}{3^2} + \frac{1}{4^2} + \cdots$$
$$= \tfrac{1}{6}\pi^2$$
$$= 1 \cdot 645.$$

Once again the value of D is not affected by the intensity of selection provided this is small, and is not very sensitive to the value of p_0.

SELECTION AT AN AUTOSOMAL LOCUS WITH INBREEDING

If inbreeding is almost complete, as in self-fertilized crop plants, the deaths of hetero-zygotes can be neglected, and equation (3) holds with sufficient accuracy. If there is partial inbreeding, suppose that gene frequencies and genotypic fitnesses are as in the last section, but the mean coefficient of inbreeding in the population is f instead of zero. Then the survivors of selection occur in the ratios

$$(p_n^2 + f p_n q_n) \mathbf{AA} : 2(1-k)(1-f) p_n q_n \mathbf{Aa} : (1-K)(f p_n q_n + q_n^2) \mathbf{aa}.$$

Hence
$$d_n = q_n[2k(1-f) p_n + K(f p_n + q_n)],$$

$$\Delta q_n = \frac{-p_n q_n [k(1-f)(p_n - q_n) + K(f p_n + q_n)]}{1 - 2k(1-f) p_n q_n - K(f p_n q_n + q_n^2)}.$$

Hence
$$D = \int_0^{q_0} \frac{2(1-f) k + f K + (1-f)(K-2k) q}{(1-q)[(1-f) k + f K + (1-f)(K-2k) q]} \, dq, \quad \text{nearly}$$

$$= [K - (1-f) k]^{-1} \int_0^{q_0} \left[\frac{K}{1-q} + \frac{(1-f)^2 \, k(K-2k)}{(1-f) k + f K + (1-f)(K-2k) q} \right] dq$$

$$= [K - (1-f) k]^{-1} \left[-K \ln p_0 + (1-f) \, k \ln \left(\frac{K - k + f k}{K + f K - f k} \right) \right] \tag{9}$$

nearly. If $(1-f) k = \mu K$,

$$D = (1-\mu)^{-1} \left[-\ln p_0 + \mu \ln \left(\frac{1-\mu}{\mu} \right) - \ln \left(1 + \frac{f}{\mu} \right) \right].$$

That is to say, the effect of partial inbreeding is very nearly to replace λ by $(1-f) \lambda$ in equation (7). The value of D is slightly reduced, as if the heterozygotes were a little fitter. But D is never as small as the value given by equation (3). If $k = \frac{1}{2}K$, D is divided by $(1+f)$. Partial inbreeding thus saves a few deaths, but has little effect on the value of D unless $\mathbf{A}$ is recessive, when it reduces it drastically.

SELECTION AT A SEX-LINKED LOCUS IN A DIPLOID

I assume males to be heterogametic. The results are the same, *mutatis mutandis*, if females are so. I assume that selection is so slow that the gene frequencies are very nearly the same in both sexes. Let the frequencies and relative fitnesses be

Genotype	AA		Aa		aa		A		a
Frequency	p_n^2		$2p_n q_n$		q_n^2		p_n		q_n
Fitness	1	:	$1-k$	:	$1-K$	:	1	:	$1-l$

In fact the frequencies of $\mathbf{a}$ differ in the two sexes by a quantity of the order of the largest of k, K and l, but this can provisionally be neglected. The selective death-rates in females and males are respectively:

$$\left. \begin{array}{l} d_{f,n} = 2k p_n q_n + K q_n^2, \\ d_{m,n} = l q_n. \end{array} \right\} \tag{10}$$

And
$$\Delta q_n = -\tfrac{1}{3} p_n q_n [2k(p_n - q_n) + K q_n + l], \tag{11}$$

since there are twice as many loci in female as in male gametes forming the next generation. Thus, the total of female selective death-rates approximates to

$$D_f = 3 \int_0^{q_0} \frac{[2k + (K - 2k)\,q]\,dq}{(1-q)\,[2k + l + 2(K - 2k)\,q]}.$$

Provided $2K + l > 2k$,

$$D_f = \frac{3}{2K - 2k + l} \int_0^{q_0} \left[\frac{K}{1-q} + \frac{(K - 2k)\,(2k - l)}{2k + l + 2(K - 2k)\,q} \right] dq$$

$$= \frac{3}{2K - 2k + l} \left[-K \ln p_0 + \tfrac{1}{2}(2k - l) \ln \left(\frac{2k + l}{2K - 2k + l} \right) \right],$$

and similarly the total for males is

$$D_m = \frac{3l}{2K - 2k + l} \left[-\ln p_0 + \ln \left(\frac{2k + l}{2K - 2k + l} \right) \right]. \tag{12}$$

If, however, $2K + l = 2k$, which implies that $k > K$, unless $l = 0$, in which case **A** is fully
recessive as regards fitness in females,

$$\left. \begin{aligned} D_f &= \frac{3}{2} \left(\frac{K}{K + l}\, p_0 - \ln p_0 \right), \\ D_m &= \frac{3l p_0}{2(K + l)}. \end{aligned} \right\} \tag{13}$$

It is possible that almost all the selective mortality should be concentrated on the males.
This will be so if K is small, provided $2K + l > 2k$. This is unlikely but not impossible. For
the reasons discussed earlier this would probably not ease the burden on the species very
greatly.

The value of p_0 would be about 10^{-4} provided that in the preliminary period **A** males
were at an appreciable disadvantage. The mean of D_f and D_m is

$$D = \frac{3}{2(2K - 2k + l)} \left[-(K + l) \ln p_0 + (k + \tfrac{1}{2}l) \ln \left(\frac{2k + l}{2K - 2k + l} \right) \right], \tag{14}$$

unless $2K + l = 2k$, when $\qquad D = \tfrac{3}{2}(p_0 - \ln p_0). \tag{15}$

If $2k > 2K + l$ an equilibrium is reached.

We see that the cost of selection at a sex-linked locus depends, as at an autosomal locus,
on $-\ln p_0$, and on the ratios of selective intensities, provided these are small. The factor
multiplying $-\ln p_0$ will seldom be large. It is, for example, 3 if $K = k = l$, and 1 if $K = l$,
$k = 0$. Thus a representative value of D is 20, and it will probably be between 10 and 40 in
most cases. It will not be greatly increased if the gene selected is completely recessive in
females, provided that it is of selective advantage in males.

SELECTION OF HETEROZYGOTES

The total death-rates of heterozygotes at an autosomal locus are given by

$$D_h = \Sigma\, 2kp_n q_n$$
$$= 2\lambda K \Sigma q_n (1 - q_n).$$

This approximates to

$$2\lambda K \int_0^\infty q(1-q)\,dt = 2\lambda K \int_{q_0}^{q_n} q(1-q)\,\frac{dt}{dq}\,dq$$

$$= 2\lambda \int_{q_n}^{q_0} \frac{dq}{\lambda+(1-2\lambda)\,q}$$

$$= \frac{2\lambda}{1-2\lambda}\,{}_{q_n}^{q_0}\!\Big[\ln\{\lambda+(1-2\lambda)\,q\}\Big].$$

If $1>\lambda>0$,
$$D_h = \frac{2\lambda}{1-2\lambda}\,\ln\left(\frac{1-\lambda}{\lambda}\right),$$

except when $\lambda=\frac{1}{2}$, when
$$D_h = 2.$$

If $\lambda=1$,
$$D_h = -2\ln p_0. \tag{16}$$

Over the range considered D_h is a monotone increasing function of λ, being 0·549 when $\lambda=0\cdot1$, and 4·944 when $\lambda=0\cdot9$. That is to say unless λ is very nearly unity, or **A** almost recessive as regards adaptive value, D_h is small. And it is always a small fraction of D. During most of the course of a gene substitution heterozygotes are rare.

It can easily be shown that in the case of a sex-linked locus the total deaths of heterozygous females are

$$D_h = \frac{3k}{K-2k}\,\ln\left(\frac{2K-2k+l}{2k+l}\right),$$

unless $K=2k$, when $D_h=3K/(K+l)$. These are also relatively small numbers.

In a recent discussion on natural selection (Haldane, 1956b) I gave the total numbers of heterozygotes produced in the course of a gene substitution, or $k^{-1}D_h$. The results are equivalent. Since so few heterozygotes are killed, there can, in the course of a gene replacement, be little selection in favour of genes raising the fitness of heterozygotes by altering dominance or otherwise, unless they affect homozygotes also.

DISCUSSION

The unit process of evolution, the substitution of one allel by another, if carried out by natural selection based on juvenile deaths, usually involves a number of deaths equal to about 10 or 20 times the number in a generation, always exceeding this number, and perhaps rarely being 100 times this number. To allow for occasional high values I take 30 as a mean. If natural selection acts by diminished fertility the effect is equivalent.

Suppose then that selection is taking place slowly at a number of loci, the average rate being one gene substitution in each n generations, the fitness of the species concerned will fall below the optimum by a factor of about $30n^{-1}$ so long as this is small. If the depression is larger we reason as follows. If a number of loci are concerned, the ith depressing fitness by a small quantity δ_i, the mean number of loci transformed per generation is $D^{-1}\Sigma\delta_i$ or about $\frac{1}{30}\Sigma\delta_i$. The fitness is reduced to $\Pi(1-\delta_i)$ or about $\exp(-\Sigma\delta_i)$. But $n=30/\Sigma\delta_i$, roughly. Thus, the fitness is about $e^{-30n^{-1}}$, or the intensity of selection $I=30n^{-1}$.

To be concrete, if a species had immigrated into an environment where its reproductive capacity was half that obtainable after selection had run its course, so that $I=\ln2=0\cdot69$,

n would be 43. This represents, in my opinion, fairly intense selection, of the order of that found in *Biston betularia*, where it has had a rapid effect because it was concentrated on a phenotypic change due mainly to a single gene. I doubt if such high intensities of selection have been common in the course of evolution. I think $n = 300$, which would give $I = 0 \cdot 1$, is a more probable figure. Whereas, for example, $n = 7 \cdot 5$ would reduce the fitness to e^{-4}, or $0 \cdot 02$, which would hardly be compatible with survival.

We do not know at how many loci two 'good' but fairly closely related species differ. Their taxonomic characters may depend mainly on as few as twenty gene substitutions. But there is every reason to think that substitutions have occurred at a great many other loci. Punnett (1932) showed that among eighteen fully recessive mutants in *Lathyrus odoratus* which he studied the viability increased with the time which had elapsed since the mutation occurred. In Table 1 I have presented the data of his Table VI in a different form. The second column is the estimated viability. If d dominants and r

Table 1. *Punnett's data on sweet peas*

	Mutant	Viability	S.E.
g_1	White	1·037	0·024
a_1	Red	1·021	0·017
b_1	Light axil	1·011	0·017
f_1	White	0·996	0·038
d_5	Picotee	0·996	0·022
a_2	Round pollen	0·990	0·024
b_2	Sterile	0·988	0·017
a_3	Hooded	0·977	0·021
e	Cupid	0·976	0·032
f_2	Bush	0·936	0·030
d_2	Blue	0·931	0·024
g_3	Mauve	0·917	0·031
d_1	Acacia	0·964	0·020
d_4	Smooth	0·940	0·020
d_2	Copper	0·909	0·040
h	Spencer	0·897	0·030
b_3	Cretin	0·886	0·048
f_3	Marbled	0·821	0·023

recessives are found out of n, this is $3r/(d+1)$ (Haldane, 1956c) and its standard error is $3\sqrt{(rn/d^3)}$. The standard errors are given in the third column. The first group of mutants occurred in wild populations, in the eighteenth, or possibly in the early nineteenth, century. The second group originated between 1880 and 1899. The third group originated between 1901 and 1912. In each group the order is that of viabilities. None of the viabilities in the first group differs significantly from unity, nor does their mean. I know of no equally satisfactory series of data in any other organism. It seems that a mutant on appearance is generally somewhat inviable. But intense selection exercised by breeders accumulates 'modifiers' which, in the course of fifty years or so, raise its viability in F_2 to normal.

Presumably the same kind of process occurs in evolution. The number of loci in a vertebrate species has been estimated at about 40,000. 'Good' species, even when closely related, may differ at several thousand loci, even if the differences at most of them are very slight. But it takes as many deaths, or their equivalents, to replace a gene by one producing a barely distinguishable phenotype as by one producing a very different one. If two species differ at 1000 loci, and the mean rate of gene substitution, as has been suggested, is one per 300 generations, it will take at least 300,000 generations to generate an interspecific difference. It may take a good deal more, for if an allel a^1 is ultimately replaced by a^{10} the population may pass through stages where the commonest genotype at the locus is a^1a^1, a^2a^2, a^3a^3, and so on, successively, the various allels in turn giving maximal fitness in the existing environment and the residual genotype. Simpson (1953) finds the mean life of a genus of Carnivora to be about 8 million years. That of a species in horotelic vertebrate evolution may average about a million.

Zeuner (1945), after a very full discussion of the Pleistocene fossil record, concluded that in mammals about 500,000 years were required for the evolution of a new species, though in the vole genera *Mimomys* and *Arvicola* the rate was somewhat greater. Some insects seem to have evolved at about the same rate, while other insects, and all molluscs, evolved more slowly. He estimated the total duration of the Pleistocene at 600,000 years, but some later authors would about halve this figure. On the other hand environmental changes during the Pleistocene were unusually rapid, and evolution, therefore, probably also unusually rapid. The agreement with the theory here developed is satisfactory.

Some writers, such as Fisher (1930, 1931), appear to assume that the number of loci at which 'modifiers', for example, genes affecting the dominance of other genes, may be selected, is indefinitely large. The number of loci is, however, finite. But even if enough modifiers were available, the selection of, say, ten modifiers which between them caused a previously dominant mutant to become recessive, would involve the death of a number of individuals equal to about 300 generations of the species concerned. Even the geological time scale is too short for such processes to go on in respect of thousands of loci. Renwick (1956) has made it very probable that dominance modifiers occur at the mutant locus, and if so recessivity may often be assured by strengthening the 'wild-type' allel (Wright, 1934; Haldane, 1939).

Can this slowness be avoided by selecting several genes at a time? I doubt it, for the following reason. Consider clonally reproducing bacteria, in which a number of disadvantageous genes are present, kept in being by mutation, each with frequencies of the order of 10^{-4}. They become slightly advantageous through a change of environment or residual genotype. Among 10^{12} bacteria there might be one which possessed three such mutants. But since the cost of selection is proportional to the negative logarithm of the initial frequency the mean cost of selecting its descendants would be the same as that of selection for the three mutants in series, though the process might be quicker. The same argument applies to mutants linked by an inversion. Once several favourable mutants are so linked the inversion may be quickly selected. But the rarity of inversions containing several rare and favourable mutants will leave the cost unaltered.

There can, of course, be other reasons for the slowness of evolution. In some cases several genes must be substituted simultaneously before fitness is increased. This process can perhaps occur in two ways. On the one hand in a species broken up into small endogamous groups such a combination of genes may be established by a random process of 'drift' (Wright, 1934 and earlier) or a single founder crossing a geographical barrier may possess them (Spurway, 1953). Or they may be linked by an inversion. But such events are not perhaps very frequent even on an evolutionary time scale. On the other hand, each gene may change by a number of small successive steps. Fisher's (1930, pp. 38–40) argument is applicable here, though he may have envisaged changes at a large number of loci, rather than successive changes at a few. In either case the cost is high and the process must, therefore, be slow. The slowness of evolution of such an organ as the vertebrate eye is thus intelligible.

Evolution by natural selection can be very rapid if a species, like the first land vertebrates, or the first colonists of an island, finds itself in an environment to which it is very ill-adapted, but in which it has no competition, and perhaps no predators and few parasites. If so selection might be so intense as to reduce the capacity for increase to one-tenth of that of its adapted descendants, and it could yet hold its own. Such episodes have doubtless been important, and account for tachytelic (Simpson, 1953) evolution. But they are probably exceptional.

On the whole it seems that the rate of evolution is set by the number of loci in a genome, and the number of stages through which they can mutate. If pre-Cambrian organisms had much fewer loci than their descendants, they may have evolved much quicker, though the possibilities open to them were more limited.

The calculations regarding heterozygotes enable us to answer certain questions. Kettlewell (1956b) has evidence that C in *Biston betularia* is now more dominant than it was in the nineteenth century. CC is now usually indistinguishable from Cc by human beings, and probably by birds. This is thought to be due to selection of one or more genes which modify dominance. The value of λ in equations (5) to (8) has decreased from about $\frac{1}{2}$ to nearly zero. If λ was originally $\frac{1}{2}$, the total number of Cc moths killed selectively was about twice the number in a generation, and since λ diminished, it can hardly be as many as this.

Now supposing a modifier M which made Cc as dark as CC had been selected by deaths of heterozygotes which did not carry it, the natural logarithm of its frequency would have increased by about 4, from equation (7). That is to say its frequency would have increased about e^4, or 55 times. This is certainly an overestimate, since fewer heterozygotes would have been killed as soon as the modifier became at all common. Probably a twenty-fold increase is the most that could be expected. This is not enough to make C almost always dominant when it was previously semi-dominant.

However, two other possibilities are open. It is quite possible that at the present time Cc has a higher adaptive value than CC, and this accounts for the persistence of cc in all populations studied. If so the proportion of Cc moths may be much higher that it would be if CC had a higher adaptive value than Cc. In fact λ may sometimes at least be negative in equation (5), leading to balanced polymorphism. Another possibility is that M improves the physiological adjustment of CC. Suppose, for example, that C is responsible for a tyrosinase or a similar enzyme absent in cc, and that CC moths produce twice as much of this enzyme as Cc. Then if the substrate concentration is low, it may not be possible for Cc moths to make enough melanin to become fully black. However, CC moths may use up most of the available phenolic substrate, and the resulting shortage may lead to ill-health. There will then be selection for a gene M which leads to the synthesis of more substrate, and incidentally permits Cc moths to make enough melanin to appear as black as CC. This is, of course, only one of many hypotheses. But it is important to realize that a dominance modifier may be selected for its effect on homozygotes.

To conclude, I am quite aware that my conclusions will probably need drastic revision. But I am convinced that quantitative arguments of the kind here put forward should play a part in all future discussions of evolution.

SUMMARY

Unless selection is very intense, the number of deaths needed to secure the substitution, by natural selection, of one gene for another at a locus, is independent of the intensity of selection. It is often about 30 times the number of organisms in a generation. It is suggested that, in horotelic evolution, the mean time taken for each gene substitution is about 300 generations. This accords with the observed slowness of evolution.

REFERENCES

BIRCH, L. C. (1954). Experiments on the relative abundance of two sibling species. *Aust. J. Zool.* **2**, 66–74.

FISHER, R. A. (1930). *The Genetical Theory of Natural Selection.* Oxford: Clarendon Press.

FISHER, R. A. (1931). The evolution of dominance. *Biol. Rev.* **6**, 345–68.

HALDANE, J. B. S. (1937). The effect of variation on fitness. *Amer. Nat.* **71**, 337–49.

HALDANE, J. B. S. (1939). The theory of the evolution of dominance. *J. Genet.* **37**, 365–74.

HALDANE, J. B. S. (1954). The measurement of natural selection. *Proc. 9th Int. Congr. Genet.* pp. 480–7.

HALDANE, J. B. S. (1956a). The relation between density regulation and natural selection. *Proc. Roy. Soc.* B, **145**, 306–8.

HALDANE, J. B. S. (1956b). The theory of selection for melanism in Lepidoptera. *Proc. Roy. Soc.* B, **145**, 303–6.

HALDANE, J. B. S. (1956c). The estimation of viabilities. *J. Genet.* **54**, 294–6.

KARN, N. & PENROSE, L. S. (1951). Birthweight and gestation time in relation to maternal age, parity and infant survival. *Ann. Eugen.* **16**, 147–64.

KERMACK, K. A. (1954). A biometrical study of *Micraster coranguinum* and *M. (Isomicraster) senonensis*. *Phil. Trans.* B, **237**, 375–428.

KETTLEWELL, H. B. D. (1956a). A resumé of investigations on the evolution of melanism in the Lepidoptera. *Proc. Roy. Soc.* B, **145**, 297–303.

KETTLEWELL, H. B. D. (1956b). Further selection experiments on industrial melanism in the Lepidoptera. *Heredity*, **10**, 287–303.

LUSH, J. L. (1954). Rates of genetic change in populations of farm animals. *Proc. 9th Int. Congr. Genet.* pp. 589–99.

NICHOLSON, A. J. & BAILEY, V. A. (1935). The balance of animal populations, Part I. *Proc. Zool. Soc. Lond.*, pp. 551–98.

PUNNETT, R. C. (1932). Further studies of Linkage in the Sweet pea. *J. Genet.* **26**, 97–113.

RENWICK, J. H. (1956). Nail-patella syndrome: evidence for modification by alleles at the main locus. *Ann. Hum. Genet.* **21**, 159–69.

SALISBURY, E. (1942). *The Reproductive Capacity of Plants.* London: Bell.

SIMPSON, G. G. (1953). *The Major Features of Evolution.* New York.

SPURWAY, H. (1953). Genetics of specific and subspecific differences in European newts. *Symp. Soc. Exp. Biol.* no. VII, Evolution.

WRIGHT, S. (1934). Physiological and evolutionary theories of dominance. *Amer. Nat.* **68**, 24–53.

ZEUNER, F. F. (1945). *The Pleistocene Period.* London: Ray Society Monograph.

EFFECTS OF DISRUPTIVE SELECTION

I. GENETIC FLEXIBILITY

J. M. THODAY

Genetics Department, Sheffield University

received 14.vi.58

THIS article, and those which will follow it, concern the results of experiments using artificial selection of the type that Mather (1953*a*) has called *disruptive* and Simpson (1944) has called *centrifugal*. Such selection may be said to occur when we maintain a single population by choosing more than one class of individuals to provide the parents of each generation. In its extreme form disruptive selection involves choosing both extreme classes and discarding intermediates.

The antithesis of disruptive selection is *stabilising selection* (Simpson's centripetal selection), which occurs when we choose, as parents of each generation, individuals at, or as close as possible to, the mean of the population from which they come.

Mather's third type of selection is the more usual *directional selection* whose effects have been widely studied.

Cyclic selection (Thoday, 1956) provides a fourth type which would occur if we were to reverse the direction of selection in different generations. It clearly has something in common with disruptive selection as Mather (1955*a*) has pointed out.

Waddington (1953, 1958) has classified selection according to the effects it may be expected to produce, rather than according to the measurable characters of the individuals selected. While of value for theoretical discussion, such a classification cannot be used in designing selection experiments and is not therefore used here.

Schmalhausen (1949), Mather (1953*a*, 1955*a*, *b*) and Waddington (1953, 1958) have discussed the consequences that might be expected to result from different types of selection. In principle we must expect effects of two kinds. Responses might occur as changes in the effective variety of genotypes, or as changes in the variability of development. The first would involve change in the amount of effective genetic variation in the population. The second would involve change in the responsiveness of the developmental system to the environmental variance to which the population is exposed, or changes in the amount or effectiveness of the accidental sources of developmental variance that Waddington, Graber and Woolf (1957) call developmental noise. We may therefore expect stabilising selection to reduce the genetic variation in a population (Waddington's normalising selection) or to increase the stability of the developmental processes mediated by the genotypes in the population (Waddington's stabilising or canalising selection), or to do both. Disruptive selection might be

Reprinted by permission of Oliver & Boyd, Ltd. from HEREDITY,
13, 187–203 (1959).

expected to have the opposite effects, increasing genetic variation and/or increasing developmental flexibility by producing epigenetic systems with alternative pathways. It might also act to reduce developmental stability or the canalisation of existing pathways.

Mather (1955a) has further argued that disruptive selection should have more profound effects. Provided that the two or more types selected are necessary to one another, disruptive selection might be expected to give rise to a polymorphic situation based on alternative pathways of development. Development might be switched into one or other path by a genetic switch mechanism, or by an environmental switch which, if available, should be equally effective and might equally well be exploited. On the other hand, if the two or more types selected are not dependent on one another, then disruptive selection could put a premium on the development of an isolation barrier and lead to the separation of different populations with different characteristics.

Mather's predictions imply that disruptive selection may be of the greatest evolutionary significance. Yet few experiments have been carried out to determine how effective either disruptive selection or stabilising selection may be. Falconer and Robertson (1956) compared the effects of stabilising and disruptive selection for weight in mice and Falconer (1957) has studied the effect of stabilising selection on abdominal chaeta-number in *Drosophila*. Neither of these experiments gave marked results though there was some reduction in variance in the mouse stabilising line. The present paper describes the results of similar experiments using sternopleural chaeta-number in *Drosophila melanogaster*. A preliminary account has already been published (Thoday, 1958a).

I. MATERIAL AND CULTURE METHODS

All the experiments have been carried out in lines that originate from a single wild stock " Dronfield." This wild stock derived from a single fertilised female captured near Sheffield in May 1954, and has been maintained at 25° C. (approximately) ever since, usually by 4-pair transfers. It is the same stock as was used for the directional selection experiments described by Thoday (1958b).

Details of culture are similar to those previously described (Thoday, 1958b). Each line is maintained by 4 cultures in each generation (three weeks per generation), each culture having a single pair of parents. The 4 cultures are labelled according to the origin of their mothers and represent 4 separate female sub-lines. A culture is assayed by counting chaeta-numbers on both sides of 20 flies of each sex, and the best 8 of each sex are selected. Of any such 8 the best is intended to continue the line, but the second, third and fourth are set up as insurance cultures in case the first fails. (When the best successful culture seemed likely to produce very few flies, virgins were sometimes collected from a second culture and used to provide extra flies to complete the assay.) The remaining 4 are set up together in a fifth (" mass ") culture to ensure absolutely against the loss of a female line. (It has only been necessary to use 8 of these in the experiments described here.) Thus each line is set up as 16 single-pair cultures and 4 four-pair cultures, though the aim is only to use 4 single-pair cultures, one from each female line. This procedure is designed to ensure against loss of female lines, and is necessitated by the insistence on single-pair cultures.

If, in selection, choice had to be made between two flies of equal chaeta-number, the more bilaterally symmetrical was chosen.

2. MATING AND SELECTION SYSTEMS

(i) Disruptive selection with negative assortative mating: the D⁻ line

The first disruptive selection line to be established was primarily intended to assess the possibility that selection might be able to bring

TABLE 1

The mating and selection systems

Parents of Generation	Culture (*i.e.* female sub-line)			
	A	B	C	D
	♀ ♂	♀ ♂	♀ ♂	♀ ♂
(a) D⁻				
n	HA × LC	HB × LD	LC × HA	LD × HB
$n+1$	HA × LD	HB × LC	LC × HB	LD × HA
$n+2$	HA × LC	HB × LD	LC × HA	LD × HB
$n+3$	HA × LD	HB × LC	LC × HB	LD × HA
etc.				
(b) D⁺				
n	HA × HC	HB × HD	LC × LA	LD × LB
$n+1$	LA × LD	LB × LC	HC × HB	HD × HA
$n+2$	HA × HC	HB × HD	LC × LA	LD × LB
$n+3$	LA × LD	LB × LC	HC × HB	HD × HA
etc.				

The entries designate the parents used to produce the culture in the generation shown in the first column. H indicates the highest, and L the lowest chaeta-number fly found in the appropriate culture. A, B, C and D indicate the culture from which the fly was selected.

about responses in the cytoplasm, and a preliminary report has been given (Thoday, 1958c) of the results from this point of view. The mating and selection system is given in table 1a.

(ii) Disruptive selection with positive assortative mating: the D⁺ line

This line was set up specifically to test the effects of disruptive selection, and was designed to ensure that cytoplasmic variables, if any, would not be subjected to consistent selection. The mating and selection system used is given in table 1b. This system ensures that there is selection for high and for low chaeta-number flies in each generation, but that high and high will be mated together, and low and low will be mated together in separate cultures.

27

At generation 21 of this line an unfortunate error was made in selection. *For this one generation the whole line was selected for low chaeta-number.* This must be borne in mind when the results are considered.

(iii) Stabilising selection: the S line

This line is maintained by exactly the same mating system as shown in table 1*b*, and originated from the generation 1 cultures of the D+ line. It was intended to provide a comparative line. The flies selected in each generation are those with chaeta-numbers nearest to the mean of the wild stock from which the lines originated. This mean has varied from 17 to 18 chaetæ, and, as males usually have rather fewer chaetæ than females, the aim is always to select females with 9 chaetæ on each side, and males with 9 on one side and 8 on the other. This aim has usually but, of course, not always been achieved. This mean of 17·5 proved a little low, so that there has been slight directional selection as well as stabilising selection.

(iv) Divergent-directional selection

Certain divergent-directional selection experiments have been carried out on the lines to test their responsiveness to directional selection. Each of these involved taking coincidentally a high selection line and a low selection line and observing their divergence over three generations. Each of these lines was maintained with 4 single-pair cultures per generation, a rotational mating system being used exactly as described in Thoday (1958*b*). The four initial cultures always included all four female sub-lines of the line under test. These test lines were run at a generation every two weeks (not three weeks as for the main lines) for three generations.

3. CHAETA-NUMBER, ASYMMETRY AND VARIANCE IN THE LINES

Fig. 1 shows the mean chaeta-numbers, arithmetic asymmetries and within-culture-and-sex mean squares for the three lines. The asymmetry values are means of the differences between the sides of the flies, sign ignored. No correction for relation between asymmetry and mean (Thoday, 1955, 1958*b*) has been made. Neither are the variances corrected for any comparable relation to mean.

The generation numbers in the figure are those applicable to the D⁻ line. Coincident generations for the three lines as plotted were cultured coincidentally.

(i) The D⁻ line

The selection practised on the D⁻ line clearly had negligible effect on mean chaeta-number in the first 10 generations. Neither variance nor asymmetry show evidence of a trend during this period.

From generation 10 to generation 17, the mean rose slowly but steadily and this was accompanied by wide fluctuations of variance which, however, was higher after this period. At the same time asymmetry rose sharply to a new level, a rise that coincided with and appears to have been confined to the period of most rapid response

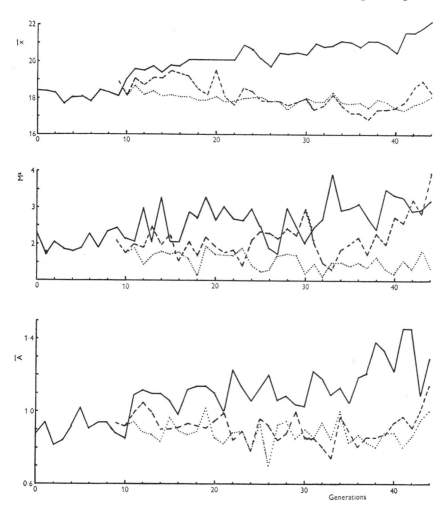

FIG. 1.—Mean chaeta-numbers ($\bar{x}$), within-sex-and-culture mean squares (M^2) and asymmetries ($\bar{A}$) in the three lines. Solid line D^-: broken line D^+: dotted S. The generations are those applicable to D^-: points plotted together represent data obtained from coincidentally raised cultures. The generation at which the selection error was made in D^+ is marked by a wavy line.

in mean. It is clear that events during this period were complex. Variance and asymmetry can both be correlated with mean and part of their rise is likely to be due to this correlation. But the fluctuations of variance, and the suddenness of the rise in asymmetry suggest that other factors are involved.

From generation 17 to generation 22 the mean was very steady indeed and the variance, though fluctuating, showed no overall change. Thereafter the mean fluctuated a little but rose slowly, variance fluctuated widely but showed a further overall rise, and asymmetry behaved similarly though its rise seems more striking in recent generations.

Apart from the rise of mean chaeta-number there is little clear evidence of any change in this line that could be attributed to disruptive selection, and the results are essentially the same as those of the corresponding mouse line of Falconer and Robertson (1956). The overall rises in variance and in asymmetry may be attributable to correlations of these measures with mean. However, inspection of the curves does suggest that changes are occurring. The relative steadiness of variance at the beginning of the experiment suggests that the fluctuations that occurred later have some real meaning, and the correlation of asymmetry with mean seems far from complete. There is also a suggestion of a cyclic behaviour of asymmetry which is subject to rises and falls, as if selection were occasionally picking out developmentally unstable genotypes, but that these were then being eliminated by natural selection. It seems that both variance and asymmetry are subject to complex causes of changes. Some of these causes may counteract one another, and some will be independent of the artificial selection. The comparatively negative results for variance cannot therefore be critical evidence that variance is little affected by the artificial selection.

(ii) The D+ line

The mean chaeta-number of this line rose during the first 9 generations and then fell until it coincided with that of the S line. Variance behaved likewise at first. There were two fluctuations of mean, the more notable being that at generation 11 (Generation D− 20 in fig. 1). Since this coincides with a period of very stable mean in D−, and is not reflected in S, it seems at first rather unlikely that some environmental fluctuation can have been responsible. However, the single generation rise in mean occurred in all four cultures of the line and an environmental factor to which only the D+ line was responsive seems to be the most probable cause.

After these fluctuations the D+ mean remained virtually identical with that of S until, at generation 21 (D− 30), the error of selection was made and it fell 0·5 chaetæ. It then remained below that of S until the most recent generations. During the period of stable mean, variance rose until at generation 21 (D− 30) it had reached the level characteristic of line D−. Over this period the variance of D+ was clearly greater than that of S, though their means were the same. There is no suggestion that their asymmetries were different, and it therefore seems very likely that disruptive selection during this period caused an increase in the effective genetic variation in the D+ line, though of course asymmetry can only be a very partial measure

30

of non-genetic variance. The error in selection made in generation 21 (D+ 30) resulted in the loss of this increased within-sex-and-culture variance. It has, however, been regained since. Variance has now risen above that of D⁻ and is still rising.

TABLE 2

Coefficients of within-sex-and-culture variation (per cent.) and coefficients of asymmetry
$(A/T \times 1000)$

D⁻ Generations		0	1	2	3	4	5	6	7	8	9	10	11	12	13	14
D⁻	CV	8·4	7·1	8·4	7·7	7·4	7·6	8·4	7·5	8·4	8·7	7·7	7·5	8·9	7·2	9·4
	A/T	48	51	45	47	51	56	50	51	51	49	45	55	58	55	57
D⁺	CV										7·5	7·3	7·5	7·3	8·2	7·2
	A/T										49	51	52	56	53	48
S	CV											7·3	7·5	6·5	7·1	7·5
	A/T											51	51	49	48	47

D⁻ Generations		15	16	17	18	19	20	21	22	23	24	25	26	27	28	29
D⁻	CV	7·1	7·3	8·4	8·2	9·0	7·3	8·9	8·3	7·8	8·2	7·9	6·9	6·4	8·5	7·7
	A/T	53	50	55	57	57	55	50	62	55	51	56	61	52	53	51
D⁺	CV	7·6	6·3	7·6	6·8	8·2	7·0	7·3	7·8	6·3	7·9	8·6	8·6	8·1	8·9	8·4
	A/T	45	48	48	50	50	49	55	47	48	42	54	51	46	50	56
S	CV	7·1	7·5	7·1	5·9	7·9	7·2	7·4	7·2	7·7	6·7	6·2	6·4	7·3	7·4	7·3
	A/T	45	50	49	51	58	48	46	50	49	43	52	40	52	55	47

D⁻ Generations		30	31	32	33	34	35	36	37	38	39	40	41	42	43	44
D⁻	CV	7·0	7·5	7·9	9·6	8·0	8·1	8·5	7·9	7·3	8·8	8·4	8·4	7·7	7·8	8·0
	A/T	50	58	57	52	53	50	57	61	65	63	58	66	67	48	58
D⁺	CV	9·6	8·3	6·9	6·1	7·8	8·2	8·6	7·5	8·8	8·1	9·5	9·1	9·6	8·8	10·9
	A/T	47	49	41	40	55	52	47	51	49	50	54	54	49	54	62
S	CV	6·6	6·8	5·9	6·6	6·8	6·6	6·9	6·7	7·2	6·4	6·3	7·3	6·5	7·7	6·3
	A/T	51	47	45	46	56	47	49	48	45	49	50	46	49	53	55

Note.—This table and figure 1 have been completed to the time of going to press. Other tables and computations do not include the most recent generations.

(iii) The S line

The mean of this line, initially a little over 18 chaetæ, declined slowly, as is to be expected since the parents in each generation averaged 17·5 chaetæ. Variance and asymmetry suggest little, if any, significant change though variance declined a little.

4. COEFFICIENTS OF VARIATION

The differences of mean chaeta number distinguishing D⁻ and the other lines, and at times distinguishing D⁺ and S, make it difficult to interpret comparisons of the variances of these lines. Coefficients of variation are often used in such situations, though coefficients of variation involve assumptions about the relation between variance and mean which are difficult to justify. Despite the problems to which these assumptions give rise, it seems worth comparing the lines in this way and table 2 lists the coefficients. There is no evidence of change of the coefficient of variation of D⁻. On the other hand there is evidence of a rise with generations in D⁺ and a fall in S. The regression of coefficient of variation on generations for D⁺ is positive and just significant $(t_{(28)} = 2\cdot03,\ P\simeq0\cdot05)$ and that for S is negative and significant $(t_{(28)} = 2\cdot48,\ P\simeq0\cdot02)$. The two regression lines meet at generation o. Table 3 gives the results of a joint analysis of variance for these two lines, showing that the joint regression is not significant, the two regressions are significantly different, and D⁺ has a significantly higher mean than S. D⁺ disruptive selection has raised, and stabilising selection has lowered the coefficient of variation.

If we accept coefficients of variation as meaningful, we must conclude that D⁺ disruptive selection has raised and stabilising selection has lowered variance. D⁻ selection has failed to raise coefficient of

TABLE 3

*Analysis of variance of coefficients of variation for the
D⁺ and S lines*

Source	n	Mean Square	P
Joint Regression on Generations .	I	16·1580	≃0·5
Difference between Regressions .	I	355·4631	<0·01
Difference between Means. .	I	968·0166	Small
Error	56	42·1597	...

variation, though it has raised mean and uncorrected variance. It is of course quite likely that the relation of variance to mean differs in different lines, and that the negative result for D⁻ is not real.

5. COEFFICIENTS OF ASYMMETRY

Sternopleural asymmetry is a partial measure of the stability of development (Thoday, 1958b), but, like variance, it may also be related to mean (Mather, 1953b) so that comparison of the asymmetry of lines whose means are different is problematical. The base stock, " Dronfield," used for these experiments is the same as that used for those described in Thoday (1958b), in which what may be called a coefficient of asymmetry was used to correct for the scaling problem. This was calculated by dividing mean asymmetry (A) by mean chaeta-number (T). Those experiments provided evidence that the correction was satisfactory for this stock and it therefore seems justifiable to use it here. Table 2 lists the A/T values (multiplied by 1,000 for convenience). There is clearly no evidence of change of A/T in D⁺ or S or of difference between them in this respect. A/T has, however, risen in D⁻. Its initial value $(\times 1,000)$ is of the order of 50 and is the same as that for D⁺ and S and for the Dronfield stock when the experiments described in Thoday (1958b) were begun. This seems a stable and characteristic value of A/T in this stock in our culture conditions.

The value has, however, risen in the D⁻ line. The regression on generations is positive and significant ($t_{(40)} = 4 \cdot 7$, P small). It seems likely, however, that the rise has not been consistent, but that it is entirely attributable to two periods in the history of the line, one at about generation 11 and the other at about generation 36. Table 4 gives the analysis of variance of D⁻ A/T for generations 0-41, the generations being combined into seven blocks of 6 generations each. Two of the six degrees of freedom for blocks of generations absorb all the significant variance. These two degrees of freedom correspond to the divisions between generations 11 and 12 and between generations 35 and 36. The first rise is that evident in fig. 1 and coincides with the first sharp rise of mean chaeta-number. Here selection of higher chaeta-number genes may have caused a deterioration of developmental stability as it did in the lines described in Thoday (1958*b*).

TABLE 4

Analysis of variance of A/T for the D⁻ line, generations 0-41
(Six-generation blocks)

Source	n	Mean Square	P
Blocks 1 + 2 v. rest . . .	1	310·2880	<0·001
Block 7 v. rest	1	246·5334	<0·001
Residual blocks . . .	4	6·0208	...
7 six-generation blocks . .	6	96·8175	<0·001
Within blocks (Error) . .	35	12·8048	...

The second rise, at generation 36, occurred in a period of stable mean and presumably reflects a direct response of developmental stability to disruptive selection.

The indications would seem to be that disruptive selection can pick out genotypes that decrease developmental stability, but that the resulting effect is slight and is rarely permanent. Of the rises in asymmetry and A/T that occurred in D⁻, only the two discussed above were sustained. Others occurred, notably at generations 17, 22 and 31, but each was followed by a fall as if natural selection were subsequently eliminating them. It must be concluded that stability of development as measured can respond but responded little to the types of selection used here. There is certainly no evidence of steady deterioration in both the D lines or of improvement in S.

It may seem that the rises in A/T which did occur in the D⁻ line should be reflected in the variances or coefficients of variation. The correlation between coefficient of variation and A/T for the D⁻ line is positive but very insignificant, so that there is no evidence of such reflection. Correlations between asymmetry and variance can occur (Thoday, 1955; Beardmore, unpub.) and might be expected to be evident in these data. That they cannot be detected may indicate that other more important causes of variation of variance are operating.

6. FERTILITY

The data available provide two measures of the fertility of the lines. Records have been kept of the cultures that failed in each generation, and of the number of flies collected in the culture used to assay each female line (except on the 8 occasions when all 4 single-pair cultures of a female sub-line failed and the mass cultures had to be used).

The failure rates are (per culture) 0·187 for D⁻, 0·184 for D⁺ and 0·254 for S. There is no evidence of difference between coincident generations of D⁻ and D⁺ in this respect, and there is no evidence of a consistent trend of failure rate in D⁻ as the experiment progressed. The difference between S and D⁺, however, is significant (100 failures

TABLE 5

The number of single-pair cultures that failed.
(From 16 cultures set up per line per generation)

D⁻ Generations	D⁻	D⁺	S
0–10	18	...	...
11–21	46	40	48
22–32	42	37	43
33–43	19	23	43

out of 528 cultures in D⁺, 134 out of 528 in S, $\chi^2_{(1)} = 6\cdot3465$ P<0·02) and there is evidence suggesting that this difference has increased with generations. (Comparing the lines in the first 11 generations $\chi^2_{(1)} = 0\cdot9697$, P>0·3, the second 11 generations $\chi^2_{(1)} = 0\cdot5823$, P>0·3 and in the third 11 generations $\chi^2_{(1)} = 7\cdot4592$, P<0·01, though the lines×generations χ^2 is not quite significant.) If this increase of difference between the lines is real it is a little difficult to interpret, for it occurs, not as increase in the number of failures in S, but as decrease of failures in D⁺ (table 5). The only firm conclusion we can draw, therefore, is that failures are more frequent in the S line than the others. However, the D⁻ data would suggest that culture conditions or the handling of the flies has varied, thus masking deterioration of fertility in S and giving a spurious improvement in D⁺. That S has in fact deteriorated is clear from other evidence (see below).

The data for productivity are more informative, despite the large error such data have. The total flies recorded for D⁺ and S (the two strictly comparable lines) are summarised in table 6. Table 7 presents the results of an analysis of variance of the D⁺ and S productivities. It seems clear that productivity has declined significantly in both lines, that it has declined more in S than D⁺, and that S is very much less productive than D⁺. D⁻ figures are similar to those for D⁺. That fertility declines with selection is well known (Mather and Harrison, 1949), but it seems surprising that stabilising selection should be the

34

more effective in producing such a decline in the present experiments. Quite apart from these data, handling the lines themselves gives a strong impression that the S line has become very poor indeed. Its

TABLE 6

Mean numbers of flies collected per culture in D+ and S

Generations	D+	S
First 8 . . .	154	134
Second 8 . .	128	91
Third 8 . .	103	76
Fourth 8 . .	122	77
Total . .	*127*	*95*

lack of vigour is similar to that of a poor inbred line or a newly-plateaued selection line and suggests that stabilising selection in conjunction with small population size may have led to increasing homozygosity and consequent unbalance.

TABLE 7

Analysis of variance of productivities of cultures: D+ and S

Source	n	Mean Square	P
Lines	1	63409	Small
Generation Blocks . .	3	39833	Small
Lines × Generation Blocks .	3	2758	<0·001
Residual Generations . .	28	6011	Small
Cultures, etc. (Error) . .	219	389	...

7. RESPONSIVENESS TO DIRECTIONAL SELECTION

It is clear that, though it provides positive clues in the D+ line and perhaps in S, variance cannot be relied upon in a negative sense as an indicator of the effects of disruptive or stabilising selection. There are too many factors that may cause it to change and some of them at least (*e.g.* inbreeding in the S line) may act to change variance in directions opposite to those in which the artificial selection might be expected to change it.

Such difficulties were anticipated when the experiments were initiated and it was planned to test the lines, using divergent directional selection experiments, to determine how much free genetic variation they possessed. Such tests have been carried out on D⁻ at generations 21, 27 and 32; on D+ at generations 13 and 23 and 34 (= D⁻ 22, 32 and 43); and on S at generations 11, 12, 17 and 22 (= D⁻ 21, 22, 27 and 32).

35

The results are presented in fig. 2 in which the rates of divergence of High and Low line means are plotted. Results are also given in

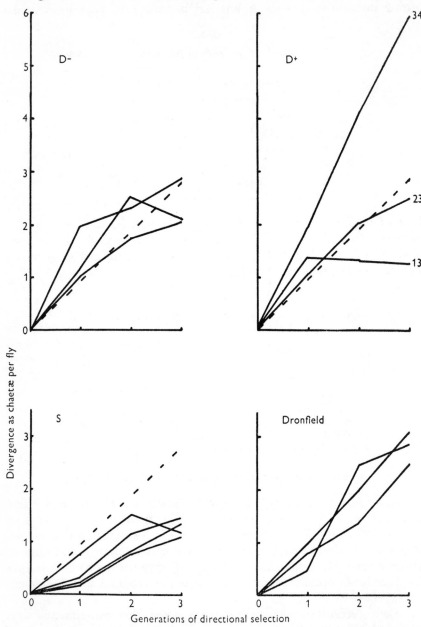

FIG. 2.—Results of divergent-directional selection tests on the lines and on the base stock (Dronfield) from which they were derived. Each solid curve represents the difference, in chaetæ per fly, between a high and a low selection line. The broken line represents the mean result of the three tests on the base stock. The generations in which D+ was tested are indicated and are those plotted with D− 22, 32 and 43 in Figure 1.

this figure for comparable tests of the wild Dronfield stock from which all the lines derive. Two of these are taken from the data of Thoday

(1958b), and the third was carried out two and a half years later (coincidentally with the tests on generation 27 D⁻ and 17 S). The agreement between these three testifies to the stability of this stock.

It is clear from the results of these tests that the D⁻ line and the S line differ. They were in fact already different when first tested and there is no evidence of subsequent further change. The D⁻ line is responsive to selection, and the S line is much less so. The S line is less responsive to selection than the Dronfield stock from which it came. The D⁻ line seems to respond more than the Dronfield stock to one generation of selection, but thereafter its response decreases so that after three generations of directional selection it has diverged no more and perhaps less than the stock.

Two of the D⁺ line tests were made at unfortunate times. The first test at generation 13 was made before variance had begun to rise in the line. It gave results in the first generation of directional selection comparable with those of the D⁻ line, but there was no further response. It was not possible to arrange to test it again until shortly *after* the error in selection had been made. It then (generation D⁺ 23 = D⁻ 32) responded exactly as the base stock. Bearing in mind that the selection error in D⁺ 21 (= D⁻ 30) had lowered the mean-square of this line from about 2·5 to about 1·5, this response is remarkable. D⁺ was tested again at generation 34 (= D⁻ 43) after it had regained a higher variance. At this test it proved most responsive, and there seems no doubt that it is now much more responsive than the base stock from which it was derived.

Together these tests make it quite clear that the D lines contain more effective genetic variation than the S line. They are genetically more flexible. There is also a suggestion that the genetic variation in the D⁻ line is more readily exploited by one generation of selection than is that in the Dronfield wild stock, and there is no doubt that disruptive selection has made the D⁺ line considerably more responsive than the stock.

These results may be used to provide estimates of heritability (realised heritability) from the formula $h^2 = \dfrac{dO}{dP}$ (where dO is the difference between the high and low line means after 1 generation of selection and dP is the difference between the selected parents used to produce the two lines). The formula is equivalent to $h^2 = \Delta P/_i$ (Lerner 1950).

The combined results for the first generations of all the divergent directional selection tests give $h^2 = 0·29$ for D⁻, 0·26 for D⁺, 0·15 for the base stock, and 0·09 for S. Heritability estimates obtained from the progeny tests of D⁻ and S figured in Thoday (1958a, fig. 3) are 0·20 for D⁻ and 0·05 for S, and are in reasonable agreement with those above.

8. DISCUSSION

Natural populations of outbreeding species are genetically diverse (*e.g.* Dobzhansky, 1955) and the causes and maintenance of this diversity present problems of great importance in the study of evolution. This genetic diversity is, in some materials at least, so great that we can speak of genetic individuality. Its study is therefore also of general philosophic importance, especially as man himself is one of the species in which (apart from identical twins) each individual is genetically unique (Medawar, 1957).

Systems that promote outbreeding help to maintain such genetic diversity. Indeed we regard the maintenance of diversity as the main function of outbreeding systems and of all the relevant aspects of genetic systems that promote heterozygosity and segregation (Darlington, 1939). But outbreeding systems cannot of themselves maintain gene frequencies indefinitely, and it is necessary to postulate selective forces that will do so. The same selective forces may be supposed responsible for the maintenance of the genetic systems themselves.

Three such selective forces have been proposed. The first is long-term selection for adaptability or genetic flexibility (*e.g.* Darlington, 1939; Mather, 1943; Thoday, 1953). Organisms have evolved in a changing environment, and selection must have, in the long run, eliminated those forms which did not maintain sufficient genetic flexibility. At the same time, short-term selection promotes genetic stability, so that high mutation rates which would permit genetic flexibility only at the expense of stability are inadequate. Heterozygous systems permit both stability and flexibility, so that stable heterozygous systems and the genetic diversity they bring about would result. Such long-term selection seems sufficient explanation to some but others doubt whether the selective forces could be adequate to account for the prevalence of outbreeding systems or the degree of diversity in contemporary populations. This quantitative objection may be valid, though it is difficult to assess, for selection against genetic inflexibility must in the long run be absolute, and the capacity of pathogens for rapid evolution implies that the long run may be shorter than we think. Nevertheless it does seem probable that other factors must be involved.

The second selective force is selection for heterozygotes. Here it is supposed that heterozygosity *per se* has some intrinsic virtue, in providing a more complex and versatile physiology. This must derive from inter-allelic interactions, or otherwise duplication could permit both alleles to become homozygous. There is evidence suggesting that such heterozygous advantage may occur, though it is always difficult to be sure what " allele " means in this context. The most cogent evidence is that of Allison (1955) and Hunt and Ingram (1958) concerning sickle-cell anaemia and the chemical structure of the haemoglobins. Here, however, there seems no good reason for invoking inter-allelic interaction. The evidence rather indicates independent action of the two alleles and there seems no reason why duplication should not ultimately occur and produce a homozygous individual capable of producing haemoglobin A and one or both the alternatives.   On the whole there seems little reason for supposing that heterozygosity had any primitive advantage (Thoday, 1955). Though some results (e.g. Wallace and Vetukhiv, 1955) are difficult to explain, it seems unlikely that superior fitness of heterozygotes can be the prime cause of heterozygosity.   The success of haploid and inbreeding species argues strongly against heterozygosity having any essential virtue other than as the prerequisite of segregation as Mather has made clear (*e.g.* Jinks and Mather, 1955).

The third type of selective force (Levene, 1953; Moree, 1953; da Cuhna and Dobzhansky, 1954; Mather, 1955*a*; Li, 1955; Robertson, 1956; Thoday, 1956) is one which may be supposed to operate in the short run to maintain the frequencies of heterozygotes.   This is continued selection for actual phenotypic (especially physiological) diversity.   Most populations occupy quite heterogeneous environments and are therefore exposed to disruptive selection.   Their environments are also subject to cyclic changes so that the populations will also be exposed to cyclic selection which is likely to have similar effects.   Robertson (1956) has shown theoretically that disruptive selection (D$^-$ in type) would be expected to maintain gene frequencies and that stabilising selection would be expected to lead to fixation. The present experiments show that this result is borne out in practice. Further, the D$^+$ line, which represents a situation likely to occur in nature more often than disruptive selection with negative assortative mating, shows that disruptive selection can actually increase the effective variation within a population.   The experiments therefore demonstrate that heterogeneity of the environment can in practice promote genetic diversity, as well as maintaining such diversity, and provide evidence favouring the view that disruptive selection is an important cause of the genetic diversity which we find in populations in nature.

9. SUMMARY

1. Three lines, each derived from the same base stock of wild *D. melanogaster*, have been maintained under different systems of selection for sternopleural chaeta-number.   One (D$^-$) was maintained under disruptive selection with negative assortative mating, one (D$^+$) under disruptive selection with positive assortative mating, and the third (S) under stabilising selection.

2. D$^-$ selection resulted in an increase of mean chaeta-number, some deterioration of developmental stability (homeostasis) as measured by sternopleural asymmetry, but little if any change of variance that could not be attributed to the correlation of variance and mean.

3. D$^+$ selection resulted in an increase of variance.

4. S selection resulted in a decrease of variance and a decline of vigour.

5. The D lines were more responsive to directional selection than the S line.

6. The D+ line has become more responsive to directional selection than the base stock from which it was derived. The S line is less responsive than the base stock.

7. Estimates of realised heritability are D⁻ 0·29, D⁺ 0·26, the base stock 0·15, and S 0·09. The D⁺ estimate is minimal as two of the three tests on which it is based were carried out at unfavourable times in the history of the line.

8. It is concluded that disruptive selection can promote and stabilising selection can decrease genetic flexibility, and, therefore, that heterogeneity of habitat may be an important cause of genetic diversity in natural populations.

Acknowledgments.—I am indebted to Mr T. B. Boam for assistance and to the Agricultural Research Council for a grant which has aided this work.

10. REFERENCES

ALLISON, A. C. 1955. Aspects of polymorphism in Man. *Cold Spr. Hbr. Symp. Quant. Biol., 20*, 239-255.

DARLINGTON, C. D. 1939. *The Evolution of Genetic Systems.* Cambridge.

DA CUHNA, A. B., AND DOBZHANSKY, TH. 1954. A further study of chromosomal polymorphism of *D. willistoni* in its relation to the environment. *Evolution, 8*, 119-134.

DOBZHANSKY, TH. 1955. A review of some fundamental concepts and problems of population genetics. *Cold Spr. Hbr. Symp. Quant. Biol., 20*, 1-15.

FALCONER, D. S. 1957. Selection for phenotypic intermediates in *Drosophila*. *J. Genet., 55*, 551-561.

FALCONER, D. S., AND ROBERTSON, A. 1956. Selection for environmental variability of body size in mice. *Z.I.A.V., 87*, 385.

HUNT, J. A., AND INGRAM, V. M. 1958. Allelomorphism and the chemical difference of the human haemoglobins A, S and C. *Nature, 181*, 1062-3.

JINKS, J. L., AND MATHER, K. 1955. Stability of development of homozygotes and heterozygotes. *Proc. Roy. Soc.* B, *143*, 561-578.

LERNER, I. M. 1950. *Population Genetics and Animal Improvement.* Cambridge.

LEVENE, H. 1953. Genetic equilibrium when more than one ecological niche is available. *Amer. Nat., 87*, 331-333.

LI, C. C. 1955. *Population Genetics.* Chicago.

MATHER, K. 1943. Polygenic balance and natural selection. *Biol. Rev., 18*, 32-64.

MATHER, K. 1953a. The genetical structure of populations. *Symp. Soc. Exp. Biol., 7*, 66-95.

MATHER, K. 1953b. Genetical control of stability in development. *Heredity, 7*, 297-336.

MATHER, K. 1955a. Polymorphism as an outcome of disruptive selection. *Evolution, 9*, 52-61.

MATHER, K. 1955b. Response to selection. *Cold Spr. Hbr. Symp. Quant. Biol., 20*, 158-165.

MATHER, K., AND HARRISON, B. J. 1949. The manifold effect of selection. *Heredity, 3*, 1-52, 131-162.

MEDAWAR, P. B. 1957. *The Uniqueness of the Individual.* Methuen, London.

MOREE, R. 1953. An unexpected relation between negative assortative mating and gene frequency. *Genetics, 38*, 677.

ROBERTSON, A. 1956. The effect of selection against extreme deviants based on deviation or on homozygosis. *J. Genet., 54*, 236.

SCHMALHAUSEN, I. I. 1949. *Factors of Evolution*. Blakiston, Philadelphia.

SIMPSON, G. G. 1944. *Tempo and Mode in Evolution*. Columbia, New York.

THODAY, J. M. 1953. Components of fitness. *Symp. Soc. Exp. Biol.*, 7, 96-113.

THODAY, J. M. 1955. Balance, heterozygosity, and developmental stability. *Cold Spr. Hbr. Symp. Quant. Biol.*, *20*, 318-326.

THODAY, J. M. 1956. Population Genetics. *Nature*, *178*, 843-844.

THODAY, J. M. 1958a. Effects of disruptive selection : the experimental production of a polymorphic population. *Nature*, *181*, 1124-1125.

THODAY, J. M. 1958b. Homeostasis in a selection experiment. *Heredity*, *12*, 401-415.

THODAY, J. M. 1958c. The cytoplasm and quantitative variation in *Drosophila*. *Proc. Roy. Soc. B*, *148*, 352-355.

WADDINGTON, C. H. 1953. Epigenetics and evolution. *Symp. Soc. Exp. Biol.*, 7, 186-199.

WADDINGTON, C. H. 1958. *The Strategy of the Genes*. London, Allen and Unwin.

WADDINGTON, C. H., GRABER, H., AND WOOLF, B. 1957. Isoalleles and the response to selection. *J. Genet.*, *55*, 246-250.

WALLACE, B., AND VETUKHIV, M. 1955. Adaptive organisation of the gene pools of *Drosophila* populations. *Cold Spr. Hbr. Symp. Quant. Biol.*, *20*, 303-310.

GENETIC ASSIMILATION OF THE *BITHORAX* PHENOTYPE

C. H. Waddington [1]

Institute of Animal Genetics, Edinburgh University, Scotland

Recieved March 17, 1955

Introduction

Some years ago it was suggested (Waddington, 1942) that if selection was practised for the readiness of a strain of organisms to respond to an environmental stimulus in a particular manner, genotypes might eventually be produced which would develop into the favoured phenotype even in the absence of the environmental stimulus. A character which had originally been an "acquired" one might then be said to have become genetically assimilated. An experimental investigation of the suggestion was carried out on *Drosophila melanogaster,* using a heat shock applied to the pupa as the environmental stimulus, and a crossveinless phenotype as the modification for which selection was practised. As has been described earlier (Waddington, 1953a), a genetic assimilation of the crossveinless phenotype was achieved in this case.

It seems possible that considerable general importance should be attached to processes of this kind, which appear able to provide a satisfactory explanation of the evolution of certain types of adaptation which have in the past been difficult to explain convincingly. It was there-fore thought desirable to investigate the genetic assimilation of other characters, so as to broaden the observational basis on which the theory rests. Mrs. K. G. Bateman in this laboratory has studied a number of rather mild developmental modifications, produced by temperature shocks applied to the pupa. These can perhaps be considered as of the same general type as the crossveinless phenotype previously investigated. The present communication deals with experiments on a phenocopy of a rather different character. This is the bithorax-like modification which can be produced by ether treatment of the young embryo (Gloor, 1947). The phenotype involves a profound modification of the normal appearance of the animal. The meta-thoracic disc, which normally gives rise to the halteres, becomes changed so as to develop into structures resembling the normal mesothorax, including the wings. If such a change occurred during phylogenesis it would certainly be accounted a macro-evolutionary phenomenon. It was felt that, if such a fundamental modification as this can be genetically assimilated, then one would have some grounds for confidence that the process was powerful enough to be invoked to explain quite far-reaching evolutionary changes.

[1] This work received financial support from the Agricultural Research Council, for which I express my gratitude.

Reprinted by permission of the author from Evolution, 10, 1–13 (1956).

42

MATERIALS AND METHODS

The stock used was a mass bred Oregon *K* wild type. Eggs were collected over a one-hour period. At the age of 2½–3½ hours after laying they were given an ether vapour treatment by inverting the watch glass on which they were laid over an open dish of ether. The duration of the treatment was normally 25 minutes. The ether-treated eggs were allowed to hatch and develop into adults, all cultures being carried on at 25° C. On emergence, which was spread over a period of about two days, the flies were classified as wild type or bithorax phenocopies. In the up selection lines from the latter category sufficient males and females (virginity uncertain) were collected every 24 hours to produce the next generation of eggs. In most generations between 2,000–3,000 flies were classified, and to produce these several hundred parents were used in each generation. Parallel with the upward selection line in which the bithorax phenocopies were used as parents, a downward selection line was carried on, in which the parents were taken from the wild type flies. Two replicates were made of this two-way selection experiment, so that there were eventually four lines, i.e. Experiment 1, Upward Selection and Downward Selection, and Experiment 2, Upward Selection and Downward Selection.

RESULTS

The two replicates were drawn from different initial stocks of Oregon R, and they started by showing rather different levels of phenocopy production. In Experiment I the first generation gave 24.5% of bithorax phenocopies, whereas Experiment II gave 48.8%. From these two initial points both the upward and the downward selections were effective. There

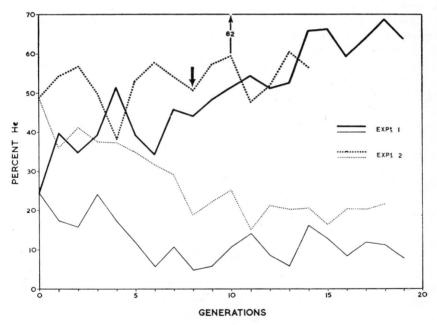

Fig. 1. Percentage of He (= bithorax-like) phenocopies in successive generations of upward and downward selection, following ether treatment of the eggs. The figures relate to flies which emerged from the puparia. At generation 10 in Experiment II, a count was made of all flies in a sample, including those failing to emerge and a percentage of 82 He found. The arrow at gen. 8 in Experiment II indicates the point at which the first assimilated stocks appeared.

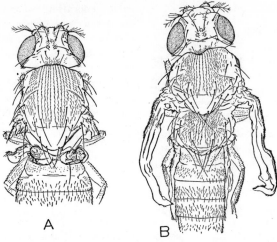

A   B

FIG. 2. Two typical phenocopies (medium and extreme in grade). Mesothoracic wings removed in 2a, metathoracic wings partly concealed by the abdomen in 2b.

is, however, not much point in quoting in detail the numbers of bithorax phenocopies which emerged in later generations, particularly in the upward selected lines. This is because a considerable proportion of high-grade phenocopies failed to emerge from the pupa cases. For instance, in generation 10 of Experiment II the proportion of phenocopies among the hatched individuals of the upward selection line was 59.5%, but from a sample of pupae in which the flies which failed to emerge were dissected out and examined, the proportion was about 82%. Normally such dissections were not done and the percentages of the phenocopies among the hatched adults, which are shown graphically in figure 1, give only a rough indication of the changes which the selection produced. It was also noted that in the upward selection lines the average grade of expression of the phenocopies rose, so that eventually a large number of very extreme bithorax types appeared (figure 2). It was in particular these most extreme types which had difficulty in emerging. The figures for the downward selection lines are probably more reliable, since in these, as the proportion of phenocopies was re-

duced, so also was the grade of expression, and there was a comparatively low incidence of failure of emergence. It will be noted that after many generations of downward selection the strains still produced a considerable and fluctuating number of phenocopies. A similar situation was found in the previous experiment with crossveinless (Waddington 1953a), where again selection did not succeed in rendering the stock completely resistant to the environmental stimulus.

The First "Assimilated" Stock

a. First set:

In each generation, besides the eggs which were collected over a timed interval for ether treatment, a number of others were collected and allowed to develop without treatment. In the early generations, as would be expected, no signs of bithorax-like phenotypes appeared, the flies being normal Oregon K wild types. However, in the eighth generation of the upward selection line of Experiment II, one fly from an untreated egg was found to show slightly enlarged halteres. In the next generation about 10 such flies were found among the untreated individuals. These were mated together in pairs and a number of "haltere-effect" or "He" lines were started. Each of these lines from the beginning threw a fairly large proportion of He flies, i.e. individuals with somewhat enlarged halteres. Selection was made amongst the lines to try to produce one in which the frequency of the haltere effect rose to 100%, or in which the phenotype was more extreme. In neither respect was success achieved. In the phenotype of an untreated individual it is very rare to find in these lines anything more extreme than the comparatively slight enlargement of the haltere illustrated in figure 3a, although in the first generation a few flies of slightly more extreme type appeared (fig. 3b).

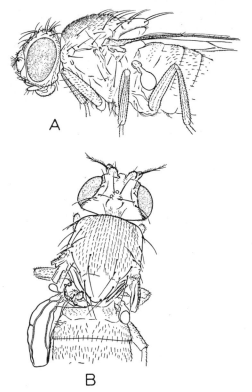

A

B

FIG. 3. Two individuals from the first set of "assimilated" stocks (He 17). Most flies of this stock show only the slightly enlarged halteres seen in 3a (cf. *Bxl*); a few have a bithoraxoid-like enlargement of the metathorax, as in 3b (from which the mesothoracic wings have been removed).

These were bithoraxoid-like; i.e. the metathorax represented the posterior part of the mesothorax (cf. Lewis, 1951). The frequency of the low grade phenotypes in one or two lines rose to 80% or slightly over, but never further.

Crosses with a C*l*B;Cy:Me stock showed that the haltere effect is due to a gene or genes on the third chromosome. In fact, the genetic condition can be perfectly balanced against Me, when it behaves exactly as though one were dealing with a single dominant gene with recessive lethal effect. Crosses to stocks containing Bxl show that the He/Bxl compound is lethal. All this is consistent with the hypothesis that the He effect is due to an allele of Bxl. The only thing which causes one any hesitation in adopting this hypothesis is the fact that in some of the "best" He stocks, and in their crosses with wild types, the numbers of He flies are higher than would be expected if He/He flies died. Thus in the selected He stocks, instead of the He individuals making up two-thirds of the progeny, they usually formed from 75% up to 85%; and in crosses and backcrosses with Oregon K and other wild types there was a consistent though not very large excess of He progeny (table 1). It was at first suspected that there might either be some polygenic tendency in the He stocks towards the enlargement of the haltere, cooperating with the major He gene, or that the lethality of the He homozygote was not absolute. Fairly extensive tests failed to confirm either suggestion. When the wild type individuals of an He strain were bred together no He's were ever produced in their progeny; nor could any He individual be found which gave rise to 100% He offspring. It was concluded therefore that the He effect is, in fact, produced by a single dominant with recessive lethal effect, but that, particularly in the strains which had been selected for a high proportion of expression, the viability of the heterozygote is somewhat greater than that of normal wild types.

TABLE 1. *Crosses of first He stocks*

Parents			He's of 1st set (He 5–He 16)			He's of 2nd set (He 17)		
♀	♂		He	Total	He %	He	Total	He %
1. He	He	Gen. 1.	2639	3436	76.8	551	753	73.4
		Gen. 2.	1713	2232	76.7			
		Gen. 3.	871	1143	76.2			
2. OrK	He		778	1476	52.7	406	822	49.4
2a. He/OrK	He		2114	3072	68.8	702	1070	65.6
2b. He	He/OrK					412	602	69.0
3. He	OrK		748	1287	58*	389	767	50.6
3a. He/OrK	He		1453	2026	72*	494	743	66.3
3b. He	He/OrK					308	484	63.6

* The wild types used in these crosses were not OrK, but were from the downward selected line of Experiment II.

b. *The second set:*

These facts show that, in this first group of stocks in which the bithorax phenotypes seem to be to some extent assimilated, the "assimilation" has not proceeded in the normal way by the selection of many minor genes acting in the required direction, but occurred by the fixation of a single major gene mutation which presumably arose *de novo* by chance. Further selection for phenocopy production was therefore continued. Experiment II was carried to the 14th generation; Experiment I was taken to generation 20, when the duration of treatment was reduced to 20 minutes till generation 26, after which it was reduced again to 15 minutes. No further sign of assimilation occurred until generation 29 in the upward selected line of Experiment I. At this time a few untreated flies were found which showed indications of a bithorax-like phenotype. In most of these the abnormal phenotype was again confined to a slight enlargement of the halteres. By breeding these together and selecting amongst their progeny another haltere-effect stock known as He17 was produced. This behaved genetically exactly like the previously obtained haltere-effect stocks, the phenotype being due to a dominant with recessive lethal effect, which is indistinguishable from that previously described.

The Second "Assimilated" Stock

Among the untreated bithorax-like flies of generation 29 in Experiment I, one or two showed not only enlarged halteres but also extra pieces of thorax-like material formed on the dorsum by the metathoracic bud. These were bred together, and selection made amongst their offspring for the development of extra thorax. A few generations of such selection produced a stock known as He*,

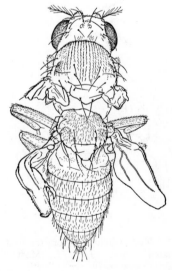

FIG. 4. An extreme, though fairly frequent, type from the second assimilated stock He*. Normal mesothoracic wings removed to show the bithorax-like metathorax.

which in mass matings gave a frequency of bithorax-like phenotypes of about 70–80%. These bithorax-like flies (fig. 4) frequently showed a large amount of extra thorax material as well as enlarged halteres. This extra material was of bithorax type, i.e. represented the anterior section of the mesothorax. The flies thus differed considerably in appearance from those of the previously described haltere-effect stocks. The difference persists even when eggs of the two stocks are given ether treatments and their phenotypic abnormalities thus exaggerated.

As a first step towards an analysis of the genetic situation in the He* stock a cross was made of an He* male to a ClB_1. Cy : Me female. No He* phenotypes appeared in the F_1. CyMe males and females from the F_1 were intercrossed and He* flies of rather weak grade were found in the F_2 in numbers which suggest that the character has a polygenic basis, the genes concerned being located both on the 2nd and 3rd chromosomes (table 2). There is no sign of any effect of recessive sexlinked factors.

This result falls in line with what one might expect if the assimilation were due to the accumulation of minor genes acting towards the bithorax phenotype. The results of crosses and back-crosses to wild types were, however, somewhat anomolous. The results of the first set of such crosses are given in table 3. It will be seen than when He* females were crossed with Oregon K males (of the stock used for Experiment II) there was a large percentage of He* individuals in the F_1,

TABLE 2. ClB; Cy; Me ♀ × He* ♂ gave no He* phenotypes in F1. $\dfrac{Cy; Me}{He*}$ mated inter se gave in F2:

Offspring	He* ♀	He* ♂	non-He*	Total	He*%
+	31	23	106	160	33.7
Cy	24	31	179	234	23.5
Me	15	16	262	293	10.6
Cy; Me	15	8	506	529	4.3

TABLE 3. He*: first set of crosses to OrK (1a, 1 bare back-crosses from 1; 2a, 2b from 2)

	Parents ♀	Parents ♂	He*	Total	He*%
	He*	He*			70–80
	Non-He* ♀ and ♂ from He* stock				10–14
1.	He*	OrK	184	398	46
1a.	He*/OrK	He*	5	419	1.2
1b.	He*	He*/OrK	98	174	56
2.	OrK	He*	0	539	0
2a.	He*/OrK	He*	3	416	0.7
2b.	He*	He*/OrK	48	276	17.4

whereas in the reciprocal cross no He* individuals appeared. The sexes were approximately equally represented in the He* F_1 individuals, from the He* female by Oregon K male cross, so that one cannot attribute the difference between the reciprocal crosses to a direct effect of recessive sex-linked factors. One must rather suppose that there is some influence of the mother, either by way of a maternal effect or possibly of a cytoplasmic nature. The series of crosses are, however, somewhat inconsistent with one another, in that many fewer He* flies were produced by the back-cross of a heterozygous He* male derived from an Oregon K mother on to an He* female (see line 2b) than had been produced when a pure wild type male had been used on an He* female (see line 1, F_1). The explanation of this was presumably to be found in the fact that there was considerable heterogeneity between the different cultures, which was taken to indicate that mass-mated He* stock was far from uniform in genotype.

An attempt was therefore made to purify the He* stock by carrying it for several generations in pair matings, amongst which those which gave the highest percentage of He* phenotypes were selected. After some generations of this procedure, a new series of matings were set up, both between the various phenotypes in the He* stock, and between the He* stock and an Oregon K wild

TABLE 4. *He*: second set of crosses to OrK*

	Parents' genotype		Parents' phenotype		Groups of pairs	Progeny		
	♀	♂	♀	♂		He*	Total	He*%
1.	He*	He*	He*	He*	10	264	387	68
					2	16	84	19
2.	He*	He*	+	He*	8	362	854	80
					1	11	85	13
3.	He*	He*	He*	+	12	429	658	63
4.	He*	He*	+	+	6	225	358	63
5.	He*	+	He*	+	—	90	592	15
5a.	He*	He*/+ ex 5	He*	He*	7	143	254	56
					1	3	29	10
5b.	He*	He*/+ ex 5	He*	+	7	91	247	37
					1	9	88	10
5c.	He*/+ ex 5	He*	He*	He*	—	7	653	1
5d.	He*/+ ex 5	He*	+	He*	—	3	358	1
6.	ex 5c	ex 5c	+	He*	3	117	187	63
					2	31	179	17
					4	14	225	6
7.	ex 5c	ex 5c	+	+	6	193	346	56
					6	9	517	2
8.	+	He*	+	He*	—	0	674	0
8a.	He*	+/He* ex 8	He*	+	—	298	610	49
8b.	+/He* ex 8	He*	+	He*	—	17	859	5
9.	ex 8b	ex 8b	+	He*	5	156	255	61
					4	8	311	2
10.	ex 8b	ex 8b	+	+	2	55	104	53
					9	14	300	3

type. As will be seen from table 4, lines 1–4, there is still some heterogeneity within the He* stock, but this had been very considerably reduced. Matings between individuals of this stock which had wild type phenotypes produced nearly the same number of He* offspring as did matings between individuals of He* phenotype, but a few pairs gave considerably fewer He* offspring than did the majority of matings. Thus it appeared that the stock had become more uniform for a genetic constitution which had produced He* phenotypes in a proportion of between 60% and 70%.

The results of crosses with wild type and back-crosses carried out at this stage are also given in table 4. It will be seen that once again the reciprocal crosses with the wild type give different results; those with a wild type mother giving no

He* phenotypes in the F₁ (line 8), whereas in the opposite cross such phenotypes do appear (line 5), though in a considerably lower proportion than was found in the earlier series of crosses with the less purified strains. In the back-crosses of the F₁ males to He* females, the numbers of He* phenotypes appearing are now in reasonable agreement with one another (lines 5a, 5b, 8a). The most interesting result appears from the back-crosses of the F₁ females to He* males and the subsequent generations. The back-crosses themselves gave rise to very few He* phenotypes (lines 5c, 5d, 8b). However, when the female offspring of these back-crosses (wild type in phenotype) were themselves crossed to their brothers (either to wild type or He* in phenotype), the families seemed to fall into two distinct groups (lines 6, 7, 9,

TABLE 5. *Hatchability in unselected wild type and selected lines of Experiment I (generation c. 35), following 25 mins. ether vapour at 2½ hrs.*

Stock	Eggs treated	Hatched	Hatched %
Or.K.	400	270	67.5
Expt. I, down selected	500	408	81.6
Expt. I, up selected	500	418	83.6

10). One group gave about 55% to 60% of He* offspring, while another group gave a low percentage of the order of 2–5%. This result can be simply explained if we suppose that an important factor in the production of the He* phenotype in these stocks and crosses is a recessive gene which has no obvious effect on males but which causes females homozygous for it to produce eggs with a strong tendency to develop into He* phenotypes. This maternal effect gene must be supposed to co-operate with a polygenic tendency towards He,* dependent on minor genes scattered throughout the second and third chromosomes.

Other Effects of the Assimilation Procedure

The ether treatment necessary to produce the bithorax phenocopy causes a certain reduction in the percentage hatch of the eggs subjected to it. This was particularly the case at the beginning of the experiment. As shown in table 5, hatchability improved in both the upward and downward selected lines. Since in both cases the selection involved breeding from survivors, this improvement is not unexpected.

It is interesting to inquire whether selection for a high rate of phenocopy production by a certain environmental stimulus produces a specific sensitivity in the selected strain, or whether one finishes with a stock which is highly sensitive against any type of abnormal environment. This question has not been studied

in detail, but the He* lines were given the hot shock treatment of the pupae which had previously been used to produce the crossveinless phenocopy, and the assimilated crossveinless strain, together with the wild Edinburgh stock from which it had been derived, were given the He treatment. The results are shown in table 6. It is clear that all the He lines had become rather more sensitive to the temperature shock to the pupae than was the wild type from which they originated. There is no evidence that the lines selected for low sensitivity to ether treatment are more resistant to the hot shock than the lines selected for high susceptibility: in fact the low line of Experiment I is the most sensitive of the group. The *cvl* line, selected for high susceptibility to hot shock, had reacted in the opposite way, and became considerably more resistant to the ether treatment than the Wild Edinburgh from which it originated. It seems then that the selections, which had certainly produced specific sensitivities or resistances to particular environmental stimuli, had not regularly resulted in corresponding changes in general developmental buffering.

TABLE 6. *He lines given cvl treatment (4 hrs. at 40° C.). Percentage of cvl phenocopies produced*

Stock	Time treatment applied after pupation	
	19–21 hrs.	21–23 hrs.
He Expt. I		
Up selected	2.3	11.8
Down selected	9.3	24.3
He Expt. II		
Up selected	2.6	13.7
Down selected	6.9	12.9
Or.K.		8.1

Lines from *cvl* expt. given *He* treatment. Percentage of *He* phenocopies produced.

cvl assimilated line	6.0
Wild Edinburgh	21.1

DISCUSSION

Selection for the ability to respond to ether treatment of the eggs by the production of bithorax-like phenocopies has on three at first sight separate occasions resulted in the appearance of stocks which exhibit this phenotype even in the absence of any special environmental stimulus. There were, firstly, the *He* stocks which arose in generation 8 of Experiment II, giving a *Bxl*-like adult; secondly, the similar stock (He 17) which arose in generation 29 of Experiment I; and thirdly, the *He** stock which appeared at the same time in Experiment I, but which gave a more *bx*-like phenotype, which was inherited in a different manner.

Such genetic assimilation of the abnormal phenotype might be due, in the first place, to the occurrence of a single new mutation which produces the character in question, and this mutation might be either spontaneous, or in some way caused by the treatment; or, in the second place, to the assembling together, by the selection pressure exerted, of already-present minor allelic differences tending in the appropriate direction; or finally, to a combination of these two mechanisms. The evidence strongly suggests that it is to the occurrence of new mutations that one must attribute the appearance of both the first group of *He* stocks and the second such stock, *He* 17. In both cases, the phenotype is dependent on a single gene, which produces its effect even in normal wild-type backgrounds, and there is no evidence that the accumulation of minor gene differences has played any significant role. Moreover, the genes are dominant in phenotypic expression, and cannot have been present in the initial population from which selection was begun.

Since the first lot of He stocks originated at quite a different time to *He* 17, and in a different selection line, the question arises whether we are dealing with two independent mutations; and if so, whether the occurrence of two apparently identical mutations in the populations involved would suggest that the treatment had caused them. As a matter of fact, since the selected stocks were basically wild-type in character, there is no absolute safeguard against the possibility that *He* 17 was a contaminant from the earlier *He* stocks which were of course present in the laboratory at the time it was found. However, concurrent experimental work has been little troubled by contamination, and there is no specific reason to suspect it in this case. If one adopts the alternative possibility, that two independent mutations to a *Bxl*-like allele have occurred, it is of interest to inquire whether the numbers of animals involved makes it all reasonable to postulate such a double event without supposing that the mutations were induced by the treatment. Unfortunately the records which were kept do not make it possible to give a completely accurate figure for the numbers. We are only concerned with the upward selected lines, since if such a mutation occurred in the downward lines, it would have been classified as a phenocopy and excluded from breeding. In Experiment II, rather over 17,000 flies had been treated and examined before the first *He*'s were found; and to these must be added a fairly considerable, though unrecorded, number of untreated sibs which were examined (and amongst which the *He*'s occurred). One can take it that at least some 20–25,000 flies had been inspected by the time the *He* mutation was found. Selection was then carried on for a further six generations in Experiment II, involving 14,000 flies examined. In Experiment I, some 87,000 flies had been inspected before *He* 17 was found in generation 29. If one makes allowance for examined untreated flies, one can conclude that a total of the order of 150,000 individuals were inspected in the whole upward selected lines of both experiments. The occurrence of two similar mutations amongst this number would give a mutation rate for the locus rather nearer 10^{-5} than 10^{-4}. Such a spontaneous mutation rate, though undoubtedly high, does not seem to be so excessive so that one is driven to postulate a direct inducing action by the environmental treatment.

In the other stock which shows assimilation, He*, the genetic changes are more far-reaching in their effects. The abnormal individuals produced by this stock are much nearer to the phenocopy, showing all grades of bithorax-like appearance up to an extreme type with a large second pair of wings and a considerable extra mesothorax. The assimilation has therefore been rather thorough. Its genetic basis certainly does not depend on the chance occurrence of only a single mutation producing this effect; the variation in the proportion of abnormal phenotypes in the various crosses clearly demonstrates that the character is affected by a polygenic system.

Since the phenocopy is induced by an environmental stimulus on the early egg, the effectiveness of which may well be supposed to depend on characteristics of the egg cytoplasm, it is perhaps not unexpected to find that an important part in the genetic constitution of the assimilated stock is played by a maternal effect. The full genetic analysis of this effect is still in progress and will be reported on later. The present data show that the genetic determinant or determinants of it are recessive. The relatively clean-cut segregation of the daughters of the back-cross of an F_1 female to an He* male into two classes (table 4, lines 9 and 10) suggests that the genetic basis of the character lies on one chromosome. It may indeed be a single gene, but it might be two or more fairly closely linked genes. If it is single, the question will arise whether it could have existed in the initial population before selection started. In crosses of He* females to wild-type males the maternal effect, operating on eggs which are heterozygous for the rest of the He* genotype, produces 15% of bithorax-like offspring. It is not yet known what effect, if any, the maternal effect genes can pro-duce in a genotype which lacks any of the rest of the He* complex. If even in these circumstances it produces some bithorax-like phenotypes, one would have to conclude that the condition had not been present in the initial population but had arisen by mutation or recombination during the course of the selection. As has been pointed out, the number of individuals runs into six figures, so that an origin by mutation would not be anything out of the way.

Whatever the origin of the maternal effect gene or genes turns out to be, there can be no doubt that the selection has brought together and concentrated a considerable number of minor alleles tending in the bithorax direction. Many if not all of these were presumably present in the original population. The attempt to assimilate the bithorax character was originally undertaken with the idea that from the evolutionary point of view it was a very bizarre aberration and would provide a good test of the powers of the mechanism of assimilation. The fact that the assimilation has been successfully carried out in a number of generations, which although long in the laboratory are very short in the time scale of nature, suggests that the mechanism can in fact be an extremely powerful one. It seems likely that any modification produced by the environment could, if it were favourable to the animal, be genetically assimilated in a relatively short time.

It is instructive to compare the process of genetic assimilation as it has occurred in the He stocks with the "organic selection" of Baldwin (1902) and Lloyd Morgan (1900). They argued that if an animal subjected to any environmental stimulus is able to respond to it in an adaptive manner, the animal and the population of which it is a member will be able to continue existing in the region where the environmental stimulus operates, until such time as a chance mutation produces a phenotypic effect which mimics the adaptive response. Now this is what seems to have happened in the first two sets of He assimilated stocks, in which a dominant allele of Bxl has appeared and produces a phenotype which has at least the lowest grade of the phenocopy appearance. The development of the full assimilation of the character in the He* stock can not, however, be accounted for in these terms. In the first place, one of the components of the genetic system, namely the maternal effect, is recessive. If we are to account for its appearance by some process other than selection for the capacity to respond to the environmental stimulus, we would have to take account not only of the low frequency with which such a mutation might be expected, but of the small probability that it would have emerged in homozygous state in these experiments, in which the inbreeding was very low. Moreover, there is no doubt that the maternal effect does increase the readiness with which the eggs respond to the ether treatment by developing bithorax phenocopies. It must surely be to this fact that its selection and concentration must be attributed, and the same applies to the other components of the He* genotype. We must be dealing with an "assimilation," produced by selection of capacity for response, rather than an "organic selection" of a chance mutation mimicking the response.

In a recent discussion by Underwood (1954) of the relevance of experiments on genetic assimilation to evolution as it occurs in Nature, some misunderstanding seems to have arisen as to what is actually being claimed for this process. It is quite true, as Underwood points out, that animals in Nature are rarely subjected to such extreme environmental stimuli as the temperature shocks used in the experiments on crossveinless phenocopies, while the ether treatment used here is even less "natural." Again it may be conceded that neither of these environmental treatments did, or could in the nature of the case, produce phenotypic changes which were adaptive. All this, however, does not in any way make it impossible that such experiments should

reveal a general mechanism, relating genotypes to selective forces acting on environmentally-influenced phenotypes, which may be of general significance, and which may operate in an essentially similar manner when the environmental stimuli are milder in character and their phenotypic effects adaptive.

Another point raised by Underwood is the consideration that if a genotype can respond adaptively to the environment it normally meets, genetic assimilation of the adaptive phenotypic characters will be unnecessary. On *a priori* grounds, the argument may seem plausible; but the fact is that most adaptive features of animals are genetically fixed, and do not alter much when development takes place in somewhat unusual conditions. It is not entirely clear why this should be so; possibly it is because it is difficult to build up a genotype which develops with the right degree of adaptive modification to the whole range of environments it has to meet, and that it "pays better" to sacrifice something of the flexibility of the developmental system and to assimilate genetically the adaptation to the most usual environment.

Underwood suggests that "we should distinguish as *primary* (genetically) *fixed adaptations* those which we believe to have arisen as such, and as *secondary fixed adaptations* those which have arisen by fixation of a facultative adaptation." This implies that the environmental modification of development is quite irrelevant to the origin of the primary fixed adaptations; and the same view is implicit in Underwood's argument "if it be necessary in the end to invoke a change of genotype to establish the suitable embryonic inductor (of callosities in the ostrich) then it may surely be invoked in the first place." Now it is certainly very usual at the present time to discuss the evolution of new characters without ever referring to the effects of environment on development, or at best to bring this in at a late stage in the discussion, as a secondary factor in the way suggested by Underwood.   But in my opinion such an approach is theoretically inadequate.   All phenotypes are modified, to a greater or lesser extent, by the environment.   All genotypes under natural conditions will be subject to selection pressures relating to the manner in which their development is modified by the environment.   The phenotypic effect of any new gene mutation must therefore be to some extent influenced by the kind of developmental flexibility which has been built into the rest of the genotype by selection for its response to the environment.   The effect of such specific developmental flexibilities may sometimes be rather slight (as it seems to have been in the first set of assimilated He stocks), or considerably greater, (as it was in respect of the maternal effect factor in the He* stock) ; but it must always be there.   The distinction between primary and secondary fixed adaptations is therefore not a real one, as Underwood has drawn it.

There is not space here for a full discussion of all the implications of the views advanced above.   It is sufficient to point out that the experiments on genetic assimilation have been designed to maximise the influence of selectively-determined developmental instabilities, since this was the aspect in the total situation to which attention was being particularly directed. The fact that they have succeeded in producing a change of macro-evolutionary magnitude in the short space of 30 generations of selection suggests that such instabilities may on occasion be of considerable importance.

SUMMARY

1. Two replicate experiments were made, in which treatment by ether vapour was given to the eggs of Drosophila melanogaster $2\frac{1}{2}$–$3\frac{1}{2}$ hours after laying, and selection practised either for the tendency to produce bithorax-like phenocopies ("upward selection"), or against it ("downward selection").   The two foundation stocks were both Oregon-K wild types, but had been bred separately for some considerable time.

2. Selection was effective in both directions, but its progress was not followed in detail owing to the death of many extreme phenocopies in the puparia.

3. In the 8th and 9th generations of the Up selected line of Experiment II, flies which showed a slight enlargement of the halteres appeared among the untreated individuals.   These gave rise to a series of stocks, which were found to contain a dominant allele of Bxl with recessive lethal effect.

4. In the 29th generation of the Up selected line of Experiment I, similar flies were again found among untreated individuals.   These gave rise to a stock (He 17), which contained a factor which was indistinguishable from that mentioned in para. 3.   It might, indeed, have arisen through contamination by flies carrying that gene; but the numbers involved in the experiment (c. 150,000) make it conceivable that both occurrences of the gene were due to independent chance mutations.

5. In the 29th generation of the Up selected line of Experiment I there also occurred, among untreated individuals, some showing the metathorax partially converted into a mesothorax.   These gave rise to a stock He*, in which the bithorax phenotype appears in high frequency and extreme grade.   The genetic basis of the character is partly a recessive gene which causes females to produce eggs developing into bithorax phenotypes (a maternal effect), and partly a number of minor genes on both the second and third chromosomes.

6. Selection for sensitivity to one type of environmental stimulus does not necessarily produce susceptibility to stimuli of a different type.

7. The fact that such a bizarre phenotype as bithorax can be assimilated, with high grade expression, in less than 30 generations, suggests that the genetic assimilation mechanism is a very powerful

one, which could have far-reaching effects during evolution.

LITERATURE CITED

BALDWIN, J. M. 1902. Development and Evolution. New York and London.

GLOOR, H. 1947. Phänokopie Versuche mit Aether an Drosophila. Rev. Suisse Zool., 54: 637–712.

LEWIS, E. B. 1951. Pseudo-allelism and gene evolution. Cold Spring Harbor Symp. Quant. Biol., 16: 159–174.

LLOYD MORGAN, C. 1900. Animal Behaviour. London.

UNDERWOOD, G. 1954. Categories of adaptation. EVOLUTION, 8: 365–377.

WADDINGTON, C. H. 1942. Canalisation of development and the inheritance of acquired characters. Nature, 150: 563–565.

———. 1953a. Genetic assimilation of an acquired character. EVOLUTION, 7: 118–126.

———. 1953b. The "Baldwin Effect," "Genetic Assimilation," and "Homeostasis." EVOLUTION, 7: 386–387.

A COMPARISON OF SELECTIVE METHODS AND A TEST OF THE PRE-ADAPTATION HYPOTHESIS

JACK BENNETT *

Department of Genetics,† University of Wisconsin, Madison, Wisconsin

Received 23.xii.59

1. INTRODUCTION

THE capacity of some species to adapt to poisons introduced into their environment has been known for many years. The work is summarised in the review articles of Crow (1957), Milani (1957), and Brown (1958).

Earlier work with DDT has produced conflicting results on the hereditary basis, and manner of selection, of resistance (Crow, 1957; Milani, 1957; Tsukamoto, 1958). Different species of insects seemed to resist the poison by different genetic mechanisms. The same species, viz., *Drosophila melanogaster*, adapted by quite different hereditary changes in different laboratories under varying conditions of culture and selection. Some resistant strains proved to have the major portion of the resistance controlled by a single dominant locus or region (Ogaki and Tsukamoto, 1957). Other strains (Crow, 1957) have been shown to have their resistance based on many factors which exert their effects additively. Some of the strains were selected by exposure of adults to aerosols, some to DDT on paper, others by exposure of larvæ to DDT in the food medium, and some by topical application. With this variety of selective methods it is not surprising that a variety of hereditary responses resulted. Furthermore, Levene, Pavlovsky and Dobzhansky (1958) have shown that replicate samples of the same population may react differently under apparently identical conditions.

Insecticide resistance is genetically similar to drug resistance in bacteria, and shares in the continuing controversy over pre-adaptation (the presence in populations of individuals with some degree of hereditary resistance before exposure to the toxic agent) and post-adaptation (the development of resistance by all, or part, of a population by physiological adaptation, which may or may not be inherited, as a result of exposure to the toxic agent). The pre-adaptational view has been well substantiated, for bacteria, by the work of Cavalli-Sforza and Lederberg (1956), the clearest evidence arising from the production of resistance without exposure to the toxic agent by means of sib-selection. The best previous evidence in favour of pre-adaptation in Drosophila has been based on the inability of selection of any kind to

* Present address : Department of Biological Sciences, Northern Illinois University, DeKalb, Illinois.

† Paper number 731 from the Department of Genetics, University of Wisconsin, Madison 6, Wisconsin. This work had been supported, in part, by grants from the Office of the Surgeon General, Department of the Army, and from the National Science Foundation.

produce significant resistance in highly inbred strains (Merrell and Underhill, 1956 ; Crow, 1957).

The present study was planned to throw light on three main points ;

1. If the adaptation is, or can be, a purely selective process, based on hereditary variability already in the population, then it should be possible to select for or against the adaptation without ever exposing the organisms in the direct ancestral line to the selective agent.

2. Will different methods of selection applied to samples of the same starting population give variant results, even with similar culture conditions ?

3. The various resistant strains of *D. melanogaster* produced in different laboratories had been selected and tested by different means. Some of these strains were obtained and cultured and tested along with the strains selected in the Madison laboratory. They can now be compared as to degree of resistance under the conditions of the Madison laboratory.

2. MATERIALS AND METHODS

The flies were tested for DDT tolerance by being exposed to DDT deposited on paper lining the vials in which they were confined. Papers were prepared with the following concentrations of DDT, in micrograms per square centimetre (10^{-6} μ gm./cm.^{2}) : 1/25 (0·04) ; 1/5 (0·20) ; 1 ; 5 ; 25 ; 125 ; 625. Some were produced with 6050 for use in the population cages with direct selection.

The DDT-lined vials were assembled into " test sets." In the initial testing, of generations 0 and 1, a " test set " consisted of 5 vials with the concentrations : 1/25, 1/5, 1, 5, 25. The number of vials was later reduced to three, and two different kinds of " test set " were produced, the " high sets " with the concentrations : 1/5 ; 5 ; and 125 (later 1, 25, 625), and the " low sets " with concentrations : 1/25 ; 1 ; 25.

The lines selected for resistance to DDT were tested by exposure to the " high sets," those selected for susceptibility to DDT were tested by the " low sets." (Exposure 18 hours, counts 24 hours later.) By using test concentrations in regular multiples it was possible to apply " Karber's Method " (Cornfield and Mantel, 1950) to obtain an estimate of the dose which would kill half of the population (LD_{50}) represented by the flies tested in each set.

The LD_{50} values for each test set were treated as units of data in the statistical analysis. In preparing a test from three to six flies were required for each vial. Thus the LD_{50} value from a particular " test set " was based on the performance of 9 to 18 flies.

All testing was done on female flies, which give more reproducible results than males (Crow, 1954). In the case of the sib-selected lines it was not practical to use females of selected size, age, and condition because of the very small number of flies available in each culture and the lack of synchrony between cultures. This choice of material undoubtedly increased the variability of the results, but seems realistic in that it involved all adult stages rather than one selected age. All tests of DDT tolerance were made in incubators adjusted to 25° C.

The test sets were serially numbered and used repeatedly in rotation for several months. Thus each set was used the same number of times and changes in potency were presumed to be proportional to the various sets. Differences between sets were presumed to be equally distributed among all tested strains.

(i) *Methods of selection*

All selections were made on samples of a heterogeneous stock, produced from 17 genetically distinct laboratory strains and 9 wild type strains derived from 9 females collected at a local fruit warehouse.

Cage 1 had no exposure to DDT at any time during the course of the experiment. It therefore can be considered a control. Cage 2 had DDT added for lengthy periods, then removed for similar periods. After early intermittent application, similar to Cage 2, Cage 3 had continuous exposure to DDT. The DDT was introduced to the cages on papers identical with those used in the test vials (except that higher concentrations were used). The papers were left in the cages for one or more weeks, being replaced periodically.

(ii) *The sib-selection lines*

An initial group of 46 pairs of flies from the heterogeneous stock were placed in a similar number of food vials and allowed to produce progenies. Thus each pair of flies produced one progeny (=sibship=family) in one food vial. Each progeny was tested for DDT tolerance. After the tests were completed the progenies were ranked according to their tolerance, as evidenced by the group of females tested from each. The parents of the next generation were chosen from the untreated sibs of the tested progeny. The most resistant 5 progenies each provided 4 males and 4 females (mated serially) toward the establishment of the " High " line. The next 15 most resistant progenies each provided 2 males and 2 females (mated serially) to the " High " line. The 20 most susceptible progenies provided similarly for the establishment of the " Low " line. In each case the flies were pair mated, with one pair to each food vial. The result was 50 vials, each with a pair of parents, to produce 50 progenies to be tested in the next generation of each line. The process was repeated for each generation of selection, except that after generation 1 duplicate sets of parents were made up for each line, with the result that two " High " and two " Low " lines were available for selection. The High and Low lines were carried in pairs through all procedures, thus High Line 1 (HL1) and Low Line 1 (LL1) were tested at the same time and were raised on the same batches of food. Similarly High and Low Lines 2 (HL2 and LL2) were carried together.

About half-way through the selection a combination of events, most importantly a series of batches of poor food medium (the nature of the poorness is unknown), led to such a reduction of numbers in all sib-selection lines that mass mating was necessary to avoid losing the lines. This interval was named the " Mass Mating Hiatus," and is so designated on the appropriate figs. The minimum effective population size during this period is unknown, but is estimated to have exceeded 25 in all lines.

3. RESULTS

In all cases where selection was practised a change in degree of tolerance of DDT was produced. The amount of change, and the final degree of tolerance, varied considerably.

(i) *The population cages*

The data on the population cages are presented in fig. 1. Here the tests on the cages are summarised by two-month periods. The fortuitous variation in the values is apparent. Cage 2 seems to vary almost at random, but with a set of values quite different from those of Cage 1. These short-term changes almost certainly represent differences in the culturing of the samples taken from the cages, rather than actual changes of the cage populations. The critical point is the final difference of tolerance between the cages. Cage 3 shows similar variation but a final greater tolerance to DDT than the other two.

If a period-by-period comparison is made between the three cages it will be noticed that the very high and very low points tend to occur together for all three. This is perhaps the best indication of a common external factor influencing the estimation of DDT tolerance of the three populations.

One may then conclude that in the case of these three cages continuous selection (Cage 3) was more effective than intermittent selection (Cage 2) as one might expect. In both cases an increase of DDT tolerance over that of the control (Cage 1) was achieved.

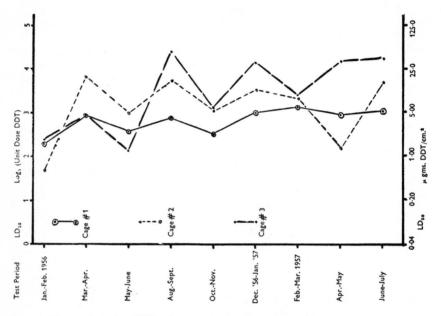

FIG. 1.—The comparative DDT tolerance of samples of 3 population cages, #1 unselected, #2 intermittent selection, #3 nearly continuous selection.

(ii) The sib-selection lines

The sib-selection lines were carried with selection for 14 or 15 generations, during the period of time that the population cages were being sampled. Fig. 2 shows clearly that the sib-selection was effective in HL1 and LL1. For the first three generations there was overlapping, and even reversal of relative positions of the values for the two lines. Then the lines quite clearly separated and remained so, with no hint of overlap at the 95 per cent. confidence level. Most of the difference between the two lines had been achieved by the 5th generation. Only relatively small gains were made later.

Fig. 3 presents a similar picture for HL2 and LL2. These lines were split off from HL1 and LL1 after generation 1. They demonstrate quite clearly that similar selective procedures on genetically near-identical stocks can have very different results.   The second lines appear to have achieved most of their separation at a time (both in strict chronology and in generations) when selection had become nearly ineffective in the first lines.   The final degree of tolerance or susceptibility to DDT produced in the first and second lines was about the same.

During the selection period various mutant phenotypes appeared repeatedly, both in samples of the population cages and in the sib-selection lines.   These were all recessives, some sexlinked, and had survived from the origin of the heterogeneous stock.

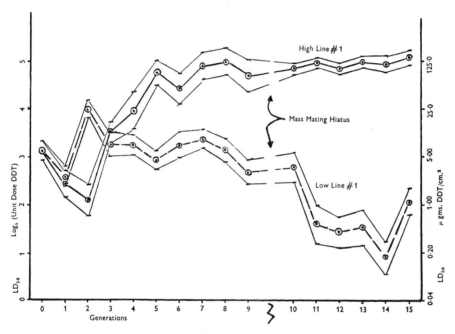

Fig. 2.—The course of selection in High and Low Lines #1.   Mean and 95 per cent. confidence limits of LD$_{50}$'s of Sibships in each generation of sib-selection.

At the end of the selection, stocks were made up from the sib-selection lines.   For each Line two representative stocks, one extreme stock and a variable number of mutant phenotype stocks were prepared. The identity of the mutant phenotypes was not determined.

Fig. 4 presents a comparison of these various stocks derived from the sib-selected lines.   It shows that the presence of the recessive mutants is not sufficient to ensure a significantly greater sensitivity to DDT.   The very fact of the persistence of these mutants during the course of selection is, of course, evidence that they were not seriously deleterious under the conditions then present.

One could imagine that selection for susceptibility could simply mean selection for general weakness, and that selection for tolerance to DDT could mean selection for general fitness. If this were so then one might expect fixation, or high frequency, of many mutants in the Low Lines and elimination of mutants in the High Lines. In fact the High Lines had as many or more mutants (both in kind and frequency) as did the Low Lines. The persistence of these mutants was caused by some selective effect more subtle than simple hardiness.

(iii) Comparison with other stocks

DDT resistant stocks obtained from other laboratories were tested to provide a comparison with the products of selection described in this study. Fig. 5 shows the results of subjecting all available selected

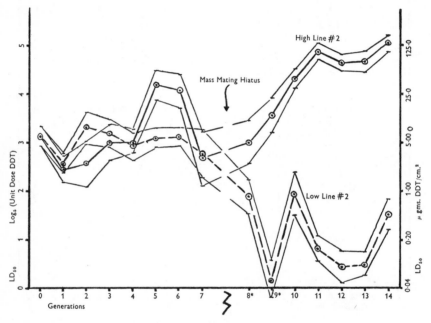

FIG. 3.—The course of selection in High and Low Lines #2. Mean and 95 per cent. confidence limits of LD_{50}'s of Sibships in each generation of sib-selection.

* Defective tests, not strictly comparable to the rest.

stocks to the same culture and testing conditions. This comparison was of particular interest because there was doubt as to the relative degree of resistance achieved in different laboratories (i.e., Tsukamoto, 1958 ; Milani, 1957).

It is clear from fig. 5 that the sib-selected Low Lines are much less tolerant of DDT than the unselected Cage 1 or any others shown, though the unselected M-5 ; Cy Pm ; Sb/Ubx[130] stock (not illustrated) was even more sensitive. One might suppose that the Low Lines represent an approach to the maximum sensitivity consistent with good viability and fertility—traits which are not characteristic of the M-5 ; Cy/Pm ; Sb/Ubx[130] stock.

The values shown for Cages 2 and 3 (in fig. 5) are those of the final two-month test period in each case. These values were chosen because they were obtained at the same time as most of the values for the other stocks. The Hikone-R strain which was selected by DDT food medium from an already resistant wild caught strain (Ogaki and Tsukamoto,

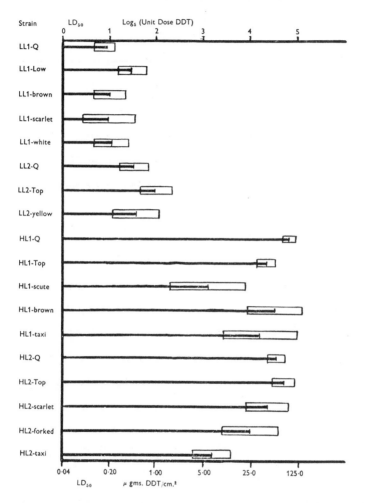

FIG. 4.—A comparison of the results of testing DDT tolerance of a number of strains and sub-strains selected for resistance and susceptibility to DDT. Mean and 95 per cent. confidence limits illustrated. (Q indicates stock made up from a representative group at the final selected generation. Top indicates stock made up from most favourable 5 progenies of the final selected generation. Low indicates stock made up from most susceptible 5 progenies of the final selected generation. Loci responsible for indicated mutant phenotypes unknown.)

1957) seems to have about the same degree of tolerance to DDT as the High sib-selected Lines. The Brown eye-R stock was selected by Crow and has been maintained in small cultures for a number of years without further selection. Its level of resistances at the time of this study was still much above that of the control and intermediate between Cages 2 and 3.

The stocks SySM-1, SyS-1002, SyS-102 and ORS-1001 were selected by King (1954, 1957) using an aerosol containing DDT as the selective agent. All of the selection was direct, survivors of a given treatment were used as parents of the next generation (as was also the case with the Hikone-R, Brown eye-R, and Cage #2 and #3

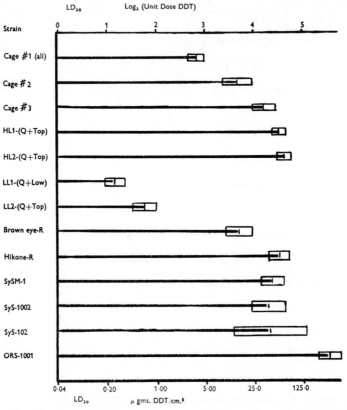

Fig. 5.—A comparison of the results of testing a number of different strains of *Drosophila melanogaster* Meigen for DDT tolerance. Mean and 95 per cent. confidence limits illustrated. ((Q+Top), (Q+Low), etc. indicate combined results for non-mutant stocks from indicated selected Line.)

stocks). The effectiveness of the sib-selection is most clearly shown here, where the sib-selection lines are seen to have become as, or more, tolerant of DDT than all of the direct selection stocks, except ORS-1001.

4. GENETIC BASIS OF RESISTANCE

The High and Low sib-selected Lines, the population cage stocks, the Brown eye-R, and Hikone-R stocks were outcrossed to M-5 ; Cy/Pm ; Sb/Ubx[130] stock and the different phenotypic classes of hybrid offspring were tested. Fig. 6 (*a* and *b*) gives graphic comparison of the results.

Probably the most obvious point in this comparison is that the Hikone-R resistance factors are clearly dominant over the susceptibility factors in the M-5 ; Cy/Pm ; Sb/Ubx^{130} stock. In fact the hybrids seem to show a degree of heterosis, in that some of the phenotypic classes have a higher mean LD$_{50}$ than did the parental Hikone-R stock.

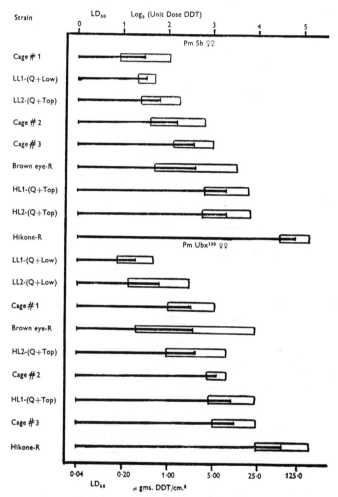

Fig. 6a.—The results of testing F$_1$ ♀♀ offspring of various strains outcrossed to the M-5 ; Cy/Pm ; Sb/Ubx^{130} stock. Grouped by similar phenotypes (Pm Sb, Pm Ubx^{130}). Mean and 95 per cent. confidence limits illustrated.

The comparisons of the other stocks are less clear. The great degree of variation within each group confuses the relative positions. The changes in relative rank, where the difference is significant, between the different phenotypic classes gives evidence of the difference in genetic basis of the resistant stocks. The interaction with the various mutant chromosomes was apparently quite different for many of the stocks. The sib-selected High stocks and the Cage 3 stock show changes in relative position in each phenotypic class. The unselected

J. BENNETT

Cage 1 stock was generally about the same as the Low sib-selected Lines in these outcrosses. Apparently the susceptibility factors were completely recessive and the resulting tolerance was simply a reflection of heterosis between genetically diverse stocks.

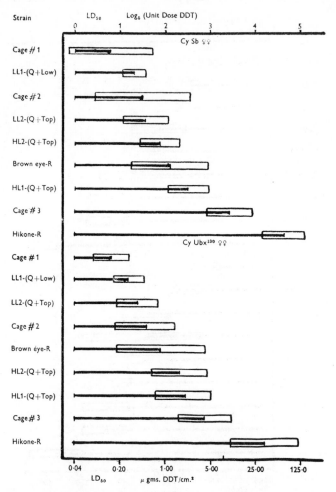

FIG. 6b.—The results of testing F_1 ♀♀ offspring of various strains outcrossed to the M-5 ; Cy/Pm ; Sb/Ubx[130] stock. Grouped by similar phenotypes (Cy Sb, Cy Ubx[130]). Mean and 95 per cent. confidence limits illustrated.

5. DISCUSSION

It is evident from figs. 1, 2, and 3 that both direct and sib-selection have been effective. The plotted curves are very similar, in general, to selection curves relating to quite different characteristics in *D. melanogaster* and other species. In this study the period of rapid change in the populations came at different times in the different lines, but was relatively early when compared with the lines developed by King (1957). Some of King's lines showed little response to selection until they had undergone 20 or 30 generations of selection. They then rose rapidly (in resistance) to high values. King's ORS-1001 finally achieved an LD_{50} nearly 35 times that of the control line after 73 generations of selection, and his SyS-1001 and SyS-1002 lines achieved values of 16 and 20 times that of the control lines after some 60 generations. These lines were selected at the 50 per cent. level by direct exposure to DDT aerosols. Their changes compare well with the following values of the difference of the sib-selected lines from their control: HL1, 34x; HL2, 35x; LL1, 1/3x; LL2, 1/8x; in 15 generations for the first Lines and 14 generations for the second Lines.

The reason for the shorter selection times for the sib-selection lines can probably be found both in their origin and in the selection method. By sib-selection those progenies from parents capable of producing resistant genotypes were selected, but non-resistant genotypes were also included by the same token. In King's lines only resistant phenotypes survived to reproduce. Thus in the sib-selection lines genes which might, in a different genotypic environment, produce resistance, were kept in the population. In the direct selection in King's lines only strongly resistant phenotypes survived, genes with the mere potentiality to produce resistance in another genotype being quickly eliminated. King's lines originated from sources of relatively little variability, The sib-selection and population cage lines reported here were started with all of the variability obtainable in 26 different sources at hand. With greater initial genetic variability, and a breeding system that tended to maintain variability, it is not too surprising that selection proceeded more rapidly in this study. There appears to be some indication (figs. 3 and 4) that the "Mass Mating Hiatus" may have allowed more effective recombination in the sib-selected lines and thus contributed to the post-Hiatus gains made by some of the lines.

The results of the outcrosses to the M-5 ; Cy/Pm ; Sb/Ubx[130] stock indicated that each of the resistant lines had a somewhat different genetic basis, at least as indicated by degree of dominance and inter-actions with the various tester chromosomes. This result is in agree-ment with King's (1957) conclusions, and seems to show again, if indeed it need be shown, that populations of similar origin will respond in different ways to similar selective pressures, and can achieve similar phenotypic endpoints with different genotypic bases. The outcrosses also show that the sib-selected high lines appear to show less dominance than the mass-selected Cage 3. This perhaps indicates that sib-selection was more likely to pick out recessives than was the mass selection in a population cage.

Crow (1957) has proposed that in a large randomly mating popula-tion selection would be strongly in favour of genes which conferred good general viability and a maximum average resistance in a variety of genotypic backgrounds. The sib-selection lines were selected primarily for resistance, and for viability only to the extent of being able to produce a minimum of 20 to 25 females, in each progeny.

Since the sib-selection lines were relatively small in size—only 25 effective pairs of parents in each generation (thus a maximum of 100 samples of each chromosome)—there would be greater likelihood of selecting chromosomes which had favourable specific interactions. Some support for the view that the selection in the sib-selected lines was not strongly for general fitness is obtained by comparing the values of resistance of each of the High Lines in the final selected generation to their mean value during the following two months, when they were mass cultured and tested, but not selected. High Line 1 had a final selection value for the LD_{50} of 133·5, but a mean value for the following two months of 57·9. High Line 2 had similar values of 137·0 and 67·8. These represent a loss of about one-half of the resistance, on the average, during this period. The fact that the lines still retained a resistance higher than Cage 3 and most of the other lines tested may reflect simply the short time available for reversion to have occurred. However, the loss may only reflect the difference of culture conditions between the relatively uncrowded vials, during sib-selection, and crowded bottles during the later period.

By sib-selection it has been possible to show that a single population can contain the genetic factors for either sensitivity or resistance to an environmental agent, and that those factors can be selected and concentrated without contact with the agent. This proof of pre-adaptation in this case does not of course eliminate the possibility of post-adaptation under some other circumstances. The proof does, however, make the hypothesis of post-adaptation superfluous.

It has been shown by Lüers (1953) that DDT is not mutagenic in *D. melanogaster*, thus eliminating the possibility that direct exposure might produce mutants, some of which might contribute to a post-adaptation. This is supported also by the fact that the directly selected lines were generally inferior to the sib-selected lines in resistance, which would hardly be expected if exposure to DDT were producing mutations that contributed to the resistance. Crow (unpublished) has shown that doses of DDT which do not kill, will not select for, or in any way increase, resistance. Thus for this species, as for some bacteria (Cavalli-Sforza and Lederberg, 1956), it is not necessary to propose any mechanism for the appearance of resistance in populations other than selection of pre-existing variation normally present in those populations.

6. SUMMARY

A heterogeneous stock of *Drosophila melanogaster* Meigen was proliferated in population cages and sub-populations extracted for selection. Samples of each of an initial group of 46 pair mating progenies were tested in vials lined with DDT impregnated paper to determine resistance to kill. The untested sibs from the 20 most resistant and the 20 least resistant progenies were used to make up 50 pair matings to start each of the prospective lines. Similar testing and selection was carried out on subsequent generations for each line.

Selection was carried on for 15 generations. At the end of this period the median lethal doses for the resistant lines were approximately 125 and 625 times as great as those for their respective paired susceptible lines, and more than 30 times as great as the median lethal dose for the control stock. Two population cages were subjected to direct contact with DDT and tested during the same period. The resistance developed by sib-selection compares favourably with the resistance of lines, from this and other laboratories, that were produced by direct selection. The pre-adaptation hypothesis is sufficient to account for the resistance of the sib-selected lines.

Acknowledgment.—The author wishes to express thanks to Dr J. F. Crow, for suggesting this problem, for many discussions of the work and results, and for making his laboratory available.

7. REFERENCES

BROWN, A. W. A. 1958. Insecticide resistance in arthropods. *World Health Org., Geneva,* 1958.

CAVALLI-SFORZA, L. L., AND LEDERBERG, J. 1956. Isolation of pre-adaptive mutants in bacteria by sib-selection. *Genetics, 41,* 367-381.

CORNFIELD, J., AND MANTEL, N. 1950. Some new aspects of the application of maximum likelihood to calculation of the dosage response curve. *J. Am. Stat. Assoc., 45,* 181-210.

CROW, J. F. 1954. Analysis of a DDT-resistant strain of Drosophila. *J. Econ. Entomology, 47,* 393-398.

CROW, J. F. 1957. Genetics of insect resistance to chemicals. *Ann. Rev. Entomology, 2,* 227-246.

KING, J. C. 1954. The genetics of resistance to DDT in *Drosophila melanogaster. J. Econ. Entomology, 47,* 387-393.

KING, J. C. 1957. Investigation of the genetic nature of resistance to insecticides developed by populations of *Drosophila melanogaster.* Final report of res. by Long Island Biol. Assoc. for Med. Res. and Dev. Board, Off. Surgeon General, Dept. of the Army, U.S.A.

LEVENE, H., PAVLOVSKY, O., AND DOBZHANSKY, TH. 1958. Dependence of the adaptive values of certain genotypes in *Drosophila pseudoobscura* on the composition of the gene pool. *Evolution, 12,* 18-23.

LÜERS, H. 1953. Untersuchung zur frage der mutangenität des kontaktinsektizids DDT an *Drosophila melanogaster. Naturwiss, 10,* 293.

MERRELL, D. J., AND UNDERHILL, J. C. 1956. Selection for DDT resistance in inbred, laboratory, and wild stocks of *Drosophila melanogaster. J. Econ. Entomology, 49,* 300-306.

MILANI, R. 1957. Genetic Research on the resistance of insects to the action of toxic substances. WHO, Div. of Environ. Sanit. Inf. Cir. on the Resistance Prob. Suppl. C-Oct. 1957. (English translation of *Rivista di Parasitologia, 17,* 233-246 (1956) and *18,* 43-60 (1957)).

OGAKI, M., AND TSUKAMOTO, M. 1957. Genetical analysis of DDT resistance in some Japanese strains of *Drosophila melanogaster.* In : *Japanese Contribution to the Study of the Insecticide Resistance Problem.* Brown, Takei, Nagesawa, Editors. Publ. by the Inst. of Insect Control, Kyoto Univ. for the World Health Organisation, 1957, pp. 28-32. (English version of "Botyu-Kagaku", *18,* 100-104 (1953)).

TSUKAMOTO, M. 1958. Genetics of insecticide-resistance in *Drosophila.* In: *World Health Organisation, Sem. on the resistance of insects to insecticides,* World Health Organisation and the Government of India, New Delhi : 27 Feb.-7 Mar. 1958, pp. 69-75. (Unpubl. working Doc. WHO/Insecticides/76) Issued : April 1958.

GENETICS OF NATURAL POPULATIONS. XII. EXPERIMENTAL REPRODUCTION OF SOME OF THE CHANGES CAUSED BY NATURAL SELECTION IN CERTAIN POPULATIONS OF DROSOPHILA PSEUDOOBSCURA

SEWALL WRIGHT AND THEODOSIUS DOBZHANSKY*

University of Chicago, Chicago, and Columbia University, New York

Received October 3, 1945

THE PROBLEM

RAPID changes in the genetic composition occur in populations of *Drosophila pseudoobscura* which inhabit certain localities on Mount San Jacinto, California (DOBZHANSKY 1943). These changes are cyclic and connected with the succession of the year's seasons. The genetic variable involved is the gene arrangement in the third chromosome. Three gene arrangements are common among the third chromosomes of the San Jacinto populations. One of them, called Standard (abbreviated ST), is most frequent in the populations in winter and in early spring, reaches its lowest frequency in early summer, and increases in frequency during middle and late summer. The second, Chiricahua (abbreviated CH), shows a cycle opposite to that of ST. The third, Arrowhead (AR), tends to follow a path resembling that of CH but with less regularity. Inversion homozygotes and heterozygotes occur in the populations with frequencies which are close to those which are expected if the carriers of the different gene arrangements mate at random.

Analysis of the data has led to the working hypothesis according to which the changes in the relative frequencies of the gene arrangements are induced by natural selection in response to the seasonal alterations in the environment. The gene arrangements may be in themselves adaptively neutral (that is, free from position effects), but they contain different gene complexes which make their carriers adapted to different seasonal environments (DOBZHANSKY 1943). Since the changes in the composition of the populations are considerable and rapid, the chromosomal types concerned must be subject to intense selection pressures. The selective advantages and disadvantages that must be postulated are, indeed, high enough to justify an attempt to detect them in laboratory experiments. The present article reports the results of experiments designed to test the validity of the above hypothesis.

APPARATUS

The problem of creating experimental populations of Drosophila even remotely comparable to the free-living ones is not easy. Attempts to solve it by increasing the size of the container in which the flies are bred are unsatisfactory. No matter how large a container, and how much food it may hold, time comes when the population must be transferred to fresh medium, and this presents as yet insuperable difficulties of the sampling technique. The nearest approach to a successful solution of the problem is that of L'HÉRITIER

---

* Experimental data by TH. DOBZHANSKY, mathematical analysis by SEWALL WRIGHT.

Reprinted by permission of Genetics, Inc. from GENETICS, 31, 125–256 (1946).

and Teissier (1933) and L'Héritier (1937), who devised population cages in which fresh food is introduced and from which the worked-out food is removed, frequently enough for the size and the age distribution of the population in the cage to remain approximately stationary. We had the privilege also of inspecting a very different model of population cage built by Mrs. G. W. Diederich.

Population cages used in the present experiments (fig. 1) are a modification of the L'Héritier and Teissier model. The cage is a wooden box with out-

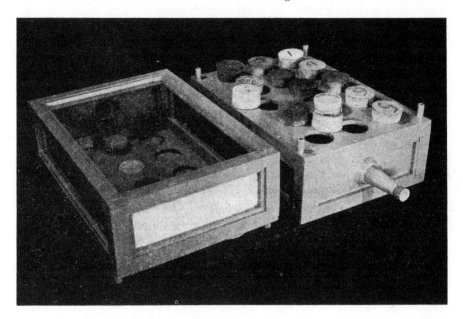

Figure 1.—The population cage. Left—view from above; right—view from below.

side dimensions $17 \times 12 \times 5\frac{1}{2}$ inches. The bottom has 15 circular openings $2\frac{1}{4}$ inches in diameter closed by tightly fitting corks. The corks are provided with wire loops that hold in place 2×1 inch Stender jars filled with cornmeal-molasses-agar culture medium. The top of the box and the long sides have glass windows. One of the shorter sides has a window for ventilation covered with wire and gauze nettings to prevent entry and escape of flies. The opposite side has a metallic funnel closed by a cork; this funnel serves as an opening through which flies can be introduced and withdrawn from the cage, and also for cleaning the glass and moistening the food while flies are breeding in the cage.

A known mixture of desired genetic types of flies, together with two or three jars with food, is introduced into the cage at the beginning of the experiment. Jars with fresh food are added, and those with worked-out food removed, at desired intervals. The withdrawal of a cork, removal and replacement of jars with food, and insertion of the cork back into its place can be done with few or no flies escaping. If the number of flies in the cage at the beginning of an experiment is small, the population increases very rapidly to numbers compatible with the quantity of food in the medium, and thereafter fluctuates within relatively narrow limits. The size of the definitive population at room temperature, and with one jar of fresh food inserted into the cage on alternate days, is of the order of 3000–5000 flies per cage. This population is reached in general within one generation from the introduction of the parent flies into the cage.

The greatest difficulty of experiments with population cages is that any mite infection that may develop in the cage is uncontrollable. As soon as mites appear, the experiment must be terminated and the cage with its contents sterilized by heat. A relatively minor difficulty is that the glass windows of the cage eventually become opaque because of the fly excreta. The glass is cleaned with the aid of a wad of cotton on a wire introduced through the funnel in the side of the cage. The food in the jars inside the cage may become too dry, in which case it is moistened with weak yeast suspension injected through a glass tube.

MATERIAL

All the flies that served as material for the experiments were descendants of individuals collected at Piñon Flats, Mount San Jacinto, California, in the summer of 1942. Chromosomes with Standard, Arrowhead, Chiricahua, Tree-Line, and Santa Cruz gene arrangements are encountered in the populations of that locality, the first three arrangements being much more frequent than the others, particularly than the fifth. Observations extending over four breeding seasons (1939–1942) showed that the relative frequencies of these gene arrangements change from month to month as indicated in table 1 and figure 2 (for further details see DOBZHANSKY 1943).

TABLE 1

Seasonal changes in the percentage frequencies of the different gene arrangements in the third chromosomes of the population of Piñon Flats, California. The symbol "n" in this and all following tables indicates the numbers of the chromosomes examined.

MONTH	ST	AR	CH	OTHERS	n
March	47.2	18.1	28.6	6.0	496
April	46.8	24.9	23.6	4.6	449
May	33.6	29.0	31.3	6.0	642
June	29.2	30.6	35.9	4.3	630
July–August	42.3	26.3	27.3	4.1	388
September	47.3	22.2	26.6	3.9	338
Oct.–Dec.	47.3	26.7	21.2	4.8	330

The frequency of ST is lowest in June, increases during the summer, remains uniformly high during autumn and winter, and decreases in spring. That of CH is highest in June, wanes in summer, is low in winter, and waxes during spring. AR behaves like CH, but the trends are less regular. No significant changes are established for the relatively rare Tree Line and Santa Cruz chromosomes.

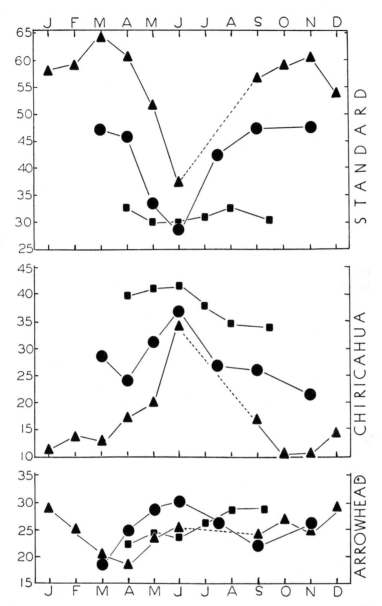

FIGURE 2.—Changes observed in the populations of *Drosophila pseudoobscura* on Mount San
Jacinto, California. The figures on the left indicate the percentage frequencies of the three gene
arrangements (Standard, Chiricahua, and Arrowhead); the letters at the top and at the bottom
stand for the months of the year; triangles—the Andreas Canyon population; circles—the Pinon
Flats population; squares—the Keen Camp population. Combined data for four years of observation.

A collection of strains descended from progenitors captured at Piñon Flats has been maintained in the laboratory since 1942; each strain is derived from a single female impregnated by one or more males. Since each female and each male progenitor carried two third chromosomes, which might have had different gene arrangements and gene contents, a strain may harbor four or more kinds of third chromosomes. However, after many generations in the laboratory, some of the ancestral chromosomes may be broken up by crossing over or lost by inbreeding, even though the strains are perpetuated in mass cultures. Theoretically, every strain kept in the laboratory should eventually become homozygous for a single kind of third chromosome. That such an uniformity has not been reached in at least some of the strains is attested by the fact that they continue to carry two or even three chromosomes with different gene arrangements. Retention in laboratory stocks of variability brought in from natural populations is observed even in strains which have have been in captivity for a decade and longer without precautions against inbreeding; some of these stocks still carry third chromosomes with different gene arrangements. A possible reason for this maintenance of variability is that many wild chromosomes carry recessive mutant genes which are deleterious when homozygous; there is a strong selection against homozygosis.

THE INITIAL POPULATION OF AN EXPERIMENTAL CAGE

In the experiments described in this report a fly population with known frequencies of different types of third chromosomes was introduced into a cage, and the incidence of these chromosome types in the progeny of the initial population was observed from time to time. The gene arrangements were determined through examination of the chromosomes in the salivary gland cells of larvae, which were, of course, killed in the process. Nevertheless, given a collection of strains with the desired gene arrangements, populations can be prepared with any initial frequencies of these chromosome types.

For this purpose, two or three dozen pair matings are made from the flies of the strains available. Eight fully grown larvae are taken from the offspring of each pair, their salivary glands stained in acetic orcein, and the gene arrangements in their third chromosomes determined by microscopic examination. With three gene arrangements, ST, AR, and CH, the following twenty-one types of matings are possible (the gene arrangements in the two chromosomes of a zygote are separated by the sign /).

PARENTS	OFFSPRING	PARENTS	OFFSPRING
ST/ST, ST/ST	ST/ST	CH/CH, CH/CH	CH/CH
ST/ST, AR/AR	ST/AR	CH/CH, ST/AR	ST/CH, AR/CH
ST/ST, CH/CH	ST/CH	CH/CH, ST/CH	ST/CH, CH/CH
ST/ST, ST/AR	ST/ST, ST/AR	CH/CH, AR/CH	AR/CH, CH/CH
ST/ST, ST/CH	ST/ST, ST/CH	ST/AR, ST/AR	ST/ST, ST/AR, AR/AR
ST/ST, AR/CH	ST/AR, ST/CH	ST/AR, ST/CH	ST/ST, ST/CH, ST/AR, AR/CH
AR/AR, AR/AR	AR/AR	ST/AR, AR/CH	AR/AR, ST/AR, ST/CH, AR/CH
AR/AR, CH/CH	AR/CH	ST/CH, ST/CH	ST/ST, ST/CH, CH/CH
AR/AR, ST/AR	AR/AR, ST/AR	ST/CH, AR/CH	CH/CH, ST/AR, ST/CH, AR/CH
AR/AR, ST/CH	AR/ST, AR/CH	AR/CH, AR/CH	AR/AR, AR/CH, CH/CH
AR/AR, AR/CH	AR/AR, AR/CH		

The chromosome constitution of the parental pair in each mating thus becomes known through examination of the chromosomes of eight or more of their offspring. The proportions of individuals with different combinations of chromosomes in the whole offspring of the pair is easily deduced. Thus, if one parent is ST/ST and the other ST/AR, half of the offspring are ST/ST and the other half ST/AR; if the parents are ST/AR and ST/AR, the offspring are one-quarter ST/ST, one-half ST/AR, and one-quarter AR/AR. When the adult offspring hatch, the desired numbers of flies are taken from each bottle, the sexes are separated, and the flies are aged for three to four days, then placed into the cage. A simple addition shows the most probable numbers of "chromosomes" with each gene arrangement introduced into the population (each fly, of course, has two "chromosomes"). These numbers in the initial populations in the different experiments are indicated in table 2.

TABLE 2

Conditions in the different experiments.

EXPERIMENT NO.	STARTED	TEMP.	LIGHT	INITIAL NUMBER OF FLIES	NUMBER OF CHROMOSOMES			KINDS OF CHROMOSOMES		
					ST	AR	CH	ST	AR	CH
1	Dec. 8, 1942	Room	Light	480	280	320	360	7	9	8
2	Dec. 8, 1942	Room	Light	480	280	320	360	7	9	8
3	Feb. 1, 1943	16½°	Dark	830	605	495	560	10	6	9
4	Feb. 3, 1943	21°	Dark	620	437	400	403	9	8	9
5	Feb. 3, 1943	25½°	Dark	585	399	372	399	9	6	9
6	Jan. 19, 1944	25½°	Dark	456	253	312	347	6	6	7
7	Jan. 19, 1944	16½°	Dark	503	303	331	372	6	6	7
8	Jan. 22, 1944	25½°	Dark	258	242	—	274	4	—	5
9	Jan. 22, 1944	16½°	Dark	226	207	—	245	4	—	5
10	June 20, 1944	Room	Light	± 5000	?	?	?	6	6	7
11	June 20, 1944	Room	Light	± 5000	?	?	?	4	—	5
12	June 28, 1944	Room	Light	1027	393	783	878	8	7	9
13	July 18, 1944	Room	Light	1390	813	—	1967	4	—	7
14	July 18, 1944	Room	Light	1002	619	1385	—	5	6	—
15	July 26, 1944	Room	Light	1464	—	930	1998	—	4	7
16	Sept. 30, 1944	16½°	Dark	897	1214	374	206	9	6	5
17	Sept. 30, 1944	16½°	Dark	562	934	—	190	5	—	4
18	Oct. 23, 1944	Room	Light	1356	539	1178	985	9	7	6
19	Nov. 15, 1944	Room	Light	639	489	—	789	5	—	6

Many chromosomes in natural populations of *D. pseudoobscura* carry recessive genes or gene complexes which, when homozygous, modify the viability, fertility, or development rate of the flies (DOBZHANSKY, HOLZ, and SPASSKY 1942). Changes that may be observed in the composition of the population of an experimental cage need not necessarily be ascribed to the properties of the chromosomes with different gene arrangements; such changes may be provoked also by differences in the gene contents of the chromosomes, which may be independent of the gene arrangement. We are interested, however, in the viability of carriers not of individual third chromosomes but of the ST, AR, and CH chromosomes as groups. Therefore it became necessary to eliminate or minimize the disturbing effects of the gene contents that vary from chromosome to chromosome with the same gene arrangement. To this end, several strains of flies with the same gene arrangement were used; in other words, the ST, AR, and CH chromosomes in the initial population of every experimental cage were derived from several different flies collected on Mount San Jacinto, frequently at different times, weeks or even months apart. The population which develops in a cage contains many individuals homozygous for the ST, AR, and CH gene arrangements. But a majority of these structural homozygotes carried two *different* chromosomes with somewhat different gene contents—that is, they were genic heterozygotes. Table 2 shows the numbers of "kinds of chromosomes" with each gene arrangement in the several experiments. In computing these numbers, it was assumed that every strain contains one and only one kind of third chromosome with each gene arrangement found in that strain. Since more than a single kind were doubtless present in some of the strains, the numbers shown in table 2 are minimum values.

SAMPLING

In order to determine the frequencies of chromosomes with each gene arrangement at different times in the experimental populations, samples were taken at approximately monthly intervals in each cage. The surface of the food in the Stender jars inserted into a cage becomes covered with fly eggs in about 24 hours. A bit of this food was cut out and placed in a regular culture bottle. Extra yeast was added when middle-sized larvae appeared. When the larvae were fully grown, their salivary glands were stained in acetic orcein; examination of the configuration of the third chromosome in one such larva permits determination of the gene arrangements in two third chromosomes, the maternal and the paternal ones. The examination of sufficient larvae should provide a fair estimate of the composition of the population in the cage.

A source of error, however, must be considered. The eggs deposited in a jar come from some but not from all the flies in the cage. To make the samples as representative as possible, the monthly samples of 300 chromosomes were sub-divided into six (seven in the early experiments) subsamples. That is, a chip of food with eggs was taken on each of six successive days, and the chromosomes of 25 larvae from each subsample were examined. This gave six groups of 50 chromosomes each, a total of 300 chromosomes. Comparison of the subsamples constituting a sample should indicate the extent to which the samples are representative of the population of a cage; χ^2's were computed to measure the homogeneity of the subsamples in 38 different samples. Among the 38 χ^2's, 15 had the probability 0.5 or higher of occurring by chance; 12 had probabilities ranging from 0.5 and 0.1; four probabilities from 0.1 to 0.05; three probabilities between 0.05 and 0.02; two between 0.02 and 0.01; and two probabilities just below the 0.01 level. The variability of the subsamples constituting a sample, therefore, was in excess of what might be expected owing to chance alone, but only slightly so. A sample may be considered a fair measure of the status of the population of a cage at the time when it is taken.

It follows from the above that the process of taking the monthly sample in an experimental cage occupies nearly a week. In tables 3 to 10 the dates of the samples are given in terms of ten-day periods; E, M, and L before the name of the month indicate the first, second, and third ten-day period, respectively. The entries in tables 3 to 10 labelled "Initial" indicate the composition of the initial population of the experimental cage, as deduced from the chromosomal constitution of the parent flies (see above). The lack of the "Initial" entries in Experiments 10 and 11 (tables 6, 10) is due to the fact that these experiments represent continuation at room temperature of Experiments 7 and 9 (tables 5, 8) carried at a lower temperature; the initial populations in Experiments 10 and 11, therefore, are the same as the final populations in the cages in Experiments 7 and 9, respectively, and their compositions are indicated by the "Control" entries.

In most experiments, a "Control" sample was taken about a week after the introduction of the initial fly population into the cage. The eggs collected at that time are bound to come from the initial population, since the F_1 generation begins to hatch in no less than two weeks from the start of the experimental cage. The incidences of the several gene arrangements in the Control sample therefore should be the same as in the initial population. Yet, more or less significant differences were observed in the second, fifth, and ninth experiments. It is possible that these differences were due merely to sampling errors. On the other hand, it should be kept in mind that the composition of the initial population is inferred from that of its parents, while the Control sample describes the genetic constitution of the eggs being deposited in the cage about a week after the beginning of the experiment. In other words, a whole generation elapses between the points to which these two sets of data are relevant. If the carriers of some gene arrangements are more and of others less favored in certain environments, differences between the Initial and Control populations may be real. It may be noted in this connection that the cultures from which the flies of the initial populations came in all experiments developed at room temperature. Since at that temperature ST chromosomes are more viable than CH chromosomes (see below), control samples are liable to show higher frequencies of ST and lower ones of CH than the corresponding initial populations. This is what is actually found wherever the two are appreciably different.

In natural populations the carriers of the different gene arrangements interbreed at random. The frequencies of inversion homozygotes and heterozygotes are in accord with expectations based on the Hardy-Weinberg theorem (DOBZHANSKY and EPLING 1944, and other work). The same holds for our samples of the populations of the experimental cages. Only the gametic frequencies of the gene arrangements are reported in tables 3 to 10, the bulkier zygotic data being kept on file.

LENGTH OF THE LIFE CYCLE

Almost from the time the initial population is introduced into an experimental cage, the number of larvae in the jars is much greater than can mature on the food available. Under these rigorous conditions the duration of the development from egg to adult is greater in experimental cages than it is in environments more nearly approaching optimum. The mass hatching of adults from pupae takes place 24 to 26 days after the insertion of the jar with food into the experimental cage at $25\frac{1}{2}°C$, in about 28 to 31 days at 21°C, and in about 35 to 37 days at $16\frac{1}{2}°C$. Some flies hatch both earlier and much later than the times indicated, but it is the date of mass hatching that is most important in this investigation, and the above figures represent the best estimates based on visual observation of jars in different experimental cages. The longevity of the flies in the cages is probably smaller than it would be under optimal conditions, and a minority of members of the initial population live long enough to meet the F_1 individuals appearing in the cage.

TABLE 3

Percentage frequencies of the different gene arrangements. First experiment—abundant food, second experiment—food scarce.

TIME	EXPERIMENT 1				EXPERIMENT 2			
	ST	AR	CH	n	ST	AR	CH	n
Initial	29.2	33.3	37.5		29.2	33.3	37.5	
Control	27.1	35.0	38.0	266	34.5	39.9	25.6	258
E January 1943	47.3	30.8	21.9	370	44.5	37.2	18.3	328
E February 1943	42.4	38.6	19.0	342	46.0	35.3	18.6	354
M April 1943	54.3	27.1	18.6	376	50.5	29.4	20.1	364
M May 1943	54.2	19.2	26.5	426	55.8	28.9	15.3	398
M June 1943	52.9	27.1	20.1	384	53.7	33.0	13.3	300

RESULTS

Among the 19 experiments performed, no two were sufficiently alike to be properly considered replications. Some of the variables are given in table 2.

The first and second experiments (table 3) were designed to test the possible influence of the food regime. In the first experiment, two jars with fresh food were given every three days. Since an experimental cage has 15 food jars (see above), each jar in the first experiment remained in the cage for 22 to 23 days and when removed contained many unhatched pupae. This puts a prize on rapid development, because all slowly developing individuals are eliminated. In the second experiment, one jar with fresh food was introduced every five days. Therefore, each jar remained in the cage for 75 days, and when finally removed, it contained no live larvae or pupae and the food was entirely consumed. The two cages stood side by side in a room which was kept very warm —25–27°C during the day, from a fraction to three degrees lower during the night. The initial populations of the cages, started in early December of 1942, contained approximately equal proportions of ST, AR, and CH chromosomes. The frequencies of ST rose and those of CH dropped with time in both cages. In about two months from the start, in early February of 1943, the frequency of ST reached 42 to 46 percent and CH declined to about 19 percent; AR remained at about the initial level (table 3). In other words, the frequency of CH was reduced in two to three generations to about half of its former value. From early February to the middle of June, when both experiments were discontinued because of mite infection, no sharp changes occurred in the populations; the samples show a further increase of the frequency of ST and a slight decline of AR in Experiment 1, and an increase of ST and a decline of CH in Experiment 2. No consistent differences in the trends which could be ascribed to the different food regimes became apparent in the two experiments. As shown below, the waxing of the frequencies of ST and the waning of CH occurred in all experiments conducted at intermediate and high temperatures.

TABLE 4

Percentage frequencies of the different gene arrangements. Third experiment—$16\frac{1}{2}$°C, fourth experiment—21°C, fifth experiment—$25\frac{1}{2}$°C.

TIME	EXPERIMENT 3				EXPERIMENT 4				EXPERIMENT 5			
	ST	AR	CH	n	ST	AR	CH	n	ST	AR	CH	n
Initial	36.5	29.8	33.7		35.2	32.3	32.5		34.1	31.8	34.1	
Control	34.7	31.2	34.1	320	41.4	31.4	27.2	360	44.2	37.1	18.7	310
M April 1943	50.0	22.3	27.7	300	45.0	32.0	23.0	300	54.0	31.7	14.3	300
M May 1943	—	—	—		46.0	29.3	24.7	300	55.7	33.7	10.7	300
M June 1943	36.0	32.0	32.0	300	45.0	29.7	25.3	300	56.1	30.1	13.8	362
M July 1943	—	—	—		47.6	39.6	12.8	250	57.3	30.7	12.0	300

Experiments 3, 4, and 5 were started early in February of 1943 in order to test the influence of temperature (table 4). The cages were placed in incubators at 21° and $25\frac{1}{2}$°C and in a cold room at $16\frac{1}{2}$°C. One jar of fresh food was given every four days in Experiment 3, every three days in Experiment 4, and on alternate days in Experiment 5; consequently, the jars remained in the cages 60, 45, and 30 days respectively, which at the low, intermediate and the high temperatures suffices for a majority of the surviving larvae and pupae to become transformed into imagoes. The initial populations contained about equal proportions of ST, AR, and CH chromosomes. Rapid increases in the frequencies of ST and decreases of CH, with AR remaining at about the same level, were observed in the fourth and fifth experiments (table 4). The changes seemed to be more rapid in the experiment (the fifth) conducted at the higher than in that (the fourth) conducted at the intermediate temperature, but the difference between the control sample and the initial population in Experiment 5 makes this uncertain. The result of Experiment 3 is somewhat ambiguous. Here the control sample coincided very well with the presumed composition of the initial population; a sample taken two months after the start, in the middle of April of 1943, showed an ostensible rise of ST and a drop of CH; no sample was taken in May, but the mid-June sample (when the experiment was discontinued on account of mite infection) agreed almost exactly with the control and with the initial population (table 4).

TABLE 5

Percentage frequencies of the different gene arrangements. Sixth and eighth experiments—$25\frac{1}{2}°C$ seventh and ninth experiments—$16\frac{1}{2}°C$.

TIME	ST	AR	CH	n	ST	CH	n
		EXPERIMENT 6				EXPERIMENT 8	
Initial	27.7	34.2	38.1		46.9	53.1	
Control	29.0	28.3	42.7	300	52.0	48.0	300
L February 1944	34.0	31.0	35.0	300	60.3	39.7	300
M March 1944	45.7	26.0	28.3	300	63.3	36.7	300
M April 1944	44.3	21.0	34.7	300	69.3	30.7	250
		EXPERIMENT 7				EXPERIMENT 9	
Initial	30.1	32.9	37.0		45.8	54.2	
Control	34.7	23.0	42.3	300	59.0	41.0	300
L March 1944	35.7	26.3	38.0	300	48.3	51.7	300
L April 1944	33.8	25.2	41.0	290	51.0	49.0	300
E June 1944	35.7	24.7	39.7	300	46.3	53.7	300

To establish beyond doubt the influence of the temperature factor indicated by the preceding experiments, four cages were started in January of 1944 (Experiments 6, 7, 8, and 9, table 5). Cages Nos. 6 and 8 were placed in an incubator at $25\frac{1}{2}°C$, and Nos. 7 and 9 in a cold room at $16\frac{1}{2}°C$. Since the foregoing experiments indicated that the frequencies of ST and CH are more subject to change than those of AR, cages Nos. 8 and 9 were populated by flies with ST and CH chromosomes only. All three gene arrangements were introduced into cages Nos. 6 and 7. Slightly more CH than ST chromosomes were put into the initial mixtures in all four experiments under consideration. The frequencies of ST rose rather sharply in the two experiments at the higher temperature, even though these experiments lasted only three months, till mid-April of 1944. The frequency of CH dropped in the eighth experiment, while in the sixth both AR and CH appear to have shared in the decline (table 5). In the eighth experiment the frequency of CH chromosomes was equal to or greater than that of ST chromosomes in January, but in April ST chromosomes were twice as frequent as CH. Contrasting with the results of the experiments at the high temperature, no appreciable and consistent changes in the frequencies of the gene arrangements occurred in the seventh and ninth experiments which lasted for five months (January–June) but which were carried on in the cold room (table 5). It may be noted that the initial populations of cages Nos. 6 to 9 consisted of sibs. The difference in the results can be ascribed only to temperature.

In June of 1944, experimental cages Nos. 7 and 9 were taken out of the cold

TABLE 6

Percentage frequencies of the different gene arrangements. Tenth to 12th experiments.

TIME	EXPERIMENT 10				EXPERIMENT 11			EXPERIMENT 12			
	ST	AR	CH	n	ST	CH	n	ST	AR	CH	n
Initial	—	—	—		—	—		19.1	38.1	42.7	
Control	35.7	24.7	39.7	300	46.3	53.7	300	22.0	38.3	39.7	300
L July 1944	38.7	25.7	35.7	300	61.7	38.3	300	28.0	40.6	31.4	300
M August 1944	52.3	19.7	28.0	300	66.3	33.7	300	39.7	35.3	25.0	300
M September 1944	48.3	22.3	29.3	300	63.7	36.3	300	50.7	30.3	19.0	300

room and placed first in a room with an open window, where they experienced
the vagaries of the summer temperatures, and in late August they were transferred to an incubator at 25°C. The numbers of these cages were changed to
10 and 11, respectively. When removed from the cold room, the cages contained numerically fully developed populations. The last (June) samples in
cages Nos. 7 and 9 (see table 5) may therefore be regarded as control samples
in cages Nos. 10 and 11 (table 6). The temperature change was soon reflected
in the incidence of the gene arrangements. Already the July samples indicated
an upward trend for ST and a downward one for CH, and by mid-August the
changes became quite significant. The experiments had to be discontinued in
September on account of an infection; the last samples did not differ from the
August ones.

TABLE 7

Percentage frequencies of the different gene arrangements. Thirteenth to 15th experiments.

TIME	EXPERIMENT 13			EXPERIMENT 14			EXPERIMENT 15		
	ST	CH	n	ST	AR	n	AR	CH	n
Initial	29.2	70.8		30.9	69.1		31.8	68.2	
L August 1944	54.7	45.3	300	48.3	51.7	300	43.0	57.0	300
M September 1944	58.3	41.7	300	55.3	44.7	300	42.0	58.0	300

Late in June of 1944, a mixture of flies in which CH and AR chromosomes
were each about twice as frequent as ST ones was introduced into cage No. 12
(table 6). The environmental conditions in the 12th experiment were the same
as in the 10th and the 11th (see above). In a month, in late July, the frequency
of ST rose from 19 percent (or from 22 percent if the control sample is taken
as the starting point) to 28 percent, and the frequency of CH fell from 43
percent (or 40 percent) to 31 percent. By mid-September ST rose to 51 percent
and CH fell to only 19 percent; the frequency of AR dwindled relatively
slightly. Thus in only three months—that is, in three to four generations—the
frequency of ST was more than doubled, and that of CH reduced to less than
half of the initial value.

It is clear that under the conditions of these experiments ST chromosomes displace CH chromosomes at high but not at low temperatures. The behavior of AR chromosomes is erratic: they either hold their own or else lose in competition with ST. To test this point further, in July of 1944 experiments 13, 14, and 15 were designed in which only two gene arrangements were introduced into each cage: ST and CH in the 13th, ST and AR in the 14th, and AR and CH in the 15th (table 7). The cages were kept first in a laboratory room with closed windows, where the populations were injured by the summer heat, then in a well ventilated laboratory room, and finally in an incubator at 25°C. By mid-September all cages developed a mite infection and had to be destroyed; thus, the experiments lasted less than two months. The results, nevertheless, are fairly clear. In the 13th experiment the frequency of ST doubled while that of CH fell from 71 percent to 42 percent. This is consistent with the results of the eighth and the 11th experiments (tables 5 and 6), in which the ST and CH gene arrangements were competing at a high temperature; at the low temperature (experiment 9, table 5, and experiment 19, table 9) the relative frequencies of ST and CH remained constant. In the 14th experiment (table 7) ST increased in frequency from 31 percent to 55 percent, while AR correspondingly dwindled from 69 percent to 45 percent. It follows that at high temperatures chromosomes with ST gene arrangement displace those with AR, provided at least, that CH chromosomes, which are still weaker competitors than AR, are absent. A comparison of the results of the 13th and the 14th experiments suggests, if the data are taken at their face value, that the displacement of CH by ST is more rapid than the displacement of AR by ST; the difference, however, is not statistically significant. The result of the 15th experiment (table 7) is not satisfactory: the August sample indicates that AR chromosomes displace CH in the absence of ST, which is consistent with the expectation, but the September sample failed to show a further drop in the frequency of CH.

The results of the experiments so far described are of two kinds. Namely, in the experiments conducted at the higher temperatures the frequencies of ST chromosomes increase and those of CH decrease, while at $16\frac{1}{2}$°C the proportions of ST, AR, and CH gene arrangements show no perceptible alterations. It is known, however, that in the population of the Piñon Flats locality from which the ancestors of the experimental flies came, a third kind of behavior of the gene arrangements is observed every spring season: the frequency of ST drops and that of CH increases. An unsuccessful attempt to reproduce experimentally this last type of change has been made. It is very probable that neither homozygotes for ST (ST/ST) nor for CH (CH/CH), but the heterozygotes ST/CH are the most favored genetic constitution. If so, the changes in the populations will proceed toward equilibrium values at which the relative proportions of the three genotypes will give the maximal degree of fitness of the population. The equilibrium values may, of course, be different at different temperatures. Now, in experiments 1 to 17 the initial populations contained either equal proportions of ST and CH, or else ST was less frequent than CH. It is possible therefore that at the low temperature these initial populations happened to contain just about the equilibrium proportions of the gene arrangements. If so, no striking changes in the composition of the populations could be expected in these experiments. Accordingly, experiments 16 and 17 were started at $16\frac{1}{2}°C$ with initial populations containing considerably more ST than CH chromosomes (table 8). The populations were kept in the cold room from September 30, 1944, till February 12, 1945, without consistent changes in the frequencies of the gene arrangements being observed. This suggests that the adaptive values of the homo- and heterozygotes for the three gene arrangements are very nearly alike in experimental cages kept at $16\frac{1}{2}°C$.

TABLE 8

Percentage frequencies of the different gene arrangements. Sixteenth and 17th experiments. Temperature $16\frac{1}{2}°C$.

TIME	EXPERIMENT 16				EXPERIMENT 17		
	ST	AR	CH	n	ST	CH	n
Initial	67.7	20.9	11.5		83.1	16.9	
L October 1944	76.3	9.3	14.3	300	86.7	13.3	300
M November 1944	63.0	19.7	17.3	300	87.7	12.3	300
L December 1944	66.0	16.3	17.6	300	89.7	10.3	300
E February 1945	61.0	24.3	14.7	300	86.3	13.7	300

STATISTICAL EVIDENCE OF SELECTION

A statistical study of the changes in chromosome frequency has been based on a grouping of the experiments according to the chromosomes present and the temperature. The largest group involved all three chromosomes at 25° (experiments 1, 2, 5, 6, 10, 12, and 18). These provide data on the changes in 30 intervals, disregarding the estimates of the initial compositions of the boxes. Experiments 3, 7, and 16 (eight intervals) involve all three chromosomes at 16.5°. Experiments 8, 11, 13, and 19 (13 intervals) involve Standard and Chiricahua at 25°, and experiments 9 and 17 (6 intervals) involve the same chromosomes at 16.5°. There remain three isolated experiments, No. 14 involving Standard and Arrowhead at 25°, No. 15 involving Arrowhead and Chiricahua at 25°, and No. 4 involving all three chromosomes at 21°. These three experiments will not be considered here beyond calling attention to the fact that the changes are in the directions expected from the other experiments.

In making a statistical analysis, it is necessary to reduce the observed changes in chromosome frequency to rates per generation. These were estimated on the assumption of an interval of 3.5 weeks between generations in the experiments at 25° and an interval of 5.2 weeks in those at 16.5°.

The first question is the statistical significance of any changes in composition that may indicate selection. Both the average rate of change per generation and the regression of rate of change on chromosome frequency must be considered. A significant average rate of change obviously indicates a selective process, but even if the average does not differ significantly from zero, a significant regression indicates a selective process which changes in amount or even in direction as chromosome frequency changes.

The principal results in the four groups of experiments referred to above are shown in table 10. Here n is the number of intervals, $\bar{q}$ is the mean chromosome

TABLE 9

Percentage frequencies of the different gene arrangements. Eighteenth and 19th experiments. Room temperature.

TIME	EXPERIMENT 18				EXPERIMENT 19		
	ST	AR	CH	n	ST	CH	n
Initial	19.9	43.6	36.5		38.3	61.7	
M November 1944	33.3	27.3	39.3	300	—	—	
M December 1944	37.7	28.7	33.7	300	53.0	47.0	300
M January 1945	39.3	30.0	30.7	300	63.3	36.7	300
L February 1945	44.3	30.0	25.7	300	60.3	39.7	300
L March 1945	42.0	39.0	19.0	300	65.3	34.7	300
L April 1945	46.7	30.3	23.0	300	65.3	34.7	300
E June 1945	56.4	27.3	16.3	282	70.4	29.6	250
L July 1945	50.3	31.7	18.0	300	72.0	28.0	300

frequency; $\overline{\Delta q}$ is the mean rate of change of chromosome frequency per generation; $b_{\Delta q \cdot q}$ is the regression of rate of change on chromosome frequency, and $\sigma^2_{\Delta q \cdot q}$ is the variance of Δq estimated for constant q. The significance of $\overline{\Delta q}$ and $b_{\Delta q \cdot q}$ are determined from their ratios (t) to their standard errors ($SE_{\overline{\Delta q}}$ and SE_b, respectively), using Students' probabilities for small numbers.

TABLE 10

Statistical analysis of the experimental data (further explanation in text)

	TWO TYPES AT 25° STANDARD (vs. CHIRICAHUA)	THREE TYPES AT 25°			TWO TYPES AT 16.5° STANDARD (vs. CHIRICAHUA)	THREE TYPES AT 16.5°		
		STAND-ARD	ARROW-HEAD	CHIRI-CAHUA		STAND-ARD	ARROW-HEAD	CHIRI-CAHUA
n	13	30	30	30	6	8	8	8
$\bar{q}$	.5492	.4201	.3182	.2617	.7040	.4927	.2169	.2904
$\overline{\Delta q}$	+.0472	+.0391	−.0122	−.0268	−.0125	−.0156	+.0167	−.0011
$SE_{\overline{\Delta q}}$	.0061	.0076	.0068	.0072	.0162	.0190	.0110	.0102
t	7.77	5.17	1.80	3.74	.77	.82	1.53	.11
Prob.	<.001	<.001	.05−.10	<.001	.40−.50	.40−.50	.10−.20	>.90
$b_{\Delta q \cdot q}$	−.346	−.387	−.394	−.261	+.036	−.237	−.614	−.055
SE_b	.057	.074	.116	.079	.092	.119	.176	.095
t	6.13	5.21	3.40	3.31	.39	1.99	3.48	.58
Prob.	<.001	<.001	<.01	<.01	.70−.80	.05−.10	.01−.02	.50−.60
$\sigma^2_{\Delta q \cdot q}$	.00048	.00172	.00139	.00154	.00163	.00290	.00096	.00083
$\bar{q}(1-q)/300$	.00079	.00078	.00071	.00062	.00059	.00075	.00055	.00065
F	.61	2.21	1.95	2.51	2.77	3.88	1.74	1.28
Prob.	.05−.20	<.001	<.01	<.001	.01−.05	<.001	.05−.20	>.20

The variance of Δq for given q is compared with that expected from accidents of sampling in a sample of 300 by Fisher's test. The following formulae were used:

$$\bar{q} = \sum q/n$$
$$\overline{\Delta q} = \sum \Delta q/n$$
$$b_{\Delta q \cdot q} = (\sum q \Delta q - \overline{\Delta q} \sum q)/(\sum q^2 - \bar{q} \sum q)$$
$$\sigma^2_{\Delta q \cdot q} = [(\sum \Delta^2 q - \overline{\Delta q} \sum \Delta q) - b^2_{\Delta q \cdot q}(\sum q^2 - \bar{q} \sum q)]/(n-2)$$
$$SE^2_{\overline{\Delta q}} = \sigma^2_{\Delta q \cdot q}/n$$
$$SE^2_b = \sigma^2_{\Delta q \cdot q}/(\sum q^2 - \bar{q} \sum q).$$

From inspection of table 10 it may be seen that there were highly significant changes in chromosome frequency in the experiments at 25° in which all three chromosomes were involved and also in those involving only Standard and Chiricahua, in spite of the small number of cases in the latter. In both sets, Standard tended to increase and Chiricahua to decrease within the range of values of chromosome frequencies in the experiments. There were, on the other hand, no significant changes in chromosome frequency in the experiments at 16.5°. This does not imply that there were no changes but merely that any changes were too small to be detected with confidence in the small number of intervals in these sets of experiments.

The regression of rate of change on chromosome frequency was highly significant for all chromosomes in the experiments at 25°. In all cases, the slope is negative and such as to indicate a reversal in the direction of change at some point. In other words, there is a tendency for any chromosome to increase in frequency when rare and decrease when sufficiently common. In the experiments at 16.5° there is one apparently significant result. The rate of change of Arrowhead falls off very rapidly as its frequency increases (probability between .01 and .02). There is a suggestion of a similar trend in the case of Standard (probability between .05 and .10) but not in the case of Chiricahua.

The estimated variance of Δq for given q is actually less, though not significantly, than expected by chance in a sample of 300 in the experiments involving only Standard and Chiricahua at 25°. On the other hand, it is consistently and highly significantly greater for the three chromosomes in the experiments involving all three at 25°. The excess could be accounted for by limitation of the number of parents but could also be due to unknown factors that affected the conditions of selection differently in the various experiments and intervals. If due solely to limitations in the effective number of parents a rough estimate of this effective number (N) may be made by equating the excess $[\sigma^2_{\Delta q \cdot q} - \overline{q(1-q)}/300]$ to $\overline{q(1-q)}/2N$, the variance expected from this cause. The estimate came out 124 from the data on Standard, 157 from that on Arrowhead, and 113 from that on Chiricahua, with an average of 131. It is probable, however, that other factors (density, condition of food, etc.) are the ones that are important.

There is a highly significant excess variance of Δq for given q at 16.5° in the case of Standard, not borne out by corresponding excesses in the cases of Arrowhead and Chiricahua where all three are involved. There is also excess variance at this temperature where only Standard and Chiricahua are involved. There can be little doubt that in most cases the rate of change of chromosome frequency, at a given frequency, varies more than accounted for by mere sampling errors.

ESTIMATES OF SELECTIVE VALUES

It is of interest next to attempt to determine the nature of the selective process and the values of the selection coefficients. Unfortunately the data at hand do not yield a unique interpretation.

The simplest assumptions are that the relative selective values of the genotypes are the same at all chromosome frequencies and that they are the same for males and females. We shall consider first the sets of experiments involving only Standard and Chiricahua at 25°. Selection must favor the heterozygotes over both homozygotes, under the above hypotheses, if there is a point of equilibrium (cf. FISHER 1922). Let s be the selective disadvantage of homozygous Standard and t that of homozygous Chiricahua, relative to the heterozygotes.

Genotype	Frequency (f)	Selective Value (W)	
ST/ST	q^2	$1 - s$	
ST/CH	$2q(1 - q)$	1	(1)
CH/CH	$(1 - q)^2$	$1 - t$	

It can easily be found that Δq is related to q by the following formula (cf. WRIGHT 1931)

$$\Delta q = q(1 - sq - \overline{W})/\overline{W}, \qquad \overline{W} = 1 - sq^2 - t(1 - q)^2 \qquad (2)$$

$$\Delta q = - q(1 - q)[sq - t(1 - q)]/\overline{W} \qquad (3)$$

$$s = \frac{1}{q}\left[1 - \left(1 + \frac{\Delta q}{q}\right)\overline{W}\right] \quad \text{from (2)} \qquad (4)$$

$$t = \frac{1}{(1 - q)}\left[1 - \left(1 - \frac{\Delta q}{(1 - q)}\right)\overline{W}\right]. \qquad (5)$$

The equilibrium point, $\hat{q}$, is that at which $\Delta q = 0$, with both chromosomes present.

$$\hat{q} = t/(s + t) \quad \text{from (3)}. \qquad (6)$$

In this set of experiments, observations were made at values of q ranging between .292 and .663. The observed values of Δq do not diverge conspicuously from the linear regression line, $\Delta q = .2375 - .3465q$. This indicates equilibrium at about $\hat{q} = .685 (= .2375/.3465)$, slightly above the highest value of q in the data. No great confidence can be placed in this, however, because of the theoretical curvilinear relation of Δq to q. The best estimate that can be made from the linear regression is probably that obtained by equating the regression coefficient to the slope of the tangent of the theoretical curve at the mean value of q.

$$\frac{d\Delta q}{dq} = \frac{\Delta q}{q} - q\left[\frac{s}{\overline{W}} + \frac{(1-sq)}{\overline{W}^2}\frac{d\overline{W}}{dq}\right] \quad \text{from (2)}$$

$$= 2\left(1 + \frac{\Delta q}{q}\right)\left(1 - \frac{\Delta q}{1-q}\right) - 1 - \frac{1}{\overline{W}} \quad \text{using (4) and (5)} \qquad (7)$$

Assuming that $\dfrac{d\Delta q}{dq}$ at $\bar{q}$ is approximated by $b_{\Delta q \cdot q}$ and substituting $\overline{\Delta q}$

and $\bar{q}$ for Δq and q respectively, $\overline{W}$ at $\bar{q}$ may be estimated from the reciprocal of the following expression.

$$\frac{1}{\overline{W}} = 2\left(1 + \frac{\Delta q}{q}\right)\left(1 - \frac{\Delta q}{1-q}\right) - 1 - b_{\Delta q \cdot q}. \qquad (8)$$

Estimates of s and t can now be made by the same substitutions with the help of the estimate for $\overline{W}$ at $\bar{q}$. For Standard and Chiricahua at $25°$

$$\overline{W} \text{ at } \bar{q} = .7747$$

$$s = .289$$

$$t = .680 \qquad\qquad (9)$$

$$\hat{q} = .702.$$

For the best estimates, however, it is necessary to use the method of least squares. As the expression for Δq in terms of q is not linear with respect to the parameters s and t (equation 3), the solution must be determined by iteration. Using trial values of s and t to estimate $\overline{W}$ for each observation (*cf.* (2)), values of s and t in the numerator of (3) can be obtained that minimize the squared deviations of observed and estimated Δq. The estimates of $\overline{W}$ may then be readjusted and the process repeated until the values of s and t calculated for the numerator agree sufficiently with those tried in the denominator. Strictly, the observations should be weighted by the reciprocals of their variances (that is, in proportion to $q(1-q)$), but as these weights would range only from 4.0 to 4.8 in this data, weighting may be ignored without serious error, in order to avoid the considerable complication which it would introduce into the calculations.

Let $y = \Delta q$, $x_1 = q^2(1-q)/\overline{W}$ and $x_2 = q(1-q)^2/\overline{W}$.

The deviations (δ) of the 13 observations from the theoretical values can be written as follows by substitutions in (3).

$$\delta = y + x_1 s - x_2 t. \qquad (10)$$

Minimizing $\sum \delta^2$ by putting $\dfrac{\partial \sum \delta^2}{\partial s}$ and $\dfrac{\partial \sum \delta^2}{\partial t}$ equal to zero gives the normal

equations:

$$\left(\sum x_1{}^2\right)s - \left(\sum x_1 x_2\right)t = -\sum x_1 y$$
$$-\left(\sum x_1 x_2\right)s + \left(\sum x_2{}^2\right)t = \sum x_2 y. \qquad (11)$$

The results of successive trials, starting from the estimates of s and t, arrived at from the regression coefficient, were as follows in terms of the values tried in the denominator and calculated (calc.) for the numerator of (3).

	IST TRIAL		2ND TRIAL		3RD TRIAL		FINAL
	TRIED	CALC.	TRIED	CALC.	TRIED	CALC.	ESTIMATES
s	.289	.3083	.2987	.3047	.3031	.3038	.304
t	.680	.7037	.6919	.6967	.6949	.6948	.695

The equilibrium point from the final estimates is $\hat{q} = .696$.

The values, $s = .30$, $t = .70$, $\hat{q} = .70$, are as accurate as the data warrant. The solid line in figure 3 shows the theoretical curve for Δq based on these values in comparison with the 13 observations.

This theory obviously fits the data as well as can be expected, but it involves the assumption that selection acts in the same way on males and females. This is not necessarily the case. Selection may occur in such factors as mating activity or fecundity rather than in mortality. It is not likely that there would be the same differentials between genotypes in the males and females in mating and fecundity. It is thus necessary to consider the effect of differences in the selective values of the sexes. Fortunately the results differ little from those obtained by assigning the average for each genotype to both sexes, as noted by WRIGHT (1942).

Let $q_f (= q + \delta q)$ be the frequency of ST in eggs and $q_m (= q - \delta q)$ be that in sperms, and let $W_{11} + \delta W_{11}$ be the selective value of genotype ST/ST in females and $W_{11} - \delta W_{11}$ be that in males, and let similar symbols be used for other selective values. Thus q is the average frequency of ST and the W's are average selective values referred to above.

Selective values

	Frequency (f)	*Females* (W_f)	*Males* (W_m)	*Average*
ST/ST	$q^2 - \delta^2 q$	$W_{11} + \delta W_{11}$	$W_{11} - \delta W_{11}$	W_{11}
ST/CH	$2q(1 - q) + 2\delta^2 q$	$W_{12} + \delta W_{12}$	$W_{12} - \delta W_{12}$	W_{12} (13)
CH/CH	$(1 - q)^2 - \delta^2 q$	$W_{22} + \delta W_{22}$ z	$W_{22} - \delta W_{22}$	W_{22}

The frequencies of Standard in eggs $(_1q_f)$ and sperms $(_1q_m)$ that function in producing the next generation are as follows, using $\overline{W}_f$ for $\sum W_f f$ and $\overline{W}_m$ for $\sum W_m f$.

$$_1q_f = \{[q^2 - \delta^2 q][W_{11} + \delta W_{11}] + [q(1 - q) + \delta^2 q][W_{12} + \delta W_{12}]\}/\overline{W}_f$$
$$_1q_m = \{[q^2 - \delta^2 q][W_{11} - \delta W_{11}] + [q(1 - q) + \delta^2 q][W_{12} - \delta W_{12}]\}/\overline{W}_m. \quad (14)$$

Let $_1q = (1/2)(_1q_f + _1q_m)$ be the average frequency of Standard after a generation and $_1\delta q = (1/2)(_1q_f - _1q_m)$ be the deviation in females from this average, and let $\overline{W}_f = \overline{W} + \delta\overline{W}$ and $\overline{W}_m = \overline{W} - \delta\overline{W}$.

$$_1q = \{[\overline{W}W_{11} - \delta\overline{W}\delta W_{11}][q^2 - \delta^2 q]$$
$$+ [\overline{W}W_{12} - \delta\overline{W}\delta W_{12}][q(1 - q) + \delta^2 q]\}/[\overline{W}^2 - (\delta\overline{W})^2] \quad (15)$$
$$_1\delta q = \{[\overline{W}\delta W_{11} - W_{11}\delta\overline{W}][q^2 - \delta^2 q]$$
$$+ [\overline{W}\delta W_{12} - W_{12}\delta W_{12}][q(1 - q) + \delta^2 q]\}/[\overline{W}^2 - (\delta\overline{W})^2]. \quad (16)$$

It may be nóted that the above value of $_1q$ differs from the expression $[W_{11}q^2 + W_{12}q(1-q)]/\overline{W}$, expected if selection acts in the same way on males and females, only by terms that are of the second degree with respect to sex differences.

On starting from any initial values of q and δq, the values in subsequent generations can be found by repeated application of (15) and (16).

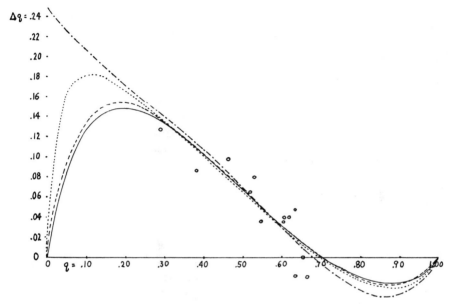

FIGURE 3.—The circles show the amounts of change per generation (Δq) in the frequency (q) of Standard chromosomes in the experiments which involved only Standard and Chiricahua at 25°. The solid line represents the theoretical relation of Δq to q that fits best under the hypothesis that the heterozygotes have a constant selective advantage over both homozygotes and that the sexes are alike in this respect. The broken line represents the same hypothesis except that the homozygotes of one sex are supposed to have considerably more selective disadvantage in relation to the homozygotes than do those of the other sex. The line in dot and dash is the case in which the relative selective disadvantage of the homozygotes in one sex is as extreme as possible. The dotted line represents the hypothesis that the heterozygotes are intermediate between the homozygotes but that each homozygote is favored when rare and opposed when sufficiently common. All hypotheses fit about equally well in the region covered by the experiments.

The effects of considerable differences between the sexes with respect to selection were tested by taking the same average values of W_{11}, W_{12}, and W_{22} arrived at above but assuming δW_{11} and δW_{22} both to be .10.

Genotype	Selective Vales			
	W_f	W_m	W	
ST/ST	.80	.60	.70	(17)
ST/CH	1.00	1.00	1.00	
CH/CH	.40	.20	.30	

The calculations were started from q=.01, δq=0 and q=.99, δq=0.

q	δq	Δq	q	δq	Δq	q	δq	Δq
.01	0	+.0252	.99	0	−.0043	.8264	+.0142	−.0249
.0352	−.0110	+.0725	.9857	+.0020	−.0061	.8015	+.0144	−.0221
.1077	−.0285	+.1375	.9796	+.0028	−.0084	.7794	+.0143	−.0187
.2452	−.0425	+.1475	.9712	+.0038	−.0113	.7607	+.0138	−.0152 (18)
.3927	−.0321	+.1062	.9599	+.0052	−.0147	.7455	+.0133	−.0121
.4989	−.0153	+.0673	.9452	+.0068	−.0185	.7334		−.010
.5662	−.0046	+.0425	.9267	+.0086	−.0222			
.6087	+.0014	+.0275	.9045	+.0104	−.0250			
.6362	+.0048	+.0183	.8795	+.0121	−.0266			
.6545		+.012	.8529	+.0134	−.0265			

The relation of Δq to q, based on these values, is shown as a broken line in figure 3. This curve differs only slightly from the solid line which shows the relation of Δq to q with the same average selective values of genotypes, but no sex difference. Thus the data are fitted substantially as well by both hypotheses.

It seemed next of interest to make the sex difference in selection value as great as possible in the homozygotes without ever exceeding the heterozygotes and subject to acceptance of the same average values, $W_{11}=.70$, $W_{12}=1.00$ and $W_{22}=.30$. This involves the assumption that CH/CH does not reproduce at all in one sex.

Selection Value

Genotype	W_f	W_m	W	
ST/ST	1.00	.40	.70	
ST/CH	1.00	1.00	1.00	
CH/CH	.60	0	.30	(19)

In this case Δq approaches .25 as q approaches 0. The values of q and δq were calculated starting from q=0 and q=.99.

q	δq	Δq	q	δq	Δq	
0	0	.25	.99	+.005	−.0070	(20)
.25	−.25	.1563	.9830	+.0070	−.0114	
.4063	−.0938	.1070	.9715	+.0115	−.0177	
.5133	−.0423	.0630	.9538	+.0180	−.0256	
.5763	−.0098	.0376	.9282	+.0263	−.0335	
.6139	+.0070	.0228	.8947	+.0352	−.0391	
.6367	+.0161	.0142	.8556	+.0426	−.0400	
.6509	+.0213	.0089	.8157	+.0466	−.0363	
.6598	+.0243	.0057	.7794	+.0468	−.0298	
.6655	+.0262	.0037	.7496	+.0446	−.0227	
.6692	+.0273	.0024	.7269	+.0413	−.0164	
.6715	+.0280	.0015	.7106	+.0382	−.0114	
.6731	+.0285	.0010	.6992	+.0356	−.008	
.6741	+.0288	.0007				

A curve from these values is plotted in dot and dash in figure 3. It differs greatly from the solid line at both low and high values of q, but in the region represented by the observations (q=.292 to .663) it does not differ much.

There is therefore no reason from the observations at hand to rule out the possibility of very great selective differences between the sexes. It would require such experiments as the competitive mating of two types of males with each type of female and competitive mating of two types of females with each type of male to distinguish these hypotheses.

So far we have assumed that the relative selective values of the genotypes remain the same at all gene frequencies. This is not necessarily, or even probably, the case where selective mating is in question, and it becomes desirable to consider the consequences where the W's are functions of q. For simplicity we shall assume that sex differences are sufficiently small that they may be ignored. The general formula for Δq is as follows (WRIGHT 1942).

$$\Delta q = q(1 - q) \sum W \frac{df}{dq} \Big/ 2\overline{W}, \qquad \overline{W} = \sum Wf. \qquad (21)$$

If the W's, as reproductive rates, involve a function of q that is the same for all, this cancels in (21) leaving Δq the same as if the function were not involved. Thus populations with the same rates of change of gene frequencies may differ widely in the values of q at which the population reproduces most rapidly ($\overline{W}$ maximum), and these points are not in general at the point of equilibrium.

There is no such cancelling if the W's involve different functions of q. It must suffice here to illustrate by one hypothesis how widely the selective values may differ from those arrived at on the assumption that they are independent of q, and still fit the data.

Assume that the heterozygotes, instead of always being superior to both homozygotes, are always exactly intermediate in selective value, but also that the selective values of the homozygotes fall off linearly as the corresponding chromosome frequencies rise.

Genotype	Frequency (f)	Selective Value (W)	
ST/ST	q^2	$1 + a - bq$	
ST/CH	$2q(1 - q)$	1	(22)
CH/CH	$(1 - q)^2$	$1 - a + bq$	

$$\overline{W} = 1 - (a - bq)(1 - 2q) \qquad (23)$$
$$\Delta q = q(1 - q)(a - bq)/\overline{W} \qquad (24)$$
$$\hat{q} = a/b \qquad (25)$$
$$a - bq = \Delta q/[q(1 - q + (1 - 2q)\Delta q] \quad \text{from (23), (24)} \qquad (26)$$

A rough determination of values of a and b to fit the observations under this hypothesis can be made by taking $\hat{q}$ as .70 (hence a=.70b from (25)) and substituting $\overline{q}$ and $\overline{\Delta q}$ in place of q and Δq in (26).

$$\begin{aligned} a &= .902 \\ b &= 1.288. \end{aligned} \qquad (27)$$

Substitution of these values in (24) gives the dotted line in figure 3. This curve differs considerably from the solid line at low values of q, but differs only slightly in the region covered by the observations and thus is a mathematically possible interpretation. How widely this hypothesis differs from that which fits the data on the hypothesis that selective values are independent of gene frequency may be seen from the following table.

	W's CONSTANT	Selective values (W) W's VARY AS IN (22)						
		$q=0$	.10	.30	.50	.70	.90	1.00
ST/ST	.70	1.90	1.77	1.51	1.26	1.00	.74	.61
ST/CH	1.00	1.00	1.00	1.00	1.00	1.00	1.00	1.00
CH/CH	.30	.10	.23	.49	.74	1.00	1.26	1.39

An hypothesis of this nature is one that might well be approximated in nature in cases in which a species occupies a heterogenous environment. Each genotype may be favored by selection when rare and unable to occupy fully the ecological niches to which it is best adapted, but selected against when so abundant that it must in part occupy ecological niches to which it is less well adapted than other genotypes. This particular hypothesis is perhaps improbable under the conditions of the experiments, but the possibility that the W's depend on different functions of the gene frequencies is not improbable. This could be tested only by special experiments.

In the most extensive experiments, three types of chromosomes and consequently six genotypes were present. The analysis is much more complicated than where only two types of chromosome are present, and we shall restrict consideration to the hypothesis that selective values are independent of gene frequencies and that sex differences may be ignored.

As a first approach, the two chromosomes, Arrowhead and Chiricahua, which tended to decrease in frequency in the data, may be grouped together in opposition to Standard, which tended to increase in frequency. Let q refer to the frequency of Standard, s to its selective disadvantage when homozygous, and t to the selective disadvantage of Arrowhead and Chiricahua combined in comparison with the heterozygotes that involve Standard. Substitution in (8) yields

$$\overline{W} = .7016 \text{ at } \bar{q}$$
$$s = .555$$
$$t = .596$$
$$\hat{q} = .518.$$

$$(29)$$

In this case, t is the weighted average of the selective disadvantages of AR/AR, AR/CH, and CH/CH relative to ST/AR and ST/CH combined. Using subscripts 1, 2, and 3 for Standard, Arrowhead, and Chiricahua, respectively, and indicating selective disadvantages of genotypes by double symbols, we may write

$$t = .596 = (s_{22}q_2^2 + 2s_{23}q_2q_3 + s_{33}q_3^2)/(1 - q_1)^2. \qquad (30)$$

If now it be assumed that the heterozygote AR/CH is at no selective disadvantage relative to the other heterozygotes (that is, $s_{23}=0$), we can estimate roughly the average selective disadvantages of the AR/AR and CH/CH by putting these the same in the above equation and substituting $\bar{q}_1=.4201$, $\bar{q}_2=.3182$ and $\bar{q}_3=.2617$ (from table 10) for q_1, q_2, and q_3, respectively. But this yields the impossible value, $s_{22}=s_{33}=1.17$ which implies that AR/AR and CH/CH suffer fates 17 percent worse than death on the average.

This lumping together of different genotypes however, is not a very satisfactory procedure, especially since it is obvious from the data that Arrowhead and Chiricahua do not react alike. Consider next the hypothesis that the three heterozygotes are equivalent in selective value ($W_{12}=W_{13}=W_{23}=1$) but that the homozygotes suffer diverse selective handicaps (s_1, s_2 and s_3).

Genotype	Frequency	Selective Value	
ST/ST	q_1^2	$1 - s_1$	
ST/AR	$2q_1q_2$	1	
ST/CH	$2q_1q_3$	1	(31)
AR/AR	q_2^2	$1 - s_2$	
AR/CH	$2q_2q_3$	1	
CH/CH	q_3^2	$1 - s_3$	

$$\overline{W} = 1 - s_1q_1^2 - s_2q_2^2 - s_3q_3^2 \tag{32}$$

$$\Delta q_1 = q_1\left[\frac{1 - s_1q_1}{\overline{W}} - 1\right] \tag{33}$$

$$\Delta q_2 = q_2\left[\frac{1 - s_2q_2}{\overline{W}} - 1\right]$$

$$\Delta q_3 = q_3\left[\frac{1 - s_3q_3}{\overline{W}} - 1\right]$$

$$\frac{\partial \overline{W}}{\partial q_1} = -2\left[s_1q_1 + s_2q_2\frac{\partial q_2}{\partial q_1} + s_3q_3\frac{\partial q_3}{\partial q_1}\right]. \tag{34}$$

$$\frac{\partial \Delta q_1}{\partial q_1} = \frac{\Delta q_1}{q_1} - q_1\left\{\overline{W}s_1 + (1 - s_1q_1)\frac{\partial \overline{W}}{\partial q_1}\right\}\bigg/\overline{W}^2. \tag{35}$$

After some reduction and noting that since $q_1+q_2+q_3=1$, $1+\dfrac{\partial q_2}{\partial q_1}+\dfrac{\partial q_3}{\partial q_1}=0$

$$\frac{\partial \Delta q_1}{\partial q_1} = 1 - \frac{1}{\overline{W}} + 2\frac{\Delta q_1}{q_1} - 2q_1\left(1+\frac{\Delta q_1}{q_1}\right)\left(\frac{\Delta q_1}{q_1}+\frac{\Delta q_2}{q_2}\frac{\partial q_2}{\partial q_1}+\frac{\Delta q_3}{q_3}\frac{\partial q_3}{\partial q_1}\right). \tag{36}$$

Assuming that all observed values of q are in the region in which relations are approximately linear, an approximate value of $\overline{W}$ may be obtained by

replacing the q's and Δq's by their mean values and replacing $\dfrac{\partial q_2}{\partial q_1}$ by the regression coefficient $b_{q_2q_1}(=-.2657)$, $\dfrac{\partial q_3}{\partial q_1}$ by $b_{q_3q_1}(=-.7343)$ and $\dfrac{\partial \Delta q_1}{\partial q_1}$ by

$b_{\Delta q_1 q_1}(=-.3865)$. With these assumptions, $\overline{W}$ comes out .7091 for the set of mean gene frequencies. The values of s_1, s_2, and s_3 can now be estimated form (33).

$$
\begin{array}{ll}
s_1 = .536 & W_{11} = .464 \\
s_2 = 1.000 & W_{22} = .000 \\
s_3 = 1.389 & W_{33} = -.389.
\end{array}
\tag{37}
$$

The estimated value of s_1 (.536) does not differ much from that obtained by lumping Arrowhead and Chiricahua (.518). The selection against AR/AR is complete and that against CH/CH is impossible, 38.9 percent greater than complete elimination. The weighted average selective disdvantage of AR/AR, AR/CH and CH/CH comes out .584, in approximate agreement with .596 where these were lumped. It appears to be impossible to account for the results on the hypothesis that the heterozygotes are all equivalent. The selective values must be allowed more latitude.

Genotypes	Frequencies	Selective Values	
ST/ST	q_1^2	W_{11}	
ST/AR	$2q_1q_2$	W_{12}	(38)
ST/CH	$2q_1q_3$	W_{13}	
AR/AR	q_2^2	W_{22}	
AR/CH	$2q_2q_3$	W_{23}	
CH/CH	q_3^2	W_{33}	

$$
\overline{W} = W_{11}q_1^2 + 2W_{12}q_1q_2 + 2W_{13}q_1q_3 + W_{22}q_2^2 + 2W_{23}q_2q_3 + W_{33}q_3^2 \tag{39}
$$

$$
\Delta q_1 = q_1 \left[\frac{W_{11}q_1 + W_{12}q_2 + W_{13}q_3}{\overline{W}} - 1 \right]
$$

$$
\Delta q_2 = q_2 \left[\frac{W_{12}q_1 + W_{22}q_2 + W_{23}q_3}{\overline{W}} - 1 \right] \tag{40}
$$

$$
\Delta q_3 = q_3 \left[\frac{W_{13}q_1 + W_{23}q_2 + W_{33}q_3}{\overline{W}} - 1 \right].
$$

At equilibrium $\Delta q_1 = \Delta q_2 = \Delta q_3 = 0$

$$
W_{11}\hat{q}_1 + W_{12}\hat{q}_2 + W_{13}\hat{q}_3 - \overline{W} = 0
$$
$$
W_{12}\hat{q}_1 + W_{22}\hat{q}_2 + W_{23}\hat{q}_3 - \overline{W} = 0
$$
$$
W_{13}\hat{q}_1 + W_{23}\hat{q}_2 + W_{33}\hat{q}_3 - \overline{W} = 0.
$$

$\overline{W}$ with its quadratic terms can be eliminated, leaving a series of linear equations to solve for two variables $\hat{q}_1$ and $\hat{q}_2$ (noting that $\hat{q}_3 = 1 - \hat{q}_1 - \hat{q}_2$). An analogous system of $(n-1)$ simultaneous linear equations would appear with n instead of three alternatives. In the present case let

$$K_1 = W_{22}W_{33} - W_{13}W_{22} - W_{12}W_{33} + W_{12}W_{23} + W_{13}W_{23} - W_{23}^2$$

$$K_2 = W_{33}W_{11} - W_{12}W_{33} - W_{r3}W_{11} + W_{23}W_{13} + W_{12}W_{13} - W_{13}^2 \qquad (42)$$

$$K_3 = W_{11}W_{22} - W_{23}W_{11} - W_{13}W_{22} + W_{13}W_{12} + W_{23}W_{12} - W_{12}^2.$$

Then

$$\hat{q}_1 = K_1/(K_1 + K_2 + K_3)$$
$$\hat{q}_2 = K_2/(K_1 + K_2 + K_3) \qquad (43)$$
$$\hat{q}_3 = K_3/(K_1 + K_2 + K_3).$$

It may be noted that in the special case considered earlier in which the selective values of all heterozygotes are 1, the condition that $\Delta q_1 = \Delta q_2 = \Delta q_3 = 0$ gives at once $s_1 q_1 = s_2 q_2 = s_3 q_3 = 1 - \overline{W}$ which gives

$$\hat{q}_1 = \frac{1}{s_1} \bigg/ \sum \frac{1}{s} \qquad (44)$$

with analogous formulae for $\hat{q}_2$, $\hat{q}_3$ (and for other q's if there are more than three alternatives).

Returning to the case in which no restriction (other than constancy) are placed on the W's, the observation equations are as follows (from 40)

$$q_1 + \Delta q_1 = (q_1^2 W_{11} + q_1 q_2 W_{12} + q_1 q_3 W_{13})/\overline{W}$$
$$q_2 + \Delta q_2 = (q_1 q_2 W_{12} + q_2^2 W_{22} + q_2 q_3 W_{23})/\overline{W} \qquad (45)$$
$$q_3 + \Delta q_3 = (q_1 q_3 W_{13} + q_2 q_3 W_{23} + q_3^2 W_{33})/\overline{W}.$$

It is convenient to let $y_1 = q_1 + \Delta q_1$, $y_2 = q_2 + \Delta q_2$, $y_3 = q_3 + \Delta q_3$, $x_{11} = q_1^2/\overline{W}$, $x_{12} = q_1 q_2/\overline{W}$ etc. The quantity to be minimized is then

$$\sum \delta^2 = \sum \left[(y_1 - x_{11}W_{11} - x_{12}W_{12} - x_{13}W_{13})^2 \right]$$
$$+ \sum \left[(y_2 - x_{12}W_{12} - x_{22}W_{22} - x_{23}W_{23})^2 \right] \qquad (46)$$
$$+ \sum \left[(y_3 - x_{13}W_{13} - x_{23}W_{23} - x_{33}W_{33})^2 \right].$$

The six normal equations with the unknown selective values written for convenience above are as follows:

W_{11}	W_{12}	W_{13}	W_{22}	W_{23}	W_{33}	
$\sum x_{11}^2 +$	$\sum x_{11}x_{12} +$	$\sum x_{11}x_{13} +$	$0 +$	$0 +$	$0 =$	$\sum x_{11}y_1$
$\sum x_{11}x_{12} +$	$2\sum x_{12}^2 +$	$\sum x_{12}x_{13} +$	$\sum x_{12}x_{22} +$	$\sum x_{12}x_{23}$	$0 =$	$\sum x_{12}y_1 + \sum x_{12}y_2$
$\sum x_{11}x_{13} +$	$\sum x_{12}x_{13} +$	$2\sum x_{13}^2 +$	$0 +$	$\sum x_{13}x_{23} +$	$\sum x_{13}x_{33} =$	$\sum x_{13}y_1 + \sum x_{13}y_3$
$0 +$	$\sum x_{12}x_{22} +$	$0 +$	$\sum x_{22}^2 +$	$\sum x_{22}x_{23} +$	$0 =$	$\sum x_{22}y_2$
$0 +$	$\sum x_{12}x_{23} +$	$\sum x_{13}x_{23} +$	$\sum x_{22}x_{23} +$	$2\sum x_{23}^2 +$	$\sum x_{23}x_{33} =$	$\sum x_{23}y_2 + \sum x_{23}y_3$
$0 +$	$0 +$	$\sum x_{13}x_{33} +$	$0 +$	$\sum x_{23}x_{33} +$	$\sum x_{33}^2 =$	$\sum x_{33}y_3.$

These could be reduced to five, taking one of the W's as standard, since only the relative values are in question. The iteration process necessitated by the use of trial values of the W's in estimating $\overline{W}$ for each observation however, is facilitated by allowing all of the W's to vary. As before, no attempt was made at differential weighting of the observations.

The initial trials were based on the estimates of $W_{11} = (.696)$, $W_{33}(=.305)$, with $W_{13}(= 1.000$ as standard), deduced from the experiments with Standard and Chiricahua only, and on preliminary deductions for W_{12}, W_{23} and W_{22}. These trial values turned out to be unsatisfactory, but approximate stability was reached at the fourth iteration. The trial values (used in $\overline{W}$) and the results from solution of the normal equations were as follows:

| | 1ST TRIAL | | 2ND TRIAL | | 3RD TRIAL | | 4TH TRIAL | | FINAL ESTIMATE |
	TRIED	CALC.	TRIED	CALC.	TRIED	CALC.	TRIED	CALC.	$W_{13}=1$
W_{11}	.696	.636	.656	.622	.60	.594	.59	.597	.43
W_{12}	2.027	1.911	1.950	1.868	1.76	1.785	1.79	1.797	1.30
W_{13}	1.000	1.281	1.189	1.347	1.44	1.411	1.41	1.394	1.00
W_{22}	.305	.034	.125	.053	.06	.081	.08	.073	.05
W_{23}	.965	.969	.968	.980	.96	.984	.98	.982	.71
W_{33}	.305	.388	.361	.340	.35	.275	.28	.284	.21

While complete stability is not reached, the values given in the last column (reduced to a scale on which $W_{13} = 1.00$) should be sufficiently accurate for the hypothesis under consideration. The reduction in the selective value of ST/ST from .696 to .43 and for CH/CH from .305 to .21 suggests increased selection against the homozygotes in the presence of three chromosomes instead of two, or, in other words, that the selective values are to some extent at least functions of the chromosome frequencies instead of constants as here assumed. The method, however, does not yield any impossible estimates of W, although the selection against homozygous Arrowhead is indicated to be almost complete.

The frequencies of the three chromosomes at equilibrium can be calculated from the above estimates of the W's by substitutions in (42) and (43).

Standard $\qquad \hat{q}_1 = .531$
Arrowhead $\qquad \hat{q}_2 = .339$
Chiricahua $\qquad \hat{q}_3 = .130$

DISCUSSION

There can be no doubt from these experiments that the three chromosome types found in the population of Piñon Flats, Mount San Jacinto, are not alike in selective value, even though the data do not yield a unique interpretation of the selective processes that take place. Under the conditions obtaining in the experimental populations, the selective values are such that a certain set of frequencies of chromosome types is in equilibrium. Furthermore, the selective values are quite different under different conditions, temperature being at least one of the modifying agents. In a general way, this makes the observation that there are marked seasonal changes in the frequencies of the chromosome types in natural populations understandable. But a detailed application of the experimental results to the interpretation of the changes observed in nature encounters difficulties.

Parallel cyclic changes occur in the populations of Piñon Flats (4000 feet above sea level) and Andreas Canyon (800 feet). In both localities the frequencies of Standard are lowest and of Chiricahua highest in June. The waning July population at Piñon shows some increase of Standard and a drop in Chiricahua; this process continues till September when Standard about reaches its annual maximum frequency and Chiricahua its minimum. Flies are rare in July and August at Andreas, but in September the population shows a materially increased frequency of Standard and a decreased one of Chiricahua. By analogy with the populations of experimental cages kept at 25°C, it is tempting to ascribe the waxing of Standard and the waning of Chricahua at Piñon and Andreas to the high temperatures prevailing during the summer months in these localities. The same analogy seems to account for the fact that Standard chromosomes are less frequent and Chiricahua more frequent at Piñon than in the warmest locality, Andreas. Furthermore, at Keen Camp (about 4500 feet elevation, ponderosa pine zone) Standard is still less and Chiricahua still more frequent than at Piñon (DOBZHANSKY 1943).

Again, no appreciable changes in the frequencies of the chromosomal types take place in any locality during the cool season, from September to March or April. This agrees with the finding that chromosome frequencies change little if at all in experimental cages kept at $16\frac{1}{2}$°C. Although Keen is the coolest of the three localities, a similar explanation is hardly satisfactory to account for the absence at Keen of the cyclic changes of the type observed at Piñon and Andreas. The selective values of the chromosomes at Keen (and Andreas) need not be the same as those at Piñon.

The frequencies of Standard drop and of Chiricahua increase from April to June at Piñon and at Andreas. Since the temperatures are increasing during spring, the observed changes in the chromosome frequencies go in the direction opposite to that found at high temperatures in the experimental populations. The causation of these changes is at present a matter of speculation.

The sensitivity of the selective differentials to environmental changes is probably the most interesting phenomenon observed in our experiments, apart from the establishment of the fact that chromosome types found in natural populations may differ in adaptive value. As shown above, the chromosome types are equivalent or nearly so at $16\frac{1}{2}$°C, but strikingly unlike at higher temperatures. An analogous extreme sensitivity to temperature has been found also in homozygotes for some individual chromosomes isolated from natural populations (DOBZHANSKY and SPASSKY 1944). It must be kept in mind that, among the mass of possible environmental variables, only temperature and the amount of food have so far been studied in population cages. It seems very improbable that the relative adaptive values of the chromosome types so greatly modified by temperature will prove to be insensitive to anything else. The changes observed at Piñon and Andreas during spring may, then, represent a selective response to factors other than temperature (for example, qualitative changes in the diet). By the same token, the causative factor of the changes taking place in the same populations in summer need not necessarily be temperature, even though temperature does induce analogous changes in population cages.

An alternative explanation has been suggested by HOVANITZ (1944)—namely, that the populations of Piñon and Andreas are swamped in summer by migration from the flourishing populations higher on the mountain, which resemble Keen in chromosome frequencies. The return of Piñon and Andreas in late summer and in fall to the frequencies of the chromosome types characteristic for the winter populations of these localities obviously cannot be accounted for by migration. It must be due to selective pressures of the sort indicated by the experiments with population cages, or even to complete extinction of the migrant population which must somehow escape crossing with the natives. Furthermore, the amount of dispersion as determined in *Drosophila pseudoobscura* by experiments in the field is not adequate (DOBZHANSKY and WRIGHT 1943). The mean square radial distance in one day from the site of release of dense populations of marked flies was 17,600m² with variance of distances increasing on subsequent days by about 8000m² per day at 72°F. The dispersion variance (close to zero below 60°F) increased by about 760m² for each increment of one degree Fahrenheit. These figures must be halved to give the variance of spread in one direction. Thus even assuming a temperature of 93°F, the increment of variance in a given direction of flies that emerge at one place on a certain day and spread by random flights is only about 12,000m² per day. In a month, the standard deviation of the group about its point of origin would be only about 600 meters. In the experiments moreover, there was evidence that about half of the flies released died in a week. Since Andreas is about 16 kilometers from Keen down the mountain, it is obvious that random dispersal from Keen at the observed rate is wholly inadequate to account for the rapid shift at Andreas to a Keen-like composition of the population. The only possibility of accounting for the May–June shift at Piñon and Andreas by migration from higher on the mountain seems to be by a directed mass movement at a rate of at least half a kilometer per day.

Cyclic changes in the composition of populations have been discovered by TIMOFEEFF-RESSOVSKY (1940) in the beetle *Adalia bipunctata*, by GERSHENSON (1945) in the hamster *Cricetus cricetus*, and by DUBININ and TINIAKOV (1945) in *Drosophila funebris*. The changes appear to be caused in all cases by natural selection in response to seasonal alterations in the environments. The situation found in *Drosophila pseudoobscura* is, thus, not unique. It furnishes, however, the only instance in which changes analogous to those taking place in natural populations can be in part reproduced in laboratory experiments.

SUMMARY

Artificial populations of *Drosophila pseudoobscura* were kept in cages constructed as a modification of the model devised by L'HÉRITIER and TEISSIER.

All the flies used in the experiments reported in this paper are descendants of parents collected at Piñon Flats, Mount San Jacinto, California. Three types of third chromosomes, Standard, Chiricahua, and Arrowhead, are common in the population of that locality. Their relative frequencies undergo cyclic seasonal changes—namely, Standard increases and Chiricahua decreases in frequency during the summer; the opposite change takes place during spring; the relative frequencies remain constant during fall and winter.

Most of the experiments began with approximately equal numbers either of two or of three chromosome types. At 25°, with initial frequencies equal or with Chiricahua more frequent than Standard, there was a highly significant increase in frequency of Standard (where present) at the expense of either of the other types but especially of Chiricahua. On the other hand, there were no significant changes in mean frequency at 16.5°C. The rate of change at 25° showed a strong negative regression on frequency in all cases, and a probably significant regression of this sort was observed in one case (Arrowhead) at 16.5°. The data further indicate that all chromosome types are favored when sufficiently rare and opposed when sufficiently common.

The simplest hypothesis is that the heterozygotes are favored over both corresponding homozygotes and that there are no sex differences. The results in the experiments at 25° in which only Standard and Chiricahua were present can be adequately explained by postulating the relative selective values .70:1.00:.30 for ST/ST, ST/CH and CH/CH, respectively. Equilibrium is indicated at 70 percent Standard, 30 percent Chiricahua.

However, there is no assurance that selection acts alike on males and females. The mathematical theory for unequal selective values in the sexes is presented. It is found that the results differ little except in extreme cases from those found with sex equality in selection. Thus the data can be fitted substantially as well by assuming selective values 1.00:1.00:.60 for females, .40:1.00:0 for males (for ST/ST, ST/CH, and CH/CH, respectively) as under the previous hypothesis in which both sexes are selected according to the averages of those figures.

It is possible that the selective values may vary with the changes in composition of the population. The mathematical theory of variable selection coefficients is discussed briefly. An extreme hypothesis of this sort (heterozygotes always intermediate while each homozygote decreases in selective value with increase in frequency) was found to fit the data reasonably well. The selective values arrived at were $(1.90 - 1.29q)$ for ST/ST, 1.00 for ST/CH and $(.10 + 1.29q)$ for CH/CH, where q is the frequency of Standard (.70 at equilibrium as before).

The mathematical theory of selection among multiple alleles is considered in connection with the cases in which three chromosome types were present. The selective values at 25°, indicated by the method of least squares, are .43 for ST/ST, .05 for AR/AR, .21 for CH/CH, 1.30 for ST/AR, 1.00 for ST/CH, and .71 for AR/CH. Equilibrium is indicated at 53 percent Standard, 34 percent Arrowhead and 13 percent Chiricahua. The hypothesis that all three heterozygotes are equal in selective value gives impossible results.

The experimental results demonstrate clearly that there may be selective differences between chromosome types derived from the same locality and that these may be of such a nature as to result in the indefinite persistence of several types in such a locality. The marked rise in frequency of Standard and decrease of Chiricahua in summer, observed to occur in nature in the locality from which the flies were collected, is analogous to the experimental reaction to high temperature, and it is tempting to compare the lack of change in artificial population at 16.5° with the constancy observed in the natural ones during fall and winter. The changes which occur in nature during spring (the reverse of those in summer) however, have not been reproduced in the population cages. Mass migration at this time from the population high in the mountains would explain the results qualitatively, but it would be difficult to reconcile this with the results of earlier experiments on the rate of dispersion of the flies in nature. It appears that there are important factors yet to be discovered.

ACKNOWLEDGMENT

Acknowledgment is made to PROFESSOR CARL EPLING of the UNIVERSITY OF CALIFORNIA who collected and sent us some of the flies used in these experiments; to MR. BORIS SPASSKY and to MISS IRENE MARKREICH who have assisted in taking care of the experiments and in the preparation of the slides for the cytological examination; to DR. CRODOWALDO PAVAN of the UNIVERSITY OF SÃO PAULO, Brazil, who introduced some improvements in the construction of the population cage; and to the DR. WALLACE C. AND CLARA A. ABBOTT MEMORIAL FUND of the UNIVERSITY OF CHICAGO for assistance in connection with the calculations.

LITERATURE CITED

DOBZHANSKY, TH., 1943   Genetics of natural populations. IX. Temporal changes in the composition of populations of *Drosophila pseudoobscura*. Genetics **28**: 162–186.

DOBZHANSKY, TH., and C. EPLING, 1944   Contributions to the genetics, taxonomy, and ecology of *Drosophila pseudoobscura* and its relatives. Pub. Carnegie Instn. **554**: 1–183.

DOBZHANSKY, TH., A. M. HOLZ, and B. SPASSKY, 1942   Genetics of natural populations. VIII. Concealed variability in the second and fourth chromosomes of *Drosophila pseudoobscura*. Genetics **27**: 463–490.

DOBZHANSKY, TH., and B. SPASSKY, 1944   Genetics of natural populations. XI. Manifestation of genetic variants in *Drosophila pseudoobscura* in different environments. Genetics **29**: 270–290.

DOBZHANSKY, TH., and SEWALL WRIGHT, 1943   Genetics of natural populations. X. Dispersion rates in *Drosophila pseudoobscura*. Genetics **28**: 304–340.

DUBININ, N. P., and G. G. TINIAKOV, 1945   Seasonal cycles and the concentration of inversions in populations of *Drosophila funebris*. Amer. Nat. **79**: 570–572.

FISHER, R. A., 1922   On the dominance ratio. Proc. R. Soc. Edinburgh **42**: 321–341.

GERSHENSON, S., 1945 Evolutionary studies on the distribution and dynamics of melanism in the hamster (*Cricetus cricetus* L.). II. Seasonal and annual changes in the frequency of black hamsters. Genetics **30**: 233–251.

HOVANITZ, W., 1944   The distribution of gene frequencies in wild populations of Colias. Genetics **29**: 31–60.

L'HÉRITIER, PH., 1937   Étude de variations quantitatives au sein d'une espèce: *Drosophila melanogaster*. Arch. Zool. exp. gén. **78**: 255–356.

L'Héritiefr, Ph., and G. Teissier, 1933   Étude d'une population de Drosophiles en équilibre. C. R. Acad. Sci. **198**: 770–772.

Timofeeff-Ressovsky, N. W., 1940   Zur Analyse des Polymorphismus bei *Adalia bipunctata.* Biol. Zbl. **60**: 130–137.

Wright, S., 1931 Evolution in mendelian populations. Genetics **16**: 97-159.

1942   Statistical genetics and evolution. Bull. Amer. Math. Soc. **48**: 223–246.

EVOLUTION AS A CREATIVE PROCESS

by

THEODOSIUS DOBZHANSKY

Columbia University, New York

The same fundamental habits of thought occur among evolutionists and biologists as among people generally. Preformation and predestination seem most attractive to some, while others choose epigenesis, creativeness, and freedom. A world view based on the first of these attitudes was set forth with greatest clarity by LAPLACE, in his famous dictum that, knowing all the forces which operate in the Universe at a given instant, a superior intelligence could deduce the past as well as the future with complete certainty. But if LAPLACE was right then life is largely an illusion. An egg cell contains the body which develops from it, this cell was itself contained in the eggs of the ancestors, and the future generations invisibly exist in the now living creatures. Evolution is mere unfolding of what was already present in the primordial virus and in primordial matter. BERGSON was probably the most brilliant exponent of the contrary view. To him, time is real, and evolution and history are creative processes; the present is not reducible to the past, nor can the future be deduced from the present. Unfortunately, in drawing these conclusions BERGSON did not avoid breaking away from the methods of study of nature, the validity of which has been tested by long experience. The « élan vital » which he supposed to bring evolution about was nothing but a fancy name for the old vital force, which belongs more to the realms of magic and witchcraft than to science.

Various forms of preformationism have been adopted by many biologists. Among its latest versions are the « one gene — one enzyme » and « one gene — one function » theories. The practical usefulness of these theories is proven by the large quantity of biochemical work which they have stimulated. But they have not been equally successful in providing a cogent picture of either the ontogenetic or the evolutionary develop-

Reprinted by permission of CARYOLOGIA from Proceedings of the
9th International Congress of Genetics: 435–449 (1954).

ment. A battery of genes which give off always the same enzymes in all kinds of cells and tissues does not add up to anything like a developing organism. Consistently preformist theories of evolution have fared even worse. Supposing that evolution unfolds the potentialities which were present in living matter at its origin from the non-living gives no insight into how evolution takes place. Assuming that evolution is propelled by an urge to reach predestined ends tells us nothing at all about it. The futility of orthogenetic and autogenetic theories of evolution is shown by their failure to provide working hypotheses that could be tested by observation and experiment.

Theories of evolution based on a synthesis of the findings of genetics with those of other biological disciplines are labelled, rather unprecisely, neo-Darwinian. These theories avoid commitments to either extreme preformism or to epigenesis, although they contain elements of both. It is the opinion of this writer that neo-Darwinism furnishes a basis for a synthesis of preformism and epigenesis that may be both scientifically and philosophically satisfactory.

The raw materials of evolution originate through mutation of the self-reproducing units of life, the genes. It seems probable that mutations are due to occasional failures of the processes of self-synthesis. Such failures often lead to structures which no longer reproduce themselves. A gene so changed that it fails to engender the synthesis of its own copy is however no longer a gene. Altered genes which reproduce their altered structures are the mutants from which new adaptive genotypes may be compounded by the sexual process and by natural selection.

Now, the mutation process is often said to be random, undirected, due to chance, or accidental. These epithets are misleading. Mutations are undirected and accidental only in the sense that which genes mutate and when, has nothing to do with the possible usefulness or harmfulness of the mutations to their carriers. To suppose that an organism produces only those mutations which are needed and only when they are needed is to believe that the organism possesses a foreknowledge of the future. But it is obvious that the mutational repertory of every gene is determined by its structure, and is released ultimately by the environmental influences in the wide sense of the word « environment ». To this extent, then, mutants are preformed in the genes, and are Laplacean rather than Bergsonian phenomena. On the other hand, the structure of a gene is an outcome of the age-long evolutionary development, extending even to the dawn of life. This development took place under the control of natural selection, and it represented, as it were, a distillation of the entire succession of the environments met with during the evolutionary history. Organisms, genotypes, and genes are time-binding machines. So considered, mutation involves epigenesis; in the long run, it is a creative process.

What has been said concerning mutation applies as well to microevolutionary changes which involve selection. The genes determine the adaptive values of their carriers in the particular environments in which the latter happen to live. Thus, in *Escherichia coli,* the carriers of certain genotypes do, and of others do not, survive in the presence of streptomycin. Hence, the contribution of some genotypes to the gene pool of subsequent generations is relatively greater than that of other genotypes. This makes the gene pool change with time. The selection of resistant genotypes gives rise to resistant strains of the bacteria. The nature, direction, and speed of microevolutionary changes are predictable when both the mutational repertory of the organism and the demands of the environment are known. Thus, in the presence of certain concentrations of streptomycin a culture of sensitive cells of *Escherichia coli* has a definite probability to give rise to a streptomycin-resistant strain.

Microevolutionary changes are not only repeatable but are also reversible. In environments free of streptomycin strains sensitive to this antibiotic may be produced. Microevolutionary changes are, then, due to selection by the environment of genetically simple alterations; the altered genotypes differ from the original one in a single or in few genes. In a very limited sense, such changes may be said to be preformed in the organism. With mutant genes available in a population or arising constantly at finite rates, microevolutionary changes are evoked rather directly by the exigencies of the environment. Selection acts here as a simple sorting-out process.

Elements of epigenesis develop when evolutionary changes involve systems of adaptively interdependent genes, instead of single or few independent genes. The genotype is an integrated system, and the degree of integration appears to be greater in higher than in lower organisms. It is also greater in animals than in plants, necessitating a more complete reproductive isolation between related species in the former than in the latter. In highly integrated genotypes the adaptive value of a gene change depends not only upon the environment but also upon the genetic system in which it occurs.

The scope of epigenesis in evolution is greatly increased by the sexual process with its twin corollaries of meiosis and Mendelian recombination.

With n genes, each capable to give rise by mutation to m different alleles, the number of possible gene combinations is, of course, m^n. Now, at least in the higher organisms, n is of the order of 1000 or 10,000, and m is probably always greater than 2. One thing which is, then, certain is that only a competely infinitesimal fraction of the possible gene combinations can ever be realized. Since the adaptive value is an emergent property of the genetic system, the sexual reproduction becomes a creative process which yields a truly vast variety of adaptive systems none of which occurred before in the history of life. Interacting with the sexual process, natural selection becomes far more than an efficient sieve. Probably in all genotypes, but especially in the highly integrated ones, the adaptive consequences of a mutational change depend upon the rest of the genotypic system in which the change takes place. This system is, however, the resultant of the changes that have occurred in the species during its phylogenetic development, which was, of course, controlled by natural selection. The present state of an adaptively integrated genotype is an epitome of its selectional history. The appearance of sexual reproduction in the history of the living world was, then, a master adaptation which has altered radically the strategy of the subsequent adaptive evolution.

The greater the reconstruction of the genetic system necessitated by an evolutionary change the more pronounced becomes its epigenetic character. Microevolution is to some extent preformistic, macroevolution is creative. This is not because microevolution and macroevolution are different in principle, or even in the basic mechanisms that bring them about. Radical changes in adaptively integrated genotypes involve however long sequences of mutational and selectional events. Now, these historical sequences are brought about by interaction of numerous variables. It would require altogether improbable coincidence to have these sequences exactly repeated or reversed. Therefore, microevolutionary changes are, at least, in principle, fully reproducible, repeatable, and reversible. Macroevolutionary changes are neither repeatable nor reversible, as morphologists and paleontologists have known for some time.

Evolutionary changes that can be observed directly, either in nature or in experiment, are for the most part strictly microevolutionary ones. This is so because the numbers of generations available for observation are usually small, and the processes of selection are difficult to study unless they involve single genes or small groups of genes. Microorganisms offer longer series of generations for study, but in these simplest forms of life the evolutionary processes remain mostly on the microevolutionary level, on account of the rarity or absence of the sexual process and the low degree of adaptive integration of the genotype. Macroevolutionary changes are, and probably will remain, outside the realm of phenomena accessible to direct observation. Macroevolution involves more or less radical alterations in body structures and functions, connected with adaptation to new modes of life. Such changes require time on geological scale, and produce new genera, families, and still higher categories.

To an experimentalist, perhaps the greatest interest attaches to changes intermediate in magnitude between micro-and macroevolution. Such changes may perhaps be referred to as mesoevolutionary. Mesoevolution involves alteration in more or less numerous genetic units, emergence of new adaptively integrated genotypes, and appearance of at least new races, or of new species and genera. The time required by mesoevolutionary changes is mostly greater than human life span. However, in some instances changes of mesoevolutionary dimensions, or at least on the borderline between micro- and mesoevolution, may be rapid enough to be studied by human observers. Breeding new varieties of domestic animals and plants proved, when analyzed by modern methods of population genetics, to involve in some cases more profound genetic alterations than formerly supposed. In these cases, selection has led not merely to changes in individual genes or in groups of genes with additive effects, but, as shown by LERNER (1950) and LERNER and DEMPSTER (1951), to construction of new integrated genotypes and to shifts in « genetic homeostasis ». Similarly far-reaching genotypic reconstructions are indicated in the irradiated populations of *Drosophila* studied by WALLACE and collaborators (1953). Experimental analysis of the heterosis connected with chromosomal inversions in natural populations of *Drosophila* permits a comparative study of microevolutionary and mesoevolutionary phenomena.

The beginnings of this story were reported to the 8th International Congress of Genetics in Stockholm. In brief, the situation, as seen in the light of the recent studies of da CUNHA, HEUTS, LEVENE, LEVITAN, PAVLOVSKY, SPIESS, TOWNSEND, WALLACE, the writer, and several others, is as follows. Most natural populations of *Drosophila pseudoobscura* and of some other species of *Drosophila* are polymorphic with respect to the gene arrangement in their chromosomes. Several variants of a given chromosome, differing in inversions of blocks of genes, coexist in many populations. The carriers of these chromosomal variants interbreed freely; inversion heterozygotes and homozygotes occur with frequencies characteristic of HARDY's equilibrium.*

Inversion heterozygotes, in which the two chromosomes of a pair are derived from the population of any one locality, usually exhibit heterosis; the adaptive values of such heterozygotes are superior to those of the corresponding homozygotes. The heterosis can be demonstrated in experiments on artificial populations, kept under controlled conditions in population cages. In such populations, the relative frequencies of the chromosomes with different gene arrangements may undergo rapid changes; the changes lead to the establishment of equilibria, at which the competing gene arrangements continue to occur in the populations, with frequencies that reflect the relative adaptive values of the heterozygotes and homozygotes.

Chromosomes with a given gene arrangement often occur over extensive territories. Thus, Standard (ST) chromosomes occur along the Pacific Coast from British Columbia to Lower California; Arrowhead (AR) chromosomes extend from British Columbia to Texas and northern Mexico; Chiricahua (CH) are found from the Pacific Northwest to central Mexico, etc. Under a microscope, chromosomes of different geographic origin are indistinguishable, provided, of course, that they have the same gene arrangement. The effects of geographically different chromosomes on the adaptive properties of their carriers may however be quite distinct. The experiments with population cages were made originally using ST, AR, and CH chromosomes derived from flies collected in a locality Piñon Flats, on Mount San Jacinto, in California. Heterosis was observed in all experiments, and adaptive values of the homo- and heterozygotes were calculated from the data. Next, experiments were made using ST, AR, and CH chromosomes from Keen Camp, a locality only 15 miles from Piñon Flats, and from Mather, in Sierra Nevada, between 300 and 400 miles distant. Heterosis was again observed, but the adaptive values of the various genotypes proved to be different for each locality. It is the gene complex contained in the

---

* Deviations from the equilibrium proportions have been observed in some populations; these deviations are due to differential mortality between the egg and the adult stage, caused by natural selection. But selection may operate also through differential fecundity, varying sexual activity, and other differences between the competing genotypes which do not lead to differential mortality. Such selection leads to no deviations from HARDY's equilibrium ratios, and natural populations, in which these ratios are undistrurbed, have been found.

chromosomes with a given gene arrangement, and not the position of these genes alone, that determines the fitness of the carriers of these chromosomes.

Further light on the situation is shed by experiments in which chromosomes with different gene arrangements and of different geographic origin compete in the same population cage. Here heterosis is no longer the rule. Only in some cages equilibria are eventually established; in such cages the heterozygotes formed by the chromosomes derived from geographically different populations are superior in fitness to the homozygotes. But in other experiments no equilibria appear, one of the competing chromosomal types tends to reach fixation, and the other is eliminated. Heterosis is evidently produced by interaction of the gene complexes carried in certain chromosomes.

Chromosomes with different gene arrangements which occur in any one population carry complexes of genes which have, through long continued natural selection, become coadapted to produce superior fitness in heterozygotes. Structural heterozygotes within a population consequently exhibit heterosis. But the processes of coadaptation have taken separate courses in different localities. In fact, unpublished experiments of Mr. Louis Levine show that the adaptive values of the inversion hetero- and homozygotes are determined by the genetic system as a whole, and not only by the genes which lie in the chromosomes in which the inversions occur. The genotype of a Mendelian population is a coadapted system. That allopatric populations of the same species may have differently integrated genotypes is strikingly apparent from the results of VETUKHOV (1953). VETUKHOV found that, although the F_1 hybrids between geographic populations of *Drosophila pseudoobscura* display a superior viability, the F_2 generation suffers a breakdown, with the viability falling below the P generation values.

The changes observed in experimental populations in which the chromosomes with different gene arrangements are of geographically uniform origin occur, then, on a microevolutionary level. These changes involve alterations only in the relative frequencies of coadapted gene complexes. But these gene complexes existed as such in the natural population from which the ancestors of the experimental flies have descended. The gene complexes, held together by the inversions, produce heterosis. In our experiments, some of the complexes become relatively more, and others less frequent with time, until they reach the equilibrium values set by the environmental conditions in which the experiments are conducted. In other words, only the relative frequencies of the genotypes present in a population, not the genotypes themselves, become altered.

The simplicity of these microevolutionary changes makes them easily reproducible. To be sure, SPIESS, DA CUNHA, and the present writer have shown that temperature and nutritional variables modify the fitness of the chromosomal types. But if the experiments are conducted with due precautions their outcomes are determinate. Fig. 1 diagrams the changes

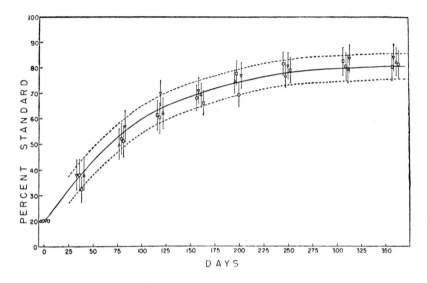

Fig. 1.

in the frequencies (in per cents) of ST chromosomes observed in four replicate experiments in which ST and CH chromosomes derived from the Piñon Flats, California, population were involved. From the data in Fig. 1 it can be computed that the adaptive values of the ST/ST, ST/CH, and CH/CH genotypes were in the ratios 0.90 : 1 : 0.41. The two dotted curves delimit the 95% confidence band for the changes expected in populations with such adaptive values. (These data will be presented in more detail in another publication).

A very different situation can be seen in Fig. 2, which shows the frequencies of ST chromosomes in six experimental populations where ST chromosomes from Piñon Flats, California, competed with CH chromosomes of Mexican origin. In these experiments the environmental conditions were controlled just as carefully as in those shown in Fig. 1, and in fact four of the experiments in Fg. 2 (those with initial frequencies of 20% of ST chromosomes) were conducted simultaneously with the four reported in Fig. 1. Nevertheless, the replicate experiments in which the intial populations were hybrids between the California and Mexico races of *Drosophila pseudoobscura* produced quite diversified results. No two of them were alike in the rates of the changes in the frequencies of ST and CH chromosomes.

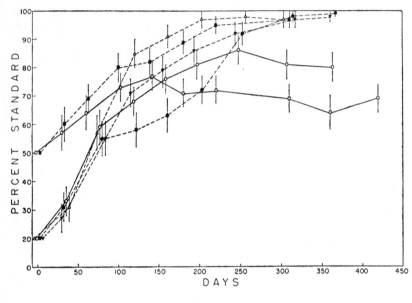

Fig. 2.

Some of the differences between the outcomes of the experiments summarized in Fig. 2 are, in fact, qualitative rather than quantitative. In two of the six populations equilibria were finally arrived at, and ST and CH chromosomes became stabilized at frequencies of about 70% ST-30% CH in one and about 80% ST-20% CH in the other population (see the solid lines in Fig. 2). In four populations no equilibria were attained, and the CH chromosomes appeared to have been well on the way to complete elimination when the experiments were terminated (see dashed lines in Fig. 2). Now, the establishment of an equilibrium means that the heterozygotes, ST/CH, have become heterotic, so that the adaptive values of the three chromosomal types are ST/CH>ST/ST> CH/CH. On the other hand, elimination of CH and fixation of ST mean that heterosis is absent, and the seriation of the adaptive values is ST/ST>ST/CH>CH/CH. A more detailed analysis of the data (to be published elsewhere) showèd an additional fact of interest. While in the populations of uniform geographic origin (Fig. 1) the adaptive values of the chromosomal types remain constant during the experiments, in the populations of mixed geographic origin they suffer alterations. The ST/CH heterozygotes were not heterotic in the foundation stocks of any of the six populations of mixed origin shown in Fig. 2. In two of these populations heterosis arose during the course of the experiments.

Fig. 3 summarizes the data for other experimental populations. In these populations, CH chromosomes derived from the population of Mather, California, competed with AR chromosomes from Mono Lake (California), from Lehman Caves National Monument (Nevada), from Bryce National Park (Utah), and from Ferron (Utah). Previous experiments showed that populations with CH and AR chromosomes from Mather reach equilibria at which CH and AR are about equal in frequency. This means that the AR/CH heterozygotes are heterotic, and that the seriation of the adaptive values is AR/CH>AR/AR = CH/CH. The outcomes of the experiments are quite different if AR chromosomes from Mather are replaced by those from the other localities named above. Fig. 3 shows that the frequencies of AR chromosomes rose at first rapidly, and rather uniformly, in all four populations. But while in three of the experiments the AR chromosomes tended to reach fixation (the dashed lines), in the fourth experiment (in which AR chromosomes came from the Lehman Caves population) an equilibrium was eventually reached at a level of somewhat more than 70% AR and somewhat less than 30% CH (the solid line in Fig. 3). In the three former experiments the AR/CH genotype was not heterotic, while in the fourth experiment heterosis has evolved. That heterosis was not present in the fourth experimental population from the start is strongly suggested by the fact that the AR chromosomes first reached the level of 83%, and then declined to only about 72%. This decline is quite significant statistically. The seriation of the adaptive values in this population has become AR/CH>AR/AR>CH/CH, while in the other three populations it remained AR/AR>AR/CH>CH/CH.

The genetic mechanisms which bring about the development of heterosis in some geographically mixed experimental populations but not in others are apparently as follows. Although there is no way at present to determine in how many genes the geographic strains of *Drosophila pseudoobscura* usually differ, one may surmise that this number is large, probably in the hundreds. The gene recombination which occurs in the populations of geographically mixed origin produces a great variety of genotypes. Even taking linkage into consideration, the number of genotypes that could arise with only 50 gene differences would be far greater than the number of individuals in all the populations combined.

Now, some of the gene combinations formed doutless possess higher

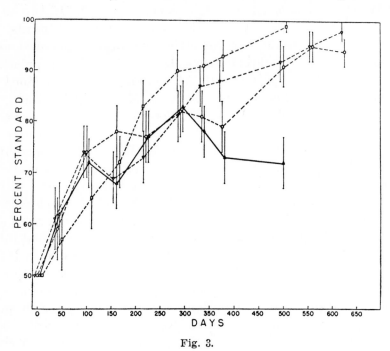

Fig. 3.

adaptive values than others. Natural selection in the experimental populations is very rigorous. It perpetuates those components of the gene pool which make the population as a whole attain the highest degree of fitness easily accessible under existing environments. Heterosis is known to be a genetic mechanism which confers high fitness on a population, despite the production of some relatively poorly adapted homozygotes. Heterotic genotypes are, accordingly, selected in those populations in which they are formed from the genetic elements contributed by the race hybridization. In other populations such heterotic genotypes have not arisen since only a small fraction of the enormous number of potentially possible genotypes are realized in any one, or in all, popul-

ations. It may also be that in some populations chromosomally homozygous genotypes have appeared, which conferred on these populations a
degree of fitness even greater than that produced by heterosis associated
with the chromosomal inversions.

The relative indeterminacy of the outcomes of the experiments on
populations of geographically mixed origin is, then, significant. It shows
that the genetic events which took place in these populations surpass the
microevolutionary and attain the mesoevolutionary order of magnitude.

When the variety of genotypes which arise through recombination
is very large, high fitness may be attained by different genetic systems in
different populations. Moreover, natural selection may evolve quite new
adaptive genotypes, which were not present at all in the populations of
the ancestral geographic races. It is unlikely that these new genotypes
existed anywhere, and least of all in the territories geographically
intermediate between those in which the parental races occur. (Arizona
and New Mexico, which lie between California and the part of Mexico
from which the ancestors of our experimental populations were derived,
are occupied by a race of *Drosophila pseudoobscura* in which ST and CH
chromosomes are relatively rare). The evolutionary events observed in
the geographically mixed populations resulted in the origin of adaptive
novelties. New races have appeared, which are adapted, presumably each
in its own way, to their environment. This environment is, of course,
the one which obtains in the laboratory population cages.

It should be clearly understood that natural selection has brought
about the changes both in the experimental populations of geographically
uniform and in those of geographically mixed origin. But the nature of
the selective processes was different in the two kinds of populations. The
replicate populations of geographically uniform origin behaved quite
similarly. The outcome of the selection processes was determined by
the genetic composition of the foundation stocks in the populations, and
by the environment in which the experiments were conducted. The foundation stocks and the environment were also uniform in the replicate
populations of geographically mixed origin. (The possibility that new
genotypes occurred by mutation can not however be excluded). The
diversity of the outcomes in the replicate experiments was a consequence
of the complexity of the adaptive processes which took place.

Evolution is deterministic on the microevolutionary level. On this
level, it is brought about by relatively simple physiological causes. The
carriers of some of the genotypes present in the foundation stock, or
formed by mutation, survive and reproduce more successfully in certain

environments than do carriers of other genotypes. When the evolutionary process reaches the meso- and macroevolutionary levels, mutation, gene recombination due to sexual reproduction, and selection remain, of course, operative. But at these levels, it is the historical sequence and the order of accumulation of the genetic changes which become progressively more and more important. Evolution becomes more and more creative as it ceases to be primarily a physiological and grows to be a historical process.

The relative indeterminacy of the outcomes of the experiments on populations of geographically mixed origins can be described as due to chance. The number of different gene combinations that may be formed is enormous, the populations are relatively small, hence a particular gene combination may appear in some populations and not in others. Many people doubt whether the operation of « blind chance » can be a basis of a creative process. FISHER (1950) gives an argument in favor of the opposite view. In FISHER'S words, « natural causation has a creative aspect.... because it has a casual aspect.... Looking back at a cause we can recognize it as creative; it has brought about something which could not have been predicted — something which can not be referred back to antecedent events. Looking forward to it as a future event, there is in it something which we can recognize as casual. It is viewed thus like the result of a game of chance; we can imagine ourselves able to foresee all its forms, and to state in advance the probability that each will occur. We can no longer imagine ourselves capable of foreseeing just which of them will occur ». MILLER (1946, 1948) has discussed the same idea in a more strictly philosophical context.

Quite regardless of any « casual » aspects that evolution may have, mesoevolution and macroevolution are creative also in a very different sense. A living organism resembles a work of art, and the evolutionary process resembles the creation of a work of art. Here we face a paradox. On the physiological level, every genotype that exists or that may be formed is a result of a chance combination of genes, of a throw of genetic dice, as it were. But the genotypes that are compounded by natural selection owe their existence to something very different from chance, namely to their fitness to maintain life. On the historical level, a genotype is not a product of chance but of adaptive integration.

In an organism, as in a work of art, one apprehends an internal coherence. This coherence is what gives life to an organism, and meaning or function to a work of art. The production of a work of art is a creative process because it involves a risk of ending in failure or yielding a miscreation. The same is true of the evolutionary process taken as a whole. The genotypes of living species are the end results on our time level of sequences of historical changes. These changes were such that the carriers of the entire series of ancestral genotypes remained in rapport with their environments. But the congruity with the environment is by no means guaranteed to the future states of the genotype by its present structure. Mutation and gene recombination constantly beget genotypes which never existed before, and which accordingly have not passed the trials by natural selection. Many of the novel genotypes are unfit for survival; most of the phyletic lines which existed in the past led to extinction and not to the now existing life. These phyletic lines were evolutionary blind alleys. This does not not make sense to a preformist theory of evolution, but it is understandable if evolution is a natural creative process.

Acknowledgments

The experimental work which is the basis of this article has been carried out in association with Mrs. OLGA PAVLOVSKY, whose conscientious assistance is gratefully acknowledged. The interpretation of the data has been discussed with many colleagues who, although in no way responsible for its flaws, have greatly contributed to its formulation; the writer is obliged especially to Drs. L. C. DUNN, H. L. CARSON, I. M. LERNER, HOWARD LEVENE, E. MAYR, D. L. MILLER, J. T. PATTERSON, G. L. STEBBINS, WILSON STONE, and BRUCE WALLACE.

LITERATURE CITED

DOBZHANSKY TH., 1949. — *Observations and experiments on natural selection in* Drosophila. Proc. Eight Internat. Congress Genetics, Hereditas, Supl., 210-224.

—, 1951. — *Genetics and the origin of species.* 3rd Edit., Columbia University Press, New York.

DOBZHANSKY Th., and O. A. PAVLOVSKY, 1953. — *Indeterminate outcome of certain experiments on* Drosophila *populations.* Evolution (in press).

FISHER R. A., 1950. — *Creative aspects of natural law.* Cambridge University Press, Cambridge.

LERNER I. M., 1950. — *Population genetics and animal improvement.* Cambridge University Press, Cambridge.

LERNER I. M. and E. DEMPSTER, 1948. — *Some aspects of evolutionary theory in the light of recent work on animal breeding*. Evolution, *2:* 19-28.

MILLER D. L., 1946. — *The meaning of evolution*. Amer. Scientist, *34:* 246-250.

—, 1948. — *The effect of the concept of evolution on scientific methodology*. Philosophy of Science, *15:* 52-60.

VETUKHOV M., 1953. — *Viability of hybrids between local populations of* Drosophila pseudoobscura. Proc. Nat. Acad. Sci., *93:* 30-34.

WALLACE B., KING J. C., MADDEN C. V., KAUFMANN B., and E. C. MC GUNNIGLE, 1953. — *An analysis of variation arising through recombination*. Genetics (in press).

WALLACE B., and C. V. MADDEN, 1953. — *The frequencies of sub- and supervitals in experimental populations of* Drosophila melanogaster. Genetics (in press).

THE THEORY OF ADAPTIVE POLYMORPHISM

A. J. CAIN AND P. M. SHEPPARD

Department of Zoology, and Genetics Laboratory, University of Oxford

Dobzhansky (especially 1951) has proposed the theory that polymorphism as such is frequently adaptive. He states (1951, p. 123) that if of two inversions coexisting in the same population one is found to be favored by selection in summer and the other in winter, then populations with both inversions will be at an advantage to populations with only one, because these will be at a disadvantage either in summer or in winter according to which inversion is present. He suggests that polymorphism will enable a species to exploit the environment more efficiently. Consequently, widespread species occurring in many habitats should be more polymorphic than those with restricted ranges. He produces evidence that this is so by comparing several species of Drosophila.

While this interesting theory may be correct, it seems that much more experimental evidence is required to support it, for the following reasons:

(1) It is not easy to understand what is meant by one population being at an advantage or being more highly adapted to a particular environment, compared with another, and no sufficiently detailed definition has yet been made. Dobzhansky has stated (1949, p. 132; 1951, p. 123) that when there is balanced polymorphism, with heterozygotes at an advantage, in a population, the "average adaptive value" ($\bar{w}$) of the population is at a maximum when equilibrium is reached. Consequently selection acts in such a way as to produce the maximum adaptive value in the population. This wording certainly suggests that a population in genetic equilibrium with heterozygotes at an advantage is in some way highly adapted. But it appears from his definition of adaptive value (1951, p. 116) that what is meant by this expression is selective value. The apparent use of "adaptation" as a synonym for "selection" does not seem to be in accordance with general practice (Darwin, 1859, and autobiography in F. Darwin, 1888; Fisher, 1930; Sommerhof, 1950). Adaptation (that is, fitness for a particular function in a particular environment) is a much wider concept than selection and can in many instances be measured by methods which involve no reference to selection coefficients. Moreover, the selection coefficient for any one gene expresses (in terms of progeny) the net effect of all the different se-

Reprinted by permission of THE AMERICAN NATURALIST from THE AMERICAN NATURALIST, **88**, 321–326 (1954).

lection pressures acting on the various effects of that gene. Consequently it can be at best only a poor estimate of the degree of adaptation produced by any one of these effects. In *Primula vulgaris*, Crosby (1949) has shown that a "gene" can spread because of an immediate intraspecific advantage (efficiency of pollination of its own and other mating types) which nevertheless produces not only a decrease in viability but also an inevitable destruction (at least in part) of an outbreeding mechanism. Clearly the selection coefficient for this gene is not a good estimate of the adaptation allowing pollen grains from plants carrying it to achieve successful fertilization in competition with other pollen grains (if this can be called an adaptation) since it takes account also of the reduced viability. Moreover, it gives no indication of the breakdown of the outbreeding mechanism which could well involve the extinction of the population. The spread by selection of such unfavorable gene-complexes has been treated in general terms by Fisher (1941).

When "adaptive value" is replaced in Dobzhansky's definitions by selective value, it is seen that his conclusion means that selection will alter the gene (or inversion) frequencies in such a way that there will be a stable equilibrium if the heterozygotes are at an advantage compared with the homozygotes, or fixation of that gene (or inversion) the homozygote of which has an advantage over the other genotypes. This is, of course, correct, but tells us nothing about the adaptation of the population concerned.

Indeed, until a precise definition of adaptation and advantage as referring to populations has been made, it will be impossible to devise experiments or collect data which will confirm or refute the hypothesis unambiguously. The consequences of different definitions are very diverse. For example (to take only two of the possible definitions), if those populations more likely to persist through environmental changes are considered to be the better adapted, then we should investigate the degree of variability in general (not only of polymorphism) and determine which populations are more likely to produce suitable genotypes when conditions change. But two populations may be exploiting (in some sense) their present environments identically in every way, and yet one may be more likely to survive than the other if it has a greater reserve of genetical variation. Consequently the present ecological state of each population cannot be taken as an indication of probable persistence. On the other hand, those populations which maintain a greater density per unit area under the same environmental conditions may be considered better adapted. If there is variation in density from population to population under the same conditions, then obviously the individuals of the different populations must be reacting differently to these conditions. This fact, of course, tells us almost nothing about the different probabilities of persistence of different populations. On this definition it would be necessary to show that the existence of polymorphism in some populations is actually the cause of their having a high density, which can happen only if the genes controlling the polymorphism are counteracting negatively density dependent factors (Haldane, 1953).

The behavior of genotypes competing in the same population gives no direct evidence on the ability of separate populations each homozygous for one of the alternative genotypes, to survive in the wild. A particular allelomorph may even be inviable when homozygous in the presence of an alternative allelomorph, as for example if more rapidly growing larvae eat so much more food that the slower growers are unable to get enough to bring them to pupation. Yet the disadvantageous homozygote (producing slow growth) may be perfectly viable as a pure stock in the wild; in fact, for equal numbers of eggs, more of the slow-growing stock may reach maturity than of a stock of rapid growers. On the other hand, a particular homozygote may be at an extreme disadvantage because of extensive dislocations of its structure and physiology that result from homozygosity, irrespective of what genotypes may be coexisting with it in the same population. In this situation the selection coefficient relative to other genotypes does give a rough measure of the homozygote's chances of survival in pure cultures. But a mere inspection of selective values of different genotypes in the same population does not allow one to distinguish between these two types of situation. Consequently, if in the presence of AR chromosomes in *Drosophila pseudoobscura*, ST chromosomes are at a selective advantage during the hot part of the year, and at a disadvantage during the cool part, this cannot be taken to mean that therefore a population containing only ST chromosomes will be in any sense at a disadvantage to others with both during the cold season. It is a matter for further experimental investigation to determine whether they are or not.

(2) If the suggestion (Dobzhansky, 1951, p. 110) that polymorphism within a single breeding community increases "the efficiency of the exploitation of the resources of the environment by the living matter" is correct, then in some sense polymorphic populations could be considered as better adapted than monomorphic ones. But this suggestion rests on an extension of Gause's principle to genotypes within the same population, an extension which needs careful examination. The analogy between species and genotypes certainly appears unsatisfactory in systems involving balanced polymorphism with heterozygotes at an advantage, in which several genotypes of different selective values do in fact continue to coexist in the same population and environment, although they appear on Dobzhansky's hypothesis to correspond to species as closely related as possible, which according to Gause should be unable to coexist. Moreover, the situation is unlike any contemplated by Gause, since any one of the "species" can appear amongst the progeny of the other two.

If on the other hand, genes (or inversions) are considered as corresponding to species, then in balanced polymorphism the allelomorphs concerned have the same selective value when in equilibrium, whereas the whole point of Gause's principle is that two species will not have or will not maintain the same efficiency in the same environment and will not arrive at a state of stable equilibrium. If it be claimed that an allelomorph in a homozygote is in a different environment from the same allelomorph in a heterozygote, then the proposed extension of Gause's principle may perhaps be acceptable. Even so, it still remains to be shown that there is in fact any increase in efficiency of exploitation of the external environment by reason of the polymorphism. Dobzhansky remarks (1951, p. 110), "A single genotype, no matter how versatile, could hardly function with maximal efficiency in all environments. Hence, natural selection has preserved a variety of genotypes, more or less specialized to render the organism efficient in a certain range of the existing environments." But this is to assume the conclusion. Is it true that the different genotypes in stably polymorphic populations are exploiting the external environment in even slightly different ways? This again is a matter for ecological research not for *a priori* genetical deduction.

(3) Dobzhansky and his colleagues have shown in some species of Drosophila that common and wide-ranging species tend to possess both a greater diversity of chromosomal inversions and a higher frequency of them in each population investigated, than closely related species which are more restricted in range and less abundant. These interesting and important facts have been interpreted as evidence that "the more polymorphic a species is, the more environments it can use or control" (Dobzhansky, Burla and da Cunha, 1950; see also Dobzhansky, 1951, p. 133). This could mean either (a) that a more polymorphic species can extend its range into a greater number of regions which differ considerably ecologically, or (b) that it can utilize a greater range of materials and conditions at any one place or, of course, both.

The greater polymorphism of the more widely ranging forms could however be the result, not the cause, of the range inhabited. In breeding communities in different environments different inversions are likely to be favored when they arise, and therefore a greater degree of polymorphism may be produced in wide-ranging species than in geographically restricted ones. In the most widespread and abundant species the chances that a generally advantageous inversion will arise are greatest; such inversions may then spread through the range of the species, increasing the number of kinds of inversion at any one locality. Consequently, the facts elucidated by Dobzhansky need not necessarily be regarded as supporting his hypothesis. Furthermore, it is known that some wide-ranging and common species have almost no inversions in wild populations, so that comparisons between different species, which may have very different capacities for variation in this respect, should be treated with reserve, as da Cunha *et al.* (1953) have pointed out.

The alternative hypothesis, that a polymorphic species can exploit (in some sense) a greater range of materials or conditions at any one locality, is also not necessarily supported by Dobzhansky's evidence, which consists only of information on distribution and frequencies of particular inversions. Polymorphism may be maintained by the superior viability or fertility for example of the heterozygotes, quite independent of heterogeneities in the immediate environment.

Allison (1954) has shown that in regions where malaria caused by *Plasmodium falciparum* is common, the gene producing sickle-cell is also common.   The reason is that in these areas, while the homozygote (si si) is highly disadvantageous because it produces sickle-cell anemia, and the normal homozygote (Si Si) is liable to severe attacks of malaria, the heterozygote is comparatively free from these disadvantages.   Obviously, if the sickle-cell homozygote were not so disadvantageous, the gene would merely spread throughout these areas exactly as genes producing industrial melanic forms have done in Lepidoptera (Ford, 1953).   The polymorphism is a result not of heterogeneities in the environment within malaria-infested regions but of the relative effect of the sickle-cell gene upon the individual, when homozygous and when heterozygous.

Da Cunha (1951) found that the relative selective values of the homo- and heterozygotes for some inversions in *Drosophila pseudoobscura* vary greatly according to the species of yeast or bacteria given as food.   But in several cases, the polymorphism was maintained by selective superiority of the heterozygotes even when only one food-species was present.   Moreover, it appears that all the food-species were eaten by all the chromosomal types. There seems no reason to believe that a pure stock of one chromosomal type could not maintain itself successfully on any or all of the food-species, but da Cunha's experiments were not designed to investigate this point. Consequently there is no evidence either way as to whether the effect of the chromosomal polymorphism in this example is to increase "the efficiency of the exploitation of the resources of the environment."

Dobzhansky and his colleagues have also shown that, in some species of Drosophila at least, polymorphism decreases towards the edges of the range, and is greatest where the greatest diversity of foods may be expected to occur (da Cunha, Burla and Dobzhansky, 1950).   This may mean only that towards the edges of the range selection is more stringent and fewer inversions are able to maintain themselves.   But in any case, no evidence that selection is affecting the degree of polymorphism in different populations is really relevant for the discussion of the hypothesis.   It is necessary in all cases to show whether the presence of polymorphism is really affecting the adaptedness of the populations concerned (in whichever sense this may be defined in future).

SUMMARY

The hypothesis of adaptive polymorphism as proposed by Dobzhansky cannot as yet be considered well established.   It is generally agreed that genetical variability enables a species to evolve in response to changes. Dobzhansky has made the important suggestion that variability also allows a population to exploit a constant, or a changing, environment more efficiently than a single genotype could do.   Consequently he believes that arrangements which maintain variability, notably balanced polymorphism, give the populations in which they occur an adaptive superiority over others.

However, it appears that by adaptive polymorphism is usually meant only polymorphism maintained by selection.   Such polymorphism can occur in a population without affecting its adaptation.   The relative adaptive

119

value of populations is a very difficult concept which has not been clearly defined. Observations on relative coefficients of selection of different polymorphs within a population give no direct evidence on the ability of any one polymorph to survive as a pure stock. And further, the evidence which has been adduced to support the hypothesis is capable of different interpretations. In no case has direct evidence been obtained that different polymorphs in a population are in any sense exploiting the environment in different ways, and thereby affecting the adaptedness of the population significantly.

ACKNOWLEDGEMENTS

We are very grateful to Dr. E. B. Ford, F.R.S., for detailed criticism of the manuscript, and to Professor Th. Dobzhansky, Professor Sir Ronald Fisher, F.R.S., and Professor J. B. S. Haldane, F.R.S., for valuable comments. One of us (P. M. Sheppard) is indebted to the Nuffield Foundation for their generous support.

LITERATURE CITED

Allison, A. C., 1954, Protection afforded by sickle-cell trait against subtertian malarial infection. Brit. Med. J., 1954 1: 290–294.
Crosby, J. L., 1949, Selection of an unfavorable gene-complex. Evolution, 3: 212–230.
Da Cunha, A. B., 1951, Modification of the adaptive values of chromosomal types in Drosophila pseudoobscura by nutritional variables. Evolution, 5: 395–404.
Da Cunha, A. B., D. Brncic, and F. M. Salzano, 1953, A comparative study of chromosomal polymorphism in certain South American species of Drosophila. Heredity, 7: 193–202.
Da Cunha, A. B., H. Burla and Th. Dobzhansky, 1950, Adaptive chromosomal polymorphism in Drosophila willistoni. Evolution, 4: 212–235.
Darwin, C., 1859, On the origin of species by means of natural selection, etc. London: Murray.
Darwin, F., 1888, The life and letters of Charles Darwin including an autobiographical chapter. London: Murray.
Dobzhansky, Th., 1949, Review and perspectives of the symposium on ecological and genetic factors of speciation and evolution. La Ricerca Scientifica, Supplement 1949: 128–135.
    1951, Genetics and the origin of species. 3rd ed. New York: Columbia University Press.
Dobzhansky, Th., H. Burla and A. B. da Cunha, 1950, A comparative study of chromosomal polymorphism in sibling species of the willistoni group of Drosophila. Amer. Nat., 84: 229–246.
Fisher, R. A., 1930, The genetical theory of natural selection. London: Oxford University Press.
    1941, Average excess and average effect of a gene substitution. Ann. Eugen. 11: 53–63.
Ford, E. B., 1953, The genetics of polymorphism in the Lepidoptera. Advances in Genetics, 5: 43–87.
Haldane, J. B. S., 1953, Animal populations and their regulation. New Biology (Penguin Books), 15: 9–24.
Sommerhof, G., 1950, Analytical biology. London: Oxford University Press.

ADAPTIVE AND SELECTIVE VALUE

A. J. CAIN AND P. M. SHEPPARD

Department of Zoology, and Genetics Laboratory, University of Oxford

We are glad that Li (1955) has entirely confirmed our conclusions (1954) as to the uselessness of w in comparing populations, and of selection co-efficients of alternatives within a population for estimating the adaptive-ness of populations homozygous for one alternative. Nevertheless, he asserts that we have deeply misunderstood the analytical method employed in gene frequency analysis. However, his comments clearly indicate that he has himself misunderstood our paper. He agrees that a standardisation of terms and avoidance of loose language is desirable, but overlooks the fact that it is *not* true that one word is as good as another if precisely defined; that depends on the accepted usages of the words in question. No one is going to say that we may as well call men fruitflies if the terms are defined precisely enough; and one of our points is that adaptation has had on the vast majority of occasions a useful meaning quite different from that of selection, that the use of adaptive value for selective value (or selection coefficient, or its derivatives) now leads to serious confusion, and that it is precisely this confusion that has led Dobzhansky to put forward the arguments which we have criticised, in which criticism Li himself supports us.

Li's misunderstanding is clearly seen in his treatment of the isolated sentence which he quotes from our paper and decorates with wrongly-placed italics. If italics are necessary, they should be used for the word "seems". We are commenting in this sentence that Dobzhansky, by using the word

Reprinted by permission of THE AMERICAN NATURALIST from THE AMERICAN NATURALIST, 90, 202–203 (1956).

adaptive where selective is appropriate, *seems* (we do not wish to be dogmatic) to believe that populations with a high value of $\overline{w}$ are necessarily more highly adapted in the usual sense of the word than those with a low value. This comment seems justified because Dobzhansky (1951, p. 123) does use selection coefficients of alternatives within a population to draw conclusions as to homozygous populations being at a disadvantage, which only makes sense if he considers that these selection coefficients do necessarily give information on the *adaptedness* to a given environment of the alternatives taken separately. We are disagreeing with this view.

A similar misunderstanding is the basis of Li's remark that our "grasp of the intra-population selection concept is somewhat incomplete" on the grounds that no selection coefficient ever gives information on the ability to survive of homozygous populations, whereas we have said that "a particular homozygote may be at an extreme disadvantage because of extensive dislocations of its structure and physiology that result from homozygosity, irrespective of what genotypes may be coexisting with it in the same population. In this situation the selection coefficient relative to other genotypes does give a rough measure of the homozygote's chances of survival in pure cultures." The example given by Li to disprove this assertion proves nothing either way; the sort of disability we were referring to was failure to hatch from the egg at all, *irrespective of what other genotypes may be in the population*. But, as we point out immediately after the quotation given above, a mere inspection of selective values does not allow one to recognise such a situation. What is necessary is both the selective value and information on the effects of the gene or inversion in question.

LITERATURE CITED

Cain, A. J. and Sheppard, P. M., 1954, The theory of adaptive polymorphism. Amer. Nat., 88: 321-326.

Li, C. C., 1955, The stability of an equilibrium and the average fitness of a population. Amer. Nat., 89: 281-295.

A. J. CAIN
P. M. SHEPPARD

DEPT. OF ZOOLOGY,
  UNIVERSITY MUSEUM, OXFORD
    January 17, 1956

THE STABILITY OF AN EQUILIBRIUM AND THE AVERAGE FITNESS OF A POPULATION

C. C. LI

Graduate School of Public Health, University of Pittsburgh

INTRODUCTION

Under a certain scheme of selection, a Mendelian population may reach an equilibrium condition other than complete homozygosis. The selection pressure is usually measured by the amount of change or "increment" in gene frequency (Δq = new q − old q) per generation. It has been noted that certain equilibrium values of q, as given by the condition $\Delta q = 0$, are stable or unstable. The nature of the stability of an equilibrium may be investigated as follows:

When Δq is positive, the value of q is increasing; if negative, q decreasing. Assume that Δq is a continuous function of q, as is the case usually. Let a and b be two values of q with a<b and Δa and Δb the values of Δq for a and b. Then if Δa is positive and Δb is negative, there exists at least one stable equilibrium value of q in the interval (a, b). Conversely, if Δa is negative and Δb is positive, there exists at least one unstable equilibrium in the region (a, b). Therefore, the number and nature of the equilibrium values will be revealed by plotting the value of Δq against those of q in the range (0, 1).

So far it sounds as if the stability of an equilibrium were solely determined by the expression Δq =a function of q. While this is undoubtedly true, it tells us very little about the meaning of a stable or unstable equilibrium except purely as an algebraic consequence of the expression for Δq. The primary purpose of the following sections is to view the stability from another angle—that of the average fitness of the population as a whole. Many of the points to be made have been discussed earlier by Professor Sewall Wright in connection with one subject or another. It seems, however, that stable equilibria are better understood than the unstable ones. What is the relationship between an unstable equilibrium and the fitness of the population? What does "unstable" mean in terms of the selection effect? In order to discuss these questions in the simplest manner, we begin with the case of two alleles and then proceed to examine briefly some other cases.

TWO ALLELES, CONSTANT SELECTIVE VALUES

Let p and q be the frequencies of the alleles A_1 and A_2, respectively, in a random mating population (p + q = 1). Further, let W_{11}, W_{12}, W_{22} be the relative selective values of the genotypes A_1A_1, A_1A_2, A_2A_2, whose propor-

Reprinted by permission of THE AMERICAN NATURALIST from THE
AMERICAN NATURALIST, 89, 281–295 (1955).

tions (f) in the population are p^2, $2pq$, q^2, respectively. The W's are assumed to be independent of the gene frequencies. Then, the *average* "fitness" of the population is

$$\overline{W} = \Sigma fW = p^2 W_{11} + 2pq W_{12} + q^2 W_{22}, \tag{1}$$

and the slope of the $\overline{W}$ curve (with respect to q) is

$$\frac{d\overline{W}}{dq} = \Sigma W \frac{df}{dq} = 2 \{-pW_{11} + (1 - 2q)W_{12} + q W_{22}\}. \tag{2}$$

The change in q per generation due to selection is thus (Wright, 1942)

$$\Delta q = \frac{pqW_{12} + q^2 W_{22}}{\overline{W}} - q$$

$$= \frac{pq}{2\overline{W}} \frac{d\overline{W}}{dq}. \tag{3}$$

Thus, we see that with fixed values of the W's, the equilibrium condition $\Delta q = 0$ is equivalent to the condition $d\overline{W}/dq = 0$, ignoring the trivial cases $q = 0$ or 1. It follows that the equilibrium values as given by the roots of the equation $\Delta q = 0$ correspond to a maximum or minimum point of the $\overline{W}$ curve (1). Putting the expression (2) equal to zero and solving, we obtain (Fisher, 1930, p. 101; Crow, 1952)

$$\hat{q} = \frac{(W_{11} - W_{12})}{(W_{11} - W_{12}) + (W_{22} - W_{12})}. \tag{4}$$

This is the most general solution for equilibrium gene frequency (other than 0 or 1) in the case of two alleles. In order that $0 < \hat{q} < 1$, the two differences $(W_{11} - W_{12})$ and $(W_{22} - W_{12})$ must be both negative or both positive. In other words, for an equilibrium value between 0 and 1 to exist, the selective value of the heterozygote must be greater, or less, than that of either homozygote.

As to the nature of the stability of an equilibrium, we find

$$\frac{d^2 \overline{W}}{dq^2} = 2 [(W_{11} - W_{12}) + (W_{22} - W_{12})].$$

If this value is negative, the point (4) yields a maximum of $\overline{W}$. If positive, a minimum. The $\overline{W}$ curve, as well as the values of Δq, for the two cases, are represented in Figures 1 and 2. Since the effect of selection is to increase the average fitness of a population, we reach the conclusion that a stable equilibrium value corresponds to a maximum point of the $\overline{W}$ curve and an unstable value corresponds to a minimum point of the $\overline{W}$ curve. From this viewpoint, the instability of an equilibrium becomes at once meaningful. An unstable equilibrium puts the population at a minimum fitness and the selection pressure constantly tends to raise the value of $\overline{W}$. Furthermore,

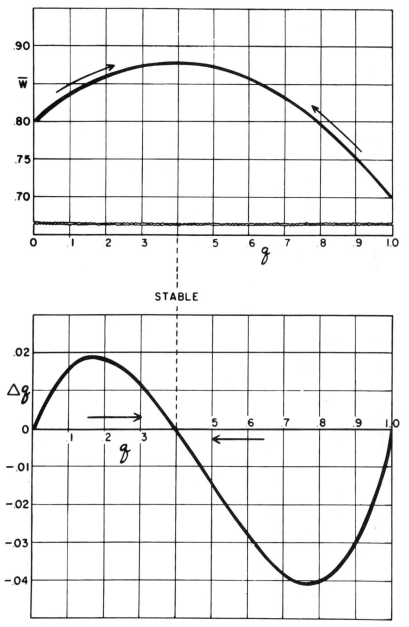

FIGURE 1. The selective values of AA, Aa, aa are assumed to be $W_{11} = .80$, $W_{12} = 1.00$, $W_{22} = .70$; the average fitness of the population is $\overline{W} = .8 + .4q - .5q^2$. The stable equilibrium point is at $\hat{q} = -2/(-2-3) = .40$, which yields a maximum value of $\overline{W}$.

125

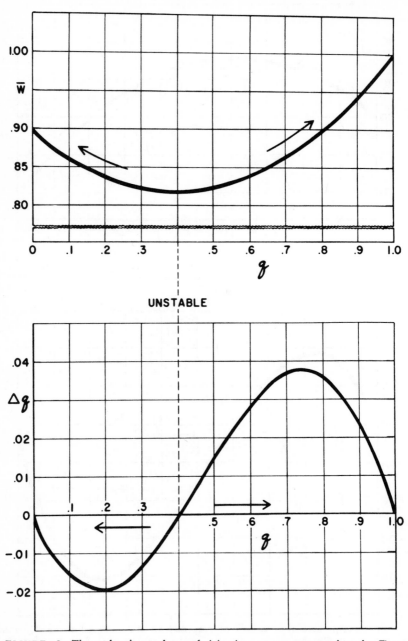

FIGURE 2. The selective values of AA, Aa, aa are assumed to be $W_{11} = .90$, $W_{12} = .70$, $W_{22} = 1.00$; the average fitness of the population is $\overline{W} = .9 - .4q + .5q^2$. The unstable equilibrium point is at $\hat{q} = 2/(2 + 3) = .40$, which yields a minimum value of $\overline{W}$.

for practical investigation, the plotting of the W curve is usually simpler than plotting the Δq curve. It seems that the $\overline{W}$ curve provides us an easy and meaningful method to determine the nature of an equilibrium.

MULTIPLE ALLELES

When there are more than two alleles, the situation becomes slightly more complicated. For the sake of simplicity and concreteness, the case of three alleles is chosen for discussion, although some obvious extensions can be made. In a random mating population let q_1, q_2, q_3 be the frequencies of the alleles A_1, A_2, A_3, respectively ($q_1 + q_2 + q_3 = 1$). The proportions and relative fitness of the genotypes are as follows:

	$A_1 A_1$	$A_1 A_2$	$A_1 A_3$	$A_2 A_2$	$A_2 A_3$	$A_3 A_3$
f:	q_1^2	$2q_1 q_2$	$2q_1 q_3$	q_2^2	$2q_2 q_3$	q_3^2
W:	W_{11}	W_{12}	W_{13}	W_{22}	W_{23}	W_{33}

Here, as before, the W's are assumed to be fixed values. Then

$$\overline{W} = \Sigma Wf = q_1 (q_1 W_{11} + q_2 W_{12} + q_3 W_{13})$$
$$+ q_2 (q_1 W_{12} + q_2 W_{22} + q_3 W_{23})$$
$$+ q_3 (q_1 W_{13} + q_2 W_{23} + q_3 W_{33})$$
$$= q_1 W_1 + q_2 W_2 + q_3 W_3 \tag{5}$$

where $W_1 = q_1 W_{11} + q_2 W_{12} + q_3 W_{13}$ may be defined as the weighted fitness of the *allele* A_1, etc. Taking $q_3 = 1 - q_1 - q_2$, $\overline{W}$ describes a surface over the $q_1 q_2$ – plane. The partial derivatives of $\overline{W}$ with respect to q_1 and q_2 are:

$$\frac{\partial \overline{W}}{\partial q_1} = 2 (W_1 - W_3), \quad \frac{\partial \overline{W}}{\partial q_2} = 2 (W_2 - W_3). \tag{6}$$

On the other hand, the increments of gene frequencies are (Wright, 1949):

$$\Delta q_1 = \frac{q_1}{\overline{W}} (W_1 - \overline{W}), \quad \Delta q_2 = \frac{q_2}{\overline{W}} (W_2 - \overline{W}). \tag{7}$$

Thus, the set of equations $\Delta q_i = 0$ is equivalent to the set $\partial \overline{W}/\partial q_i = 0$, both yielding the solution $W_1 = W_2 = W_3 = \overline{W}$. It follows that the equilibrium values $(\hat{q}_1, \hat{q}_2)$ correspond to maximum or minimum points on the $\overline{W}$ surface.

The values of $\hat{q}_1$ and $\hat{q}_2$ are functions of the W's. Writing out the equilibrium equations, we obtain immediately

$$\hat{q}_1 = \frac{D_1}{D}, \quad \hat{q}_2 = \frac{D_2}{D}, \tag{8}$$

where

$$D = \begin{vmatrix} (W_{33} - W_{13}) + (W_{11} - W_{13}), & (W_{12} - W_{23}) + (W_{33} - W_{13}) \\ (W_{33} - W_{23}) + (W_{12} - W_{13}), & (W_{22} - W_{23}) + (W_{33} - W_{23}) \end{vmatrix}$$

$$= \begin{vmatrix} W_{33} - W_{13}, & W_{12} - W_{23} \\ W_{33} - W_{23}, & W_{22} - W_{23} \end{vmatrix} + \begin{vmatrix} W_{11} - W_{13}, & W_{33} - W_{13} \\ W_{12} - W_{13}, & W_{33} - W_{23} \end{vmatrix} + \begin{vmatrix} W_{11} - W_{13}, & W_{12} - W_{23} \\ W_{12} - W_{13}, & W_{22} - W_{23} \end{vmatrix}$$

$$= D_1 \quad + \quad D_2 \quad + \quad D_3$$

These are identical with the expressions given by Levene, Pavlovsky, and Dobzhansky (1954, p. 342), despite their apparent different forms. The expressions (5), (6), (7), (8) of this section are analogous to (1), (2), (3), (4), respectively, of the previous section.

In the special case that all heterozygotes have the same fitness ($W_{12} = W_{13} = W_{23} = 1$) but homozygotes have a lower fitness value of $W_{ii} = 1 - s_i$, we have the stable equilibrium, corresponding to a maximum point of the $\overline{W}$ surface. The value of q_1 is

$$q_1 = \frac{\begin{vmatrix} s_3 & 0 \\ s_3 & s_2 \end{vmatrix}}{\begin{vmatrix} s_3 + s_1 & s_3 \\ s_3 & s_3 + s_2 \end{vmatrix}} = \frac{s_3 \, s_2}{s_3 s_2 + s_1 s_3 + s_1 s_2} = \frac{\dfrac{1}{s_1}}{\dfrac{1}{s_1} + \dfrac{1}{s_2} + \dfrac{1}{s_3}}, \qquad (9)$$

in agreement with the results of Wright (1949). Conversely, if $W_{ii} = 1 + s_i$, and $W_{ij} = 1$, the equilibrium point has the same value but the point is a minimum of the $\overline{W}$ surface and therefore the equilibrium is unstable.

It may also be shown that if a heterozygote (say, $A_1 A_2$) is not only superior in selective value to all homozygotes but also much superior to all other heterozygotes (i.e. $W_{12} > 1 + 2 s_1$), the population will eventually reach an equilibrium involving only alleles A_1 and A_2; the others will be eliminated (Wright, 1949, p. 372).

DIFFERENTIAL LOCAL SELECTIONS

Next, let us consider a large random mating population of which various portions are subject to differential selections. This is the case when more than one ecological niche is available in the area occupied by the population (Levene, 1953). Suppose that there are k types of niches or localities in the area, and each type has its own selection scheme. We assume, as did Levene, that after selection the survivors from the various niches form one random mating population, so that in the next generation the initial zygotic frequencies in each niche are all the same, viz., p^2, $2pq$, q^2, where q is the gene frequency of the entire population. Let $W_{11}^{(i)}$ be $W_{12}^{(i)}$, $W_{22}^{(i)}$ be the genotypic values in the i-th niche, $\overline{W}_i$ be the average fitness of this niche, and c_i the proportion of the total survivors to be found in this niche

($\Sigma c_i = 1$). Hence, after selection, the net total change in q for the entire population is

$$\Delta q = c_1 \Delta q_1 + \ldots + c_k \Delta q_k \qquad (10)$$

where Δq_i is the change in q in the i-th niche. Now for each niche, our fundamental formula (3) holds. Thus,

$$\Delta q = \frac{q(1-q)}{2} \left[\frac{c_1}{\overline{W}_1} \frac{d\overline{W}_1}{dq} + \ldots + \frac{c_k}{\overline{W}_k} \frac{d\overline{W}_k}{dq} \right]. \qquad (11)$$

On the other hand, if we define the average fitness of the entire population as,

$$\overline{W} = \overline{W}_1^{c_1} \overline{W}_2^{c_2} \ldots \overline{W}_k^{c_k}, \qquad (12)$$

then

$$L = \log \overline{W} = c_1 \log \overline{W}_1 + \ldots + c_k \log \overline{W}_k. \qquad (13)$$

Hence,

$$\Delta q = \frac{q(1-q)}{2} \frac{dL}{dq}. \qquad (14)$$

This is a general form of the expression given by Levene (1953) except that our q is his 1-q. When there is only one type of selection scheme for the entire population, (14) is identical with (3). Here, the equilibrium condition $\Delta q = 0$ (other than trivial cases) implies that $dL/dq = 0$, which, in turn, implies that $dW/dq = 0$. It follows that the equilibrium points, if existant, correspond to the maximum or minimum points in the $\overline{W}$ (or L) curve.

Two simple examples are given here to illustrate the various possibilities of such a selection scheme. One is taken from Levene (1953). Suppose that there are only two types of niches, in one of which the genotypic selection values are 2, 1, 1.1; and in the other, .5, 1, 1.1, so that $\overline{W}_1 = 2 - 2q + 1.1q^2$ and $\overline{W}_2 = .5 + q - .4q^2$. For the sake of simplicity, let us further assume that the survivor proportions $c_1 = c_2 = \frac{1}{2}$; thus, $\overline{W} = \sqrt{\overline{W}_1 \overline{W}_2}$ which is plotted in Fig. 3 together with corresponding values of Δq. It is seen that $\hat{q} = .40$, the stable equilibrium point, corresponds to a maximum point of the $\overline{W}$ curve, while the unstable point $\hat{q} = .65$ corresponds to a minimum point of the $\overline{W}$ curve.

As a second example, we may assume that in one set of niches the genotypic selection values are $.5 : 1 : .5$, and in the other $3 : 1 : 3$, so that $\overline{W}_1 = .5 + q(1-q)$ and $\overline{W}_2 = 3 - 4q(1-q)$. As before, taking $c_1 = c_2 = \frac{1}{2}$, $\overline{W} = \sqrt{\overline{W}_1 \overline{W}_2}$ which is plotted in Fig. 4. Here there are two stable equilibrium values at $\hat{q} = .146447$ and $\hat{q} = .853553$, and an unstable point at $\hat{q} = 50$. An example with three niches has been given by Li (1955, p. 265).

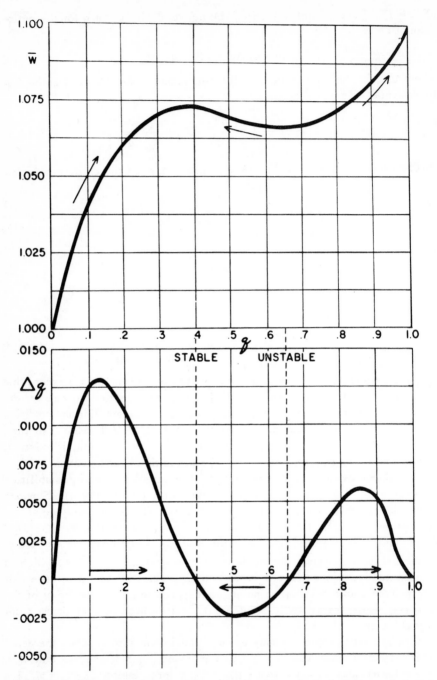

FIGURE 3. The genotypic selective values in one ecological niche are 2, 1, 1.1, and in the other .5, 1, 1.1. The average fitness of the entire population, assuming survivors from each niche to be equally numerous, is $\overline{W} = \overline{W_1}^{1/2}\,\overline{W_2}^{1/2}$. The stable equilibrium point is at $\hat{q} = .40$, yielding a maximum value of $\overline{W}$, and the unstable point is at $\hat{q} = .65$, yielding a minimum of $\overline{W}$.

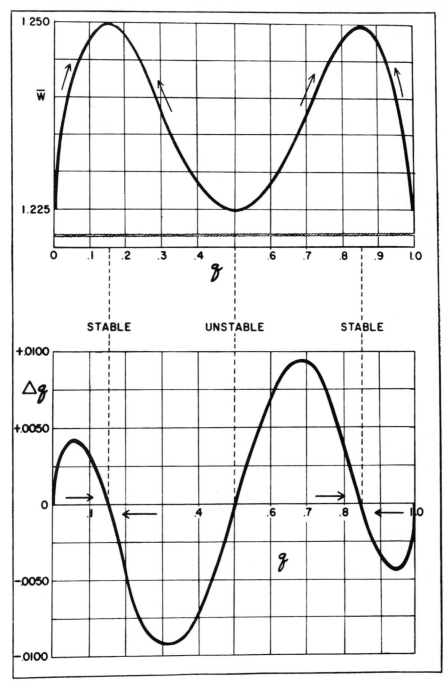

FIGURE 4. The genotypic selective values in one ecological niche are .50, 1.00, .50, and in the other 3, 1, 3. The average fitness of the entire population, assuming survivors from each niche to be equally numerous, is $\overline{W} = \overline{W}_1^{1/2} \overline{W}_2^{1/2} = [(.50 + pq)(3 - 4pq)]^{1/2}$. The two stable points are at $\hat{q} = .15$ and .85 approximately and the unstable point is at $\hat{q} = .50$.

VARIABLE SELECTIVE VALUES

In some cases, probably more often than we thought in natural populations, the genotypic selective values (W_{11}, W_{12}, W_{22}) are functions of gene frequencies themselves. In such a case our previous formulas no longer hold. If we still define the average fitness of the population as $\overline{W} = \Sigma fW$, then

$$\frac{d\overline{W}}{dq} = \Sigma W \frac{df}{dq} + \Sigma f \frac{dW}{dq}. \tag{15}$$

Note that the term on the right, $\Sigma f(dW/dq)$, is the average value of (dW/dq) of the various genotypes in the population and thus may be written $\overline{(dW/dq)}$. It measures the average effect of changing gene frequencies on the genotypic selective values (Wright, 1949, p. 375). This term of course vanishes when the W's are constants, whereupon (15) reduces to (2).

On the other hand, proceeding the same way as in deriving (3) and still assuming panmixia, we obtain (Wright, 1942, 1949)

$$\Delta q = \frac{q(1-q)}{2\overline{W}} \Sigma W \frac{df}{dq}. \tag{16}$$

It is noted that the equilibrium condition $\Delta q = 0$ here no longer implies that $d\overline{W}/dq = 0$; but, instead, implies that

$$g(q) = \Sigma W \frac{df}{dq} = \frac{d\overline{W}}{dq} - \overline{\left(\frac{dW}{dq}\right)} = 0. \tag{17}$$

In words this equation says: the equilibrium value of gene frequency should be such that its effect on the average fitness of the entire population is balanced by its average effect on the individual selective values. If we regard the W's as constant in any particular instant and define the average fitness as

$$G(q) = \int g(q)\, dq + \text{constant}, \tag{18}$$

then again the equilibrium values of q will correspond to the maximum or minimum points of the G curve, depending upon whether they are stable or unstable.

As an example we may cite the case of selection against heterozygotes born to recessive mothers with respect to the Rh locus in man. If the recessive mothers tend to compensate their loss by having more children (Glass, 1950), then we have (Li, 1953)

$$W_{11} = 1, \qquad W_{12} = 1 - \tfrac{1}{2}\,sq, \qquad W_{22} = 1 + tq(1-q)$$

where s and t are positive fractions, denoting the selection and compensation coefficients, respectively. Here

$$g(q) = -sq + 2(s+t)q^2 - 2tq^3, \tag{17'}$$

$$G(q) = 1 - \tfrac{1}{2}\,sq^2 + \tfrac{2}{3}\,(s+t)q^3 - \tfrac{1}{2}\,t\,q^4. \tag{18'}$$

When the G curves are plotted, it will be found that the unstable equilibrium values of q tabulated by Li (1953) are their minimum points.

POPULATIONS WITH INBREEDING

The genotypic frequencies of a population with an inbreeding coefficient F are $(1 - F)p^2 + Fp$, $2(1 - F)pq$, $(1 - F)q^2 + Fq$. The average fitness of the population is thus

$$\overline{W} = (1 - F)\overline{W}_R + F\,\overline{W}_I, \tag{19}$$

where $\overline{W}_R$ is the same as expression (1) and is the average fitness of the random component of the population, and $\overline{W}_I = pW_{11} + qW_{22}$ is the average fitness of the inbred component. The corresponding expression for Δq has been given by Wright (1942, 1949) and need not be repeated here. Suffice it to observe that the condition $\Delta q = 0$ does not imply $d\overline{W}/dq = 0$. However, if we give double weight to the selection effects on the inbred homozygotes and define a new average fitness as

$$\overline{W}' = (1 - F)\,\overline{W}_R + 2F\overline{W}_I, \tag{20}$$

then the condition $\Delta q = 0$ implies that $d\overline{W}'/dq = 0$; and the equilibrium point corresponds to the maximum or minimum point of the $\overline{W}'$ curve. The situation is similar to those shown in Figs. 1 and 2. Only the equilibrium value of q now becomes

$$\hat{q} = \frac{(1 - F)(W_{11} - W_{12}) + F(W_{11} - W_{22})}{(1 - F)\left[(W_{11} - W_{12}) + (W_{22} - W_{12})\right]} \tag{21}$$

Note that when $W_{11} = W_{22}$, $\hat{q} = \frac{1}{2}$. Generally, in order that $\hat{q}$ be a positive fraction, not only the two differences $(W_{11} - W_{12})$ and $(W_{22} - W_{12})$ should be both positive or both negative, as noted before, but the inbreeding coefficient should be

$$F < \frac{W_{22} - W_{12}}{W_{11} - W_{12}} \quad \text{or} \quad < \frac{W_{11} - W_{12}}{W_{22} - W_{12}}, \tag{22}$$

depending upon which is a proper fraction.

SELECTION AND MUTATION

The effect of mutation on the equilibrium values of q has been discussed by Wright in various papers. Only a few remarks will suffice for the sake of completeness of our discussion. If μ is the mutation rate of allele A to a, then

$$\Delta q = \mu(1 - q) + \frac{q(1 - q)}{2\overline{W}}\frac{d\overline{W}}{dq} \tag{23}$$

The equilibrium value of q here does not exactly correspond to a maximum point of the W curve but is very close to it on account of the small term involving μ. As a simple example, suppose that $W_{11} = W_{12} = 1$, $W_{22} = 1 - s$, so that $\overline{W} = 1 - sq^2$, then, when $\Delta q = 0$, we obtain $\hat{q} = \sqrt{\mu/s}$. At this point, $\overline{W} = 1 - s(\mu/s) = 1 - \mu$, instead of 1. In general, the equilibrium point deviates from the maximum or the minimum point of the $\overline{W}$ curve (or surface) only by a distance of the order of magnitude of the mutation rate. Except for this small deviation, the general situation is much the same as in the previous cases.

DISCUSSION

From the above analysis it should be clear that equilibrium in a population is a consequence of the genotypic selective values of the population. The method adopted involved a study of the manner in which gene frequency changes from generation to generation and the ultimate genotypic composition of the population under a given selection scheme. To compare the "adaptiveness" of one population with another is entirely another problem. In fact, the absolute values of W_{11}, W_{12}, W_{22}, and $\overline{W}$ are quite irrelevant in this type of analysis. As long as their *relative* magnitudes remain the same, they yield the same values of Δq per generation (Li, 1955, p. 273). These W's may thus be called the "intra-population genotypic selective values." It is meaningless to say that a population with $\overline{W} = 1.50$ is "better" than one with $\overline{W} = .95$, when $\overline{W}$ is defined the way we did. Our model for differential local selections illustrates this point very well. In that section, intra-niche comparisons were considered (Levene, 1953) and not the absolute viabilities in the different niches. Furthermore, the absolute number of survivors in the different niches is also irrelevant when the proportions (c_i) of survivors contributed by each niche to the total population are used.

It should also be clear that the words "maximum" and "minimum" are conventional mathematical terms and have no connotations of value judgement. A population in a stable equilibrium state, attaining a maximum value of $\overline{W}$, does not at all mean that the population is "the best on earth." By the same token, an unstable equilibrium population (if existant) with a minimum value of $\overline{W}$, is not to be taken as a very "poor" population. It is just a mathematical method to describe the nature of the stability of an equilibrium. All it means is that under the given selection scheme, the population will be at a standstill at that particular point and no further change is expected under the same circumstances. To my understanding, when Dobzhansky (1951, p. 123) says "the adaptive value $(\overline{W})$ of the whole population under balanced polymorphism can be shown to reach the highest level when the equilibrium proportions of the competing variants, $q = s_2/(s_1 + s_2)$, are established," he is referring to a situation shown in our Fig. 1, in view of the definitions he set on p. 116. Perhaps he should have added that this is strictly an intra-population business.

If the $\overline{W}$ curve or surface assumes a complicated form with several maxima and minima, it is even possible that one "minimum" point may be actually higher than at least one of the "maximum" points on the same $\overline{W}$ scale; yet the populations at the (lower) maximum point will be stable and that at the (higher) minimum point will be unstable. From this view-point, one could object to Dobzhansky's wording, such as "the highest level." Even when a population occupies a maximum point, it still does not mean that it is at the highest of all the maximum points available in the $\overline{W}$ curve or surface. Sewall Wright has explained this aspect of equilibrium repeatedly in various papers. Dobzhansky could be defended on the ground that he is referring to the case where only one stable equilibrium point exists.

However, despite the somewhat loose language used by Dobzhansky and the fact that some of his sweeping assertions have not been well established by experimental evidence, the writer fears that Cain and Sheppard (1954) have some misunderstanding about the nature and limitations of the current methods of selection analysis. Some of their arguments are semantic, concerned with the meaning and usage of certain words. In this paper the writer is also guilty of using "fitness" and "selective value" synonymously, but has succeeded in avoiding the word "adaptive." Although one word is as good as another, when it is precisely defined, a standarization of the terms and avoidance of loose language would be desirable, especially in a subject like ours.

With respect to the statement: "When there is balanced polymorphism, with heterozygotes at an advantage, in a population, the average adaptive value ($\overline{W}$) of the population is at a maximum when equilibrium is reached. Consequently selection acts in such a way as to produce the maximum adaptive value in the population," Cain and Sheppard (1954, p. 321) commented: "This wording *certainly* suggests that a population in genetic equilibrium with heterozygotes at an advantage is in some way *highly* adapted" (italics mine). This one comment suffices to show how deeply Cain and Sheppard misunderstood the analytical method employed in gene frequency analysis. Their whole discussion seems to have stemmed from this fundamental misapprehension. The fact is that the above statement is not only true as it stands, but it could be made much more general.

If the expression "adaptive value" is as misleading as claimed by Cain and Sheppard, the writer wishes to point out that Fisher (1930, p. 100), in describing the same phenomenon, has employed the same phraseology— "that is, if the heterozygote is either better or worse *adapted* than both the homozygotes." The only thing that has escaped the attention of Fisher is the relationship between Δq and $d\overline{W}/dq$.

It should be noted that Cain & Sheppard at times seem to realize that the method applies only to intra-population selection. "The behavior of genotypes competing in the same population gives no direct evidence on the ability of separate populations each homozygous for one of the alternative genotypes, to survive in the wild" (p. 323). With this the writer of course fully agrees. In addition to the example of rapidly growing larvae versus slower growers cited by them, one may add the familiar example of Rh selection in man. The frequency of the rh allele is increasing or decreasing in the American population, depending upon the selection scheme, but no one ever even hinted that a population of homozygous Rh negatives would be in any respect better or worse than a population of homozygous Rh positives. The important point is that when both alleles are present in a population, there will be selection effect; that is, one or the other allele will be at a "disadvantage," so to speak. There can be no selection in the absence of alternatives.

Cain and Sheppard, however, continued: "On the other hand, a particular homozygote may be at an extreme disadvantage because of extensive dislocations of its structure, irrespective of what genotypes may be co-existing with it in the same population. In this situation the selection coefficient relative to other genotypes does give a rough measure of the homozygote's chances of survival in pure cultures." This shows that their grasp of the intra-population selection concept is somewhat incomplete. The truth is "No, not even in this situation." Should man become a one-legged animal, we cannot be sure that mankind will perish from earth when raised "in pure cultures."

As to the example of *Primula vulgaris* (Cain and Sheppard, p. 322) in which a gene is of selective advantage in the gametic stage and of disadvantage in the zygotic stage, a stable equilibrium is also possible (Li, 1955, p. 264).

With respect to the association between abundance and variability of a species, Dobzhansky is inclined to think that greater variability leads to greater abundance, while Cain and Sheppard think that "greater polymorphism of the more widely ranging forms could be the result, not the cause, of the range inhabited." The writer is certainly unable to say anything definitive except to point out that, like other evolutionary factors, there may not be a fixed rule as to which is invariably the cause and which the result. It is not impossible that the cause-and-effect relationship may be reversed from one case to another. Also, there could be a chain process: viz. variability leads to abundance, which in turn leads to greater variability, and so on. It is hoped that critical experiments may be performed to shed more light on this important subject.

SUMMARY

The effect of intra-population selection on gene frequency in a large random mating population has been examined. In the absence of other forces when the genotypic selective values are independent of gene frequencies, a stable equilibrium value of gene frequency yields a maximum value of the average fitness of the population and an unstable equilibrium yields a minimum average fitness. This relationship is best illustrated by plotting both the $\overline{W}$ curve and the Δq curve on parellel q axis of the same scale. In more involved cases, it is often possible to define a modified average fitness of the population so that the above conclusion holds.

Only relative magnitudes of the intra-population selective values are relevant. It was emphasized that they cannot be used as a basis for comparison between two separate populations under two different environments. A comparison of absolute adaptiveness of two populations cannot be done until "absolute adaptiveness" is defined and measured.

ACKNOWLEDGEMENT

I am very grateful to Professor Howard Levene for reading the manuscript and checking the formulas.

LITERATURE CITED

Cain, A. J. and Sheppard, P. M., 1954, The theory of adaptive polymorphism. Amer. Nat. 88: 321-326.

Crow, J. F. 1952, Mimeographed lecture notes. Unpublished.

Dobzhansky, Th., 1951, Genetics and the origin of species. 3rd ed. New York: Columbia Univ. Press.

Fisher, R. A., 1930, The Gentical theory of natural selection. pp. 100-101. Oxford: Clarendon Press.

Glass, B., 1950, The action of selection on the principal Rh alleles. Amer. J. Human Genet. 2: 269-278.

Levene, H. 1953, Genetic equilibrium when more than one ecological niche is available. Amer. Nat. 87: 331-333.

Levene, H., O. Pavlovsky, and Th. Dobzhansky, 1954, Interaction of the adaptive values in polymorphic experimental populations of *Drosophila pseudo-obscura*. Evolution 8: 335-349.

Li, C. C., 1953, Is Rh facing a crossroad? A critique of the compensation effect. Amer. Nat. 87: 257-261.

1955, Population Genetics, Chapter 19, Selection. Chicago: Univ. of Chicago Press.

Wright, S. 1942, Statistical genetics and evolution. Bull. Amer. Math. Soc. 48: 223-246.

1949, Adaptation and selection. *In* Genetics, Paleontology, and Evolution, ed. G. L. Jepsen, 365-389. Princeton Univ. Press, New Jersey.

GENETICS OF NATURAL POPULATIONS. XXIV DEVELOPMENTAL HOMEOSTASIS IN NATURAL POPULATIONS OF DROSOPHILA PSEUDOOBSCURA

THEODOSIUS DOBZHANSKY[1] AND HOWARD LEVENE[2]

Departments of Zoology and Mathematical Statistics, Columbia University, New York City

Received March 25, 1955

IN his important book on *Genetic Homeostasis*, LERNER (1954) concludes "that heterozygosity has a dual function in the life of Mendelian populations. On the one hand, it provides a mechanism for maintaining genetic reserves and potential plasticity, and on the other, it permits a large proportion of individuals to exhibit combinations of phenotypic properties near the optimum. Underlying both processes is the superior buffering ability of heterozygotes as compared with homozygotes." The foregoing article of DOBZHANSKY, PAVLOVSKY, SPASSKY and SPASSKY (1955) describes the heterozygosity in the second chromosomes of a natural population of *Drosophila pseudoobscura*. The purpose of the present article is to examine the buffering ability of the heterozygotes and homozygotes for some of these chromosomes. To this end, "The ideal test would consist of comparisons of environmental variability in fitness of these types" (LERNER 1954). Our material permits an approach to this "ideal test", although the data obtained so far are limited to examination of only the viability between the egg and adult stages of the carriers of certain heterozygous and homozygous genotypes under a relatively limited variety of environmental conditions. The viability is, of course, a component of fitness but is not synonymous with it.

THE DATA

The nature of the material used and the experimental techniques employed are described in the companion article of DOBZHANSKY, PAVLOVSKY, SPASSKY and SPASSKY. The essentials relevant to our present purposes are as follows. Nineteen second chromosomes were isolated from a natural population of *Drosophila pseudoobscura*. Ten of these, noted in the tables below by H ("High") produced normally viable or supervital homozygotes in cultures raised at 25°C and fed on Fleischmann's yeast (F). Nine chromosomes, denoted by an L ("Low"), produced subvital homozygotes under the same conditions. The viability of these nineteen homozygotes was then tested in nine different environments. These environments involved four different temperatures—27°, 25°, 16°C, and a variable temperature regime ranging from 4° to 25°C, and feeding on three different yeasts, namely Fleischmann's *Saccharomyces cerevisiae* (F), a species of Klockeraspora (K), and of Zygosaccharomyces (Z). Twenty-seven crosses were made in which heterozygotes for different combinations of H and L chromosomes were obtained (see table 2).

[1] The work reported in this article has been carried out under Contract No. AT-(30-1)-1151, U. S. Atomic Energy Commission.

[2] Research under contract with Office of Naval Research.

All tests of the homo- and heterozygotes in a given environment were carried out simultaneously; the experiments with the F yeast were done somewhat earlier than those with K and Z yeasts.

Six replicate cultures containing the offspring of the same group of parents were made to test the viability of every homozygote and of every heterozygous combination of chromosomes. Counts of the flies with and without the marking mutant gene (Bare) were made in all cultures. The primary data consist, then, of records of the numbers of Bare and non-Bare flies in the different cultures. The frequencies of the non-Bare flies are expressed in percentages of the totals. The statistics discussed below are derived from these percentages.

ANALYSIS OF VARIANCE

The body of data at our disposal furnishes three kinds of quantities for analysis. (1) The first and most basic of these is the average viability of the homozygotes and heterozygotes for certain chromosomes, expressed as percentages of non-Bare (wild type) flies. The values of these viabilities are given in table 4 of the preceding paper (DOBZHANSKY, PAVLOVSKY, SPASSKY and SPASSKY 1955). (2) Quantities which we will call microenvironmental variances. The replicate cultures were grown under conditions which were kept as nearly uniform as practicable in large-scale experiments. Nevertheless, the conditions did vary because of the different amounts of food in the different culture bottles, different degrees of crowding, as well as minor differences in temperature, microorganisms in the food, etc. Accordingly the observed variance between replicate cultures consists of two distinct components. One is the ordinary binomial sampling variance, the other the variance in viability due to the differences between replicate cultures. By subtracting the calculated binomial sampling variance from the observed variance we obtain an estimate of the second component, which we call microenvironmental variance. If p_i is the observed percentage of wild type and n_i the total number of flies in the ith culture, and c is the number of cultures, we then let $\overline{p} = (\sum p_i)/c$ be the unweighted mean viability, and then estimate the binomial sampling variance as $\sigma_b^2 = (\sum \frac{\overline{p}(100 - \overline{p})}{n_1})/c$

(See the similar computation in WALLACE and MADDEN 1953). The means of microenvironmental variances for all genotypes of a given kind raised at a given temperature on a given yeast are given in table 1. (3) The third kind of quantity we will consider is the macroenvironmental variance; i.e. the variance of the survival rates of a given genotype over the different macroenvironments or yeast-temperature combinations. These are obtained in a similar way to the microenvironmental variances. We let p_i and n_i now be the percentage of wild type and number of flies in the combined cultures of a particular macroenvironment, and subtract σ_b^2, defined as above, from the observed variance of the viability of that genotype over all nine macroenvironments. The resulting quantity will be called the macroenvironmental variance. Values of these variances for each of the genotypes in this study are given in table 2.

Each of the three types of quantity discussed above adds something to our understanding of the situation, and they will be analyzed separately. We first consider

139

TABLE 1

Microenvironmental variance between replicate cultures raised under different conditions. L—chromosomes which are subvital, and H—chromosomes which are supervital when homozygous. F—Fleischmann's yeast, K—Kloeckeraspora yeast, Z—Zygosaccharomyces yeast

Environment	Homozygotes L	Homozygotes H	Heterozygotes L × L	Heterozygotes L × H	Heterozygotes H × H
F 25°C	19.98	8.58	−0.84	3.57	3.52
F 27°	6.06	37.63	−6.46	4.87	−3.56
F 16°	12.50	6.66	−3.39	3.82	−2.64
F 4°	5.69	3.98	10.23	−5.02	1.50
K 25°	18.06	3.88	8.17	7.41	5.74
K 27°	36.14	13.80	2.84	2.49	10.18
K 16°	4.87	5.12	2.91	4.15	6.42
Z 25°	47.00	11.62	0.96	5.36	18.51
Z 27°	13.52	33.02	17.29	18.36	9.44
Mean	18.20	13.81	3.53	5.00	5.46
Std. Error	±3.88	±1.96	±1.45	±1.59	±1.89

the analysis of the basic data, the viabilities per se. To start with, we restrict ourselves to a particular kind of cross, such as low homozygotes or low × low heterozygotes. The data then fall into a two way analysis of variance with replications. One criterion of classification is genotype: the particular chromosome or combination of chromosomes involved. The other criterion is the nine macroenvironments formed by the combinations of yeast and temperature tested. For each combination of genotype and environment there are six viability values from the replicate cultures. A standard analysis of variance is then performed and the effects of genotype, environment and genotype-environment interaction are tested. A significant effect of genotype implies that different genotypes have different mean viabilities when averaged over all nine environments. Similarly, a significant effect of environment means that the mean viability of all the genotypes of a certain kind varies from environment to environment. Finally, a significant F statistic for interaction implies that in addition to any possible average effects of genotype and environment, there are also unpredictable results for specific genotype-environment combinations. Mathematically, if there were no interaction, the true viability of a particular genotype-environment combination would be equal to the grand mean of all combinations, plus the difference between the average viability of that genotype and the grand mean, plus the difference between the average viability in that environment and the grand mean; and the observed viability would differ from this only because of the random variability between replicate cultures. A simple numerical example may clarify the idea of interaction. Let the grand mean be 33, and let genotype I be one less on the average and genotype II one more, while environment A is 2 less on the average and environment B, 2 more. Then the predicted values without interaction would be IA = 30, IB = 34, IIA = 32, IIB = 36, while a possible set of values with interaction would be IA = 31, IB = 33, IIA = 31, IIB = 37. In the first case the difference of I and II is 2 in environment A and 2

TABLE 2

Macroenvironmental variance between series of cultures raised in different environments.
L—chromosomes which are subvital, and H—chromosomes which are supervital when
tested in homozygous condition on Fleischmann's yeast at 25° C

Homozygotes		Heterozygotes	
Chromosome no.	Variance	Chromosome combination	Variance
L 14	12.23	L 14 × L 31	1.11
L 31	156.42	L 31 × L 39	8.32
L 39	8.22	L 39 × L 43	6.31
L 43	2.09	L 43 × L 53	3.28
L 53	31.78	L 81 × L 120	7.12
L 81	13.65	L 120 × L 121	5.62
L 120	48.46	L 121 × L 140	1.95
L 121	27.10	L 140 × L 14	1.20
L 140	36.61		
Mean L	37.40	Mean L × L	4.36
H 1	4.41	H 1 × L 14	2.69
H 10	1.67	H 10 × L 31	1.20
H 16	10.02	H 16 × L 39	2.98
H 50	0.23	H 50 × L 43	2.18
H 57	2.66	H 57 × L 53	4.01
H 62	10.87	H 106 × L 81	−0.63
H 106	27.08	H 150 × L 120	6.18
H 150	27.87	H 158 × L 121	−1.50
H 158	1.71	H 202 × L 140	1.77
H 202	4.85		
Mean H	9.14	Mean H × L	2.10
		H 1 × H 10	10.46
		H 10 × H 16	5.03
		H 16 × H 50	2.60
		H 50 × H 57	3.56
		H 57 × H 62	3.75
		H 62 × H 106	3.13
		H 106 × H 150	3.60
		H 150 × H 158	5.28
		H 158 × H 202	3.13
		H 202 × H 1	4.10
		Mean H × H	4.46

in environment B, while in the second this difference is 0 in environment A and 4 in environment B. Hence the departure of the viability of a genotype-environment combination from the predicted value is a measure of the interaction. In biological terms the interaction is a measure of the specific biological interaction of genotype with environment; e.g. a genotype which has a superior viability in some environments may be inferior in others.

141

TABLE 3

Analysis of variance of viabilities

	Genotypes			Environments			Interaction			Error	
	MS	df	F	MS	df	F	MS	df	F	MS	df
L	78.8	8	3.93***	219.4	8	10.95***	20.04	64	2.98***	6.717	405
H	21.85	9	3.56**	71.4	8	11.65***	6.13	71	1.066	5.749	445
L × L	5.46	7	1.65	22.45	8	6.78***	3.31	56	.918	3.605	360
L × H	5.62	8	1.70	16.37	8	4.96***	3.30	64	.754	4.376	405
H × H	13.12	9	3.13**	31.19	8	.45***	4.19	72	.956	4.379	450

** Significant at the 1% level.
*** Significant at the 0.1% level.

The analysis of variance is given in table 3. The error mean square is used to test the interactions, while the interaction mean squares are used for testing the main effects. This is done because the main effects are not biologically meaningful unless they are significantly larger than the interactions. The effect of macroenvironment is highly significant for all five types of cross, as might be expected, since these environments are extremely different. The effect of genotype is highly significant for low homozygotes, significant at the 1% level for high homozygotes and high by high heterozygotes, and not significant but possibly present for low by low and high by low heterozygotes. There is also a significant interaction for low homozygotes, but in the other four types of cross the variance between replicates explains all departures from the values predicted from the main effects.

The fact that only one significant interaction is found seems to contradict the findings in the companion paper on the unpredictability of the behavior of different genotypes in different environments. However, this was most striking for L homozygotes, where we *do* find significant interaction. The unpredictability in the H homozygotes, which were selected because they were supervital in one environment (F25), shows up mainly as a regression toward the expected viability for random homozygotes in other environments. Statistically, this appears as a main effect (lower average viability in the other environments), rather than as interaction, in the analysis of the H homozygotes. The behavior of the heterozygotes, on the other hand, is more predictable.

We now turn to the analysis of the microenvironmental variance. Here each microenvironmental variance is calculated from the six replicates, giving a single figure for each genotype-macroenvironment combination. Consequently there is no error mean square against which to test the interaction mean squares. Accordingly the interaction will not be tested. In the light of the comparative unimportance of interaction for the viability itself, this seems not too serious a loss.

The analysis of variance for the microenvironmental variances is given in table 4. While the effect of genotype and macroenvironment are both larger for homozygotes than for heterozygotes, the interaction, or error, is also larger, so that only the effect of environment is significant, and this only for high homozygotes. In addition the effect of macroenvironment is barely significant for low by low heterozygotes, but this could well be due to chance, since one F out of nine would often be sig-

TABLE 4

Analysis of variance for microenvironmental variances

	Genotypes			Environments			Interaction	
	MS	df	F	MS	df	F	MS	df
L	2050	8	1.68	1695	8	1.39	1223	64
H	475.9	9	1.40	1221.9	8	3.58**	340.8	71
L × L	245.9	7	1.61	430.1	8	2.82*	152.3	56
L × H	179.1	8	.88	332.4	8	1.62	204.7	64
H × H	164.7	9	.51	469.9	8	1.46	321.4	72

* Significant at the 5% level.
** Significant at the 1% level.

nificant at the 5% level. Even the result for high homozygotes appears upon inspection to be due solely to a high microenvironmental variance in one of the nine macroenvironments, namely, Fleischmann's yeast at 27°. There is thus no evidence for any consistent average effects of either genotype or environment on microenvironmental variance.

No analysis of variance is possible for macroenvironmental variance for a given type of cross, since there is only one value for each genotype. Formally, it would be possible to use a test for homogeneity of variances, but for various technical reasons such a test was not felt to be valid for this data.

We turn now to comparisons between different types of cross. The mean viabilities, with their standard errors, for each type of cross as given in the companion paper, are as follows: L, 27.91 ± 0.99; H, 30.68 ± 0.49; L × L, 33.56 ± 0.28; L × H, 34.31 ± 0.26, H × H, 34.4 ± 0.38. In each case the standard error is the square root of the mean square for genotypes divided by the number of genotype-environment combinations. The reason for this is that we desire to draw general conclusions about the types of crosses, and the mean viability of "low" homozygotes, for example, would have been quite different if some other set of nine chromosomes had been used. A measure of the expected difference due to this cause is given precisely by the mean square for genotypes. The actual viabilities given above are in precisely the order one might expect, with low homozygotes the poorest and high by high heterozygotes the best. However, the differences between the three classes of heterozygotes are not significant. The difference between low homozygotes and high homozygotes is significant at the 5% level, while the difference between homozygotes and heterozygotes is significant at the 0.1% level, giving clear evidence of heterosis.

A similar analysis was made for microenvironmental variance. In this case the standard error was calculated from the interaction mean square, since none of the effects of genotype was significant, and the interaction afforded more degrees of freedom, permitting the use of tables of the normal distribution rather than STUDENT's *t*. The mean values and their standard errors are given in table 1. The microenvironmental variance is greater for low than for high homozygotes but not significantly so. Homozygotes are very significantly higher than heterozygotes (*P* less than 0.1%), and there are no significant differences between classes of heterozygotes.

The analysis of the figures for macroenvironmental variance in table 3 must be done in a slightly different way. Homeostasis resulting from heterozygosity would be evidenced by fairly uniformly low macroenvironmental variance for heterozygotes, and by a higher value for at least some of the homozygotes, and this is what is observed. However, the variability of these values among homozygotes is so high as to attach a large standard error to their means, and this obscures the difference between the mean of homozygotes and the mean of heterozygotes. Since the larger standard error is itself evidence of a difference between homozygotes and heterozygotes, it is valid to compare the difference of the means with the error calculated from heterozygotes alone. Accordingly, the pooled sum of squares for heterozygotes was divided by its degrees of freedom, and then multiplied by the sum of the reciprocals of the number of homozygotes and number of heterozygotes, and used as the variance of the difference. Similarly the sum of squares for high homozygotes was used to test the low versus high homozygote comparison. The result is similar to those before. There is no significant difference between heterozygotes. The difference between homozygotes and heterozygotes is highly significant ($t = 6$), and the difference between low and high homozygotes also gives $t = 6$. The macroenvironmental variance for L31, 156.42, far exceeds all the others. However, even if it is excluded, the mean for lows (22.3) is significantly higher than that for highs.

Finally, a remarkable fact should be noted. The actual values of macro- and microenvironmental variances averaged over all experiments for a given type of cross are closely comparable. In other words the "minor" fluctuations in environment between replicate cultures seem to have as great an effect on viability as the major differences in yeast and temperature. This point seems worthy of further study.

VARIANCE AND VIABILITY

The broad outline of the situation is now clear. The overall viability of homozygotes is, in most environments, lower than that of heterozygotes. The viability of homozygotes is also very sensitive to both micro- and macroenvironmental differences, while the viability of heterozygotes is relatively stable. Since the viability of heterozygotes tends to be uniformly high, and that of homozygotes tends to be frequently but not uniformly low, the viability and sensitivity to environmental changes are really two sides of the same coin. It should be kept in mind that some chromosomes (H) were chosen because they produced in a certain environment highly viable homozygotes, and other chromosomes (L) because they gave subvital homozygotes. When the environment was varied, the H homozygotes remained on the average more viable than the L homozygotes, though with many exceptions. The H homozygotes showed also lower variances than did L homozygotes (tables 1 and 2). On the other hand, the L homozygotes show a significant interaction of viability in the different environments, and both classes of homozygotes show differences among themselves in average viability in different environments. The heterozygotes are more uniform. There are no differences between H × H, H × L, and L × L heterozygotes, and no average differences or interactions with the environment for different heterozygous combinations.

The relationship we have repeatedly observed between low viability and high environmental variability is so important that it is desirable to study it more directly.

Accordingly a scatter diagram was prepared, plotting the macroenvironmental variances for the various low and high homozygotes against the corresponding mean viabilities. Homozygotes for chromosome L31 had by far the largest variance and smallest viability. Even after deleting this point the remaining points showed considerable correlation, giving $r = -0.78$, which for 16 degrees of freedom is significant at the 0.1% level, giving a 95% confidence interval of -0.45 to -0.9. The correlation of the same mean viabilities with the corresponding microenvironmental variances was -0.57, which is significant at the 2% level, giving a 95% confidence interval of -0.1 to -0.8. The corresponding correlation of micro- and macroenvironmental variances was $+0.41$, which is not significantly different from 0. Calculation of the corresponding partial correlations gives slightly smaller values for the first two, but a value of only -0.02 for the partial correlation of micro- and macroenvironmental variances after removing the effect of viability. Evidently then, the chromosomes with low mean viability are usually the ones which are poorly adapted to some but not all of the tested macroenvironments and therefore show large variability. To a lesser extent such chromosomes also react erratically to the smaller environmental differences between replicate cultures. On the other hand there seems to be no interrelationship between macro- and microenvironmental variability except to the extent that both tend to be associated with low mean viability.

Looking at the data differently, and using the unweighted average values of all low and high homozygotes in each macroenvironment, the correlation between viability and microenvironmental variance is -0.34, giving a 95% confidence interval of -0.7 to $+0.2$. There is thus indication that less favorable macroenvironments may produce greater microenvironmental variances. Finally separate scatter diagrams were made for L and H, plotting microenvironmental variances against the corresponding viabilities for each genotype-environment combinations. The result for L's was a widely scattered constellation of points showing no apparent correlation. A statistical test confirmed the absence of any correlation. The result for H's was similar, but with some slight appearance of negative correlation that was barely significant at the 5% level. The difference from the previous results is due to the facts that only microenvironmental variances are available here, the regularizing effect of averaging is missing, and the larger number of experimental values permitted separating the L from the H homozygotes.

Finally it should be said that there is no evidence of any correlation between viability and variances for the heterozygotes. This is not surprising since the observed viability range for the heterozygotes is very much smaller than for homozygotes, and the number of different heterozygotes studied is limited (27).

DISCUSSION

Some analogies of our results with those observed in maize are worth mentioning. Differences we observe between viability of different hybrids are due to what maize geneticists call "Total combining ability" of the parent homozygotes. The present data is not well suited to separating general and specific combining ability. In maize such characters as yield in F_1 hybrids of two inbred strains show a low correlation with the corresponding character of the two parent inbred strains (see e. g. the review by SPRAGUE 1946). We might expect less correlation for viability, since natural selection will reduce the additive genetic variance or heritability for this character. ROJAS and SPRAGUE (1952) have studied the interactions of genotype with year and locality for F_1 hybrids in maize and find these components of variance to be of the same order of magnitude as the main effects of genotype, but much smaller than the main effects of year and locality. In our data, on the other hand, for the most part neither main effects of genotype nor genotype-environment interactions are significant for heterozygotes. Again this is probably due to greater selection for the character, viability, that we are studying.

In recent years, several investigators have, largely independently, arrived at the conclusion that heterosis, the high fitness of heterozygotes relative to homozygotes, is often due to the superior buffering abilities met with in many heterozygotes. ROBERTSON and REEVE (1952) noted that the environmental variance of the wing length is greater in inbred lines of *Drosophila melanogaster* than in F_1 hybrids between these lines. They suggested that the decrease of the variance following hybridization may be due to greater biochemical versatility of the heterozygotes. The heterokaryons of Neurospora studied by EMERSON (1952) and others may be regarded as models showing how such a biochemical versatility could arise. DOBZHANSKY and WALLACE (1953) compared the survival rates in replicate cultures of homozygotes and heterozygotes for certain chromosomes from natural populations of *Drosophila pseudoobscura*, *D. persimilis*, and *D. prosaltans*, and from experimental populations of *D. melanogaster*. The survival rates were heterogeneous in homozygotes more often than in heterozygotes in all four species. The mean viability of the homozygotes was decidedly lower than that of the heterozygotes. Therefore it could be inferred that the developmental paths of most heterozygotes are better buffered against environmental disturbances, are more homeostatic, than the developmental paths of most homozygotes. It was further surmised that the superior homeostatic properties of the heterozygotes are a consequence of coadaptation of the gene contents of the chromosomes composing the gene pool of a Mendelian population. The coadaptation is the outcome of natural selection.

MATHER (1953) found that the numbers of sternopleural bristles on the two sides of the body in the same individual are more often different in inbred lines of *D. melanogaster* than in the F_1 and F_2 hybrids between these lines. MATHER's interpretation parallels rather closely that given by DOBZHANSKY and WALLACE (see above), except that MATHER speaks not of homeostasis but of "canalization", a term suggested by WADDINGTON (1942). LEWIS (1954) observed that, in a certain environment, the F_1 hybrids between two lines of tomatoes are less variable with respect to the flower number than are these lines themselves. However in a different environment the variability was uniform. LEWIS suggests an interesting model which relates the phenotypic stability of a trait with the degree of dominance in variable environments of the genes which influence that trait. The interesting experiments of TEBB and THODAY (1954) lead them to conclude that heterozygosity does not necessarily promote homeostasis and that coadaptation of gene alleles or gene complexes may be necessary to bring homeostasis about. On the other hand, LERNER (1954) has critically reviewed the evidence concerning this homeostatic adjustment in homo- and heterozygotes. He is inclined to believe that, at least in domestic animals, "mere diversity of alleles at different loci may provide a sufficient basis for what is usually referred to as heterosis," although it is possible that "coadaptation of the genetic contents of homologous chromosomes plays a greater role in natural than in domestic populations."

The evidence presented above shows very clearly that the average environmental variance of the survival rates is greater in homozygotes than in heterozygotes. The heterozygotes are better buffered, both with respect to the microenvironmental and the macroenvironmental variations. This much is a confirmation of the results of DOBZHANSKY and WALLACE (1953). Now we can go somewhat further. In contrast to DOBZHANSKY and WALLACE, we have not worked with a random sample of chromosomes from a population. The H chromosomes were selected because they produced, in a certain macroenvironment, homozygotes which were about as viable as an average heterozygote. The L chromosomes produced, in the same environment, subvital homozygotes. The homozygotes for H chromosomes were, however, not as fit as the heterozygotes when the environment was altered. Not only is the mean viability of the homozygotes often below that of the heterozygotes (cf. table 4 in the companion paper by DOBZHANSKY, PAVLOVSKY, SPASSKY, and SPASSKY), but both the micro- and the macroenvironmental variances for H homozygotes are significantly greater on the average than those for the heterozygotes (see tables 1 and 2). In fact, the environmental variance for H homozygotes (13.81 ± 1.96) is not sig- nificantly smaller than that for L homozygotes (18.20 ± 3.88). We may conclude that the homozygotes for some of the chromosomes found in natural populations of Drosophila are "narrow specialists". Such homozygotes do quite well in a restricted range of environments, but they lack the resilience necessary to maintain their fitness in other environments. By contrast, the heterozygotes are more often many- sided and versatile in their adaptedness, hence able to live successfully in a broader range of environments.

The objection may be raised that it is high, rather than uniform, rate of survival in different environments that is necessary for adaptedness. A lethal which dies in all environments is surely not well adapted. But this is sheer confusion; high survival is correlated with versatility in a range of environments; homeostasis results in high as well as uniform survival rates. The survival rates of the heterozygotes, measured in percentages of non-Bare flies in the cultures, are high (table 4 in the companion paper) as well as relatively uniform (table 2 of the present paper). The variations in these percentages in different environments may be due as much to the environ- mental sensitivity of the Bare as of the non-Bare flies. Conversely, the homozygotes show lowered as well as variable survival rates. It should of course be realized that all the Bare flies contain heterozygous combinations of a Bare chromosome and one of the tested chromosomes, since homozygous Bare rarely survives, and that hence the Bare flies in our cultures may be expected to behave more like the heterozygotes than like homozygotes for chromosomes taken from nature.

To understand clearly the relation of homeostasis to adaptedness, it must be kept in mind that homeostasis does not imply a stationary state (WADDINGTON 1953) but a dynamic stability. According to CANNON (1932), "In an open system, such as our bodies represent, compounded of unstable materials and subjected continually to disturbing conditions, constancy is in itself evidence that agencies are acting, or ready to act, to maintain this constancy." Action is, however, change; homeostasis is brought about by changes in some processes which result in stability of other processes. Among the vertebrates, the composition of the blood is maintained fairly constant; this constancy is due. however, to the activities of the kidneys which function differently under different circumstances. What is essential about homeostasis is that it enables life to continue despite the variations in the environment. Homeostatic adjustments permit the development, whether that of an embryo or that of an adult, to follow one of a limited variety of paths established in evolution under the control of natural selection. Straying away from these paths results in death (LERNER 1954, see particularly his fig. 6). On the other hand, homeostasis does not prevent the development from switching from one of these historically established paths to another established path. The ability of the organism to follow any one of these paths is, in fact, highly adaptive. Thus, on the human level, the plasticity of behavioral developmental patterns confers a very high adaptability on our species. What homeostasis does is to avoid the developmental processes being deflected in haphazard ways, resulting in non-adaptive modifications (morphoses according to SCHMALHAUSEN 1949).

The simplest form of homeostasis is exemplified by reversible physiological reactions which permit the functioning of the body and the organs to continue unimpeded. Kidney function, temperature regulation, and functional hypertrophy or atrophy of organs are good examples. By insensible gradations this *functional homeostasis* merges with physiological reactions which result in *developmental homeostasis*. Developmental homeostasis, which WADDINGTON (1942, 1953) prefers to call canalization, permits the development to keep to a definite path or to switch over to a closely related path. SCHMALHAUSEN'S (1949) physiogenic modification is also a related concept. A given repertory of functional and developmental homeostatic mechanisms is, of course, determined by the norm of reaction of each genotype. LERNER'S (1954) *genetic homeostasis* refers to self-regulatory properties not of individual organisms but of Mendelian populations. It may seem that genetic homeostasis is a phenomenon entirely separate from functional and developmental homeostasis. But LERNER argues, and we believe convincingly, that the genetic homeostasis is brought about by essentially the same mechanisms of heterozygosity and coadaptation of gene alleles and gene complexes as those which underly the other forms of homeostasis.

Surely, the relationships between the different forms of homeostasis, between homeostasis and heterosis, and between homeostasis and adaptedness are far from completely understood. The scene is too diverse and contradictory. The field is a new one, and more data are needed. It is particularly important to know to what extent these phenomena are due to what LERNER (1954) has called "mere diversity of alleles" and to what extent to previous selection and coadaptation of these alleles. LERNER'S summary of the pertinent evidence now available suggests rather that the situation may be different in organisms with different types of reproductive biology.

SUMMARY

The viability of homozygotes for 19 different second chromosomes, and of 27 different heterozygous combinations of the same chromosomes, has been studied. These homozygotes and heterozygotes have been exposed to 9 different "macroenvironments" (different temperatures and nutrient media) and to different "microenvironments" (environmental differences which occur in replicate cultures in the same macroenvironment). Homozygotes show greater mean macroenvironmental and microenvironmental variances of survival rate than do heterozygotes. The developmental patterns of the heterozygotes are more homeostatic, better buffered against environmental disturbances than those of the homozygotes. The viability and the homeostatic buffering are positively correlated, the viability and the environmental variances show a negative correlation. The relationships between viability, homeostasis, and variability are discussed.

LITERATURE CITED

CANNON, W. B., 1932   The Wisdom of the Body. New York, Norton.
DOBZHANSKY, TH., and B. WALLACE, 1953   The genetics of homeostasis in Drosophila. Proc. Nat. Acad. Sci. U. S. **39**: 162–171.
EMERSON, S., 1952   Biochemical models of heterosis in Neurospora. Heterosis, Ames, Iowa, Iowa State College Press.
LERNER, I. M., 1954   Genetic Homeostasis. New York, John Wiley.
LEWIS, D., 1954   Gene-environment interaction: A relationship between dominance, heterosis, phenotypic stability and variability. Heredity **8**: 333–356.
MATHER, K., 1953   Genetical control of stability in development. Heredity **7**: 297–336.
ROBERTSON, F. W., and S. C. R. REEVE, 1952   Heterozygosity, environmental variation and heterosis. Nature **170**: 286.
ROJAS, B. A., and G. F. SPRAGUE, 1952   A comparison of variance components in corn yield trials: III. General and specific combining ability and their interactions with locations and years. Agron. J. **44**: 462–466.
SCHMALHAUSEN, I. I., 1949   Factors of Evolution. Philadelphia, Blakiston.
SPRAGUE, G. F., 1946   The experimental basis for hybrid maize. Biol. Rev. **21**: 101–120.
TEBB, G., and Y. M. THODAY, 1954   Stability in development and relational balance of X-chromosomes in Drosophila melanogaster. Nature **174**: 1109.
WADDINGTON, C. H., 1942   Canalization of development and the inheritance of acquired characters. Nature **150**: 563–565.
   1953   The "Baldwin effect", "Genetic Assimilation" and "Homeostasis". Evolution **7**: 386–387.

INTER–POPULATION HYBRIDS IN *DROSOPHILA MELANOGASTER* [1]

BRUCE WALLACE

The Biological Laboratory, Cold Spring Harbor, New York

Received November 17, 1954

Until recently the gene pool of a population was regarded as a relatively uniform assemblage of "wild-type" genes with a scattering of recessive mutant alleles at various loci; a precise description of a gene pool of this type and of the population of individuals carrying it at any instant could be formulated in terms of gene frequencies (the *allelotype* of Strandskov, 1950). The concept of coadaptation (Dobzhansky, 1950) pointed up the role of selection as an integrating force consolidating intra-population genetic systems on the basis of specific interactions between their different parts. In its original form coadaptation referred to chromosomal inversions within local populations of *D. pseudoobscura*. Evidence that selection operates within populations to establish heterozygosis through the retention of multiple allelic series at many loci (Wallace *et al.*, 1953; Dobzhansky and Wallace, 1953) has led to the more inclusive concept that coadaptation involves the entire gene pool. Coadaptation can be defined, then, as the mutual adjustment of interacting alleles within the gene pool of a Mendelian population brought about (a) by selection of heterozygous genotypes possessing superior adaptive values, and (b) by the occurrence of genetic recombination between successive generations. An excellent treatment of the theoretical aspects of this problem has been given by Lerner (1954) in a discussion of genetic homeostasis.

Experimental evidence for the existence of specific gene interactions responsible for phenotypic traits of individuals of isolated or local populations has been reported in the viability studies of Wallace *et al.* (1953), Vetukhiv (1953, 1954), and Brncic (1954), and studies on DDT resistance by King (1955). The demonstration rests in each case upon the contrasts between interactions observed in intra- as opposed to inter-population gene combinations.

The experiments reported in this paper deal with the ability of *D. melanogaster* larvae to develop under near-starvation conditions. The original purposes for the study were two. Both Vetukhiv and Brncic reported that inter-population hybrids of *D. pseudoobscura* were heterotic. Would a cosmopolitan species such as *D. melanogaster* with a worldwide exchange of populations owing to accidental transport by man also exhibit inter-population heterosis? If heterosis is exhibited by inter-population hybrids, what is its genetic basis? Two experiments were made. The results of the first posed an additional problem for the second: Are the gene interactions observed in inter-population crosses ascribable to the disruption through crossing-over of an intra-chromosomal organization established originally by natural selection?

MATERIAL AND METHODS

The basic techniques of the two experiments were the same. Wild type *D. melanogaster* of diverse geographic origins were mated systematically for several generations to obtain larvae carrying a variety of gene combinations. Definite numbers of such newly hatched larvae were transferred to vials containing measured amounts of food and the numbers of adults hatching in the vials were recorded.

[1] This work was done under contract No. AT-(30-1)-557, U. S. Atomic Energy Commission.

Reprinted by permission of the author from EVOLUTION, **9**, 302–316 (1955).

Different populations of flies were used in the two experiments. In the first, flies were obtained from our experimental populations number 1 and number 3 (described in Wallace and King, 1951), from an Amherst, Mass. population (M) and from a Syosset, N. Y. population (S). Populations number 1 and number 3 were originally derived from an Oregon-R strain but had been maintained separately for nearly 115 generations. Population M had been kept in an experimental cage for two or three generations at the time we obtained our sample; population S had been in the laboratory for about 35 generations.

In experiment II, flies from five populations were used. Four of these were natural populations from the following places: (1) a fruit store in Blacksburg, Virginia; (2) a citrus grove at Riverside, California; (3) a vineyard near Santiago, Chile; and (4) a fruit orchard near Jerusalem, Israel. The fifth population was the Syosset, N. Y. strain maintained in a laboratory cage at this time for 45 generations.

The author wishes to express his appreciation for the kindness of the following persons who supplied the flies used in these experiments: Drs. Danko Brncic, Elizabeth Goldschmidt, J. C. King, Paul Levine, Max Levitan, and Timothy Prout.

The matings used were similar in the two experiments. The purpose was to obtain larvae carrying definite proportions of genes from different populations in a variety of combinations. A brief account describing experiment II will serve to describe the first as well. The original flies consisted of 12 strains (a-l) from each of the five populations (1-Virginia, 2-California, 3-Chile, 4-Israel, and 5-New York). Each strain was started with 1–3 fertilized females captured in the "field." The following crosses were made between strains designated by the same letters: 1×2, 1×3, 1×4, 1×5, 2×3, 2×4, . . . 3×5, 4×5, 1×1, 2×2, 3×3, 4×4, and 5×5 (15 crosses, 12 bottles (a-l) of each). The next step entailed

setting up an F_2 from each of the 10 types of inter-population crosses and, using the intra-population cultures, in remaking the same series of 15 crosses as in the first step. The F_2 series served to introduce cross-over chromosomes from hybrid females into males. The third cross consisted of mating F_2 males with hybrid females of the corresponding type [$(1a \times 2a)$ F_2 ♂♂ $\times$ $(1a \times 2a)$ ♀♀, etc.] and using the intra-population cultures $(1 \times 1, 2 \times 2, \text{ etc.})$ for setting up once more the same series of 15 crosses as described in the first step. The intra-population cultures of this generation, however, were made *between* strains ($1a \times 1b$, $1b \times 1c$, $1c \times 1d$ . . . $1f \times 1a$, $1g \times 1h$, $1h \times 1i$, . . . $1l \times 1g$). The cross of F_2 males with hybrid females introduced another series of crossover chromosomes into the males; the F_3 males hatching from these cultures carried approximately 75% chromosomes from hybrid females and 25% chromosomes passed down through males with no recombination. These males were considered equivalent to hybrid females and were used interchangeably with these females whenever recombinant chromosomes were desired. The series of 12 bottles for each type of cross were now divided into two groups; strains a through f were designated A and strains g through l, B. For each cross in the next step males were taken from one of these groups and females from the other; this precaution insured the maximum heterozygosity in crosses where both parents carried genes from the same population.

The flies ultimately available for mating were F_3 hybrid males that carried crossover chromosomes, F_1 hybrid females that would transmit crossover chromosomes in their gametes, F_1 hybrid males carrying mixtures of chromosomes from two different populations but which could transmit only non-crossover chromosomes, and intra-population males and females carrying random combinations of chromosomes from their respective localities.

The final matings differed between the

two experiments. In the first where only four populations (1, 3, M, and S) were involved, all 55 possible matings were made between hybrid and non-hybrid flies: 11×11, $[= (1 \times 1) \times (1 \times 1)]$, 11×13, $11 \times 1M$, $11 \times 1S$, 11×33, $11 \times 3M$, $11 \times 3S$, . . . $MS \times MS$, $MS \times SS$, and $SS \times SS$. In this series F_3 males and F_1 females were considered equivalent; the 55 matings were tabulated as indicated and the type used as males alternated, with minor exceptions, from left to right in successive crosses. Six additional matings were made using F_1 males: 13×13, $1M \times 1M$, $1S \times 1S$, $3M \times 3M$, $3S \times 3S$, and $MS \times MS$.

In the second experiment more emphasis was placed on the use of F_1 males. In this experiment it was impractical to study all possible combinations. Those studied in the series utilizing F_3 males (or hybrid females) were of the following types: 11×12 and all other crosses of a non-hybrid of one population with a hybrid between that population and another, 11×23 and all other crosses between a non-hybrid of one population and a hybrid between two other populations, and 12×34 and all comparable "double-cross" hybrids. Besides these crosses there were those in which hybrid parents were not used: 11×11 and other intra-population crosses and 11×22 and similar inter-population crosses. There were 80 different kinds of crosses in this series. The second series made use of F_1 hybrid males. The crosses studied were 12×12 and all other crosses of F_1 males and females, 12×33 and all corresponding crosses of hybrid males with non-hybrid females of an entirely different population, and 12×34 and all comparable crosses of hybrid males with hybrid females of two other populations. There were 70 kinds of crosses in this series. In both experiments the final crosses were designated by code numbers to conceal their nature until collection of the data was completed.

The next aspect of the experimental technique involves larval collection and the transfer of larvae to vials. In the first experiment with only 61 kinds of crosses, 4 replicate sets of 61 mating vials were set up with 7–15 females and males in each. Wooden spoons with regular yeasted Drosophila medium were inserted each morning and the flies were allowed to oviposit for 24 hours. Four workers transferred larvae from the spoons to vials with needles. Each worker dealt with one set of 61 crosses each day, exchanging the old spoon for a fresh one in every vial and then transferring 40 freshly hatched larvae from each of the 61 spoons into an appropriately labelled vial. Each person took a different set of vials every day until the fifth and last day when he worked once more with his original set. At the end of the transferring period there were, consequently, 20 vials (4 persons × 5 days) of 40 larvae each for each of the 61 crosses.

Collecting and transferring larvae for all 150 vials of the second experiment was more than one person could do in a day. These vials were divided into two replicate groups of 80 vials each (F_3 males) and another two of 70 vials each (F_1 males). Ten–twenty males and females were placed in each mating vial. The procedure for gathering larvae was the same as in the first experiment. Transfers were made, however, by six persons for 4 days. Only 25 larvae were transferred into each vial. With six persons transferring from four groups of vials (two of 80 and two of 70) it was necessary for two pairs of persons to work on two of the groups each day. At the end of the four days, each of the six persons had transferred larvae from every one of the 150 vials of each of the two replicate sets. There were, then, 12 vials of 25 larvae each for each of the 150 crosses.

The type and quantity of medium to which the larvae were transferred also differed in the two experiments. In the first, $1'' \times 4''$ shell vials containing 2 cc. of cornmeal-molasses-agar medium with Tegosept-M (a mold preventative) were used. Live yeast was transferred with the larvae and, despite the fact that the food dried considerably, this amount of food was more than ample to support most of the developing larvae. In the second experiment the medium consisted of 1 part blackstrap molasses : 7 parts of 1½% agar-water solution. Propionic acid (0.5%) was added to inhibit the growth of the live yeast which clung to the transferred larvae. The vials were ½″ × 1¾″ shell vials; each vial contained 2 cc. of the molasses-agar medium.

In both experiments the vials with developing larvae were kept at 25°. In the first experiment, counts were made on the 11th, 15th, and 17th days. The total hatch obtained by the 17th day was so large that the results are virtually meaningless; the discussion of the data will deal exclusively with the number of adults which hatched on and before the 11th day. The figures obtained reflect primarily the relative developmental rates of the different types of larvae. In the second experiment development was very slow; counts were made on the 22nd, 26th, and 28th days. For some unknown reason—possibly the propionic acid was omitted from the medium or traces of brewers yeast contaminated the agar—the development in one set of vials was noticeably better than in the others. These vials were counted only on the 20th and 24th days; nevertheless, 20 of the 1800 vials of this experiment went into second generation. The 20 vials giving more than 25 adults are scattered throughout 6 of the 8 large groups we wish to compare and so these counts are left in the data. Finally, in the first experiment, data from 3 of the 1220 vials are missing—no larvae in one, flies escaped from the second, and an obvious contamination of the third; data for these vials were completed by a technique for supplying missing information described in Snedecor (1946, p. 274).

It will be useful at this point to discuss definitions, methods of classification of larvae, and the analysis of the data. It is obvious from the nature of the crosses described that the tested larvae can be described in several ways: (1) whether loci on homologous chromosomes carry alleles from the same or different populations, (2) whether genes at loci along a single chromosome have come from the same or different populations, (3) whether different chromosomes, although not cross-over chromosomes themselves, have come from the same or different populations.

We will refer to individuals carrying alleles from different populations at homologous loci as "heterozygous"; this is strictly an operational use of this term and quotation marks will be used to emphasize this fact. Although it is impossible to specify which loci are "heterozygous" in all cases, it is possible to speak of the average proportion of "heterozygosity" for any type of cross: 11 × 11, 0% "heterozygous"; 11 × 12, 50% "heterozygous"; 12 × 34, 100% "heterozygous"; 12 × 33, 100% "heterozygous"; 12 × 13, 75% "heterozygous"; etc. It must be re-emphasized that there was no inbreeding in this material; in every instance in which two alleles from the same population occupied homologous loci, these alleles came from different strains of that population. Chromosomes transmitted by hybrid *inter-population* females or F_3 males will be referred to as "derived" chromosomes. This term emphasizes the fact that these chromosomes are recombinants between chromosomes of different populations—a recombination that could not have occurred in natural populations. A chromosome that is not "derived" is, consequently, "natural." For simplicity we will assume that all chromosomes transmitted by hybrid females or F_3 males are crossover chromosomes; the tested larvae can be classified according to the proportion of derived chromosomes they carry: 11 × 11, 0% derived; 11 × 12, 50% derived; 11 × 22, 0% derived; 12 × 34, 100% derived, etc.

Through common usage the term "heterozygous" is frequently used in reference to individuals rather than to the genes carried by these individuals; we will use the term "derived" in the same way and will occasionally refer to "derived" individuals.

Finally, in those crosses involving F_1 hybrid males, larvae are formed that have received from their fathers mixtures of natural chromosomes from two different populations—derived haploid sets: 12 F_1 ♂ × 33 ♀♀, 100% "heterozygous," 0% derived chromosomes, derived haploid set from father; 12 F_1 ♂ × 34 ♀♀, 100% "heterozygous," 50% derived chromosomes (from hybrid mother), derived haploid set from father; 12 F_1 ♂ × 12 ♀♀, 50% "heterozygous," 50% derived chromosomes, derived haploid set from father; etc.

The primary importance of the data for our present purpose lies in contrasting the effect of "heterozygosity" and of recombination (measured by derived chromosomes and derived haploid sets) on the survival of larvae under starvation conditions. In our statistical treatment of the data we have not attempted a complete analysis of variance; instead, we have obtained estimates of experimental error and have used these estimates in comparing the average survival of larvae classified according to proportions of "heterozygous" loci and derived chromosomes. The estimate of error in the first experiment was based on the variance between replicated sets; the estimate in the second experiment was based on the variance within all 12 vials of the two replicated sets. In each case the estimated error is too large but these estimates are accurate enough for our purposes.

A schematic representation of the chromosomal constitution of the different classes of flies synthesized in the two experiments is shown in figure 1. In each instance only one of many possible combinations of populations is shown (for instance, six different crosses in experiment I and ten in experiment II gave rise to

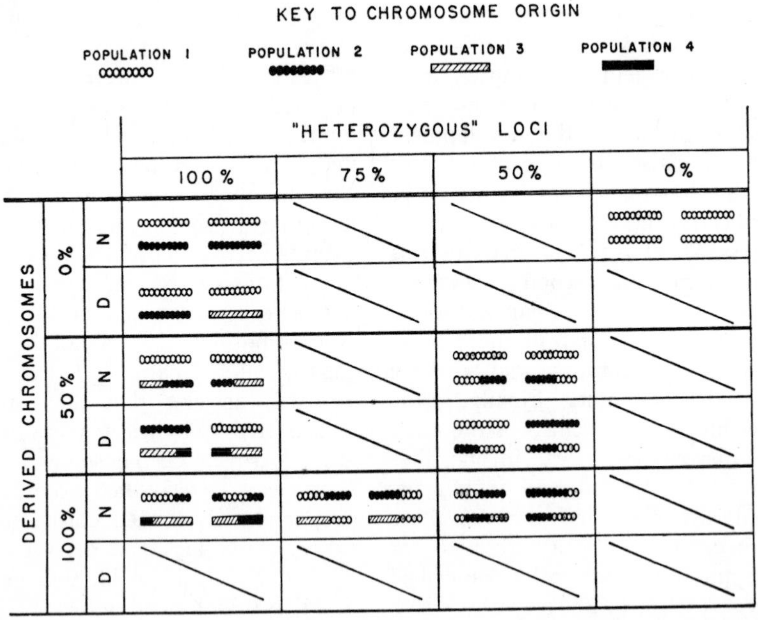

FIG. 1. A schematic representation of the types of gene combinations carried by the flies developing under starvation conditions. Each diagram represents the diploid number of two chromosomes. "Heterozygous" loci gives for each class of flies the average proportion of loci carrying alleles from two different populations. "Derived chromosomes" gives the approximate proportion of chromosomes which carry genes from two different populations (crossover chromosomes from inter-population hybrid females or F_3 males). Derived and natural haploid sets are indicated D and N; a derived haploid set is a combination of non-crossover chromosomes from two different populations obtained from an F_1 hybrid male.

100% "heterozygous," 0% derived individuals with natural haploid sets). It has been possible to indicate only one combination of genes in those classes possessing derived chromosomes or derived haploid sets; it must be remembered that an almost infinite variety of combinations is possible in these instances.

Results and Conclusions

Maternal Effect

In evaluating the effects of different genotypes on the survival of larvae under adverse conditions, it is necessary to eliminate any advantage gained by larvae through the genotypes of their mothers. In a preliminary analysis (Wallace, 1954b) of the data from experiment I, the existence of a maternal effect was not detected. A more careful analysis of data from experiment II revealed such an effect and re-examination of the earlier data revealed it there as well.

The detection of a maternal effect depended upon the fact that in certain types of crosses only one hybrid parent was involved; this parent was either an F_1 hybrid female or an F_3 male. The data were grouped so that one population was considered at a time and the average number of adults hatching in crosses involving "homozygous" females was compared with the number hatching in analogous crosses using "heterozygous" females. The results of these tests were as follows: Experiment I: $\bar{d}$ (the average difference) = 5.145, $\sigma_{\bar{d}}$ = 2.25, $\bar{d}/\sigma_{\bar{d}}$ = 2.29, degrees of freedom = 55, p = probability = .02 − .03. Experiment II: $\bar{d}$ = 10.28, $\sigma_{\bar{d}}$ = 4.78, t = 2.15, d.f. = 12, p = .05. In both instances the chances that the observed differences are due to chance are small; the agreement between the experiments makes it almost certain that a hybrid maternal genotype increases the chances of survival of developing larvae. Further analysis failed to reveal any indication that the maternal effect was limited only to larvae of certain genotypes or that

only some hybrid females produced the effect. Consequently, correction factors for crosses involving homozygous female parents were calculated from the analyzed data; these were 1.04 for experiment I and 1.06 for experiment II. Squares of these factors were used in calculations involving variances.

Following the adjustment for maternal effects, the data of experiment II were examined once more for evidence of interactions between the X and Y chromosomes and the cytoplasm when these were of different origins. No evidence for such interactions was found.

Larval Viability

The total numbers of survivors in all tested combinations are given in tables 1 and 2. Data on the number of survivors in individual vials are too voluminous for publication. Figures in the tables which have been corrected for maternal effect (nearest whole fly) are marked by an asterisk. The data for experiment I represent counts made on the 11th day after the transfer of larvae.

In tables 3 and 4 the crosses listed in tables 1 and 2 have been grouped on the basis of "heterozygosity," derived chromosomes, and derived haploid sets. The mean number of surviving adults and the error of the mean are shown for each class. Pairs of classes which differ significantly (p < .05) are indicated by arrows in figures 2 and 3; the arrows point toward the class with the fewer survivals.

In general the experiments agree reasonably well. The striking aspect of both figures 2 and 3 is the downward sweep of the arrows. This pattern is especially noticeable in figure 2 in which the arrows fan down from the two upper corners. A combined summary of the direction of the arrows in the two experiments is given in table 5. Twenty-seven of 32 arrows point downward; the greater the proportion of recombined chromosomes, the smaller the numbers of surviving individuals. "Heterozygosity" is not nearly as

TABLE 1. *The 61 different combinations of genes from populations 1, 3, M, and S (see text for origin of these flies) studied in experiment I*

The combinations are grouped according to proportion of "heterozygous" loci (H) and proportion of derived chromosomes (d) as explained in text. The group indicated by $F_1 \male$ possesses a derived haploid set of non-recombinant chromosomes. n = the number of flies hatched by the 11th day, a measure of relative developmental rates. The original number of larvae in each instance was 800 (20 vials, 40 larvae each).

0% H, 0% d	n	100% H, 100% d	n	50% H, 50% d	n
11×11	631*	13×MS	561	11×13	580*
33×33	511*	1M×3S	593	11×1M	604
MM×MM	588*	1S×3M	533	11×1S	586*
SS×SS	640*			13×33	566
		75% H, 100% d		1M×MM	567
100% H, 0% d		13×1M	566	1S×SS	607
11×33	615*	13×1S	621	33×3M	514*
11×MM	643*	13×3M	559	33×3S	470
11×SS	636*	13×3S	587	3M×MM	556*
33×MM	602*	1M×1S	528	3S×SS	603*
22×SS	599*	1M×3M	521	MM×MS	603
MM×SS	610*	1M×MS	494	MS×SS	577
		1S×3S	522		
100% H, 50% d		1S×MS	524	**50% H, 50% d ($F_1 \male$)**	
11×3M	571*	3M×3S	546	13×13	524
11×3S	544	3M×MS	521	1M×1M	568
11×MS	591	3S×MS	528	1S×1S	610
13×MM	558*			3M×3M	579
13×SS	508*	**50% H, 100% d**		3S×3S	537
1M×33	517	13×13	499	MS×MS	596
1M×SS	593*	1M×1M	543		
1S×33	574*	1S×1S	550		
1S×MM	567	3M×3M	553		
33×MS	674*	3S×3S	516		
3M×SS	544*	MS×MS	541		
3S×MM	482*				

* Adjusted for maternal effect (×1.04).

important; of the 32 arrows indicating significant differences in survival, 10 point to the left and 10 to the right. Whatever the differences between the genetic systems of the various tested populations, these differences are manifested much more by recombination than by inter-population "heterozygosity."

Finally, inter-population hybrids (100% "heterozygous," 0% derived, natural haploid sets) on the average do exhibit heterosis in this species. This is certainly true with the five populations studied in experiment II and is quite probably true for the four of experiment I as well although the difference here was not statistically significant (p = .08).

Thus, answers to the questions listed

earlier are already available. In spite of the accidental transport of large numbers of individual *D. melanogaster* from one part of the globe to another, local populations have diverged genetically. This is indicated by the difference between intra- and inter-population crosses. It is re-emphasized by the average decrease in viability that accompanies inter-population recombination. Not only have the original populations diverged but this divergence has involved the formation within these populations of mutually compatible gene combinations.

The data presented above lead to certain conclusions regarding the genetic basis of inter-population heterosis. Vetukhiv (op. cit.) suggested that heterozygosity

TABLE 2. *The 150 different combinations of genes from five natural populations (1, Virginia; 2, California; 3, Chile; 4, Israel; 5, New York) studied in experiment II grouped according to proportion of "heterozygous" loci (H) and derived chromosomes (d)*

Those groups indicated by $F_1 \sigma$ possess a derived haploid set of non-recombinant chromosomes. n = the total number of flies hatched. The original number of larvae in each instance was 300 (12 vials, 25 larvae each).

0% H, 0% d	n	100% H, 50% d	n	100% H, 100% d	n	100% H, 0% d ($F_1\sigma$)	n	100% H, 50% d ($F_1\sigma$)	n
11×11	173*	11×23	161	12×34	171	12×33	242*	12×34	159
22×22	154*	11×24	153*	12×35	105	12×44	164*	12×35	116
33×33	166*	11×25	162	12×45	154	12×55	106*	12×45	123
44×44	176*	11×34	153	13×24	131	13×22	155*	13×24	176
55×55	111*	11×35	170*	13×25	198	13×44	146*	13×25	129
		11×45	146*	13×45	131	13×55	158*	13×45	109
100% H, 0% d		12×33	184*	14×23	152	14×22	145*	14×23	159
11×22	218*	12×44	217	14×25	158	14×33	126*	14×25	194
11×33	145*	12×55	176	14×35	151	14×55	130*	14×35	128
11×44	222*	13×22	174*	15×23	135	15×22	130*	15×23	149
11×55	121*	13×44	146*	15×24	134	15×33	173*	15×24	139
22×33	176*	13×55	138*	15×34	173	15×44	131*	15×34	147
22×44	216*	14×22	212	23×45	140	23×11	173*	23×14	172
22×55	174*	14×33	230*	24×35	130	23×44	163*	23×15	180
33×44	173*	14×55	140	25×34	138	23×55	136*	23×45	160
33×55	134*	15×22	172*	**50% H, 50% d**		24×11	173*	24×13	161
44×55	139*	15×33	164	11×12	159*	24×33	170*	24×15	134
		15×44	161	11×13	171	24×55	174*	24×35	117
		22×34	172	11×14	152*	25×11	137*	25×13	133
		22×35	173*	11×15	146	25×33	110*	25×14	155
		22×45	146*	12×22	153	25×44	179*	25×34	146
		23×44	192*	13×33	203	34×11	202*	34×12	175
		23×55	139*	14×44	169*	34×22	190*	34×15	160
		24×33	133	15×55	128*	34×55	119*	34×25	135
		24×55	158*	22×23	141	35×11	164*	35×12	203
		25×33	159	22×24	193*	35×22	167*	35×14	90
		25×44	184	22×25	193	35×44	172*	35×24	159
		33×45	172*	23×33	170	45×11	200*	45×12	139
		34×55	162*	24×44	156	45×22	144*	45×13	167
		35×44	110	25×55	163*	45×33	195*	45×23	139
				33×34	167				
				33×35	218			**50% H, 50% d ($F_1\sigma$)**	
				34×44	138			12×12	217
				35×55	112*			13×13	154
				44×45	145			14×14	128
				45×55	143*			15×15	139
								23×23	175
								24×24	140
								25×25	172
								34×34	177
								35×35	150
								45×45	138

* Adjusted for maternal effect (×1.06).

per se was responsible for the heterosis of F_1 hybrids observed in his experiments since selection can not operate to coadapt the genetic systems of two isolated populations. However, it is quite apparent from figures 2 and 3 that heterozygosity alone does not explain the heterosis found in our material. Eight classes of individuals tested in the two experiments are 100% "heterozygous"; of these only the inter-population hybrids (100% "heterozygous," 0% derived) are consistently

TABLE 3. *Mean number of flies present at 11th day in vials of experiment I grouped on the basis of proportion of "heterozygous" loci and derived chromosomes*

These figures are only 1/4th as large as those in table 1 because the analysis of variance was based on four replicated sub-experiments. For comparative purposes the material is presented in the same form as figure 1 even though certain classes of individuals were not tested in this experiment.

			"Heterozygous" loci			
			100%	75%	50%	0%
derived chromosomes	0%	N	154.38 ±2.34			148.13 ±2.91
		D	not tested			
	50%	N	140.06 ±2.20		142.36 ±2.17	
		D	not tested		142.25 ±3.10	
	100%	N	140.58 ±3.96	135.77 ±2.00	133.42 ±3.53	
		D				

more viable than flies from local populations. The difference between the F_1 hybrids and the others lies in the amount of

TABLE 4. *Mean number of flies in final counts of vials in experiment II grouped on the basis of proportion of "heterozygous" loci and derived chromosomes*

These figures are equivalent to those of table 2 since the analysis and estimate of error was based on the 12 vials of each combination. For comparative purposes the material is presented in the same form as figure 1 even though certain classes of individuals were not tested in this experiment.

			"Heterozygous" loci			
			100%	75%	50%	0%
derived chromosomes	0%	N	171.80 ±1.94			156.00 ±2.95
		D	159.13 ±1.13			
	50%	N	165.30 ±1.17		161.00 ±1.52	
		D	148.43 ±1.05		159.00 ±1.90	
	100%	N	146.73 ±1.61	not tested	not tested	
		D				

recombination that has occurred. The F_1 hybrid carries two haploid sets obtained intact from local populations; the others possess at least one haploid set in which genes from two populations have been recombined. Heterosis in our material must, then, be ascribed to heterozygosity for selected gene complexes rather than mere heterozygosity. The large drop in the number of survivors among individuals 100% "heterozygous," 100% derived relative to those 100% "heterozygous," 50% derived (table 4) indicates

FIG. 2. A diagrammatic representation of the significance of the figures given in table 3. Each arrow is drawn between classes that differ significantly ($p < .05$) in the number of flies hatched by the 11th day. The arrow points from the class with the greater number to the one with the lower number. Stippled areas denote classes not subject to study by the experimental technique used or (partially stippled) classes not included in experiment I.

that one "natural" haploid set is capable of functioning quite well in the presence of one which carries genes from two different populations This effect is not evident, however, in the data from experiment I (table 3)

Among the types of flies tested in experiment I were six crosses in which F_1 hybrid males were used as parents. Flies obtained by these crosses were 50% "heterozygous" and 50% derived just as those of one other class in this experiment. The two classes differed in the presence of a natural haploid set in the individuals of one class and a derived haploid set in the other. The mean numbers of flies counted in the two classes were nearly identical, a fact which led to the suspicion that inter-chromosomal interactions were relatively unimportant in determining developmental rates. To test this possibility a greater emphasis was placed on the use of F_1 males in the second experiment. The answer is immediately apparent: Inter-population hybrids carrying two different haploid sets (100% "heterozygous," 0% derived) are more viable than individuals carrying a haploid

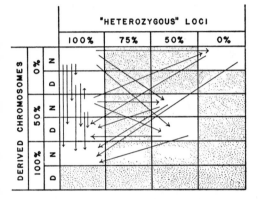

Fig. 3. A diagrammatic representation of the significance of the number of survivors given in table 4. As in figure 2 each arrow connects two classes that differ significantly (p < .05) and points toward the class with the smaller number. Stippled areas denote classes impossible to form by the technique used or (partially stippled) classes not included in experiment II.

set from one population and a second set consisting of chromosomes from two different populations even though these chromosomes have segregated without crossing over. Inter-chromosomal interactions, therefore, do influence the viability of hybrids. The existence of this type of interaction renders the experimental technique useless for demonstrating the "organization effects" suggested by experiment I. This does not imply that such effects do not exist (see Levitan, 1954) but that their demonstration requires another type of experimental analysis.

TABLE 5. *An analysis of the directions in which the arrows of figures 2 and 3 point*

"Heterozygosity" decreases from left to right; the amount of recombination increases from top to bottom.

	Right	Vertical	Left	Total
Up	1	1	0	2
Horizontal	2	xxxxxx	1	3
Down	7	11	9	27
Total	10	12	10	32

In some respects the results of the two experiments differ. In experiment I, for instance, the two classes of flies, 100% heterozygous–50% derived and 100% heterozygous–100% derived, did not differ significantly while the same classes in experiment II differed markedly. Furthermore, in experiment I more flies were counted among intra-population crosses than among those 100% heterozygous, 50% derived, natural haploid set; just the reverse was found in experiment II. In part these differences must reflect the

TABLE 6. *The probability that the observed differences in survival of flies of various genotypes would have occurred were the gene pools of different populations actually identical*

These results are based on the survival of larvae in a series of crosses in which genes from two populations have been combined in comparable ways with genes from other populations.

Experiment I

	1	3	M	S
1	x	.03	.07	.90
3	.03	x	.01	.015
M	.07	.01	x	.75
S	.90	.015	.75	x

Experiment II

	1	2	3	4	5
1	x	.13	.57	.80	.05
2	.13	x	.03	.09	.003
3	.57	.03	x	.18	.90
4	.86	.09	.18	x	.01
5	.05	.003	.90	.01	x

use of different populations, different media, and the analysis of two different characters (developmental rate and total survival). The differences between the two experiments probably reflect, too, some shortcomings of the experimental technique. Some classes of larvae were genetically uniform while those in other classes were genetically variable. Thus, where recombination had occurred, a variety of genotypes was produced; the F_1 hybrids were, of course, more or less uniform. The effect of population density on survival among homogeneous and heterogeneous collections of larvae could easily differ. For these reasons, the rather high survival in experiment II of individuals 100% "heterozygous," 50% derived, carrying a natural haploid set of chromosomes is probably misleading. As mentioned above, the relation between this class and the 0% "heterozygous," 0% derived class is reversed in the two experiments. Furthermore, this same class (100% "heterozygous," 50% derived) has more survivors than the class 100% "heterozygous," 0% derived, with a derived haploid set; if real, this difference is difficult to explain. In view of these discrepancies, it seems doubtful that the apparent decrease in viability accompany a decrease in heterozygosity between the class 100% "heterozygous," 50% derived, natural haploid set, and the class 50% "heterozygous," 50% derived, natural haploid set reflects the real situation.

Individuals 50% "heterozygous," 50% derived, with derived haploid sets were more viable than individuals 100% "heterozygous," 50% derived, with a derived haploid set. The *decrease* in viability accompanying this *increase* in heterozygosity is probably real. First, the difference is large. Second, the number of survivors in each of these classes compares well with that found in a corresponding class involving the same combination of populations. In this instance, the 50% "heterozygous" individuals are obtained by inbreeding F_1 males and females. Only two populations are involved in any one of the

ten kinds of crosses included in this class. Through the union of gametes carrying complementary portions of important gene combinations, it is possible that a number of larvae obtained genotypes substantially similar to those of either F_1 hybrids or intra-population flies. This could easily be the case in our experiments since naturally occurring inversions were not eliminated from the material used. (Contrast our inter-population F_2 flies with those of Vetukhiv who worked with inversion-free material; in his case the inter-population F_2 individuals were less viable than the intra-population flies.) There is virtually no opportunity for larvae of the 100% "heterozygous" class to possess genotypes essentially similar to those of either F_1 hybrids or intra-population individuals. This is so because the 100% "heterozygous" class involves portions of the gene pools of *four* rather than *two* different populations.

Comparing Gene Pools

A type of analysis for which these data are useful is the comparison of gene pools of different populations. In the past such comparisons have been based primarily on frequencies of recessive lethal or visible mutations. This type of study has of necessity dealt with chromosomes in the homozygous condition. There are several interpretations possible when significant differences are found. Assume, for instance, that one population of *D. melanogaster* is found to have 20% second chromosome lethals and another to have 30% and that this difference is significant. This difference will suggest to one person a difference in effective population size and a greater accumulation of lethals in the larger one. Another person might consider mutation rates as the causative factor. A third will make assumptions regarding the number of lethal loci, frequencies of lethals at each locus, allelism of these lethals and will conclude—all other things being equal—that the fitness of one population is slightly less that of the other. A fourth might regard this difference as merely an overt manifestation of fundamental differences in genetic modifiers, polygenic complexes—the whole genetic network—upon which the populations are built. Except in the last instance, a tacit assumption is that the nonlethal alleles at various loci are alike in the two populations and that the information on lethals offers a substantial basis for inter-population comparisons. The experiments discussed in this paper offer a much better opportunity for comparing gene pools of different populations—comparisons based on the interactions between substantial segments of these pools when in novel combinations. For instance, to compare populations 1 (Virginia) and 2 (California) of experiment II we can compare the viability of the following classes of larvae: 11×11 vs. 22×22, 11×33 vs. 22×33, 11×34 vs. 22×34, 14×35 vs. 24×35, etc. There are seventeen comparisons one can make between any two populations of experiment I; forty in experiment II. The assumption in each instance is that the two populations are alike; using the difference in the number of survivors and the error of this difference, the probability of obtaining this difference by chance can be computed. These individual probabilities can be combined by Fisher's method ($-2\Sigma\ln p_i = \chi^2$ with $2N$ degrees of freedom, where N = number of comparisons and p_i = any of the individual probabilities); the result is the probability of observing the entire array of probabilities through chance alone. The finding of a maternal effect changes the results substantially from those published earlier (Wallace, 1954b). The summarized results of these experiments are given in table 6. It is apparent that in about one half of all comparisons in either experiment, the two populations are found to differ significantly. There are indications, too, that these differences reflect specific interactions between the genes of different populations: In experiment I, $1 = S$ ($p = .90$) and $M = S$ ($p = .75$) but the probability that $1 = M$ is only .07;

in experiment II, $1 = 2$ ($p = .13$) and $1 = 3$ ($p = .80$) but 2 does not equal 3 ($p = .03$); $3 = 4$ ($p = .18$) and $3 = 5$ ($p = .90$) but 4 does not equal 5 ($p < .01$). These data offer additional support to the hypothesis that alleles are selected within populations on the basis of interactions with alleles at the same and/or different loci; the phenotypic manifestations of these alleles are altered by the substitution of novel combinations for the original coadapted complexes of the local populations.

Discussion

The data presented above bear on a number of genetic and evolutionary problems. The discussion of these data will be limited to their bearing on the concept of an integrated gene pool and on heterosis.

In the first section of this paper a definition of coadaptation was given that involved two phenomena, the adaptive superiority of heterozygous individuals and the mutual adjustment of interacting alleles within Mendelian populations. The experiments have dealt solely with the second of these two phenomena; they have no direct bearing on the question of intrapopulation heterozygosity. The results clearly indicate that the gene pools of different local populations of *D. melanogaster* do consist of mutually adjusted gene combinations. These gene combinations were disrupted by inter-population gene recombination.

The presumed basis for coadaptation lies in polygenic complexes. The data indicate that the interacting complexes of the material studied include genes of different chromosomes. Data pertinent to this point were obtained through the use of F_1 inter-population hybrid males as parents in certain crosses. The chromosomes transmitted by such males to their offspring are non-crossover chromosomes but, within the haploid set transmitted, there are mixtures of chromosomes from different populations. The viability of individuals 100% "heterozygous" receiving these "derived" haploid sets was lower than that of F_1 hybrids. Crossing-over and intra-chromosomal recombination resulted in still lower viabilities. Not only are the elements of the interacting complexes distributed between different chromosomes but those portions on individual chromosomes can be disrupted by recombination. The latter point is especially emphasized in the results of Brncic (1954) who restricted his studies to the third chromosome of *D. pseudoobscura*.

If a coadapted combination of genes occupies several chromosomes with a number of factors on each chromosome, this combination can be properly referred to as "polygenic." The concept of polygenic complexes has been questioned recently in this journal (Goldschmidt, 1953) but it looks very much as though in his denial of such complexes, Goldschmidt adequately though perhaps inadvertently described just such a gene system in the following passage: ". . . he (Dubinin) selected simultaneously and without discrimination a) for homozygosity of the simple Mendelian mutant *net,* b) for homozygosity of the mutant *blistered* (or *balloon* or both?) in the same chromosome, c) for the combined presence of both (or more) mutants in different homozygous or heterozygous combinations, d) for dominance enhancers, e) for multiple alleles of the loci involved (. . .), and f) for enhancers of expressivity." The necessary raw materials are all here; if we reject Goldschmidt's notion that these genes merely "float" in populations, we can assume that selection brings about a mutual adjustment of these genes and thereby produces a coadapted complex.

In a number of recent papers (Dobzhansky, 1950, 1952; Vetukhiv, 1953, 1954; Lerner, 1954) a distinction has been made between heterosis observed within Mendelian populations (euheterosis) and the hybrid vigor characteristic of inter-population or inter-specific hybridization (luxuriance). The distinction is based on the role of selection in bringing about euheterosis and the inability of selection to cause or influence luxuriance. Coadap-

tation can arise only within populations of interbreeding individuals.

It seems, however, that euheterosis and luxuriance can, in some instances, be referred to a common genetic basis; the data presented above help in identifying this basis. It was seen that the only class of flies that was substantially heterotic relative to the individuals of the local populations were the F_1 hybrids between these populations. These hybrid individuals carried two haploid sets of chromosomes each of which contained a combination of genes established by selection within a local, inter-breeding population. In synthesizing these hybrids no chromosomal mechanisms were provided to maintain and perpetuate these combinations and, as tables 3 and 4 show, heterosis was lost by recombination. If heterosis of integrated gene combinations were a general phenomenon, it might be expected that genetic systems capable of exploiting this type of heterosis would be established by natural selection within local populations. These systems would include chromosomal mechanisms capable of preventing recombination; the inversions commonly found in Drosophila populations are just this type of mechanism. Inversions, however, do not provide a perfect solution to the problems posed by recombination (Wallace, 1953, 1954a): Double cross-overs can remove blocks of genes from within long inversions. Certain combinations of overlapping inversions may permit a serial transfer of genes from chromosomes of one arrangement to chromosomes of a different arrangement. Inversions in one chromosome modify (increase, as a rule) the amount of crossing-over on other chromosomes. In addition to these short-comings of inversions as a mechanism for maintaining isolated blocks of genes, the populations face additional problems raised by mutation and the introduction of "alien" genes by migrant individuals from more or less remote localities. Consequently, it would seem reasonable in the case of Mendelian populations to regard euheterosis as a manageable fraction of luxuriance. The higher average viability of inter-population F_1 hybrids is a measure of the price paid by local populations for an integrated gene pool capable of being transmitted successfully from generation to generation.

Finally, it is interesting to contrast the conclusions based on studies of natural and artificial populations of Drosophila with those based on studies of self-fertilizing species or inbred material. Smith (1952), for instance, found that non-allelic interactions were not an important source of variation in studies on *Nicotiana*. Gowen (1952) reported a linear increase in egg production accompanying a chromosome-by-chromosome increase in heterozygosity in crosses between two inbred strains of *D. melanogaster*. The techniques used by corn breeders (that of Jenkins, for instance) to predict the yield of double-cross hybrids would be highly inefficient if recombination disrupted interacting gene combinations. In these studies, heterozygosity rather than recombination seems to play the dominant role in determining the hybrid and partial-hybrid phenotypes. The type of co-adapted gene combinations revealed by studies of Vetukhiv, Brncic, and by our own material seem to be lacking in the inbred material; either such systems were never present or they were abandoned upon the assumption of new mating patterns.

Summary

Two experiments were made to answer the following questions: (1) Do inter-population hybrids of *Drosophila melanogaster* exhibit hybrid vigor? (2) If it exists, what is the genetic basis of this heterosis? Flies from eight populations were used: two experimental, laboratory populations and six natural populations from Virginia, California, Massachusetts, New York, Chile, and Israel. The characters studied were relative developmental rates (experiment I) and survival ability (experiment II) under starvation conditions.

Through systematic matings between flies from different populations larvae were obtained that could be classified according to percentages of "heterozygous" loci and proportions of "derived" chromosomes (definitions of these terms are given in the text). Definite numbers of these larvae were grown in small amounts of food. The greatest numbers of survivors were found among the F_1 inter-population hybrids. The greater the amount of recombination (measured in terms of "derived" chromosomes or "derived" haploid sets) the smaller the number of survivors. Recombination was much more important in determining viability than was "heterozygosity."

It was concluded that heterozygosity for integrated gene complexes produces the heterosis exhibited by inter-population hybrids. Recombination destroys these complexes and, simultaneously, the heterosis dependent upon them. It was suggested that local populations of Drosophila exploit to the extent permitted by their breeding structures, heterosis resulting from heterozygosity of integrated gene combinations. Viewed in this way, euheterosis can be considered as a fraction of luxuriance that is compatible with problems concerning the transmission of these integrated systems through successive generations.

Literature Cited

Brncic, D. 1954. Heterosis and the integration of the genotype in geographical populations of *Drosophila pseudoobscura*. Genetics, **39**: 77–88.

Dobzhansky, Th. 1950. Genetics of natural populations. XIX. Origin of heterosis through natural selection in populations of *Drosophila pseudoobscura*. Genetics, **35**: 288–302.

——. 1952. Nature and origin of heterosis. In, John W. Gowen (ed.), Heterosis: 218–223, Iowa State College press.

——, and B. Wallace. 1953. The genetics of homeostasis in Drosophila. Proc. Nat. Acad. Sci., **39**: 162–171.

Goldschmidt, R. B. 1953. Pricking a bubble. Evol., **7**: 264–269.

Gowen, J. W. 1952. Hybrid vigor in Drosophila. In, John W. Gowen (ed.), Heterosis: 474–493, Iowa State College press.

KING, J. C. 1955. DDT resistance and the integration of the gene pool. Am. Nat. 89: 39–46.

LERNER, I. MICHAEL. 1954. Genetic Homeostasis. Oliver and Boyd, Edinburgh.

LEVITAN, M. 1954. Additional evidence of position effects in natural populations. Records of the Genetics Soc. of Amer. (abstract).

SMITH, H. H. 1952. Fixing transgressive vigor in *Nicotiana rustica*. In, John W. Gowen (ed.), Heterosis: 161–174, Iowa State College press.

SNEDECOR, G. W. 1946. Statistical Methods. Iowa State College press.

STRANDSKOV, H. H. 1950. The genetics of human populations. Cold Spring Harbor Symp. Quant. Biol., 15: 1–11.

VETUKHIV, M. 1953. Viability of hybrids between local populations of *Drosophila pseudoobscura*. Proc. Nat. Acad. Sci., 39: 30–34.

——. 1954. Integration of the genotype in local populations of three species of Drosophila. Evol., 8: 241–251.

WALLACE, B. 1953. On coadaptation in Drosophila. Am. Nat., 87: 343–358.

——. 1954a. Coadaptation and the gene arrangements of *Drosophila pseudoobscura*. IUBS Symposium on Genetics of Population Structure. IUBS Series B, Vol. 15: 67–94.

——. 1954b. Radiations and populations. Annual Report of The Biological Laboratory, Cold Spring Harbor, N. Y., No. 64: 32–38.

——, AND J. C. KING. 1951. Genetic changes in populations under irradiation. Am. Nat., 85: 209–222.

————. 1952. A genetic analysis of the adaptive values of populations. Proc. Nat. Acad. Sci., 38: 706–715.

——, J. C. KING, C. V. MADDEN, B. KAUFMANN AND E. C. McGUNNIGLE. 1953. An analysis of variability arising through recombination. Genetics, 38: 272–307.

POPULATION GENETICS OF
ABNORMAL HUMAN HAEMOGLOBINS

By A. C. ALLISON

Ten genetically controlled abnormal haemoglobin types have now been characterized (haemoglobins S, C, D, E, G, H, I, J, K and M). Their properties have recently been summarized by *Zuelzer*, *Neel* and *Robinson* [1956]. The genes for haemoglobins G, H, I, J, K and M seem to be rather uncommon in most populations, so that they can properly be regarded as mutants which are kept at a low frequency by the operation of selection against them; this occurs when any two abnormal haemoglobin genes come together in the same individual and thereby produce an anaemia.

On the other hand, the genes for haemoglobins S, C and E, and the thalassaemia gene, have attained high frequencies in many human populations despite the fact that selection operates against homozygotes and against those who carry two different abnormal haemoglobin genes. These characters are undoubtedly polymorphic. The case of haemoglobin D, which seems to be present in about 2 per cent of Sikhs and to produce a homozygote with polycythaemia as the only detectable abnormality (*Bird* and *Lehmann* [1956]) is marginal, but probably represents a true polymorphism.

An adequate explanation for the polymorphism of the sickle-cell character in East Africa is available. Electrophoretic analyses performed in 729 African infants show the proportion of sickle-cell homozygotes expected from the *Hardy-Weinberg* law, which confirms that there is no significant selection against sickle-cell homozygotes *in utero*. Similar analyses carried out on 6840 adult Africans show that on both the East and West sides of the continent the proportion of sickle-cell homozygotes surviving to adult life is less than 20 per cent of the average survival of all genotypes (*Allison* [1956b]) This order of survival is confirmed by

Reprinted by permission of S. Karger A. G., (Basel) from ACTA GENETICA, 6, 430–434 (1956).

clinical studies. The sickle-cell heterozygote seems to have a considerable advantage—up to 25 per cent—over other genotypes. The advantage can be attributed mainly to resistance against *falciparum* malaria, although other factors (e.g. resistance to hookworm infestation—*Raper* [1956] may play a subsidiary part. It can now be taken as established that children who are heterozygous for the sickle-cell gene have lower malaria parasite counts than other children. Since the mortality from *falciparum* malaria is known to be related to the height of the parasite count (*Field* [1949]), it seems reasonable to conclude that the mortality from malaria will be lower in sickle-cell heterozygotes than in other genotypes. And there is direct evidence that the heterozygotes rarely, if ever, develop potentially fatal complications of malaria, such as cerebral malaria and blackwater fever (*Raper*, loc. cit.). The advantage of the heterozygote appears also in their significantly higher incidence in adult than in infant African populations (*Allison* [1956b]). The distribution of the sickle-cell gene is also in accordance with this hypothesis: in Africa and elsewhere high frequencies are attained only in malarious regions. Thus, the equilibrium of the sickle-cell gene and its normal allelomorph in East Africa seems to be stable, with the sickle-cell heterozygote at an advantage and the homozygote sub-lethal.

In West Africa the position is complicated by the presence of a third allelomorph, the haemoglobin C gene. A year ago, when the position was reviewed by *Allison* [1956a], the only information available was that the haemoglobin C gene was present at a frequency of about 5 per cent in the Southern Gold Coast and had not been found in East Africa. Since it was known that persons who inherit the sickle-cell gene from one parent and the haemoglobin C gene from the other sometimes develop a condition very like sickle-cell disease (see, e.g. *Smith* and *Conley* [1954]), *Allison* postulated that the sickle-cell and haemoglobin C genes must tend to be mutually exclusive in human populations. Extensive data published since then (*Edington* and *Lehmann* [1956], *Allison* [1956b]) have provided a fair overall picture of the distribution of the sickle-cell and haemoglobin C genes in West Africa and have confirmed *Allison*'s postulate. The frequency of the haemoglobin C gene rises to 13.5 per cent in the Dagomba tribe of the Northern Territories of the Gold Coast; in this tribe the frequency of the sickle-cell gene is only 2 per cent. On all sides of this main focus the populations tested have shown a cline of descending frequencies of the haemoglobin C gene and increasing frequencies of the sickle-cell gene. The negative correlation between the frequencies of the two abnormal genes appears in fig. 1.

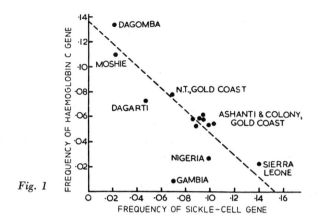

Fig. 1

Allison [1956b] has also made a preliminary calculation of the fitnesses of the various genotypes on the basis of electrophoretic tests of haemoglobin specimens in 1042 adult Africans from the Gold Coast. The reduced viability of sickle-cell and haemoglobin C homozygotes and the sickle-cell : haemoglobin C heterozygote is reflected in the relatively low frequency of persons with these genotypes in the adult population. Equating viability between birth and reproductive age with fitness, the following estimates of fitness were obtained (symbols of *Allison* [1955]):—

$$Hb^A/Hb^S = 1.138 \qquad Hb^C/Hb^C = 0.550$$
$$Hb^A/Hb^C = 1.103 \qquad Hb^S/Hb^C = 0.407$$
$$Hb^A/Hb^A = 0.976 \qquad Hb^S/Hb^S = 0.192$$

All homozygotes are at a disadvantage, the normal less than the abnormal; the Hb^S/Hb^C heterozygote is also at a disadvantage, but the other heterozygotes are favoured.

The conditions required for genetic equilibrium of three allelomorphs have been analysed by *Owen* [1953] and by *Penrose, Smith* and *Sprott* [1956]. The latter have shown that with the fitness values quoted above the equilibrium is stable but only by quite a small margin. It is uncertain whether Hb^S and Hb^C would, in fact, return to the same proportion if there were a chance variation. By slightly altering the fitness values, a semi-stable equilibrium is obtained, in which, if the frequencies are disturbed from the equilibrium values within a definable subspace, they will remain at their new values. If they are moved outside the subspace, they will be restored by selection to some point within the subspace, not necessarily the original point.

In this instance the equations determining the subspace lead to a single equation $162a_2 + 127a_3 = 24$, where a_2 is the frequency of Hb^S

and a_3 is the frequency of $Hb\,^C$. It is therefore interesting to see whether the values of $Hb\,^S$ and $Hb\,^C$ observed in different West African populations fit this equation. The data so far published are given in table 1.

Table 1

Population	Number tested	Hb^S	Hb^C	$162a_2+$ $127a_3$	Observer
Dagomba, N. Gold Coast	71	0.021	0.134	20.42	1
Moshie, N. Gold Coast	115	0.022	0.105	16.95	1
Dagarti, N. Gold Coast	97	0.047	0.072	16.76	1
Miscellaneous, N. Gold Coast . .	275	0.069	0.078	21.09	2
Zabrama, Togoland	63	0.103	0.048	22.79	2
Ashanti, Gold Coast	102	0.108	0.044	23.09	2
Ga, S. Gold Coast	174	0.098	0.043	21.34	2
Fanti, S. Gold Coast	156	0.103	0.052	23.29	2
Ewe, S. Gold Coast	167	0.112	0.045	23.85	2
Twi, S. Gold Coast	104	0.101	0.048	22.46	2
Miscellaneous, S. Gold Coast . .	283	0.096	0.049	21.74	1
Miscellaneous, Nigeria	247	0.109	0.027	21.18	2
Miscellaneous, Sierra Leone . . .	218	0.140	0.023	25.60	2
Miscellaneous, Gambia	1442	0.070	0.009	12.48	2

Observers: (1) *Edington* and *Lehmann* [1956]; (2) *Allison* [1956b].

In view of the relatively small number of individuals on which the gene frequency and fitness estimates are based, the values of $162a_2+127a_3$ are in fair agreement with expectation in all populations except the Gambians. Most of the observed values are somewhat below 24, which suggests that the estimates of fitness may not be quite correct. The Gambia seems to be a marginal region with a very heterogeneous population in which the frequencies of the abnormal haemoglobin genes may not yet have been stabilized by selection (*Allison* [1956b]). On the whole, these results suggest that the other West African populations tested have lived long enough in relatively uniform environments to show frequencies of the abnormal haemoglobin genes close to those predicted for a semi-stable equilibrium from the estimated fitnesses of the several genotypes.

With such a system, there is only a small probability that the haemoglobin C gene could have attained the high frequencies now observed if it had arisen by mutation in a population already having a high frequency of the sickle-cell gene. The most likely inference is that the haemoglobin C gene has been favoured in some population in or near the Northern Gold Coast having a low frequency of the sickle-cell gene. The haemo-

globin C gene diffused out of this area into populations with higher frequencies of the sickle-cell gene, and through selection the frequencies of
the two abnormal genes have been brought to various points close to the
subspace for a semi-stable equilibrium as defined above.

The population genetics of haemoglobin E and thalassaemia in South-
East Asia and the Mediterranean countries have not been worked out,
but it seems likely that the situation will turn out to be quite similar to
that obtaining in the case of the sickle-cell and haemoglobin C genes in
Africa.

REFERENCES

Allison, A. C.: Science *122*, 640, 1955.
— Cold Spr. Harb. Symp. quant. Biol. *20*, 239, 1956 a.
— Ann. hum. Genet. *21*, 71, 1956 b.
Bird, G. W. G. and *H. Lehmann:* Man *56*, 1, 1956.
Edington, G. M. and *H. Lehmann:* Man *56*, 34, 1956.
Field, J. W.: Trans. R. Soc. trop. Med. Hyg. *43*, 33, 1949.
Owen, A. R. G.: Heredity 7, 151, 1953.
Penrose, L. S., S. M. Smith and *D. A. Sprott:* Ann. hum. Genet. *21*, 90, 1956.
Raper, A. B.: Brit. med. J. *1*, 965, 1956.
Zuelzer, W. W., J. V. Neel and *A. R. Robinson:* Progr. Haemat. *1*, 91, 1956.

Discussion:

J. V. Neel (Ann Arbor, Michigan): Dr. *Lehmann* and Dr. *Allison* have presented in a
beautifully clear fashion certain aspects of the problems associated with the abnormal
hemoglobins. It is a comment on the swift progress of the field of human genetics that until
8 years ago we did not even recognize the existence of abnormal hemoglobins.

First of all I should like to endorse Dr. *Lehmann*'s plea for an elastic terminology.
My collaborators and I have evidence that gene responsible for hemoglobin C_1 is not an
allele of the gene responsible for hemoglobin S. The Thalassæmia locus seems separate from
both of these, while there are theoretical reasons for postulating that the production of
hemoglobin F depends upon activity at still another locus. This is going to be a situation
of some genetic complexity, where the need for an adjustable and descriptive terminology
is great.

Secondly I would mention the recent finding of my collaborators and myself that
hemoglobin J otherwise known on the basis of a single family, occurs in approximately 1 %
of Liberians. It is tempting to speculate from the known distributions of hemoglobins J,
C and S that here are three successive stages in the process whereby a "new" human gene
becomes established and disseminated.

Finally, with respect to the "malaria hypothesis", as I pointed out last year in the
Galton lecture, the hypothesis demands a higher death rate from malaria than many
malariologists would accept. If the malaria hypothesis becomes firmly established, and
results in a reappraisal of malaria deaths, here is a new example of the uses of the genetic
approach. I would hope that in accepting the malaria hypothesis we not abandon the
search for other factors of importance in maintaining this polymorphism, since here we
have a situation which will be widely quoted, and the need to be critical is great.

HOMEOSTASIS IN A SELECTION EXPERIMENT

J. M. THODAY

Genetics Department, University of Sheffield

Received 11.xii.57

In his stimulating book, Lerner (1954) argues that *Genetic Homeostasis* (the tendency of populations of outbreeding species to resist the effects of artificial selection) arises because selection brings about inferior *Developmental Homeostasis* (canalisation of individual development). He argues, from the frequently observed inferior developmental homeostasis of homozygotes, that in these species good control of development depends on heterozygosity as such. Selection necessarily involves inbreeding and must therefore reduce the heterozygosity of the population and hence produce impaired developmental homeostasis. Natural selection will therefore operate in favour of heterozygosity and resist the artificial selection. In due course the selection pressures will balance and the artificial selection will cease to be effective.

This thesis supposes that the three following hypotheses are generally applicable to artificially selected populations. First, artificial selection must produce deterioration of developmental homeostasis. Second, this poor homeostasis must be the result of decreased heterozygosity. Third, the poor homeostasis must limit significantly the rate of response to artificial selection. The experiment to be reported here bears on the first two of these hypotheses.

1. THE MEASURE OF DEVELOPMENTAL HOMEOSTASIS

The kinds of quantity that may be taken as indicating the degree that development is under control have been discussed elsewhere (Thoday, 1953, 1956), and reasons have been given for preferring measures of within-individual variation to measures of between-individual variation. In selection experiments, since their whole success depends upon genetic heterogeneity, between-individual variance can only provide a measure of developmental homeostasis if the proportion of total variance that is genetic can be accurately estimated : a measure of within-individual variation is therefore peculiarly appropriate. The convenient character first studied by Mather (1953a), bilateral asymmetry of sternopleural chaeta-number in *Drosophila melanogaster*, has therefore been used in this work.

The choice of this character was based in the first place on the reasonable supposition that in a well-canalised individual the end-results of development on the two sides of the fly are likely to be very similar, whereas in a poorly-canalised individual any tendency

Reprinted by permission of Oliver & Boyd, Ltd. from HEREDITY,
12, 401–415 (1958).

J. M. THODAY

for development of the two sides to diverge will be inadequately buffered (Mather, 1953a). Such theoretical considerations alone will not convince everyone, and the author has heard doubts of the value of sternopleural asymmetry as a character, and even doubts of the value of using chaeta number as a character in any experiment in quantitative genetics. These doubts seem to be based on a feeling that chaeta number is a trivial character of little, if any, adaptive significance.

There can, however, be no doubt that chaeta number has adaptive

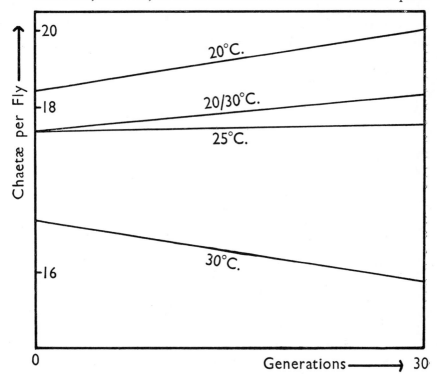

Fig. 1.—The regression lines of sternopleural chaeta number on generations in populations adapting to different environments. Each line is obtained from 3 populations each started from an F_1 cross between the inbred lines Oregon and Samarkand. (Log scale). From Beardmore (1956).

significance, for it is affected by *natural* selection. On general grounds alone this is clear : different species of *Drosophila*, and different populations of a species have different characteristic chaeta numbers, and the variance of chaeta number is very much less than the potential genetic variance can be shown to be by appropriate selection experiments (*e.g.* Sismanides, 1942 ; Mather and Harrison, 1949 ; Rasmusson, 1955). These facts must imply a history of effective stabilising selection (Mather, 1953b).

The conclusion based on these general considerations is supported by the behaviour of sternopleural chaeta number in populations of *Drosophila melanogaster* studied by Beardmore (1956) who has kindly

permitted me to outline them. Beardmore established three populations in each of four environmental conditions, 20° C., 25° C., 30° C.
and an incubator in which the mean temperature is 25° C., but in
which there is a smooth diurnal temperature cycle from 20° midnight
to 30° C. midday. All the populations were maintained by, as far
as possible, a three-weekly transfer of ten pairs of flies and had been
started from the same cross between two lines, Oregon and Samarkand,
both long inbred at 25°. (Great difficulty was experienced in maintaining the 30° populations, and their incubator was at first left at
28° and only gradually raised to 30°. They have not yet adapted
to 30° and, periodically, resort has to be made to insurance cultures
kept for one generation at 25° to prevent them dying out.)

TABLE 1

Significance of changes of chaeta number in adapting populations

(From Beardmore, 1956)

Environment	Joint regression	Sign of b	Differences between three replicate populations	
			Difference of regressions	Difference of means
20° C.	$t_{(54)} = 3 \cdot 366$ P. $\simeq 0 \cdot 001$	+	P. large	P. large
25° C.	$t_{(60)} = 2 \cdot 407$ P. $< 0 \cdot 02$	+	P. $< 0 \cdot 05$	P. $< 0 \cdot 001$
30° C.*	$t_{(42)} = 2 \cdot 789$ P. $< 0 \cdot 01$	−	P. large	P. $\simeq 0 \cdot 01$
F. 20°/30° C.	$t_{(66)} = 2 \cdot 811$ P. $< 0 \cdot 01$	+	P. large	P. $< 0 \cdot 01$

* See footnote to Table 2.

Fig. 1 illustrates the results. The first point of note is that adaptation to the new environments does involve changes of chaeta number.
The regressions of chaeta number on generations are significant
(table 1), and the slopes are greater in the new environments than
in the old. Further, in the old environment the regressions of replicate
populations are not consistent, whereas in the new environments
they are.

The second point is that the directions of change in 20° and 30°
differ, which can only be taken as evidence that it is a good thing for
flies developing at 20° to have more chaetæ, and a good thing for
those developing at 30° to have less chaetæ. In other words, chaeta
number measures something of adaptive significance.

A third point is of the greatest importance. It is well known
(Plunkett, 1927) that *Drosophila* cultured at higher temperatures
produce fewer chaetæ than those cultured at lower temperatures.
This environmental effect is the reason for the differing chaeta numbers
of the flies at the start of Beardmore's experiments (fig. 1).

Without Beardmore's results, interpretation of this phenotypic
effect of the environment would be difficult. It might on the one
hand be held that the environmentally caused modification of chaeta

number arose through poor canalisation of individual development. On the other hand it might be held that the modification of chaeta number arises because the individual is capable of adapting its development so as to produce a phenotype approaching the optimum required in the environment in which development takes place. This is the standard problem, discussed by Thoday (1953), of determining whether inter-individual variation is evidence of good or bad developmental homeostasis. Beardmore's results seem to settle the question for this character, this environmental variable and these flies. The genetic changes in his 20° and 30° populations augment the standard effects of the environment. It follows that the individual fly modifies its development *adaptively* in producing more chaetæ in lower temperatures and fewer chaetæ at higher temperatures.

TABLE 2

Significance of changes of asymmetry in adapting populations
(From Beardmore, 1956)

Environment	Joint regression	Sign of b	Differences between three replicate populations	
			Difference of regressions	Difference of means
20° C.	$t_{(54)} = 1\cdot887$ P. $<0\cdot1$	—	P. large	P. large
25° C.	$t_{(60)} = 0\cdot008$ P. large	+	P. large	P. large
30° C. *	$t_{(42)} = 2\cdot530$ P. $<0\cdot02$	—	P. large	P. $<0\cdot2>0\cdot05$
F. 20°/30° C.	$t_{(66)} = 2\cdot989$ P. $<0\cdot01$	—	P. large	P. $\simeq0\cdot05$

* The 30° regressions ignore the data obtained before the incubator had been raised to 30° C.

It cannot, of course, be argued from this that higher variance of chaeta number is always to be taken as a measure of higher developmental homeostasis. There is in fact evidence (Thoday, 1956) that high within-culture non-genetic variance is sometimes evidence of low developmental homeostasis (see also Lewontin, 1956), which merely serves to underline the value of measures of within-individual variance such as have been used by Mather (1950, 1953*a*), Jinks and Mather (1955), Paxman (1956), Thoday (1953, 1956), and Tebb and Thoday (1954).

Beardmore's results show that sternopleural number is of adaptive importance, a fact of significance for our argument. If this were not so, it would be less easy to suppose that sternopleural asymmetry might be of importance. His results also provide direct evidence that sternopleural asymmetry is a character of adaptive significance. Table 2 demonstrates the significance of changes in sternopleural asymmetry in his adapting populations. Asymmetry was measured by summing the differences of chaeta number between the two sides of a standard number of flies, a measure differing from that used by

Mather (1953a), but the same as that used by Tebb and Thoday (1954). There is no indication of regression on generations in the 25° populations. Each of the other populations (in new environments) shows a negative regression of asymmetry on generation and this is significant in the F. 20/30° and in the 30° populations. The regression in the 20° populations is not quite significant, but that this regression should be the least significant is to be expected, since 20° seems to be as good an environment as 25° for Oregon/Samarkand F_1 flies (Thoday, 1953). Furthermore, the rise in chaeta number in the 20° populations might be expected to raise asymmetry as a result of the scaling phenomenon referred to below, and this would mask any improvement of symmetry that was occurring. This same scaling problem somewhat weakens the evidence provided by the 30° populations whose chaeta number decreased. It cannot, however, affect conclusions based on the fluctuating environment populations, so that the overall result is clear : sternopleural asymmetry decreased as the populations adapted to particular new conditions. It must be concluded that natural selection promoted sternopleural symmetry, which, therefore, is of adaptive significance. The same conclusion follows from the experimental results of Tebb and Thoday (1954).

It would in fact be very surprising if bilateral symmetry of chaeta number were not of adaptive significance, since chaeta number must measure some of the attributes of a particular set of differentiation fields, and hence numerical symmetry must be a partial measure of the similarity of the comparable differentiation fields on the two sides of the fly.

A further point arises concerning the relevance of sternopleural asymmetry as a measure of homeostasis. Mather (1953a) argued that asymmetry is not so much a result of variation of external environment, but a consequence of internal " accidents of development ". Similar arguments have been used by Reeve and Robertson (1954) concerning abdominal chaetæ and Waddington, Graber and Woolf (1957), who refer to asymmetry as developmental "noise". Our own results (Thoday, 1956 ; Tebb and Thoday, 1954 ; Beardmore, 1956) clearly show that major changes of external environment can affect sternopleural asymmetry, but this does not mean that the divergence of the two sides in development is initiated by a difference of the external environment of the two sides : accidents of development may be more frequent or less well buffered in an unfavourable environment. It is quite probable that we are, in fact, dealing with accidents of development, but this has little, if any, bearing on the validity of sternopleural asymmetry as a measure of the competence of developmental control. Just as a " good " genotype will buffer the individual against undesirable effects of external variables, so a " good " genotype will lead to fewer accidents of development and better buffering of the individual against the effects of such accidents as do occur.

2. SCALING PROBLEMS

One disadvantage of sternopleural asymmetry is that it presents problems of scaling when it is desired to use it for the comparison of two populations whose mean sternopleural chaeta numbers differ. Mather (1953a) found that there was sometimes no relationship between asymmetry and total sternopleural chaeta number, but that in other types of fly there was a positive relationship. The control lines used in the present experiment show a highly significant positive relationship (calculation by Beardmore, 1956). The experiment involves lines selected for sternopleural chaeta number and some scaling correction is therefore required. The correction used by Thoday (1956), which involves dividing summed asymmetry by total chaeta number, seems to be satisfactory for the population used here since it gives comparable results for high and low selection lines. Asymmetry results are therefore presented as A/T, that is, the summed differences between the two sides of a set of flies (sign ignored) divided by their total chaeta number.

3. MATERIAL AND METHODS

The experiments began with a wild stock ("Dronfield") of *D. melanogaster,* derived from the progeny of a single inseminated female captured near Sheffield. Since its capture the stock had been maintained for six months by standard culture at 25° C., 4 pairs of flies being transferred each generation. This stock was then split into two lines, I and II, and in the next generation 4 single-pair cultures labelled *a, b, c* and *d* were set up from each. Assay and selection for number of sternopleural chaetæ began with the progeny of these eight pairs.

Assay of any line in any generation involved counting the sternopleural chaetæ on each side of 20 females and 20 males from each of four single-pair cultures except in generation O in which 24 of each sex were counted. In this generation the first four were used to establish control lines. From the remainder, the four with highest chaeta numbers were used to establish high selection lines and the four with lowest chaeta numbers were used to establish low lines.

Thus in generation O the following flies were selected from line I : 4 random females and 4 random males from each culture *a* to *d* ; the 4 highest flies of each sex numbered 1 to 4 from each of the four cultures and the 4 lowest flies likewise. These groups of flies were used to establish lines I C, I H, I L.

Each such line was set up by mating the female a_1 to male b_1, a_2 to b_2, a_3 to b_3, a_4 to b_4, b_1 to c_1, c_1 to d_1 and d_1 to a_1 and so on, providing 16 single-pair cultures. Culture $a_1 \times b_1$ was labelled a_1 and provided this was successful a_2, a_3 and a_4 were discarded. If a_1 failed, a_2 was used. If a_1 and a_2 failed, a_3 was used, etc. (An additional mass culture (4 random pairs) was also set up to insure against loss of all four single-pair cultures. Resort to this culture was only necessary on four occasions, that is for 4 of the 244 cultures assayed.) The progeny of the successful culture were assayed and selected and the next generation set up as before except that the mating system was changed to $a \times c$, $b \times d$, $c \times a$, $d \times b$. In the following generation the mating was $a \times d$, $b \times a$, $c \times b$, $d \times c$, and in the following the first mating system was repeated. Thus the four single pairs used in each generation are maintained as one population and the labels *a, b, c* and *d* merely designate female lines.

In the control lines the first 4 flies of each sex that were counted from each culture were labelled 1 to 4 and used. In the selection lines the "best" 4 were used. "Best" was defined as, *e.g.* in a high line, the fly with the most sternopleural chaetæ, but, if choice were necessary, the most symmetrical fly was used, that is, that with the most nearly equal numbers of chaetæ on its two sides.

In addition to the lines, F_1 cultures were also obtained in most generations from crosses between I C and II C, I H and II H, I L and II L and between High and Low lines. Each F_1 assay involved 20 flies of each sex from each of 4 single-pair cultures, two of each reciprocal cross. In the H×L F_1s the four cultures were of

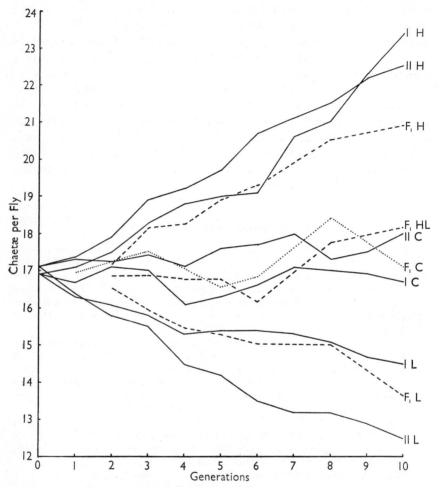

Fig. 2.—Mean sternopleural chaeta number in the lines and their F_1 crosses. Solid curves, the lines. Broken curves, the F_1s between selected lines. Dotted, the F_1s between the control lines. (The F_1s are plotted with the generation with which they were cultured.)

4 crosses, I H× II L, II L× I H, II H× I L and I L× II H. Parents for F_1 cultures were chosen at random.

All cultures were set up in standard half-pint milk bottles with standard corn-meal black-treacle agar medium, inoculated with live baker's yeast. Counts and matings were made on Tuesdays and Wednesdays, the mating pairs being placed in 2×1 in. tubes. The cultures were set up on Saturday (having been poured on Thursday and yeasted Friday), and the parents were removed on Tuesday. Emergence of adults began the following Monday and the flies were sexed and separated morning and evening until and including Thursday, by which time emergence was usually complete. The flies were preserved until Tuesday for counting. This routine means keeping the flies for some time and forces a three-week generation, but it is simple to manage and usually permits collection of all the progeny before selection, a matter that may be of some importance (*cf.* Durrant, 1955).

4. RESULTS

Fig. 2 shows that the response to selection in the four selection lines was good, and that the control lines, though differing somewhat, remained fairly steadily near their original chaeta numbers.

Table 3 gives the A/T figures, multiplied by 1000 for convenience, for each of the six lines, and for each of the four F_1s which are classed with the generations with which they were grown.

TABLE 3

A/T × 1000 for the lines and their F_1 crosses

Generation :	0	1	2	3	4	5	6	7	8	9	10
I Control . .	52	56	53	46	58	50	53	52	46	50	53
II Control . .	49	49	55	54	58	62	53	54	56	50	51
F_1 .	...	50	57	58	48	55	53	...	54	...	60
I High . .	...	47	59	60	51	50	58	62	53	58	59
II High . .	...	50	54	62	62	54	62	61	63	57	66
F_1 . .	...	...	50	57	62	58	57	...	48	...	56
I Low . .	...	55	48	53	56	57	57	54	55	57	64
II Low . .	...	55	58	49	57	52	59	52	56	55	62
F_1 . .	...	...	49	55	53	53	55	...	58	...	62
High/Low F_1 .	...	...	54	50	56	56	58	...	55	...	58

Fig. 3 shows A/T for the selected and the control lines and table 4 the corresponding analysis of variance. The following points emerge :

1. A/T is higher in the selection lines than in the controls.
2. There is no significant difference between mean A/T for high and low lines, indicating that A/T is a measure satisfactorily compensating for the relationship between arithmetical asymmetry and total chaeta number.
3. A/T does not vary significantly with generation in the controls, but there is a highly significant increase with generations of selection. Furthermore there is no suggestion of differences between the regression slopes of the four selection lines. Both high and low selection result in such an increase. (The regression coefficients of A/T ×1000 on generation are : I C $-0·3000$, II C $0·1091$, I H $0·6545$, II H $1·2545$, I L $0·8364$, II L $0·6091$).

The mean bristle numbers for the F_1 cultures are illustrated in fig. 2, along with those of the lines. They are plotted with the generation with which they were cultured, not with that which provided their parents. Having due regard to the fact that the parents of the F_1 cultures were chosen at random, it seems clear that the bristle numbers of F_1 flies show little evidence of overall dominance.

177

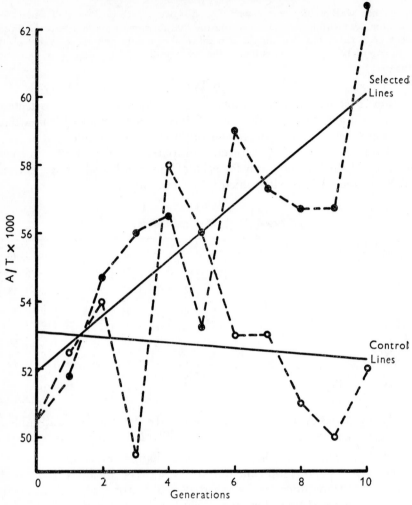

FIG. 3.—Asymmetry in the selected and control lines.

TABLE 4

Analysis of variance of $A/T \times 1000$ for the lines

Source	Sum of squares	N	M.S.	P
Joint regression on generations	183·4909	I	183·4909	≃0·001
Difference selected and control regressions	127·9704	I	127·9704	<0·01
Difference High and Low regressions	5·9113	I	5·9113	...
Difference selected and control means	150·6439	I	150·6439	<0·01
Difference High and Low means .	31·0834	I	31·0834	...
Residual differences between means	66·4090	3	22·1363	...
Error	866·2638	53	16·3446	...
Total . . .	1431·7727	61	...	...

Table 3 lists the A/T values for the F_1 cultures and those for the F_1s between the selected lines are illustrated in fig. 4. Table 5 gives

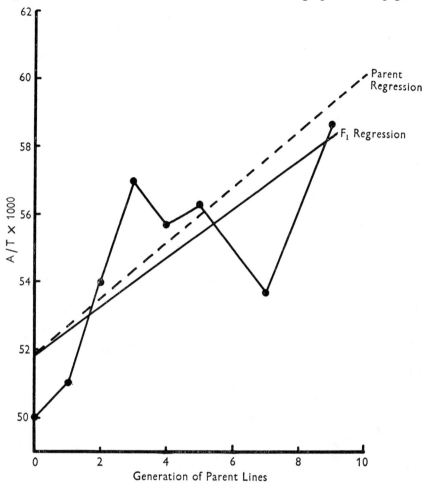

FIG. 4.—Asymmetry of the F_1s between selected lines. The regression for the selected lines is plotted as well as the F_1 joint regression. (The F_1s are plotted with the generation that provided their parents.)

TABLE 5

Analysis of variance of F_1 $A/T \times 1000$. Selected and controls

Source	Sum of squares	N	M.S.	P
Joint regression on generations	120·8989	1	120·8989	≃0·01
Difference between selected and control regressions	1·8169	1	1·8169	...
Residual difference between regressions	42·0739	2	21·0369	...
Error	309·1791	24	12·8825	...
Total . . .	473·9688	28	...	...

the analysis of variance of F_1 A/T. The joint regression of A/T on generation for the F_1s is significant and there is no significant difference of behaviour over the generations between the different types of F_1. However, the control F_1 regression is not by itself significant and it is lower than the joint regression for the selected F_1s. The control F_1s do not therefore provide sufficient data to be useful. The F_1s between the selected lines, on the other hand, do. It is clear (fig. 4) that the F_1s between the selected lines increase in A/T in exactly the same way as the selected lines themselves.

Now if the deterioration of the selected lines arose because of increasing homozygosity, their F_1s should show lower A/T values than the lines, unless the lines crossed to give the F_1s had identical genotypes, which is unlikely for all and impossible for the H ×L F_1s. It would therefore appear that increasing homozygosity in the selected lines cannot be invoked as an explanation of their increasing asymmetry.

There is, however, one possibility that might render this conclusion invalid. If asymmetry were a character *entirely* determined by maternal genotype and completely independent of the genotype of the individual in which it is measured, then the F_1s would be expected to show the same asymmetry as the parent. If this asymmetry arose from maternal homozygosity, we should then expect reduced asymmetry in F_2, for the F_2 would have heterozygous mothers. Mather (1953*a*) did in fact find some evidence that asymmetry might *in part* be determined by maternal genotype, but only *complete* maternal inheritance would invalidate the conclusion reached above. Further, 25 F_2 cultures raised from the High ×Low F_1 after the completion of the experiment gave A/T values identical with those of 16 contemporaneously reared F_1 cultures (A/T ×1000 F_1 56·3, F_2 56·0), and it seems clear that maternal inheritance cannot be important in this experiment. It must be concluded that homozygosity is not an important factor determining the observed increase of asymmetry.

5. DISCUSSION

The results presented show clearly that directional selection can cause deterioration of the systems responsible for developmental homeostasis as here measured, and to this extent they are in agreement with Lerner's thesis. They do not, however, lend any support to Lerner's hypothesis that increasing homozygosity is the cause of the deterioration.

There are two alternative explanations which may account for the increased asymmetry. The first is similar to that put forward by Mather to explain declining fertility in selection lines. Selection produces unbalance in gene complexes linked to the genes directly concerned with the character under selection and the result is impaired fertility (Mather and Harrison, 1949). The increased asymmetry may merely be another manifestation of this poor balance.

In a discussion of the results obtained part way through the present experiment, and of those obtained with some other lines, the author (Thoday, 1956), put forward a second explanation similar to that discussed by Falconer and Robertson (1956). This was that, in selecting for a given character, we may pick out from a population not only individuals whose genotypes determine directly an extreme value for that character, but also individuals whose genotypes render them exceptionally subject to modification by the environmental variation in the culture, or exceptionally incompetent at buffering the effects of internal accidents of development, or exceptionally subject to such accidents. Selection of these latter types would lead to increase of genotype-environment interaction and/or deterioration of developmental stability. That such genes exist in *Nicotiana* has been made abundantly clear by the work of Mather and his associates (Jinks and Mather, 1955 ; Paxman, 1956), and in addition Mather (1953a) has demonstrated that sternopleural asymmetry in *Drosophila* is itself a character responsive to artificial selection. Such genes would be selected in this experiment. Provided that the same genes, or some of the same genes, that affect inter-individual variance of sternopleural number also affect asymmetry in the same direction, the present increase of A/T in the selection lines is formally explicable on the basis of such selection.

Evidence concerning coefficients of variation in the lines of this experiment might be expected to provide relevant information. Unless new mutants arise or fixed variability becomes freed at a greater rate than the available genetic variance is used up, genetic variance must decline in lines undergoing inbreeding, such as the control lines in this experiment, and in selection lines. Phenotypic variance must therefore decline unless genotype-environment interaction and/or developmental variation caused by intrinsic accidents during development increase. Selection for increase of these will, on the other hand, arrest the decline and may even produce an increase of phenotypic variance. The final result will depend upon the relative variance arising from stability genes and additive genes at the beginning of selection.

In these experiments, the variance of the control lines behaved as expected. Some of the selection lines, on the other hand, increased in variance. Furthermore, the regression slopes for coefficients of variation for the different lines fall in the same order as those for A/T, which supports the view that A/T and coefficient of variation have some common causes. The changes in variance are therefore in agreement with the hypothesis that the decline of developmental homeostasis observed in the selection lines results from the selection for low developmental stability, which in small or large degree is a necessary consequence of directional selection. This evidence is, however, of no real value, for the changes of variance are not significant and are open to other interpretations. The alternative balance hypothesis would explain them and the freeing of fixed variability in the selection lines would also explain them.

Distinction between the balance hypothesis, and that involving direct selection of genes for poor homeostasis is, however, possible. If the deterioration of homeostasis arises as a result of the selection of unbalanced gene-complexes linked to chaeta number genes, then increase of asymmetry should be greatest when the selection of extreme chaeta number genotypes is most effective. If, on the other hand, increase of asymmetry arises because of the selection of individuals whose extreme chaeta-number is caused by poor developmental canalisation instead of an extreme chaeta-number genotype, then

TABLE 6

Correlation between increase of asymmetry and $\mathrm{h}^2 = \Delta\mathrm{P}/i$ *in the selected lines*

Generation	0-1	1-2	2-3	3-4	4-5	5-6	6-7	7-8	8-9	9-10
I H A/T increase	−4·9	11·7	1·0	−8·5	−0·5	7·3	4·0	−8·6	4·5	1·5
h^2	0·05	0·19	0·30	0·17	0·05	0·04	0·39	0·13	0·33	0·27
II H A/T increase	1·4	4·3	7·6	0·4	−8·2	8·2	−1·1	1·4	−5·7	8·8
h^2	0·06	0·17	0·26	0·09	0·19	0·30	0·14	0·08	0·21	0·07
I L A/T increase	3·1	0·8	4·8	3·4	−8·5	9·2	−2·7	1·2	2·0	7·1
h^2	0·33	0·07	0·06	0·10	−0·26	0·00	0·06	0·13	0·20	0·08
II L A/T increase	6·3	7·5	−8·2	8·0	−4·8	6·6	−6·3	−3·5	−0·7	6·6
h^2	0·32	0·27	0·15	0·44	0·14	0·32	0·13	0·26	0·19	0·37

increase of asymmetry should be greatest when the selection of extreme chaeta-number genotypes is least effective.

Accordingly the regression of increase of asymmetry in a generation on the advance of chaeta number made in that generation, measured by the heritability formula $h^2 = \Delta P/i$ (Lerner, 1950), has been calculated (table 6).

The regression is positive and just significant ($t_{(38)} = 2\cdot22$, $\mathrm{P} < 0\cdot05$) suggesting that the balance hypothesis is the more important, and providing no evidence that the other effect is operative. It should, however, be borne in mind that the two hypotheses are not mutually exclusive and that direct selection of instability genes may also be effective. It might even be more important than the balance effect if heritability were relatively low and response of the primary character to selection were small, as was suggested in explanation of the behaviour of the *vg* line described by Thoday (1956).

We may now suggest the following history for poor homeostasis in a longer term selection experiment. If, at the start of the experiment, the available genetic variance directly affecting the primary character is relatively high, selection will be effective in changing the mean, but development will become gradually less stable as linked gene complexes affecting stability become unbalanced. The resulting decrease in heritability of the primary character may render more likely the direct selection of instability genes (as might occur if heritability were low at the beginning). Stability should therefore deteriorate at an increasing rate except in so far as the genetic variance of stability is used up. If, however, after a period of selection, new genetic variance directly affecting the primary character were to be produced in the line, either by mutation, recombination, or gene-interactions increasing the expressivity of existing heterozygous loci, then a new balance of selection pressures would be set that might permit rapid improvement of stability. Accelerated response to selection, or the crossing of selection lines might therefore, on these grounds, result in improvement of stability. Such was the behaviour of the *dp* line described by Thoday (1956), which showed a clear improvement in sternopleural symmetry at the same time as an accelerated response to selection. After such a response we would expect stability to begin to deteriorate once more. Whether or no the final level of instability reached might prove an effective bar to full exploitation of the genetic variance directly affecting the primary character would depend on the degree of correlation of stability with fitness in the particular population and environment. If it were an effective bar, coincident artificial selection, both for the primary character and for stability, might in the long run produce more satisfactory results than selection for the primary character alone.

6. SUMMARY

(1) It is argued from results of Beardmore that asymmetry of sternopleural chaeta number is a useful measure of developmental homeostasis.

(2) Ten generations of selection for high or low sternopleural chaeta number produced a deterioration of developmental homeostasis so measured.

(3) This decline of developmental homeostasis was not caused by increasing homozygosity, for the same deterioration was observed in crosses between the selected lines.

(4) Two alternative hypotheses are suggested. One involves direct selection of " poor-homeostasis " genes. The other involves the deteriorating balance of gene complexes linked to those directly affecting bristle number. The results indicate that the second of these is correct, but it is suggested that direct selection of instability genes may be more important when heritability is relatively low, the balance effect being more important when heritability is high enough to permit good response to selection.

Acknowledgments.—The author is greatly indebted to Mr T. B. Boam, who maintained all the cultures and assayed half the cultures in every generation, and did all the experimental work in generations 7-9 while the author was away. The experiment could not have been undertaken without the assistance of a grant made by the Agricultural Research Council.

7. REFERENCES

BEARDMORE, J. A. 1956. Environmental variation and developmental stability. Ph.D. Thesis, Sheffield.

DURRANT, A. 1955. Effect of time of embryo formation on quantitative characters in *Drosophila*. *Nature, 175,* 560.

FALCONER, D. S., AND ROBERTSON, A. 1956. Selection for environmental variation of body size in mice. *Z.I.A.V., 87,* 385-391.

JINKS, J. L., AND MATHER, K. 1955. Stability of development of heterozygotes. *P.R.S.,* B, *143,* 561-578.

LERNER, I. M. 1950. *Population Genetics and Animal Improvement.* Cambridge University Press.

LERNER, I. M. 1954. *Genetic Homeostasis.* Oliver and Boyd, Edinburgh.

LEWONTIN, R. C. 1956. Studies on homeostasis and heterozygosity. *Amer. Nat., 90,* 237-256.

MATHER, K. 1950. The genetic architecture of heterostyly in *Primula sinensis. Evolution, 4,* 340-352.

MATHER, K. 1953a. Genetical control of stability in development. *Heredity, 7,* 297-336.

MATHER, K. 1953b. The genetical structure of populations. *Symp. Soc. Exp. Biol., 7,* 66-95.

MATHER, K., AND HARRISON, B. J. 1949. The manifold effects of selection. *Heredity, 3,* 1-52, 131-162.

PAXMAN, G. J. 1956. Differentiation and stability in the development of *Nicotiana rustica. Ann. Bot.,* N.S., *20,* 330-347.

PLUNKETT, C. R. 1927. The interaction of genetic and environmental factors in development. *J. Exp. Zool., 46,* 181-245.

RASMUSSON, M. 1955. Selection for bristle-number in some unrelated strains of *Drosophila melanogaster. Acta Zool., 36,* 1-49.

REEVE, E. C. R., AND ROBERTSON, F. 1954. Studies in quantitative inheritance. VI. Sternite chaeta number in *D. melanogaster. z. Vererbungslehre, 86,* 269-288.

SISMANIDES, A. 1942. Selection for an almost invariable character in *Drosophila. J. Genet., 44,* 204-215.

TEBB, G., AND THODAY, J. M. 1954. Stability in development and relational balance of X-chromosomes in *Drosophila melanogaster. Nature, 174,* 1109.

THODAY, J. M. 1953. Components of fitness. *Symp. Soc. Exp. Biol., 7,* 96-113.

THODAY, J. M. 1956. Balance, heterozygosity and developmental stability. *Cold Spr. Harbr. Symp. Quant. Biol., 21,* 318-326.

WADDINGTON, C. H., GRABER, H., AND WOOLF, B. 1957. Iso-alleles and response to selection. *J. Genet., 55,* 246-250.

THE ROLE OF HETEROZYGOSITY IN *DROSOPHILA* POPULATIONS[1]

Bruce Wallace[2]

POPULATIONS of a species in which two or more phenotypically distinct forms occur sympatrically with relatively high and constant frequencies have been known for a long time. These are known as "polymorphic" species; the phenomenon is referred to as "balanced polymorphism" (Ford, 1940). Fisher (1930) outlined a genetic basis for the maintenance of a polymorphic system. The essential part of his argument lies in the selective superiority of heterozygous individuals; virtually any equilibrium frequency can be maintained in a population if the two homozygotes are to some extent at a selective disadvantage relative to the corresponding heterozygote.

The known cases of balanced polymorphism have increased in number since 1930. Not only have the recognized instances of phenotypic polymorphism been extended but numerous instances of "cryptic" polymorphism have been discovered as well. The latter cases include the numerous naturally occurring inversion systems in *Drosophila* and other Diptera (see Da Cunha, 1955), the cytologically altered chromosomes in grasshoppers (reviewed by White, 1954), and the chromosomal interchanges common in certain plant species (see, for example, Cleland, 1958).

For the purposes of the present discussion I will consider heterosis as equivalent to the selective advantage of heterozygous individuals which results in balanced polymorphism. Heterosis used in this sense corresponds to *euheterosis* as used by Dobzhansky (1952). I will not be concerned with the underlying mechanisms which give rise to heterosis; various possibilities are listed in Table I. It will be noted that heterosis *per se* can be explained as shown in the table on the basis of pleiotropic gene action which is equivalent in principle to the exploitation of diverse ecological niches or temporal fluctuations in environmental conditions; it can also be explained on the basis of properties of heterozygotes which are unique and which cannot be copied by either of the two homozygotes (Haldane, 1954; Robertson and Reeve, 1952).

At the present time there are probably more known—and better understood— instances of cryptic than of non-cryptic polymorphism. The so-called "cryptic" polymorphic traits, however, are really morphological traits made visible by cytological examination of chromosomes. The number of recognizably different, co-existent "cryptic" systems is frequently large. Dobzhansky and his co-workers in Brazil (Da Cunha, *et al.*, 1950; Dobzhansky and Da Cunha, 1954) have described a number of populations of *D. willistoni* in which the average number of inversion differences per individual is eight or more. The existence of these inversions appears to be correlated with the local diversity of ecological niches available to the species. Quite obviously the number of cytologically detectable polymorphic systems is limited by the chromosomal complexity which confronts the investigator, the clarity of the cytological picture which the species provides, and the limit of microscopic visibility. One may be excused, then, for speculating on the frequency of truly

[1]The work reported in this paper has been done under Contract No. AT–(30–1)–557, United States Atomic Energy Commission.
[2]Biological Laboratory, Cold Spring Harbor, N.Y., U.S.A.

Reprinted by permission of University of Toronto Press from
PROCEEDINGS XTH INTERNATIONAL CONGRESS OF GENETICS, 1,
408–419 (1958).

TABLE I

SEVERAL POSSIBLE MECHANISMS BY WHICH HETERO-
ZYGOUS INDIVIDUALS MAY ATTAIN HIGHER AVERAGE
FITNESSES THAN THEIR CORRESPONDING HOMO-
ZYGOTES

	AA	Aa	aa
1*	1	1	$1-s_1$
2	$1-s_2$	1	1
3	$1-s_3$	1	1
4	1	1	$1-s_4$
.	.	.	.
.	.	.	.
.	.	.	.
i	$1-s_i$ (or 1)	1	1 (or $1-s_i$)
Product	$1-s_A$	1	$1-s_a$

*The succession of numbers 1, 2, 3, . . . , i may
represent: (a) different ecological niches within a
single locality (Levene, 1953); (b) different environmental conditions prevailing in successive
generations (Dempster, 1955); (c) different developmental processes governed by pleiotropic
gene action (Caspari, 1950).

cryptic, heterotic systems; instances of heterosis at individual gene loci, for
example, which are not detectable by presently available techniques.

In essence, one would like to estimate, if possible, the frequency of heterozygosity in terms of gene loci at which representative individuals of a population
are heterozygous. It is entirely inadequate for this purpose to estimate the proportion of individuals heterozygous for genes at one or more loci; surely the proportion
of such individuals approaches 100 per cent even in the absence of heterosis.
Rather, what is needed is some technique for screening individuals with the
purpose of determining the mean frequency of loci occupied by dissimilar alleles
and the distribution of frequencies about this mean. At the same time, it would
be desirable to exclude from the estimated mean frequency those instances of
heterozygosis which arise passively from mutation pressure, from an influx of non-
heterotic alleles by migration, and from relic alleles favorable at some earlier time
but now in the process of being eliminated from the population.

Our experimental approach to this problem has consisted of an anlysis of the
viability effects of radiation-induced mutations in heterozygous condition. Underlying our approach is the tacit admission that present techniques do not allow us to
recognize all possible differences between alleles and, therefore, do not assure us
of recognizing heterozygosity as such where it exists. On the other hand, we do
have techniques which allow us to create individuals which are homozygous for
genes at large numbers of loci (entire chromosomes or, if desirable, entire sets of
chromosomes). We should be able, then, to draw inferences concerning the
viability effects of these genes if we determine the average effect of newly induced
mutations in heterozygous condition. We must assume, of course, that the new
mutations are distributed at random among loci and represent an adequate sample
of the array of alleles which might arise spontaneously at any locus.

The rationale for this type of approach is represented in Figure 1 by contrasting
one's expectations under two extreme models—one based on the universal selective
superiority of homozygous individuals and the other on that of heterozygotes. In

SITUATIONS PREDICTED BY
EXTREME MODELS BASED ON

	HOMOZYGOTE SUPERIORITY	HETEROZYGOTE SUPERIORITY
SELECTION'S GOAL— THE "IDEAL" GENOTYPE	$\underline{ABCDEFGH}$ ········· $\overline{ABCDEFGH}$ ········	$A_1 B_9 C_2 D_7 E_3 F_5 G_4$ ·· $\overline{A_7 B_5 C_6 D_2 E_1 F_4 G_3}$ ··
GENOTYPE OF AN AVERAGE INDIVIDUAL UNDER ORDINARY CONDITIONS	$\underline{ABCDeFGH}$ ····· $\overline{aBCDEFGH}$ ·····	$A_1 B_9 C_7 D_6 E_4 F_5 G_8$ ·· $\overline{A_1 B_6 C_5 D_7 E_4 F_9 G_{23}}$ ··
GENOTYPE OF AN INDIVIDUAL WHICH IS HOMOZYGOUS FOR A CHROMOSOME OF THE SORT COMMONLY FOUND IN POPULATIONS	$\underline{ABCDeFGH}$ ····· $\overline{ABCDeFGH}$ ·····	$A_1 B_9 C_7 D_6 E_4 F_5 G_8$ · $\overline{A_1 B_9 C_7 D_6 E_4 F_5 G_8}$ ··
GENOTYPE OF AN INDIVIDUAL SIMILAR TO THE ONE ABOVE BUT NOW WITH A NEW MUTATION (') IN THE HETEROZYGOUS CONDITION	$\underline{ABCDeFGH}$ ···· $\overline{Ab'CDeFGH}$ ····	$A_1 B_9 C_7 D_6 E_4 F_5 G_8$ · $\overline{A_1 B' C_7 D_6 E_4 F_5 G_8}$ ·

FIGURE 1. A schematic representation of expectations based on two extreme genetic models of population structure. A possibility for differentiating between these two models experimentally is outlined in the text.

the former we postulate that there is a "normal" or "type" gene at each locus, that mutant alleles are invariably deleterious when homozygous, and that heterozygous individuals never exceed the normal homozygotes in fitness or in viability. In the second model we postulate that at each locus there are a number of alleles which in heterozygous combinations give rise to "normal" individuals; the average fitness or viability of these heterozygotes exceeds that of individuals homozygous for any of the individual alleles. One need not postulate that every allele is capable of taking part in these heterotic combinations; certain mutations may be deleterious in virtually all gene combinations.

The first two entries under each theoretical model shown in the figure emphasize that the extreme situation predicted by either model (complete homozygosis of every individual for the "type" genes of a species or heterozygosity at every locus in the second model) does not exist in any real population. Homozygous superiority does not lead to complete homozygosity even in the absence of heterosis; mutations and alterations in selective pressures serve to maintain a small proportion of heterozygous loci. Similarly, in the absence of any mechanism for maintaining a series of unique alleles at every locus, some homozygosis must occur in a population even though heterozygotes are favored at each of these loci.

The third entry in the figure represents the genotype of an individual homozygous for a chromosome chosen at random from a population. It is well known for *Drosophila* that such individuals have an average viability lower than that of individuals heterozygous for two different chromosomes chosen at random. The lower viability of these homozygotes is predicted by both models. Even though selection may favor individuals homozygous for normal alleles, deleterious mutant genes are

187

sufficiently common that one or more of these is likely to be included among the genes carried by a given chromosome. The few that are included in this way are the limiting factors in determining the viability of individuals homozygous for an entire chromosome. The alternative model also predicts that individuals homozygous for an entire chromosome will be less viable than one heterozygous for two different chromosomes since, by definition, the genes present in the population have been selected on the basis of an average selective superiority of heterozygous individuals.

The last entry in the figure shows how one might possibly distinguish between the two models experimentally and decide which is more nearly correct. A homozygous individual is shown which is identical in all respects to that of the third entry except for the presence of a new, randomly induced mutation in one but not in the other of the two chromosomes. If selection favors "normal" homozygotes, most genes in a population will be represented by "normal" alleles; consequently, a new mutation induced at random will most likely be one that changes a normal gene to a deleterious allele. In order for a random mutation to improve the viability of the homozygous individual, the newly induced mutant allele must interact specifically and favorably with the few deleterious mutations already present or it must represent a back-mutation at a locus occupied by a deleterious allele. Both of these can be regarded as highly unlikely events. In contrast to these expectations, viability improvement as a result of a random mutation need not be a rare event if heterosis is a common phenomenon. First, no matter what locus on the chromosome is affected by radiation, the new mutation results in heterozygosis at that locus; this is a matter of definition. Second, the probability that this heterozygosity will increase the viability of the otherwise homozygous individual depends upon the relative proportions of alleles which act in a heterotic fashion or in a deleterious manner in combination with the original allele. Although the proportion of heterotic alleles may be small, one might hope, if selection does in reality favor heterozygous individuals, that it is large compared to the probability of getting a "beneficial" mutation under the alternative model.

An experimental technique for testing the effect of random mutations on viability is illustrated in Figure 2. A full description of this method has been published elsewhere (Wallace, 1958); for the present it is sufficient to give a simple outline of the system. In *Drosophila melanogaster* entire second chromosomes can be manipulated in breeding experiments by the use of a genetically marked (*Cy*, curly wings; *L*, lobe eye) chromosome carrying two large inversions which act as crossover suppressors. The *CyL* chromosome is maintained in a stock (*CyL/Pm*) whose other second chromosome is marked by the dominant gene *Pm* (plum eye color).

The upper portion of Figure 2 illustrates the isolation of a second chromosome from an experimental population (our population no. 18; see Wallace, 1956). Wild-type males from the population were mated with *CyL/Pm* females. Single *CyL/+* F_1 males were backcrossed with *CyL/Pm* females. Several *Pm/+* F_2 males and *CyL/+* F_2 females of each culture were mated, brother with sister, to give F_3 cultures containing, among other types of flies, wild-type individuals homozygous for one of the second chromosomes carried by each of the original wild-type males. Four chromosomes which gave viable, fertile homozygous individuals were chosen from among those tested.

The center portion of Figure 2 illustrates how each of the four chromosomes was transferred by repeated backcrossing into the genetic background of our

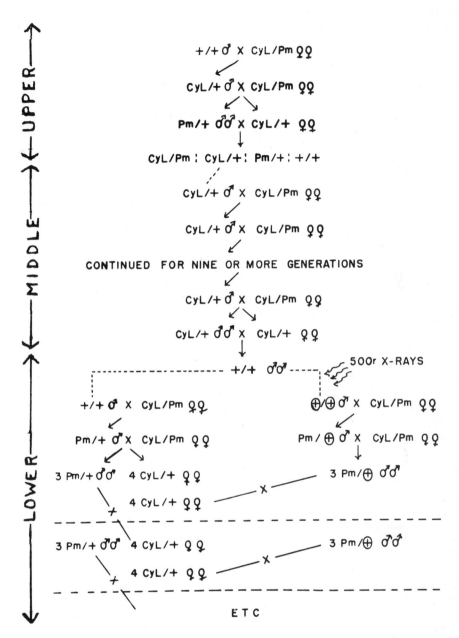

FIGURE 2. Mating scheme used to test the effects on viability of new mutations in hetero-zygous condition.

CyL/Pm stock of flies. Each generation a single $CyL/+$ male was chosen from each of the four chromosomal strains and these males were mated with CyL/Pm females. After nine or more generations of backcrosses it is most likely that all of the chromosomes other than the wild-type second were replaced by those of the balancer stock. The use of a single $CyL/+$ male in each of these crosses prevented an accumulation of a variety of wild-type second chromosomes in this material.

The lower portion of the figure illustrates the experimental crosses which lead to the evaluation of the viability effects of new mutations in heterozygous condition. Males homozygous for any one of the four chromosomes were obtained by mating $CyL/+$ males and females from one of the backcross cultures. These males (approximately four hundred in number) were divided into two groups of which one was exposed to about 500 r X-radiation. Both exposed and non-exposed males were mated individually with CyL/Pm females in vials. Single $Pm/+$ F_1 males from each vial were backcrossed to CyL/Pm females. In the irradiated material, three $Pm/(+)$ F_2 males were obtained from each culture. (Irradiated wild-type chromosomes are designated as $(+)$.) From the non-irradiated cultures, three $Pm/+$ F_2 males and eight $CyL/+$ F_2 females were collected. Four of the $CyL/+$ females of each culture were mated with $Pm/(+)$ males of an X-ray culture; the offspring expected from these matings are CyL/Pm, $CyL/(+)$, $Pm/+$ and $+/(+)$ in equal proportions. The remaining four $CyL/+$ females of each culture were mated with $Pm/+$ males of a different control culture; the offspring expected from these matings are also CyL/Pm, $CyL/+$, $Pm/+$ and $+/+$ in equal proportions.

These two series of cultures allow us to determine the average effect of newly induced mutations in heterozygous condition. With the exception of those mutations induced by irradiation, the two series of cultures—control and X-ray—are virtually identical. Thus, differences in the amount by which the Mendelian ratios are distorted by differential viabilities of developing larvae in the two series can be ascribed to mutations induced by exposure to X-radiation.

The mating scheme outlined above can be—and has been—modified in different experiments so that (1) the $Pm/+$ flies of the X-ray series rather than the $CyL/+$ flies carried an irradiated chromosome, and (2) the chromosomes other than the second in the control cultures were exposed to radiation as were those of the X-ray series.

The results of seven large experiments involving the examination of more than nine thousand cultures and the counting of more than three and a quarter million flies are summarized in Table II. On the left are listed the average viabilities of CurlyLobe, Plum, and wild-type flies of the control and X-ray series in each of the different experiments; the viability of CyL/Pm flies is 1.000 in all cases. Although significant differences in the viability of $+/+$ and $+/(+)$ flies were observed in only two of the individual experiments (2–9M, 15–22F), the viability of $+/(+)$ individuals exceeds that of the control homozygotes in all six experiments. The over-all probability that the mean difference observed (1 1/2 per cent) is the result of chance is .002. (Note that the seventh experiment involves not homozygous wild-type flies but flies heterozygous for two different chromosomes.)

The relative viabilities of CurlyLobe flies in the X-ray series ($CyL/(+)$) are larger than those of their corresponding controls ($CyL/+$) in four of five experiments; in one experiment (2–9M) the difference is significant at the 5 per cent level. The over-all probability that the mean difference observed (0.9 per cent) is the result of chance is .04.

190

TABLE II

RESULTS OF SEVEN EXPERIMENTS IN WHICH THE VIABILITY OF INDIVIDUALS CARRYING RANDOMLY INDUCED MUTATIONS IS COMPARED WITH THAT OF THEIR NON-IRRADIATED CONTROLS

Experiment	C X	A			Number of cultures	B		
		$CyL/+$ $CyL/(+)$	$Pm/+$ $Pm/+$	$+/+$ $+/(+)$		$CyL/+$ $CyL/(+)$	$Pm/+$ $Pm/+$	$+/+$ $+/(+)$
2–9M	C	1.094	1.146	1.008	766	.955	1.000	.880
	X	1.115	1.137	1.033	764	.981	1.000	.909
6–14F	C	1.093	1.139	1.000	676	.960	1.000	.878
	X	1.108	1.140	1.007	672	.972	1.000	.883
15–22F	C	1.105	1.137	.989	636	.972	1.000	.870
	X	1.110	1.145	1.015	637	.969	1.000	.887
19–26M	C	1.100	1.143	.979	596	.962	1.000	.857
	X	1.108	1.136	.989	598	.975	1.000	.871
	C	$CyL/+$	$Pm/+$	$+/+$		$CyL/+$	$Pm/+$	$+/+$
	X	$CyL/+$	$Pm/(+)$	$+/(+)$		$CyL/+$	$Pm/(+)$	$+/(+)$
11–18M	C	1.098	1.127	.983	639	1.000	1.026	.895
	X	1.095	1.125	.990	637	1.000	1.027	.904
37–43M	C	1.154	1.189	.992	499	1.000	1.030	.860
	X	1.147	1.201	1.002	496	1.000	1.047	.874
	C	$CyL/+$	$Pm/+$	$+^1/+^2$		$CyL/+$	$Pm/+$	$+^1/+^2$
	X	$CyL/(+)$	$Pm/+$	$+^1/(+^2)$		$CyL/(+)$	$Pm/+$	$+^1/(+^2)$
23–34H	C	1.185	1.215	1.143	839	.975	1.000	.941
	X	1.182	1.222	1.155	837	.967	1.000	.945

A. CyL/Pm, not shown, has viability 1.000 by definition. B. Figures listed under "A" readjusted so that the class of flies ($Pm/+$ or $CyL/+$) of the X-ray series which is free of an irradiated second chromosome becomes the standard for comparing relative viabilities.

The viabilities of Plum flies heterozygous for non-irradiated wild-type chromosomes do not differ significantly between the two series in any single experiment or in the consolidated results of all experiments.

On the right side of the table we have adjusted the viabilities listed on the left so that the class of flies free of an irradiated chromosome in the X-ray series has been assigned in both the X-ray and control series a relative viability of 1.000. It can be seen once more that the $+/(+)$ flies of the X-ray series have consistently higher viabilities than those of the controls. As for the $CyL/(+)$ flies of the X-ray series, we now find that in two of the five experiments their relative viabilities are lower than those of the $CyL/+$ flies of the control series.

A full discussion of the additional tests to which these experimental data have been subjected will be given elsewhere (Wallace, 1958). For the moment we will simply mention that the two series of cultures, X-ray and control, did not differ significantly in mean culture size (mean difference of less than one fly in cultures whose average size was about 350 flies); classes of flies which were expected to have the same mean viabilities in the two series did in fact have the same viabilities; the mean variances of viabilities and even the distributions of these variances (Figure 3) of different classes and of numbers of flies per culture did not, with the

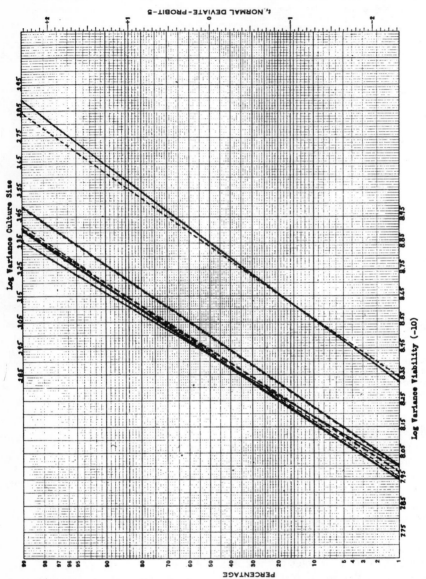

FIGURE 3. Distributions of log variances of relative viabilities of CurlyLobe, Plum, and wild-type flies (lower scale) and of numbers of flies per culture (upper scale). Variances are between cultures (usually twenty) counted by various individuals in each experiment. Dotted lines represent X-ray series of cultures; solid lines, control. The CurlyLobe and wild-type flies of both series of the two series have very similar mean variances; these are the four curves clustered at the left; heavy lines are wild type, light lines are CurlyLobe. The Plum flies of the two series are not expected to differ; these two curves are those which are nearly superimposed and which lie to the right of the four previous curves. The two curves for variances of numbers of flies per culture

exception of the $CyL/+$ and $CyL/(+)$ classes, differ significantly between the two series. The mean variance of the viabilities of the CurlyLobe flies did not differ but the distribution of variances for $CyL/+$ flies of the control cultures was somewhat more uniform than that of the corresponding class $(CyL/(+))$ of the X-ray series. We conclude, therefore, that the two series of cultures are comparable, that the larger proportion of wild-type flies in the X-ray series is real, and that this represents an actual increase in viability (or developmental rate) caused by the newly induced mutant alleles. We admit that these conclusions are tentative and that they may be modified by a more elaborate analysis of available data or by additional experiments. However, we can, on the basis of these conclusions, anticipate some of the more obvious alternative explanations of our results, explanations which avoid or restrict the role of heterosis.

There are a number of alternative explanations for these results which do not rely on heterosis. First, for example, one can claim that most radiation-induced mutations are dominant enhancers of viability. This possibility has been rejected because it raises problems more serious than the one it answers. It suggests that in large populations selection leads to the fixation of deleterious alleles at most loci but it gives no logical explanation why this should be so. Furthermore, it suggests that were we to test irradiated chromosomes in homozygous condition, we would find the same improvement in viability that we have seen in our experiments; this is contrary to the experience of radiation geneticists. We include in this rejected hypothesis the suggestion that the mutations we have induced improve viability of homozygotes because these are "abnormal" individuals. According to the model based on the superiority of homozygotes, an individual which is homozygous for a given chromosome differs only slightly from an individual heterozygous for two different chromosomes. To say that a random mutation improves the viability of homozygotes because these are "abnormal" is equivalent to claiming that specific, compensatory interactions are the rule and not the exception. An additional implication of this last argument is that the effect of mutations on viability is that of a regression towards the mean—individuals with poor viability would be improved and those with high viability would be harmed by new mutations; the average viability of individuals in a population would, in that case, represent a stable equilibrium based on mutation but virtually independent of mutation rates.

A second possible explanation for our data can be based on the recessivity of deleterious mutations and the dominance of mutations which improve viability. The average increase in viability observed in our experiments would, according to this scheme, result from the detection of dominant (not heterotic) viability modifiers only. This explanation, too, has been rejected. First, dominance and recessivity are not sufficiently complete to make this hypothesis entirely convincing. Second, even if dominance and recessivity were complete, the absolute minimum number of mutational changes per locus for any set of genes having a given effect on viability can be shown to equal $d\sqrt{(us)}$ where d is the observed increase in viability, u the spontaneous mutation rate, and s the reduction in viability characteristic of the genes of this particular set. By absolute minimum we mean that every induced mutation would be a mutation of the minus modifier present on the chromosome to its normal allele only. The number of mutations per chromosome demanded by this explanation appears to be unreasonably high even for material such as ours which has been obtained from a population whose past history includes chronic exposure to radiation.

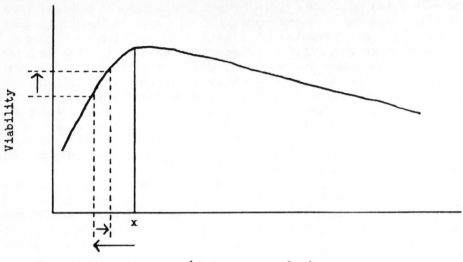

FIGURE 4. An illustration depicting how "optimal hybridity" might possibly explain the experimental results listed in Table II. If heterozygosis at x per cent of all loci is optimal, the viability of the homozygous control flies is lowered as indicated by the lower arrow. Induced mutations, by partially restoring the optimal proportion of heterozygosity (small arrow), might be expected to result in a slight increase in viability as well. See text for reasons for discarding this hypothesis.

A final alternative explanation for our results can be found in the postulate of "optimal hybridity" or "optimum heterozygosity," a postulate which admits the existence of heterosis but restricts it to a small fraction of all loci. According to this hypothesis our control homozygotes $(+/+)$ had less than the optimal degree of heterozygosity and through irradiation we improved viability by partially restoring this optimum (Fig. 4).

Unless the above hypothesis is extended to include an optimum of 100 per cent heterozygosity, it too is rejected. X-ray induced mutations are presumably distributed at random among loci and, hence, there does not appear to be a fixed set of loci reserved for heterotic effects. If the optimal proportion of heterozygous loci is small, geographically isolated populations would most likely utilize multiple allelic series at different loci in maintaining this optimum within their individual members. The probability that exactly the same loci would be utilized by isolated populations would be negligible. One would predict, then, that inter-population F_1 hybrid individuals would have more than the optimum proportion of heterozygosity and as a result would be somewhat inviable. On the contrary, these inter-population hybrids are almost always more viable than are members of a single population; inviability, if it occurs in *Drosophila*-strain hybrids, is primarily a consequence of recombination in the F_2 and later generations (Vetukhiv, 1952, 1954, 1956; Wallace, 1955; Wallace and Vetukhiv, 1955).

A second version of the same explanation—optimal hybridity—is also rejected. In this version the optimal proportion of heterozygosity per individual is a low percentage which is met at the population level not by many alleles at a few loci but by a low frequency of mutant alleles at many loci. This is rejected because of the improbability, should the number of heterotic alleles at each locus be restricted, that a random mutation will give rise precisely to that allele which produces the heterotic effect. It is rejected on the additional grounds that wild-type "isoalleles" are not uncommon in nature. Stern and Schaeffer (1943) found that of three wild-type alleles at the ci locus in $D.$ $melanogaster$ which they examined, each was demonstrably different from the other two. It is difficult to reconcile this finding with a predominantly common "normal" gene and a family of rare but heterotic mutant alleles at each locus.

As a result of the studies described above, we are adopting the tentative conclusion that heterosis plays a fundamental role in the genetic structure of Drosophila populations. We feel that at every locus there are heterozygous combinations of alleles which, on the average, give rise to individuals of higher viabilities or greater fitnesses than do homozygous combinations of the same alleles. Subject to the limitations imposed by chance elimination of alleles, by mating of close relatives, and by the finite number of alleles at a locus, we feel that the proportion of heterozygosis among gene loci of representative individuals of a population tends toward 100 per cent.

We suspect, though, that the heterotic effect exhibited by two alleles at one locus is not independent of the proportion of heterozygosity at other loci. It is difficult, for example, to imagine under the conditions of our experiments an increase in viability of 1½ per cent per locus (or per few loci) accompanying mutations at each of hundreds of additional loci. On the other hand, we do not visualize the change in sign for the viability effects of heterozygosity that the hypothesis of optimal hybridity seems to demand. That heterosis at a locus is a function of the background genotype has been suggested by the work of Robertson and Reeve (1955), Tantawy (1957), and Tantawy and Reeve (1956). These workers suggest that under a program of inbreeding it becomes increasingly difficult to attain homozygosis at unfixed loci as the proportion of fixed loci increases. Our experiments represent another approach to this question and appear to confirm the above suggestion for the improvement in viability accompanying the first increment of heterozygosity appears to be too large to accompany each additional increment.

REFERENCES

CLELAND, R. E. 1958. The evolution of the North American Oenotheras of the "biennis" group. Planta 51: 378–398.

DA CUNHA, A. B. 1946. Polymorphism in natural populations of a species of $Drosophila$. J. Hered. 37: 253–256.

——— 1955. Chromosomal polymorphism in the Diptera. Advance. Genet. 7: 93–138.

DA CUNHA, A. B., H. BURLA, and TH. DOBZHANSKY. 1950. Adaptive chromosomal polymorphism in $Drosophila$ $willistoni$. Evolution 4: 212–235.

DA CUNHA, A. B., and TH. DOBZHANSKY. 1954. A further study of chromosomal polymorphism in $Drosophila$ $willistoni$ in its relation to the environment. Evolution 8: 119–134.

DOBZHANSKY, TH. 1952. Nature and origin of heterosis. In Heterosis: A Record of Researches Directed toward Explaining and Utilizing the Vigor of Hybrids, ed., J. W. GOWEN, pp. 218–223. Ames, Iowa: Iowa State College Press.

FISHER, R. A. 1930. The Genetical Theory of Natural Selection. Oxford: Clarendon Press.

FORD, E. B. 1940. Polymorphism and taxonomy. In The New Systematics, ed., J. S. HUXLEY, pp. 493–513. Oxford: Clarendon Press.

HALDANE, J. B. S. 1954. The statics of evolution. In Evolution as a Process, eds., J. S. HUXLEY, A. C. HARDY, and E. B. FORD, pp. 109–121. London: Allen and Unwin.

ROBERTSON, F. W., and E. C. R. REEVE. 1952. Heterozygosity, environmental variation and heterosis. Nature *170*: 286.

———— 1955. Studies in quantitative inheritance. VIII. Further analysis of heterosis in crosses between inbred lines of *Drosophila melanogaster*. Zschr. indukt. Abstamm. *86*: 439–458.

STERN, C., and E. W. SCHAEFFER. 1943. On wild-type iso-alleles in *Drosophila melanogaster*. Proc. Nat. Acad. Sc. U.S. *29*: 361–367.

TANTAWY, A. O. 1957. Genetic variance of random-inbred lines of *Drosophila melanogaster* in relation to coefficients of inbreeding. Genetics *42*: 121–136.

TANTAWY, A. O., and E. C. R. REEVE. 1956. Studies in quantitative inheritance. IX. The effects of inbreeding at different rates in *Drosophila melanogaster*. Zschr. indukt. Abstamm. *87*: 648–667.

VETUKHIV, M. 1952. Viability of hybrids between local populations of *Drosophila pseudoobscura*. Proc. Nat. Acad. Sc. U.S. *39*: 30–34.

———— 1954. Integration of the genotype in local populations of three species of *Drosophila*. Evolution *8*: 241–251.

———— 1956. Fecundity of hybrids between geographic populations of *Drosophila pseudoobscura*. Evolution *10*:139–146.

WALLACE, B. 1955. Inter-population hybrids in *Drosophila melanogaster*. Evolution *9*: 302–316.

———— 1956. Studies on irradiated populations of *Drosophila melanogaster*. J. Genet., Cambr. *54*: 280–293.

———— 1958. The average effect of radiation-induced mutations on viability in *Drosophila melanogaster*. Evolution *12*: 532–552.

WALLACE, B., and M. VETUKHIV. 1955. Adaptive organization of the gene pools of *Drosophila* populations. Sympos. Quant. Biol. *20*: 303–310.

WHITE, M. J. D. 1954. Animal Cytology and Evolution. 2nd revised edition. London and New York: Cambridge University Press.

HOW STABLE IS BALANCED POLYMORPHISM?*

By Theodosius Dobzhansky and Olga Pavlovsky

DEPARTMENT OF ZOOLOGY, COLUMBIA UNIVERSITY

Communicated November 24, 1959

Natural populations of many species of organisms are polymorphic, i.e., are composed of two or more distinct kinds of individuals. Several genetic mechanisms may participate in the maintenance of polymorphism in populations.[1-5] One of the most widespread and interesting ones is balanced polymorphism. It has long been known[6-8] that if the heterozygotes for a pair of alleles, A_1A_2, are superior in adaptive value to the corresponding homozygotes, A_1A_1 and A_2A_2, natural selection will, in sexually reproducing and cross-fertilizing populations, establish an equilibrium state at which the two alleles, A_1 and A_2, will continue to occur in the gene pool of the population with certain predictable frequencies. This will happen even if one or both of the homozygotes are deficient in fitness, or are inviable, provided only that the heterozygote enjoys the advantages of hybrid vigor.

The mean adaptive value of the population is maximized when stable equilibrium frequencies of the alleles A_1 and A_2 are achieved. Nevertheless, the poorly adapted homozygotes continue to be born generation after generation in populations under balanced polymorphism. In other words, the population fails to reach the level of adaptedness which it would have if it were monomorphic for a genotype with an adaptive value equal to that of the A_1A_2 heterozygotes. Suppose, then, that a mutation produces an allele A_3, such that the fitness of the homozygote A_3A_3 is equal to that of the heterozygote A_1A_2. Natural selection is expected to lead to gradual elimination of A_1 and A_2, and to establishment of a population monomorphic and homozygous for A_3A_3.

These considerations have led to the view[9, 10] that balanced polymorphisms " . . . are to be regarded as temporary makeshifts that arose in the stress of comparatively rapid evolutionary flux and that are due to be rectified ultimately, when a long-term natural selection repairs its short-term imperfections and miscarriages."

Reprinted by permission of the authors from PROCEEDINGS OF THE NATIONAL ACADEMY OF SCIENCES, 46, 41–47 (1959).

The flaw in the above argument lies in the implied assumption that whatever level of adaptedness may be reached by a heterozygote A_1A_2, it can always be equalled, if not exceeded, by mutations yielding a superior allele A_3. Experimental verification or invalidation of this assumption is evidently difficult, especially if it is not specified just how "temporary makeshift" the balanced polymorphisms are expected to be. Natural populations of many species of Drosophila are balanced polymorphic systems of several gene arrangements, differing in inversions of sections of chromosomes. Although some early speculations which ascribed to inversion polymorphisms an antiquity ascending to Eocene and to Cretaceous times[11] appear to have been not well founded, there is good evidence that balanced polymorphs may not be easily replaceable. Thus in *Drosophila willistoni*, which is a species not closely associated with man, some inversion heterozygotes occur over vast territories, including much of the intertropical zone of the Western Hemisphere. A genetic variant must have existed assuredly for a long time to have spread to, and become incorporated in the gene pools of populations so numerous and so remote.

Laboratory experiments on balanced polymorphisms cover time intervals obviously small compared to the persistence of such polymorphisms in natural populations. There are two considerations, however, which make experimental approaches to the problem hopeful. In the first place, experiments are carried in laboratory environments which are of necessity unlike the natural ones. Experimental populations are thus faced with environmental challenges, to which they may respond by genetic changes adapting them to the experimental environments. A serviceable monomorphism may then be substituted for a balanced polymorphism. Secondly, what is sometimes described picturesquely as a "genetic revolution," may be produced by making experimental populations derived from founders obtained by hybridization between geographically distinct (allopatric) natural populations or races. Segregation and recombination of the genes in which the races differ supply an abundance of genetic variance. Natural selection in the experimental environments is then called upon to construct a new adaptive system, which may or may not include balanced polymorphism.

Many experimental populations of Drosophila flies, polymorphic for naturally occurring inversions, have been studied by various investigators since 1946. In most of these populations apparently balanced equilibria were attained, provided that the foundation stocks of these populations were of geographically uniform origin. It is, of course, arguable that experiments were usually discontinued too soon, before substitution of monomorphism for polymorphism could take place. The few recorded exceptions are therefore interesting. In experiments with *Drosophila pseudoobscura*, a population containing third chromosomes with ST and TL gene arrangements became, in about a year after its foundation, almost monomorphic for ST. It may be noted that TL chromosomes are relatively rare in the natural population from which the foundation stock came.[12]

In an experiment with the same species, in which chromosomes of Texas origin with AR and PP gene arrangements were involved, two experimental populations were started with equal frequencies of the two kinds of chromosomes. Some 605 days later the populations contained about 95 per cent AR and 5 per cent PP chromosomes.[13] It may be noted that in the natural populations of Texas, PP chromosomes are considerably more frequent than AR chromosomes. This shows how different may be the relative fitness of the same karyotype in natural and in experimental environments. Lewontin's experiments with similar populations brought confirmatory results.[14, 15] But in addition, Lewontin observed that the progress of the selection in the experimental populations was such as to indicate either that the environment, or that the relative fitness of the karyotypes were changing during the experiments. If the latter possibility is correct, it would follow that an evolutionary process was here enacted which led to the abrogation of the balanced polymorphism in favor of monomorphism.

That this is not a general rule for experimental populations of geographically uniform origins, is shown by the data in Table 1. These populations, of *D. pseudo-*

TABLE 1

FREQUENCIES (IN PER CENTS) OF AR CHROMOSOMES IN POPULATIONS OF *Drosophila pseudoobscura*
CONTAINING AR AND CH CHROMOSOMES KEPT AT 25°C

Days	Generations	Populations			Chi Square
		173	176	181	
0	0	20.0	20.0	20.0	..
35	1.4	39.3	40.0	40.7	0.12
70	2.8	45.0	48.3	41.3	2.92
105	4.2	50.0	50.3	*	0.15
118	4.7	..	..	55.3	..
140	5.6	60.7	56.7	*	1.21
175	7.0	57.3	..	..	..
264	10.6	..	..	67.7	..
275	11.0	*	66.3	*	1.75
302	12.1	64.3	..	..	..
365	14.6	64.3	71.3	67.7	3.37
488	19.5	..	..	69.0	..
583	23.3	*	78.3	*	8.96
610	24.4	72.7	..	..	..
649	26.0	..	..	66.3	..
790	31.6	74.7	79.7	..	1.83
980	39.2	72.0	..	60.7	8.27

obscura, contained AR and CH chromosomes from southern California (Piñon Flats). In experimental, as well as in natural populations, AR chromosomes have an advantage over CH; an equilibrium is therefore established with AR outnumbering CH. The progress of selection in three populations, Nos. 173, 176, and 181, though they were started at different times, was very similar for at least a year. This is shown by the small chi-square values in the rightmost column in Table 1; (these chi-squares have mostly 2 degrees of freedom; where samples were not taken at similar ages, interpolation was made between the successive samples; such interpolations are marked in Table 1 by asterisks). The experimental populations were kept at 25°C, but the population No. 181 spent several months at 15° when it was about 1½ years old, and was later returned to 25°. The sojourn at 15° has apparently altered its genetic properties, and it reached an equilibrium at a lower frequency of AR chromosomes than did populations Nos. 173 and 176. The chi-squares computed for the 583 day and 980 day stages indicate significant differences between No. 181 and the other two populations. All samples contained 300 chromosomes.

The progress of natural selection in populations Nos. 173 and 176, and in No. 181 during the first year of its career, can be accounted for on the assumption that the adaptive values of the three karyotypes were as follows:

AR/AR	AR/CH	CH/CH
0.78	1	0.42

The course of selection predicted on the basis of these values gives a satisfactory fit, thus indicating that the adaptive values of the karyotypes have remained constant during the course of the experiment. The aberrant behavior of No. 181 after it was exposed to changes in the temperature regimen shows, however, that even in populations of uniform geographic origin, genetic variance may be available which may be used to alter the equilibrium position of the balanced polymorphism. And the alteration was, in the present case, towards making the two gene arrangement more nearly equal in frequencies than they were in other populations, not at all towards monomorphism.

Some geographic populations of the sibling species, *Drosophila willistoni, D. paulistorum,* and *D. tropicalis* are remarkable in having more than 50 per cent of the individuals heterozygous for certain inversions in their chromosomes.[16]   In these populations, one half of the zygotes formed in every generation are handicapped genetically enough to suffer a differential mortality, even under the near-optimal conditions in laboratory cultures.   It would seem that natural selection in populations of this sort should be especially likely to lead to a monomorphic condition that would free them from the necessity of paying the "costs" of balanced polymorphism.   In August, 1956 we started two experimental populations of D. *willistoni,* using in one (No. 168) progenies of the flies collected some months earlier near Recife, Brazil, and in the other (No. 169) flies from Guaramiranga, Ceará, Brazil.[17]   The results obtained are reported in Table 2.

About 60 per cent of the individuals in the Recife population were originally heterozygous for an inversion J, in the third chromosome (IIIJ), which was present in 55 per cent in the Ceará population (Table 2).   An inversion E in the right limb

TABLE 2

Frequencies (in per cents) of Heterozygotes for Inversions IIRE, IIIJ, and IIIP in Experimental Populations of *Drosophila willistoni* Derived from Parents Collected in Two Localities in Brazil

Days	Population No. 168 (Recife) IIRE	IIIJ	IIIP	Population No. 169 (Ceara) IIRE	IIIJ
0	14	61	32	65	55
140	30.0	61.5	31.0	53.5	42.5
420	?	59.5	?	59.5	53.5
835	49.0	32.0	11.0	47.0	43.0
1110	51.0	44.0	9.0	50.0	45.0

of the second chromosome (IIRE) was, however, heterozygous in about 65 per cent of the individuals in the Ceará population, but in only 14 per cent at Recife. Moreover, about 32 per cent of the Recife population was heterozygous for the inversion P in the third chromosome (IIIP), which did not occur in Ceará at all.   Samples of 200 larvae were examined when the populations were 140, 835, and 1,110 days old from the start.   The 420-day samples were obtained by testing the zygotic constitution of 200 adult flies per population[17]; these samples are not entirely comparable with the rest.   Table 2 shows that, when the populations were slightly more than three years old, the balanced polymorphism was retained.   The frequencies of the heterozygotes have, however, undergone changes; the frequencies of IIRE and IIIJ heterozygotes decreased somewhat in the Ceará population, as did the IIIJ and especially the IIIP heterozygotes in the Recife population. The frequency of IIRE heterozygotes in the Recife population has, however, increased quite strikingly—it has more than trebled.

An unpremeditated experiment of a much longer duration, up to 211 generations, was performed by maintaining laboratory strains of *Drosophila psuedoobscura*, the wild progenitors of which were heterozygous for certain chromosomal inversions.[18] Although the maintenance of laboratory stocks involves some inbreeding, only 3 of the 27 strains which were originally polymorphic became monomorphic in the course of time. The adaptive advantage of the chromosomal heterozygotes in these populations was evidently strong enough to counteract the effects of inbreeding and genetic drift. At the same time, no well-adapted homozygotes have developed which would have permitted replacement of the polymorphism by monomorphism. It may, of course, be objected that inbred strains do not possess sufficient genetic variance to enable such evolutionary changes to take place. This stricture does not apply to experiments described below.

Chromosomally polymorphic experimental populations of Drosphila have been made using for the foundation stocks hybrids between strains of flies coming from different geographic regions. Such populations of geographically mixed origin often behave quite differently from those of geographically uniform origin.[13, 19, 20] The process of natural selection in populations of mixed geographic origin is characteristically erratic, and often quite different in replicate experiments. The balanced chromosomal polymorphism is sometimes retained and sometimes lost. The selective processes which are enacted in such populations lead to compounding of new adaptive systems from genetic fragments yielded by the hybridization of the geographic races. The replacement of the balanced polymorphisms present in the parental races by chromosomal monomorphisms certainly proves that acquisition in evolution of a balanced polymorphic condition need not be irreversible; the population is not, so to speak, committed to remain polymorphic forever. On the other hand, retention of the polymorphism shows that it may be advantageous even when the adaptive system in a population undergoes reconstruction. It has been cogently argued[14, 15] that balanced polymorphism is most likely to be retained in populations living in variable environments, and replaced by monomorphism in uniform environments. Although the environmental conditions in the experimental populations are not quite uniform, yet they are almost certainly more nearly so than in the natural habitats of Drosophila.

Levine and Beardmore[21] have maintained an experimental population of *Drosophila pseudoobscura* of mixed geographic origin (California + Mexico) for about 53 months (66 generations). In about 20 generations from the start, the population established an equilibrium of about 30–35 per cent CH and 65–70 per cent AR chromosomes, and kept it till the end of the experiment, with occasional fluctuations up to 40 per cent and down to 25 per cent of CH.

We have considered most suitable for testing the stability of balanced polymorphism the populations of *Drosophila paulistorum* and *D. willistoni* which contain, in nature, more than 50 per cent of heterozygotes for certain inversions (see above and the references 16 and 17). Two experimental populations of *D. paulistorum* were set up, with the foundation stocks of mixed geographic origin. In about 10 months, corresponding to 12–15 generations, the balanced polymorphism broke down and the populations became virtually monomorphic.[17]   A different outcome was, however, observed in the populations Nos. 178 and 179 (Table 3), the founda-

TABLE 3

Frequencies (in per cents) of Heterozygotes for Inversions IIRE and IIIJ in Experimental Populations of *Drosophila willistoni* of Hybrid Origin

| | Population No. 178 | | Population No. 179 | |
Days	IIRE	IIIJ	IIRE	IIIJ
0	41.75	52.0	41.75	52.0
300	27.5	45.0	34.0	38.0
400	33.75	35.0	38.0	34.0
640	40.5	42.0	45.5	35.0
820	45.5	45.5	52.0	34.5
980	44.0	46.0	53.5	37.0

tion stocks of which were hybrids between the experimental populations of *D. willistoni* Nos. 168 and 169 (see Table 2).

As shown in Table 3, the frequencies of the heterozygotes for the inversion IIRE decreased at first in both populations; instead of progressing towards monomorphism, the heterozygotes became, however, more frequent again, and, in fact, reached frequencies higher than they had in the foundation stocks.   The incidence of the heterozygotes for the inversion IIIJ also declined in both populations.   In No. 179 a new equilibrium was established at a level lower than in the foundation stock; in No. 178 the frequency of heterozygotes diminished at first, but later recovered a part of this initial loss, and became stabilized.   These populations apparently did not possess genetic materials from which monomorphic genetic systems conferring high adaptedness could be built.

Conclusions and Summary.—As a method of adaptation, balanced polymorphism is a costly one, since it entails production of some relatively unfit homozygotes. Balanced polymorphism is nevertheless widespread in natural populations of Drosophila and probably in other sexually reproducing organisms as well.   There is every reason to think that the chromosomal balanced polymorphisms in Drosophila are stable.   This is shown by the wide geographic distribution and the apparent antiquity of many natural polymorphisms, and also by their retention in experimental populations in which opportunities are offered for adaptive reconstruction of the genetic system.   On the other hand, establishment of balanced polymorphism in a population is not an evolutionary blind alley, as shown by the emergenec of secondary monomorphisms in some experimental populations.

From a long-range view, the evolutionary advantages of genetic systems based on balanced polymorphisms may lie, as suggested by Lerner[22] and others, in their great adaptational plasticity and in the possession of the property of genetic homeostasis.   It may also be that the fitness conferred upon their carriers by heterozygosis for balanced supergenes is not easily equalled in homozygotes.   How important are balanced polymorphisms in the genetic systems of man and of other higher organisms with limited fecundity is an open question.[23]   Chromosomal inversions of the kind known in Drosophila are unlikely to be common in mammals, but other genetic mechanisms which form and maintain balanced supergenes may exist. The losses of the homozygotes of lower fitness are more difficult to put up with, but they can be reduced by development of numerous heterotic supergenes acting like multiple alleles of single loci.

* The work reported in this article has been carried out under Contract No. AT-(30-1)-1151, U.S. Atomic Energy Commission.

[1] Dempster, E. R., *Cold Spring Harbor Symp.*, **20**, 25–32 (1955).

[2] Lewontin, R. C., *Evolution*, **9**, 27–41 (1955).

[3] Levene, H., *Amer. Natur.*, **87**, 331–333 (1953).

[4] Ludwig, W., *Neue Erg. Probl. Zool.* (Klattfestschrift), (1950).

[5] Ludwig, W., in G. Heberer's *Die Evolution der Organismen*, **1**, 663–712 (1959).

[6] Haldane, J. B. S., *Proc. Cambridge Philos. Soc.*, **26**, 220–230 (1926).

[7] Fisher, R. A., *The Genetic Theory of Natural Selection*, (Oxford: Clarendon, 1930).

[8] Wright, S., *Genetics*, **16**, 97–159 (1931).

[9] Muller, H. J., *Amer. Jour. Human Genetics*, **2**, 111–176 (1950).

[10] Muller, H. J., *Proc. X Internat. Congr. Genetics*, **1**, 306–317 (1959).

[11] Epling, C., Carnegie Inst. Washington, Publ. 554 (1944), pp. 145–183.

[12] Dobzhansky, Th., *Genetics*, **33**, 588–602 (1948).

[13] Dobzhansky, Th., *Cold Spring Harbor Symp.*, **22**, 385–393 (1957).

[14] Lewontin, R. C., *Cold Spring Harbor Symp.*, **22**, 395–408 (1957).

[15] Lewontin, R. C., *Evolution*, **12**, 494–503 (1958).

[16] Pavan, C., Th. Dobzhansky, and A. B. da Cunha, these PROCEEDINGS, **43**, 226–234 (1957).

[17] Dobzhansky, Th., and O. Pavlovsky, these PROCEEDINGS, **44**, 622–629 (1958).

[18] Levene, H., and Th. Dobzhansky, *Heredity*, **12**, 37–49 (1958).

[19] Dobzhansky, Th., *Genetics*, **35**, 288–302 (1950).

[20] Dobzhansky, Th., and O. Pavlovsky, *Evolution*, **11**, 311–319 (1957).

[21] Levine, L., and J. A. Beardmore, *Amer. Natur.*, **93**, 35–40 (1959).

[22] Lerner, I. M., *Genetic Homeostasis*, (New York: John Wiley, 1954).

[23] Wallace, B., and Th. Dobzhansky, *Radiation, Genes, and Man.* (New York: Henry Holt, 1959).

INTERACTION BETWEEN INVERSION POLYMORPHISMS OF TWO CHROMOSOME PAIRS IN THE GRASSHOPPER, *MORABA SCURRA*.

R. C. Lewontin

Department of Biology, University of Rochester, N. Y.

AND

M. J. D. White

Department of Zoology, University of Melbourne, Australia

Received August 11, 1959

Introduction

In studying the evolutionary dynamics of polymorphisms in natural populations, most of the work in the past has concentrated on single genetic entities. The Work of Dobzhansky and his collaborators on the inversion sequences in the third chromosome of *Drosophila pseudoobscura*, the studies of Lamotte (1951) on shell color and banding in the snail *Cepaea nemoralis*, and those of Allison (1955) on abnormal hemoglobins in man are examples of genetic studies of polymorphisms controlled by alleles at a single locus, or else by blocks of genes which act in heredity as single loci.

A new order of complexity is introduced when an attempt is made to study *simultaneously* two or more segregating systems in the same population because of the possibility, indeed the probability, that the evolutionary fates of the different polymorphic systems are not independent. Such will be the case if there is interaction between the different loci in the determination of the fitness of various genotypes. For example, the fitness of individuals of the genetic constitution AA may be greater than those with the constitution aa if at a second locus these individuals are, let us say, BB; but this fitness relationship may be reversed in the presence of bb at the second locus. In such cases the polymorphisms A,a and B,b are not independent in their fates in the population. Levitan (1955, 1958) in his studies of the

inversion polymorphisms of *Drosophila robusta* has evidence of a small interaction of this sort and Cain and Sheppard (1954a, 1954b) have found such interactions for shell color and banding in *Cepaea nemoralis*.

One of the most favorable materials for the study of these interactions and their evolutionary consequences is the Australian grasshopper, *Moraba scurra*. In an earlier paper (White, 1957) evidence was presented that the pericentric inversions, carried on two different chromosome pairs in this species, are not combined at random in the adult male individuals of certain natural populations. The deviations from random combination were regarded as proof of a genetic interaction between the two systems of cytological polymorphism, so far as their effects on viability are concerned. The significance of this interaction effect has been discussed and a hypothesis as to how it could have arisen has been suggested (White, 1958).

The present paper has two purposes. First we shall present added data on the interaction effect from recent collections. The data published previously relate to six adult male samples collected in 1955 and 1956 at various localities in South Eastern Australia. Further data on two of these populations (at Wombat, New South Wales, and Royalla "B," Australian Capital Territory) were obtained in 1958 and 1959. Statistical analysis of the more recent data provides

Reprinted by permission of the authors from Evolution, **14**, 116–129 (1960).

additional evidence for the interaction effect, which is thus shown to be no mere "flash in the pan," but a consistent phenomenon, occurring in at any rate most of the populations in which both chromosome pairs are polymorphic, and manifesting itself regularly each year.

Second we shall present a method for dealing with observations that is designed to provide a better understanding of the past and future evolution of such complex polymorphic systems. Specifically we shall attempt to answer two questions. Is the present genetic composition of the populations what one would expect from the estimates of fitness of the various genotypes? What is likely to be the future genetic history of these populations?

THE 1958 COLLECTIONS

The chromosome frequencies given in table 1 were calculated from adult male samples collected during the winter

TABLE 1. *Chromosome frequencies in 1956, 1958, and 1959*

		1956	1958	1959
Wombat:	Blundell CD	0.84800	0.85246	0.87500
	Tidbinbilla EF	0.14950	0.13866	0.13955
Royalla "B":	Blundell CD	0.66667	0.67267	
	Tidbinbilla EF	0.20333	0.22823	

	χ^2	d.f.	P
Wombat CD	4.61	2	≃.1
Wombat EF	1.01	2	≃.6
Royalla CD	0.07	1	≃.8
Royalla EF	1.59	1	≃.2

months. The results of our analyses carried out in 1958 are presented in tables 2 and 3. In these populations there are two sequences of the "CD" chromosome, *Standard* and *Blundell* and two of the "EF" chromosome, *Standard* and *Tidbinbilla*. The Standard chromosomes are both metacentric, Blundell and Tidbinbilla being acrocentric elements. For information on the life cycle of *Moraba scurra*, location of the colonies studied, appearance of the chromosomal inversions and other details, reference should be made to the

TABLE 2. *Composition of the population at Royalla "B," 1958, with deviations from proportionality to marginal frequencies*

		Chromosome CD			
		St/St	St/Bl	Bl/Bl	
Chromosome EF	St/St	22 (+4.61)	96 (+4.43)	75 (−9.04)	193
	St/Td	8 (−3.53)	56 (−4.73)	64 (+8.26)	128
	Td/Td	0 (−1.08)	6 (+0.31)	6 (+0.77)	12
		30	158	145	333

$\chi^2_{(4)} = 6.29$, P ≅ 0.18.

earlier papers (White 1956, 1957, White and Chinnick, 1957).

It will be seen that no significant changes have occurred in the chromosome frequencies of either the Wombat or the Royalla "B" population from 1956 to 1959 (table 1), since none of the chi squares approaches statistical significance. Thus, for some purposes it might be legitimate to simply add together our samples of 1956, 1958 and 1959. However, in tables 2, 3 and 4, the data of the later years are presented separately, for comparison with those previously published.

We test for the interaction effect by

TABLE 3. *Composition of the population at Wombat, 1958, with deviations from proportionality to marginal frequencies*

		Chromosome CD			
		St/St	St/Bl	Bl/Bl	
Chromosome EF	St/St	16 (+4.28)	141 (+6.27)	379 (−10.55)	536
	St/Td	0 (−4.13)	42 (−5.51)	147 (+9.64)	189
	Td/Td	0 (−0.15)	1 (−0.76)	6 (+0.91)	7
		16	184	532	732

$\chi^2_{(4)} = 8.227$, P ≅ 0.09.

TABLE 4. *Composition of the population at Wombat, 1959, with deviations from proportionality of marginal frequencies*

		Chromosome CD		
		St/St	St/Bl	Bl/Bl
Chromosome EF	St/St	7 (−0.38)	100 (+7.01)	324 (−6.63)	431
	St/Td	3 (+0.55)	22 (−8.85)	118 (+8.30)	143
	Td/Td	0 (−0.17)	4 (+1.84)	6 (−1.67)	10
		10	126	448	584

$\chi^2_{(4)} = 5.949$, P = .20.

determining the deviations from proportionality to the marginal frequencies, in the case of each of the nine genotypes. These deviations were found to be similar to those encountered previously (e.g., the Bl/Bl, St/St genotype is always deficient, the St/Bl, St/St and Bl/Bl, St/Td genotypes are present in excess, etc.). It should be pointed out that deviations calculated in this manner cannot be due to heterosis, although heterosis is undoubtedly present.

As with the earlier data the deviations of the two samples, considered separately, are not statistically significant, as shown by chi square tests. What we need, clearly, is a statistical test which can be applied to the data as a whole, including samples collected at different localities and in different years, and which show different chromosome frequencies. In the earlier paper (White, 1957) a statistical analysis by Dr. B. Griffing was presented which involved the partitioning of the $\chi^2_{(4)}$ into four orthogonal components. This procedure established that an interaction between the two systems of cytological polymorphism does, in fact, exist. However, since the analysis is of a relatively sophisticated type, a simpler test of significance may be preferable. The results of such a test (suggested by Professor J. B. S. Haldane *in litt.*), applied to the six samples considered in the earlier paper as well as to the samples studied in 1958 and 1959, are given in table 5. Each 3 × 3 contingency table is condensed to a 2 × 2 table by adding the rarer homozygous classes to the heterozygotes $\left(\text{e.g. for Wombat, 1958, we have } \dfrac{157 \mid 379}{43 \mid 153} \right)$. We then calculate a $\chi^2_{(1)}$ for each 2 × 2 table. Values of χ are then calculated; those for samples with negative deviations in the top right and lower left cells are regarded as positive, those with negative deviations in the other two cells as negative (in the case of the 9 samples in table 5 all χ's are positive). The statistic $t = \dfrac{\Sigma \chi}{\sqrt{n}}$ is used as a normal deviate. The result of this test is to establish the reality of the interaction effect with virtual certainty (p $\simeq$ 0.00001).

If we assume that panmixia occurs in these populations, the relative viabilities of the nine genotypes in each of the samples may legitimately be estimated by the ratio of the number of individuals actually found to those expected on the binomial square rule. The fact that no significant changes in the chromosome frequencies are taking place from generation to generation, in these populations, renders the objections of Wallace (1958) and Novitski and Dempster (1958) to

TABLE 5. *Test of significance of the interaction effect*

		$\chi^2_{(1)}$	χ
Wombat	1956	0.81887	0.90491
Wombat	1958	3.90552	1.97624
Wombat	1959	2.17920	1.47621
Hall	1955	1.29005	1.13580
Hall	1956	4.22536	2.05557
Royalla "A"	1955	2.81785	1.67865
Royalla "B"	1956	0.75647	0.86975
Royalla "B"	1958	4.09607	2.02387
Williamsdale	1956	2.88523	1.69860
			13.81960

$\dfrac{\Sigma(\chi)}{\sqrt{N}} = \dfrac{13.81960}{3} = 4.607$, P $\cong$ 0.00001.

TABLE 6. *Estimated relative viabilities of the 9 genotypes in 1956, 1958 and 1959, calculated from the deviations from expectation (on the basis of the Hardy Weinberg ratios) by the method of Haldane (1956)*

St/Bl; St/St arbitrarily taken as 1.000 in each sample.

		Chromosome EF	Chromosome CD		
			St/St	St/Bl	Bl/Bl
Wombat	1956		0.789	1.000	0.922
Wombat	1958		1.353	1.000	0.924
Wombat	1959	St/St	0.970	1.000	0.917
Royalla	1956		0.791	1.000	0.834
Royalla	1958		0.932	1.000	0.752
Wombat	1956		0.801	0.876	1.004
Wombat	1958		0.000	0.919	1.113
Wombat	1959	St/Td	1.282	0.672	1.029
Royalla	1956		0.670	1.006	0.901
Royalla	1958		0.573	0.976	1.086
Wombat	1956		0.000	1.308	0.645
Wombat	1958		0.000	0.272	0.564
Wombat	1959	Td/Td	0.000	1.506	0.645
Royalla	1956		0.657	0.657	1.067
Royalla	1958		0.000	0.707	0.688

such a procedure inapplicable in the present instance. The relative viabilities for the 1958 and 1959 samples, calculated by the method of Haldane (1956), which includes a correction to remove bias, are given in table 6, which may be compared with table 8 of White, 1957. The St/Bl; St/St genotype is used as a standard (viability = 1.000) in the case of each sample.

Such calculations suffer from one serious weakness, namely the very considerable sampling error in the case of five of the nine genotypes, whose numbers are in all cases very small. Thus it is only the relative viabilities enclosed within the dotted line in table 6 that should be regarded as at all reliable. It will be noted that, in the case of the values within the dotted line, there is good agreement between those for 1956, 1958 and 1959, and that this agreement is especially close for the most numerous Bl/Bl; St/St genotype. In view of this, and because the chromosome frequencies of these populations have not changed from 1956 to 1959, we have thought it legitimate to pool the data for the three years (table 7). It seems likely that the relative viabilities in table 7 are more

reliable estimates, in the case of the rarer genotypes, than those in table 6. But it would obviously be necessary to study samples ten to a hundred times larger in order to obtain any close accuracy in the case of such rare genotypes as St/St; Td/Td. We feel that any differences in the viability constants which may occur from one year to another in the same locality are likely to be trivial compared to the inevitable inaccuracy of the method by which they are determined. Differences between the chromosome frequencies from one locality to another, however, clearly imply that the relative viabilities of the genotypes are not the same throughout the distribution area of the species, and may vary over a distance of a few miles. The Royalla A and B localities are about a mile apart and both are situated on a strip of ungrazed land along a railroad. These populations were no doubt formerly continuous and are probably not completely cut off from one another even now. There is no significant difference between the frequencies of the CD sequences at these localities ($\chi^2_{(1)} = 0.21$), but a real difference may exist in the frequencies of the EF sequences ($\chi^2_{(1)} = 3.5495$). It would hence be dangerous to pool the data for Royalla A and Royalla B in order to estimate the relative viabilities of the nine genotypes.

THE ADAPTIVE SURFACES

If estimates are available of the fitnesses or adaptive values of the various

TABLE 7. *Estimated relative viabilities, calculated in the same manner as in table 6, but with the data of 1956, 1958, and 1959 combined*

			Chromosome CD		
			St/St	St/Bl	Bl/Bl
Wombat		St/St	1.002	1.000	0.927
Royalla			0.842	1.000	0.808
Wombat		St/Td	0.646	0.849	1.044
Royalla			0.636	0.997	0.974
Wombat		Td/Td	0.000	1.054	0.626
Royalla			0.393	0.682	0.916

(Chromosome EF is indicated for the left grouping rows.)

genotypes in a population, it is possible to predict what the eventual genotypic composition of the population will be and at what rate gene frequencies should change, given that the population has a certain composition at any particular time. Particularly, one would like to know whether the population will reach a stable polymorphic condition or whether it will tend to monomorphism. A general theoretical treatment of evolution in multi-locus systems is not appropriate here and will be dealt with in a separate paper. There is enough in the existing literature, however, to provide a basis for the present analysis. Rigorous demonstrations and original expositions of the concepts to be used here may be found in the papers of Wright (1949, 1956), Li (1955), Kimura (1956), and Lewontin (1958).

In a polymorphic system of two loci with two alleles at each locus, there will be nine genotypes: AABB, AABb, AAbb, AaBB, etc. To each genotype is assigned a weight, W, which is the fitness or adaptive value of that genotype. Denoting the frequency of the ith genotype by Z_i and the fitness by W_i, the mean adaptive value of the population, $\overline{W}$, is defined as

$$\overline{W} = \sum Z_i W_i.$$

Mean adaptive value, so defined, will be different for different genotypic compositions of the population; it will be higher when genotypes with larger values of W_i predominate and lower when less fit genotypes are in greatest frequency. In a random mating population the frequency of any genotype at one locus is given by the binomial square rule and if we ignore the effects of linkage between the loci, the frequency of genotypes for the loci simultaneously will be the appropriate term in the product of the two binomial expansions of the separate loci. Thus, if the frequency of A is q_1 and that of B is q_2, the genotype frequencies at the A locus are: q_1^2 AA, $2q_1(1 - q_1)$ Aa, and $(1 - q_1)^2$ aa, while for the B locus

the frequencies are: q_2^2 BB, $2q_2(1 - q_2)$ Bb and $(1 - q_2)^2$ bb. For the combined genotypes the frequencies will be:

AABB AaBB $\cdots$aabb
$q_1^2 q_2^2$ $2q_1(1-q_1)q_2^2 \cdots (1-q_1)^2(1-q_2)^2$
$$(1)$$

Although it is often assumed that there is no complication due to linkage when the genes are on different chromosomes, this is incorrect and the frequencies given above are only approximate even for cases of free recombination. Because the effects of linkage can be shown to be small, however, we will ignore them in the discussion.

Using the distribution of genotypes given in (1) it is then possible to calculate $\overline{W}$ for any combination of gene frequencies q_1 and q_2 and this may be put in the form of a surface or topography. The two horizontal dimensions represent the frequencies q_1 and q_2 and the vertical height at each point represents the mean fitness, $\overline{W}$. Thus, a sort of "adaptive landscape" is formed with peaks, valleys, slopes, and saddles. At any particular time the population may be represented as a point on the q_1, q_2 plane and a change in q_1 and q_2, that is the movement of the point, will be governed by the conformation of the topography. If the fitnesses of the various genotypes are constants and do not depend upon the frequencies of the genotypes, it can be demonstrated that the gene frequencies will change in such a way as to increase the value of $\overline{W}$. That is, the population will tend to "ascend" the slopes of the topography, coming to rest on a "peak." If there are several adaptive peaks in the landscape, the one to which the population moves will be governed by the present position of the population and by the slope of the landscape in the neighborhood of that position. Thus, the population may easily reach an equilibrium genetic composition which does not correspond to the maximum possible $\overline{W}$ over the whole landscape, but may come to rest on a relatively low peak. This is another way of saying that natural selection is opportunistic and that evolution does not always result in the "best of all possible worlds."

In figures 1–10 we give the topographies calculated for each of the 8 samples, and for the pooled data of 1956 and 1958 in the case of Royalla "B" and Wombat populations. The method of computing these topographies was as follows. The frequencies of Blundell CD chromosomes (q_1) and of Tidbinbilla EF chromosomes (q_2) were varied between 0 and 1 at intervals of .05. The 21 values of q_1 (.00, .05, .10 ··· 1.00) and the 21 values of q_2 in all possible combinations give 441 points on the q_1q_2 plane. For each combination of q_1 and q_2 the frequencies of the 9 genotypes were computed according to expression (1). These frequencies, Z_i, were then multiplied by the appropriate value of W_i taken from table 6 and summed to give $\overline{W}$. A value of $\overline{W}$ thus resulted for each of the 441 possible points on the q_1q_2 plane. By interpolation between points it was then possible to draw the continuous topographic lines connecting points of equal mean adaptive value.[1] The black dot on each topography represents the actual composition of the population and the arrow indicates the direction in which that composition should change in future generations if the topography truly represents the mean adaptive values at each of the 441 points on each surface.

All the topographies have certain features in common. They show a kind of ridge running obliquely across the surface from some point on the upper side of the square to a point on the right hand side. On either side of the ridge, but especially in the direction of the lower left hand corner, the surface falls away steeply. In the case of those samples in which no St/St; Td/Td individuals were encountered the mean

---

[1] These lines might be called "isodapts."

viability at this corner of the topography appears as zero.

The two ends of the ridge are higher than the middle, so that there is a kind of saddle. Moreover, in every instance the actual population is located on this saddle. This is especially clear for the Royalla samples, Hall, 1956, and Williamsdale. The topographies for Wombat, 1956, and Hall, 1955, look somewhat different from the others but Wombat, 1958, and the topography for the Wombat data of 1956 and 1958 look fairly similar to the "typical" topographies. In figure 11 we give a diagrammatic representation of a typical topography, showing how each of the four corners corresponds to a cytologically monomorphic population. We may speak of the ridge as orientated in the AB direction or axis, the axis which crosses the saddle perpendicular to the ridge being referred to as the CD axis.

The general similarity of the topographies which we have calculated is extremely striking, when we consider how remote the relationship between the different colonies must be. The Wombat population belongs to the 17-chromosome race, and the others to the 15-chromosome race, so that to find a common ancestor of the Wombat population and the remaining colonies it might be necessary to go back several million years (i.e., generations). The two Royalla colonies ("A" and "B") are situated only about a mile apart and hence must be regarded as closely related. These localities are about six miles from Williamsdale and about 30 miles (in the opposite direction) from Hall. The vagility of this wingless insect is so low that to find a common ancestor of the Hall and Royalla populations it would probably be necessary to go back at least 3,000 years.

Such topographies obviously include considerable sampling errors, as previously pointed out. Such sampling errors, however, are almost certainly not large enough to obscure the general

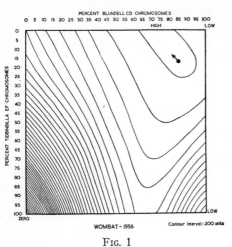

FIG. 1

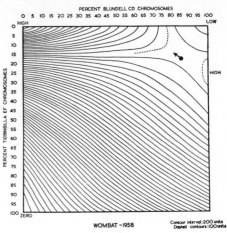

FIG. 2

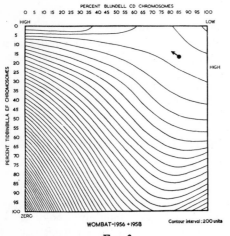

FIG. 3

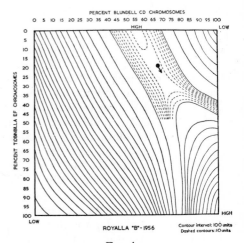

FIG. 4

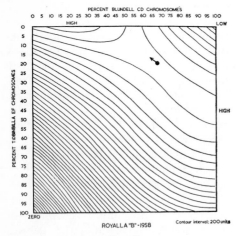

FIG. 5

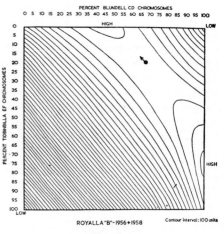

FIG. 6

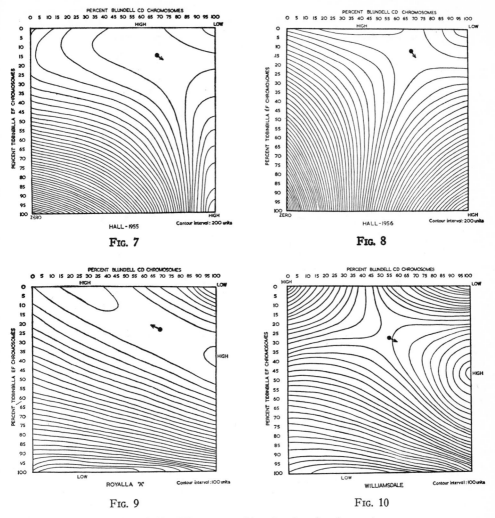

FIGS. 1–10. The topographies (explanation in text).

features of the adaptive landscape. That this is so is demonstrated by comparing the topographies calculated from different years in the same locality. If one takes the extreme position that no real change in adaptive values takes place from year to year, a position that is hardly credible considering the lack of constancy of physical factors of the environment, then the differences between topographies in two different years from the same locality can be regarded as due entirely to sampling error. While the different years certainly do not produce identical topographies, the general fea-tures are the same. The location of the saddle point remains virtually unchanged from year to year and the general orien-tation of the ridge remains "northwest" to "southeast." The main change from year to year is a shift in the angle of the ridge with a resultant shift of the peak positions along the margin. This phe-nomenon is shown for Wombat (figs. 1 and 2) and Royalla "B" (figs. 4 and 5). The combined topographies (fig. 3 for Wombat and fig. 6 for Royalla) can be regarded as the mean surfaces for the two years and are intermediate between them. The two samples of the Hall

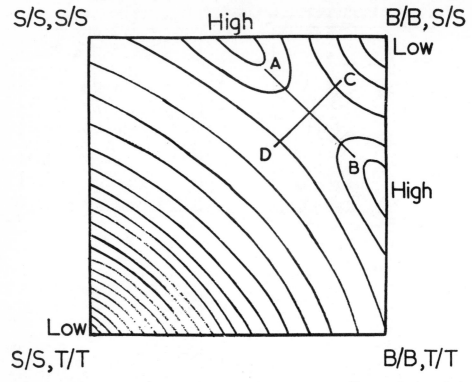

FIG. 11. Diagrammatic representation of a typical topography. The constitution of the monomorphic populations at the four corners is indicated. AB and CD are the two axes discussed in the text.

population (figs. 7 and 8) show practically no change.

THE GENETIC EQUILIBRIUM OF THE POPULATIONS

The topographies refer solely to one component of the selective value, namely male viability up to the adult stage. They take no account of other components such as female viability, sexual activity and fecundity in both sexes; all of which must be involved in the determination of the genetic equilibrium. Moreover, they are based on the assumption that panmixia obtains, an assumption which may not be strictly true (see White, 1957, p. 326). In spite of these reservations we believe it is worth while to discuss the genetic equilibrium which appears to obtain in these populations in the light of the

evidence provided by the topographies. It is at any rate evident that in all the localities where these samples were collected a population consisting mainly of St/St, Td/Td individuals would be severely handicapped, whatever the fecundity of that genotype.

Stability in the direction of the CD axis seems assured for all populations, i.e., there is little likelihood of them "slipping down off the ridge." Equilibrium along the AB axis is less certain. At first sight it would seem that each population should in future generations "climb" from its present position on the topography up whichever slope is steeper until it reaches the highest point. The apparent final equilibrium state of each sample is shown in table 8. It should be pointed out that the surfaces in the immediate vicinity of the dots that indi-

TABLE 8. *Apparent final equilibrium state of the samples*

Hall	1955 & 1956	Bl/Bl; Td/Td
Wombat	1956	St/Bl; St/St
Wombat	1958	St/St; St/St
Wombat	1956 + 1958	St/St; St/St
Royalla A	1955	St/Bl; St/St
Royalla B	1956	Bl/Bl; Td/Td
Royalla B	1958	St/Bl; St/St
Royalla B	1956 + 1958	St/Bl; St/St
Williamsdale	1956	Bl/Bl; St/Td

cate the existing composition of the samples are in several instances so nearly horizontal that a relatively minute change in the slope would determine whether the population should move along the AB axis towards A or towards B.

The following hypotheses concerning these populations may be considered:

I. There is no true equilibrium and the populations will in actuality climb from their present position towards either A or B.

II. An equilibrium exists.

IIa. An equilibrium exists because the actual selective values are different from the relative viability constants, i.e., the various components of the selective value are imperfectly correlated. For example, the high viability of some genotypes may be accompanied by low fecundity.

IIb. An equilibrium exists, because the selective values of some or all of the genotypes are frequency-dependent. In particular, the selective values of some genotypes may decline as these genotypes become more frequent in the population.

IIc. A pseudo-equilibrium exists, the direction of the slope along the AB axis in the immediate vicinity of the existing constitution undergoing a periodic reversal every few generations (see fig. 12 in which it is assumed that such a reversal is related to "wet" and "dry" years).

Hypothesis I states essentially that the present composition of the populations is an historical relic, the populations being still in a state of directed gene frequency change. Agaist such a hypothesis is the fact that each population is at *its own saddle point*. The loca-

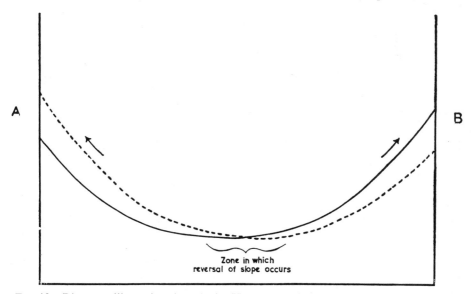

FIG. 12. Diagram illustrating hypothesis II c. The figure represents a section of a topography along the AB axis. The full line is supposed to indicate the slope in a wet year, the dotted line is the slope in a dry year. The zone in which reversal of the slope occurs is indicated.

tion of the saddle for each population is slightly different as is the location of the point representing the actual gene frequencies. That each population should have reached its own saddle but not begun to climb the ridge is difficult to accept especially if these populations are tens of thousands of generations old, as we believe them to be. This objection is somewhat mitigated by the extreme flatness of the adaptive surface around the saddle point so that predicted changes in gene frequency would be of the order of .0002 to .0003 per generation. While this slow rate of change might account for a stalling of the evolutionary process near the saddle point, it would not in itself explain why each population should pass near the saddle point on its way to one or the other of the peaks.

Some insight into this problem can be gained by calculating the theoretical path of a population along the gene frequency plane under the influence of the estimated gradients in mean adaptive value. This can be done by regarding a system of two segregating loci with two alleles at each locus as if it were a single locus with four alleles. These alleles, which are the four gametic types, are St;St, St;Td, Bl;St, and Bl;Td. Assigning the symbols x, y, z, and u to the frequencies of these four gametic phases respectively, the change per unit time in the frequency of the alleles can be represented by four differential equations:

$$\frac{dx}{dt} = x[W_x - \overline{W}] - rW_H(xu - yz) \quad (2)$$

$$\frac{dy}{dt} = y[W_y - \overline{W}] + rW_H(xu - yz) \quad (3)$$

$$\frac{dz}{dt} = z[W_z - \overline{W}] + rW_H(xu - yz) \quad (4)$$

$$\frac{du}{dt} = u[W_u - \overline{W}] - rW_H(xu - yz) \quad (5)$$

where W_x, W_y, W_z and W_u are the average fitnesses of the phases St;St, St;Td,

Bl;St, and Bl;Td in all their combinations, $\overline{W}$ is the average adaptive value of the population at the given combination of gene frequencies, r is the proportion of recombination between the two loci, which for our case is .50 since we are dealing with two different chromosomes, and W_H is the fitness of the double heterozygote St/Bl;St/Td. One method of deriving these equations can be found in Kimura, 1956. The variable of time can be eliminated from these equations and the set of four dependent equations reduced to three independent equations by dividing (2), (3), and (4) by (5). The simultaneous solution of the three new equations $\frac{dx}{du}$, $\frac{dy}{du}$ and $\frac{dz}{du}$ will give the path of gametic frequency change of a population starting with some initial composition x_0, y_0, z_0 and u_0. Finally the gametic frequencies can be converted into gene frequencies by noting that

$$(u + z) = \text{frequency of Bl},$$
$$(u + y) = \text{frequency of Td}.$$

Such equations are not easily soluble by analytic methods so that we have employed numerical solutions using the Runge-Kutta and Milne methods adapted to the IBM 650 computer.

The results of the solution of these equations are shown in figure 13 for the Royalla "B" sample of 1956. Given in the figure is the topographic map of the adaptive surface as shown in figure 1, upon which has been superimposed the calculated trajectories for populations starting with different initial gene frequencies.

Two points emerge from this analysis. First, the population may go to either of the two adaptive peaks, depending upon the starting point of the population. Second, and more interesting, is the fact that the population generally does not pass directly to the peak from a low point, but goes to the peak *by way of the saddle*. This is true, at least, for populations whose initial composition is either St;Td, or Bl;St.

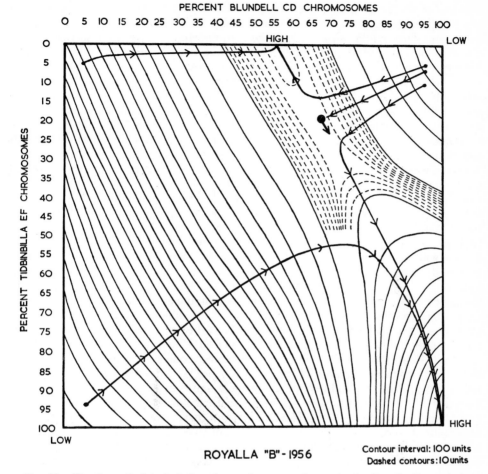

FIG. 13. The theoretical trajectories of gene frequency change in the Royalla B population, superimposed onto the adaptive topography for that surface. Arrows indicate the direction of the trajectories in time. Data of 1956.

Thus we might imagine, if hypothesis I were the correct one, that the present location of the populations near their saddle points is an historical relic due to the very slow rate of gene frequency change near the saddle and to the initial composition of the populations either at the time the inversions arose or at the time of establishment of the colonies.

We do not favor this hypothesis because of the high degree of coincidence that seems necessary to it and because the rate of gene frequency change, slow as it is, would result in considerable changes over a period of 500 to 1,000 generations. Nevertheless we cannot completely reject this hypothesis, unlikely as it may seem, since all evolutionary changes seem unlikely in retrospect.

A formal decision among hypotheses IIa, IIb, and IIc does not seem possible but experimental verification of one or a combination of them is possible. These hypotheses are not incompatible with one another and all three may be true to some extent.

Hypothesis IIa seems to imply that genetic co-adaptation of the inversion sequences has proceeded differently in the case of the genes affecting the various components of fitness. What data exist from Drosophila suggest that the opposite is true and that viability, fecundity, and longevity are positively, rather than negatively correlated (see especially Vetukhiv, 1954, 1956, 1957, and Wallace, 1948). This hypothesis is then rather unattractive but without experimental disproof cannot be rejected out of hand.

Hypotheses IIb and IIc seem much more plausible. If we assume that the various genotypes are to some extent occupying various different niches within the general environment, then as a particular genotype becomes more abundant it will tend to "spill over" from its preferred niche into others where it is less favored. Thus to some extent, frequency-dependent selective values should be expected on general ecological principles. By now, of course, it is well known that such frequency-dependent selection does exist. This has been shown for polygenic systems by Lewontin (1955) and for inversion systems by Dobzhansky, Pavlovsky and Levene (1954) and by Spiess (1957). The most important theoretical consideration arising in gene frequency-dependent selection is that the *stable equilibrium point may not coincide with an adaptive peak.* This is most easily demonstrated for a single locus, but applies in general. Suppose there are two alleles at a locus and the fitnesses of the three genotypes are:

AA	Aa	aa
1	1	$1.5 - q$

where q is the frequency of the allele *a*. In such a case the fitness of the genotype *aa* will decrease as its frequency increases and a stable equilibrium is reached at q = .50. However, the mean adaptive value at this equilibrium point is 1 while it is greater than 1 for lower frequencies of the allele *a*. For example, $\bar{W} = 1.016$ when q = .40. Thus, the

saddle points for our *Moraba* populations may well represent points of stable equilibrium and indeed if these points prove to be stable, this is almost *prima facie* evidence of frequency-dependent fitness values.

The type of slope reversal shown in figure 12 might also be expected on meteorological grounds. It is, however, difficult to accept hypothesis IIc as the sole cause of the genetic equilibrium, since one would expect in this case that sooner or later a number of similar years would follow one another so that the population would evolve beyond the zone in which slope reversal occurs. Whenever this happens the population would thereafter continue to climb the ridge to A or B, in spite of any slope reversals in the region of the saddle. Again, the gradient is so flat in the region of the saddle that the populations might be stalled in this region for an indefinite period. Such a maintenance of an unstable equilibrium has been suggested by Li (1953) for the Rh alleles in human populations.

In summary, some combination of hypotheses IIb and IIc seems the most probable explanation of the observed apparent equilibrium of the inversion systems in *Moraba* with frequency-dependent selection being the more important of the two.

SUMMARY

All the data currently available on the frequencies of inversions in chromosomes CD and EF of the grasshopper *Moraba scurra*, in certain populations in southern New South Wales, indicate an equilibrium condition in which the Blundell arrangement for chromosome CD and the Standard arrangement for chromosome EF predominate. Estimates of viability based on deviations of adult frequencies from binomial-square proportion show that there are epistatic interactions between the non-allelic arrangements in determining genotypic fitness.

From these estimates adaptive surfaces have been constructed which reveal that each population sampled is at a "saddle" or minimax point of the adaptive surface. The possible reasons for the apparent equilibrium condition of the populations at such an unstable point have been examined, and it is tentatively hypothesized that the equilibrium is maintained by a combination of gene frequency-dependent selection and yearly fluctuations in the physical factors of the environment.

Literature Cited

Allison, A. 1955. Aspects of polymorphism in man. Cold Spring Harbor Symposia on Quantitative Biology, **20**: 239–255.

Cain, A. J., and P. M. Sheppard. 1952. The effects of natural selection on body color in the land snail *Cepaea nemoralis*. Heredity, **6**: 217–231.

————. 1954. Natural selection in *Cepaea*. Genetics, **39**: 89–116.

Dobzhansky, Th., O. Pavlovsky, and H. Levene. 1954. Interaction of the adaptive values in polymorphic experimental populations of *Drosophila pseudoobscura*. Evolution, **8**: 335–349.

Haldane, J. B. S. 1956. The estimation of viabilities. Journal of Genetics, **54**: 294–296.

Kimura, M. 1956. A model of a genetic system which leads to closer linkage by natural selection. Evolution, **10**: 278–287.

Lamotte, M. 1951. Recherches sur la structure génétique des populations naturelles de *Cepaea nemoralis* L. Bulletin Biologique de France et Belgique Supplement, **35**: 1–239.

Levitan, M. 1955. Studies in linkage in populations. I. Associations of second chromosome linkages in *Drosophila robusta*. Evolution, **9**: 62–74.

Lewontin, R. C. 1955. The effects of population density and composition on viability in *Drosophila melanogaster*. Evolution, **9**: 27–41.

————. 1958. A general method for investigating the equilibrium of gene frequency in a population. Genetics **43**: 419–434.

Li, C. C. 1953. Is Rh facing a crossroad? A critique of the compensation effect. American Naturalist, **87**: 257–261.

————. 1955. The stability of an equilibrium and the average fitness of a population. American Naturalist, **89**: 281–296.

Novitski, E., and E. R. Dempster. 1958. An analysis of data from laboratory populations of *Drosophila melanogaster*. Genetics, **43**: 470–479.

Spiess, E. B. 1957. Relation between frequency and adaptive values of chromosomal arrangements in *Drosophila persimilis*. Evolution, **11**: 84–93.

Vetukhiv, M. 1954. Integration of the genotype in local populations of three species of Drosophila. Evolution, **8**: 241–251.

————. 1956. Fecundity of hybrids between geographic populations of *Drosophila pseudoobscura*. Evolution, **10**: 139–146.

————. 1957. Longevity of hybrids between geographic populations of *Drosophila pseudoobscura*. Evolution, **11**: 348–360.

Wallace, B. 1948. Studies on "sex-ratio" in *Drosophila pseudoobscura*. I. Selection and "sex-ratio." Evolution, **2**: 189–217.

————. 1958. The comparison of observed and calculated zygotic distributions. Evolution, **12**: 113–115.

White, M. J. D. 1956. Adaptive chromosomal polymorphism in an Australian grasshopper. Evolution, **10**: 298–313.

————. 1957. Cytogenetics of the grasshopper *Moraba scurra*. II. Heterotic systems and their interaction. (With a statistical appendix by B. Griffing.) Australian Journal of Zoology, **5**: 305–337.

————. 1958. Restrictions on recombination in grasshopper populations and species. Cold Spring Harbor Symposia on Quantitative Biology, **23**: 307–317.

————, and L. J. Chinnick. 1957. Cytogenetics of the grasshopper *Moraba scurra*. III. Distribution of the 15- and 17-chromosomal races. Australian Journal of Zoology, **5**: 338–347.

Wright, S. 1949. Adaptation and selection. Chapter 20, in: Genetics, Paleontology and Evolution. pp. 365–389. Ed., G. L. Jepson, G. G. Simpson, and E. Mayr.

————. 1955. Classification of the factors of evolution. Cold Spring Harbor Symposia on Quantitative Biology, **20**: 16–24D.

EVOLUTIONARY CHANGES IN COMPONENTS OF FITNESS AND OTHER POLYGENIC TRAITS IN *DROSOPHILA MELANOGASTER* POPULATIONS

ADRIANO A. BUZZATI-TRAVERSO *
Istituto di Genetica, Universita', Pavia, Italy
and
Scripps Institution of Oceanography, University of California,
La Jolla, California, U.S.A.

Received 12.x.54

I. INTRODUCTION

CHARLES DARWIN's theory and current genetic interpretations regard natural selection as the main determinant of evolutionary events. In the course of succeeding generations, a population copes with a given environment through a process of trial and error. The errors, that is, the variations which are less fitted to the environment, are lost, successful trials or variations better fitted are preserved ; the process responsible for the fate of different variations is based on the fact that unlike types leave different average numbers of adult progeny in the next generation. If such unlikeness is at least partly hereditary the variations responsible for it persist for longer or shorter periods. In the course of time the population thus becomes better adapted to its surroundings, and this adaptation is made apparent by a series of changes in the morphology and physiology of the organism concerned. These changes in time are generally referred to as evolution.

Morphological and physiological characters which may undergo change fall under the control of genetic determinants which, for the sake of simplicity, have been classified by Mather (1943) under two main categories : unifactorial (or oligogenic) and multifactorial (or polygenic). Evolutionary change may thus be described either (1) in terms of variations in frequency of those genes that primarily affect single traits, or (2) in terms of variations in the mean values of morphological and physiological characters that show continuous variability and are controlled by polygenes.

While most of our genetic knowledge on evolutionary processes is derived from the study of variations in the frequency of oligogenes and chromosomal types, the significance of changes of the type indicated under (2) needs be stressed because of the following facts. In the first place, most of the paleontological evidence on the historical process of evolution is inferred from successions of fossils differing in shape and size, and the traits concerned were most likely controlled by polygenic systems. In the second place, zoo- and phyto-geographic data indicate that living organisms may differ, over their distribution

---

* The experimental part of this work was done at the Istituto Italiano di Idrobiologia, Pallanza and at the Istituto di Genetica, Pavia.

range, in morphological and physiological traits which are considered to be adaptive and are known to be mostly of polygenic type. In the third place, the components of fitness, such as fecundity, fertility and the like, fall under the control of polygenes in the majority of the studied forms.

In spite of the importance of polygenic characters in evolution, however, no experiments have been reported thus far, which might show how natural selection operates on polygenic systems over a number of generations. The work reported here is an attempt to analyse the changes in such systems which natural selection can produce in experimental populations.

2. TECHNIQUES FOR BREEDING POPULATIONS

The classic paper of L'Héritier and Teissier (1934) was the first to demonstrate the effects of natural selection on single gene differences present in artificial populations of *Drosophila melanogaster*. Since that time variations in the frequencies of genes and of chromosome types, produced by natural selection, have been described in many *Drosophila* species kept in population cages. These are small boxes in which the amount of food available to the population is kept relatively constant ; that is, every day or every few days fresh food is introduced and the worked-out food is removed. The population of the cage will reach an approximately stationary number, regardless of the original number of flies introduced, provided that the supply of fresh food as well as other environmental factors, such as temperature, remain constant. The amount of available food at any particular time determines the number of flies that reach the adult stage. This number is smaller than the number of zygotes represented by the fertilised eggs because of mortality in the larval and pupal stages. The struggle for existence and reproduction may also occur in the adult stage because of high population density. The genotypes better adapted to the prevailing conditions will accordingly become more frequent than those less well adapted.

Different experimental techniques have been used by other authors. In order to evaluate the relative selective values of eleven mutants of *D. melanogaster*, Wiedemann (1936) crossed them with wild-type flies. In the F_1, F_2 and succeeding generations the first 50 adults to emerge were used as parents of the following generation. A comparison between the observed frequencies of various phenotypes and the ones calculated for Mendelian ratios in succeeding generations, using Jennings' formulas, provided a measure of the relative viability of the various mutants. Nikoro and Gusev (1938), with a similar technique, kept populations of flies with various genotypes in large bottles and collected at random in each generation 100 pupæ, which were transferred to a new bottle where they could hatch and breed. Kalmus (1945) started an experiment with five homozygous wild-type females and five homozygous *ebony* males, in one breeding bottle. The progeny was counted and 150 flies were chosen at random and subdivided into 5 groups of thirty flies each to become parents of the following generation in five separate bottles. Records were kept of the numbers of wild-type and ebony flies appearing in each generation. This procedure was repeated for several generations in eight parallel series kept at different temperature and humidity conditions. Reed and Reed (1948) used the " population bottle," consisting of two half-pint milk bottles, the mouths of which were connected by rubber tubing. Each milk bottle had a paper cap perforated with two or three quarter-inch holes which allowed passage of the flies but prevented food and debris from being pushed from one bottle to the other by larvæ. The experiments were started with five pairs of flies in one bottle, the second bottle being added after two months. Two months later the first bottle was removed and a fresh one substituted. By repeating this operation the population can be kept going at will. Techniques such as these seem to be less reliable for a thorough study of natural selection phenomena than the population cages of L'Héritier and Teissier because : (*a*) the population number is smaller and thereby random fluctuations in the frequency of a gene may give a biased picture of the selection process ; (*b*) a periodically changing environment (such as that of the " population bottle ") or arbitrary choice of parents in each generation may emphasise some and neglect other of the viability factors which are of significance for the competitive success of a given genotype.

The technique used in the work to be reported here is more laborious than those previously described, but provides a wider range of information on the dynamics

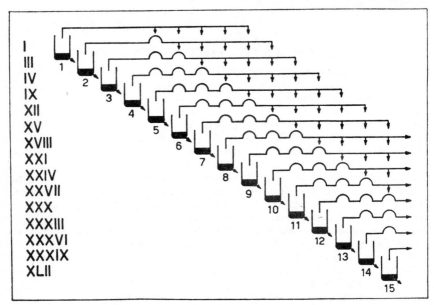

FIG. 1.—Schematic representation of the breeding technique used for the experimental populations. The vials are indicated with successive Arabic numbers ; the arrows protruding from them indicate the transfer of the adult individuals from one vial to the next, which occurred every three days (indicated in Roman numbers). The lines originating from the vials and the downward arrows indicate that the adult progeny of each vial was added to the population ; there are three arrows for each vial to show that the adults hatching from each vial were collected and added to the population over a period of 15 days (3 × 5) ; after that the vial was discarded.

of the populations under study. This method, already described in an earlier paper (Buzzati-Traverso, 1947*a*), takes advantage of the knowledge derived by Pearl (1927) while studying the growth of Drosophila populations. The experiment is started by introducing a certain number of adult flies of the kinds desired into a vial with food. After one, two or three days, according to the type of experiment one wishes to carry out, the flies are transferred to a new vial of the same size and with the same amount of fresh food. The transfer is repeated to new vials with the chosen constant periodicity. With a three day periodicity the number of flies in the first three vials of the series will be the same, unless some die in the meantime. At 25° C., adults of *Drosophila melanogaster* emerge on the ninth day after eggs have been laid, and therefore, some young flies will be found in the first vial on the tenth day from the beginning of the experiment. These are counted, and added to the original group of flies, which, by this time, will be in the fourth vial.

Every day the flies emerging in the earlier vials are transferred to the last one, which, as time passes, will have an increasing number of adult individuals (fig. 1). Such increase will continue up to a point when an equilibrium is reached between the amount of available food and space and the number of individuals which can live under such conditions. The equilibrium will be an approximately stationary one under constant conditions, although, as it will be shown later, this is not always true.

By means of this procedure, one can obtain : (1) data on the number, sex and phenotypic ratios of the flies present in the population at the time of each transfer to a new vial ; (2) data on the birth rates of the two sexes and of the phenotypes in each vial. This information makes it possible to evaluate at any particular time : (*a*) variations in the population size ; (*b*) variations in the sex ratio of the population as a whole or of its constituent phenotypes ; (*c*) variation in the gene frequencies ;

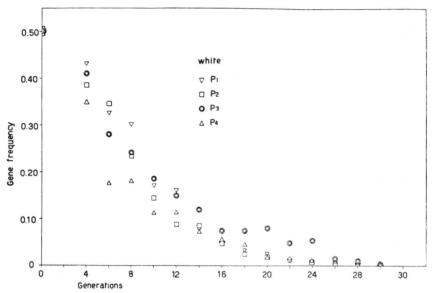

FIG. 2.—Elimination of the mutant *white* in the four experimental populations (P₁, P₂, P₃, P₄).

(*d*) the mean life length of adult individuals ; (*e*) selection differentials for the developmental stages and for imagoes ; (*f*) the total productivity of the population at any given time.

3. THE EXPERIMENT

In the experiment to be described here, four populations of *Drosophila melanogaster* were kept at 25° C., on the standard corn-meal, agar, molasses medium seeded with a constant amount of baker's yeast. Two of these (P₁ and P₂) were started about one year earlier than the other two (P₃ and P₄). The foundation stock of all four populations consisted of 10 virgin females and 10 males of wild-type Oregon-R strain, and 10 virgin females and 10 males of another strain homozygous for the sex linked genes *white* and *Bar*. The populations were bred in glass vials 12 cm. high and 3·5 cm. in diameter for about 100 generations over a period of four years. After equilibrium was reached the population numbers fluctuated around 700 flies at first, but increased later. A total of about 2,000,000 flies were counted and classified for sex and phenotype.

Figs. 2 and 3 summarise the elimination of the mutant genes in competition with their wild-type alleles. As it will be seen, the mutants *white* and *Bar* were completely replaced by their normal alleles in the course of approximately 30 generations. The selection coefficients of the two genes were very similar throughout the experiment. As has been previously pointed out (Buzzati-Traverso, 1947), the selective value of these genes remains the same irrespective of its absolute frequency in the population. This conclusion is based on a plot of

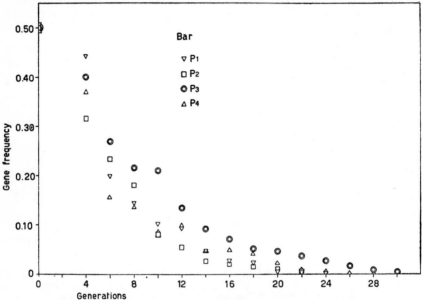

FIG. 3.—Elimination of the mutant *Bar* in the four experimental populations
(P_1, P_2, P_3, P_4).

the logarithms of observed gene frequencies against time expressed in generations.

At their face value, the results obtained with the four populations showed no more than what might have been expected from similar data published by other authors. (L'Héritier and Teissier, 1934 and 1937 ; Reed and Reed, 1948 and 1950 ; Merrell, 1933*a* and *b*). The technique employed in this experiment, however, makes possible, as it has been pointed out before, to get more detailed information on the selection mechanism responsible for eliminating the mutant alleles. This aspect of the experiment will be analysed in a separate paper. Here only two facts brought out by the detailed analysis need to be mentioned in view of the discussion to follow : (1) the average generation time was 15 days ; (2) the mean life of the adult flies in the experimental populations averaged 8·82 days.

Disregarding for the time being the obvious changes which occurred, when in thirty generations two genes, originally present in half the individuals, completely disappeared, one can still raise the question whether natural selection also brought about other genetic changes not so easily detectable but perhaps of even greater significance for adapting the fly populations to the conditions described. In other words, were the wild-type flies constituting the population after the disappearance of the mutant types genetically identical to the Oregon-R and *white-Bar* strains ? These certainly differed from each other not only in the characters of the eye which made them easily distinguishable, but also in an indefinite number of genetic factors affecting other morphological and physiological characters. Now, did natural selection also affect this part of the genotype of the two original strains ? Is it possible to find whether any genetic changes were produced in this respect and if so, of what sort ? And, if any such changes did occur during the process of eliminating the *white* and *Bar* alleles, did the populations undergo similar changes in later generations, when their members had become all wild type ? How different and how much better adapted to the cultural conditions might the flies be after natural selection had operated for many generations ?

In order to find the answers to these and to similar questions, the populations were continued for another seventy generations, and were subjected to tests which will be analysed in the following sections.

4. CHANGES IN COMPONENTS OF FITNESS

The characters which most likely have been influenced by the process of natural selection are those directly responsible for the fitness of the flies. It is clear that the individuals having greater viability under the chosen experimental conditions had a better chance of contributing their genetic material to the following generations. In an experiment of this type viability can accordingly be defined in terms of relative survival value in competition. Various factors may contribute directly or indirectly to the production of a greater survival value, and it is possible to devise various tests to measure some of them. If we observe that one strain has a higher survival value than another, we may try to relate this difference to different values of some measurable characters such as fecundity, fertility, rate of development, etc. (see below). If such factors are inherited at all, one should be able to find whether their values in the experimental populations were greater than in the two original strains. It is known that in *Drosophila melanogaster* such characters are indeed heritable largely on the basis of a multifactorial or polygenic scheme. With this idea in mind samples of the two original strains and of the four populations were tested at different times. The following characters were measured: (*a*) percentage of sterile females ; (*b*) fecundity of single females, measured by the number of eggs laid per day ; (*c*) fertility, in the sense of Pearl (1932), *i.e.* the percentage of adults emerging from a known number of eggs ; (*d*) rate of development, or the average time between the laying of the egg and the emergence of the imago ; (*e*) adult longevity, or the average time between emergence of the adult and its death.

(a) Sterility

Approximately 20-30 individuals of both sexes were taken at random from the Oregon-R, the *white-Bar* strains and from the four populations and were transferred to 300 c.c. culture bottles. Female offspring from these matings were cultured singly with three brothers each in $3 \cdot 5 \times 12$ cm. vials. Every four days the flies were transferred to a new vial with fresh food, such transfer being repeated five times. If by the 24th day no larvæ were observed on the medium, the female was considered to be sterile. The number of sterile females was recorded, after due allowance for accidental deaths. Table 1 shows clearly that the incidence of sterile females in the original stocks was reduced to zero in the experimental populations. If one takes

TABLE 1

Sterility of females of original strains and of experimental populations

Strain or population	No. ♀♀ tested	No. ♀♀ sterile	Percentage sterility
Oregon-R	252	4	*1·58*
white-Bar . . .	252	32	*12·69*
P$_1$	250	0	*0*
P$_2$	248	0	*0*
P$_3$	251	0	*0*
P$_4$	252	0	*0*

the average viability as measured in terms of sterility of the two parental strains as being equal $1 \cdot 00$, the viability of the four populations improved by a factor of $1 \cdot 07$.

(b) Fecundity

Samples of about 20-30 individuals of both sexes were taken at random from the two original strains and from the four populations and were cultured in 300 c.c. culture bottles (only in the case of tests performed in May 1948, see table 2, were the flies directly derived from the population bottles.) Virgin female progeny were isolated and mated singly within 24 hours from their emergence to three brothers in $3 \cdot 5 \times 12$ cm. vials. The surface of the medium in these was covered with a disc of blue absorbent paper soaked in a suspension of yeast. The flies were transferred every day to a new vial of this type and the number of eggs laid on the blue paper during the previous 24 hours was recorded. Egg laying took place at $25°$ C., and the recording was continued to the 20th day of life of the female or to the time of her death. For each test and day the quantity and quality of food and laying medium was the same for both strains and all experimental populations.

Table 2 gives the results of various tests for fecundity at different times. Data are presented separately for the first ten days and for the first fifteen days of life of the females, because some of the females died before the fifteenth day. The mean life of flies in the populations being approximately nine days, it did not seem worthwhile to extend egg counts beyond the 15th day. Because of the laboriousness of egg counting over a period of several days, no counts were made for the two original strains in the May 1948 test. The relatively low figures for the four populations in this test are probably due to the fact that the females were sampled directly from the population bottles. They

TABLE 2

Fecundity of females of original strains and of experimental populations at various times

Strain or population	Date	Generation tested	10-day period		15-day period		Total no. eggs
			No. ♀♀ tested	Mean no. eggs/day	No. ♀♀ tested	Mean no. eggs/day	
Oregon-R .	2/48	...	6	*11·50*	4	*10·50*	1330
	1/49	...	13	*11·74*	10	*13·58*	2683
w-B . .	2/48	...	6	*6·45*	6	*9·53*	1107
	1/49	...	11	*15·00*	9	*16·63*	2397
P₁ . .	2/48	59	6	*32·45*	6	*29·46*	4297
	5/48	65	11	*22·34**	11	*29·85**	5940
	1/49	82	12	*37·36*	12	*35·70*	7748
P₂ . .	2/48	59	6	*31·90*	6	*30·30*	5104
	5/48	65	12	*25·38**	11	*29·72**	6140
	1/49	82	12	*31·31*	12	*37·09*	6843
P₃ . .	2/48	32	6	*27·46*	6	*26·26*	4318
	5/48	38	11	*22·03**	11	*26·00**	4925
	1/49	56	12	*28·70*	12	*28·64*	6063
P₄ . .	2/48	32	6	*33·43*	6	*34·33*	6537
	5/48	38	12	*16·55**	11	*20·65**	4232
	1/49	56	12	*34·83*	12	*34·17*	7296

* All the values of the May 1948 test are systematically lower for reasons explained in text.

were thus therefore certainly less well fed than those in the other tests, a factor of significance in egg production, since it is known that culture conditions during larval development affect fecundity (Hadorn and Zeller, 1943). Table 3 shows the results of the analysis of variance of the square roots of the actual numbers of eggs counted. The comparison between the mean number of eggs of the two original strains and those of the four populations gives a value of F which is significant beyond the P = 0·01 value. Differences between various samples of the same strain or population, on the other hand, are not significant, with the exception of the *white-Bar* strain in which the

average number of eggs per day changed from 9·53 to 16·63 in the
course of about one year.   Even though the means of the populations

TABLE 3

Analysis of variance of transformed (square root) values of
egg production for 15 days

	February 1948				January 1949		
	DF	SSQ	MS		DF	SSQ	MS
Total Populations.	33 5	1039 795	159	Total Populations .	66 5	1797 632	126·4
	28	244	8·71		57	1165	20·4
	F = 18·25**				F = 6·19**		
	Oregon-R				*white-Bar*		
	DF	SSQ	MS		DF	SSQ	MS
Total Samples	13 1	167 10	10	Total Samples	14 1	214 120	120
	12	157	13		13	94	7·23
	F = <1				F = 16·56**		
	Population 1				**Population 2**		
	DF	SSQ	MS		DF	SSQ	MS
Total Samples	28 2	559 12	6	Total Samples	28 2	891 12	6
	26	547	21		26	879	33·8
	F = <1				F = <1		
	Population 3				**Population 4**		
	DF	SSQ	MS		DF	SSQ	MS
Total Samples	28 2	330 4	2	Total Samples	28 2	1078 169	84·5
	26	326	12·5		26	909	34·9
	F = <1				F = 2·42		

for the February 1948 and January 1949 tests (table 2) are markedly
different, especially in the case of P1 and P2, their F values are not

226

significant due to the wide range in the number of eggs of different females of the same population. Fig. 4 gives the mean cumulative fecundity of the two strains and the four populations over a period of 15 days and brings out in a very clear way the considerable difference in fecundity at the time of the last test between the original strains and the experimental population, derived from them. In spite of the already mentioned lack of significance between samples within populations, and disregarding the May 1948 test there seems to have been a trend toward higher values in each population as the selection experiment proceeded. The May 1948 test had smaller values than

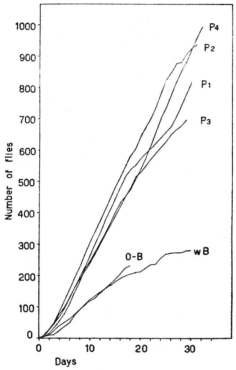

Fig. 4.—Comparison between the cumulative fecundities of the two original strains (O-B, *w-B*) and of the four experimental populations.

either of the others, but they were highly significant with respect to both tests on the original strains. Calculating the average means for Populations 1 and 2 on the one hand, and those of Populations 3 and 4 on the other, one can arrange the fecundity of females with respect to the number of generations as follows :

Generation 32   30·44 eggs per day
       ,,   56   31·76   ,,
       ,,   59   32·17   ,,
       ,,   82   37·33   ,,

227

This pooling of data of the various populations seems justified by the remarkably parallel behaviour of the populations in every other respect, which makes the trend toward a continuous improvement in the fecundity very clear. If we take now the average viability as measured in terms of fecundity of the two parental strains at the first test as equal to 1·00, the average viability of Populations 1 and 2 at the 82nd generation had improved by a factor of 3·69.

(c) *Fertility*

Fertility, or the percentage of imagoes emerging from a known number of eggs, is influenced by the age of the mother, as shown by Hadorn and Zeller (1943). As a consequence, it was not possible

TABLE 4

Fertility of original strains and of populations at various times during the selection experiment

	Oregon		w-B	
	Egg no.	Per cent. emergence	Egg no.	Per cent. emergence
June 1947 . . .	200	*61·5*	200	*66·5*
Nov. 1947 . . .	200	*62·0*	200	*50·0*
Jan. 1949 . . .	3320	*64·51*	3320	*60·18*
Mar. 1949 . . .	1800	*79·00*	2040	*61·42*

Date	Generation	P_1		P_2		P_3		P_4	
		Egg no.	Per cent. emergence	Egg no.	Per cent. emergence	Egg no.	Per cent. emergence	Egg no.	Per cent. emergence
4/48	35	...	...	...	...	200	*73·5*	200	*81·00*
6/47	40	200	*90*	...	...	...	...	...	...
1/48	51	200	*81·5*	200	*93·5*	...	...	...	...
12/48	55	...	...	...	...	2430	*88·35*	2430	*92·75*
3/49	60	...	...	...	...	1360	*84·26*	1320	*89·92*
12/48	81	2430	*88·97*	2430	*86·62*	...	...	...	...
2/49	86	1020	*91·17*	1400	*84·28*	...	...	...	...

to use egg samples taken directly from a strain or population because of the uncertain age of the females concerned. Young daughters of flies sampled from the Oregon-R and the *white-Bar* strains as well as from the experimental populations were mated to several brothers and used as egg producers for the determination of fertility. Two tests were performed in 1947, for the sole purpose of determining fertility. In this case, groups of 20 eggs were transferred to 3·5 × 12 cm. vials; after developing at 25° C. the number of adults present in the vials was recorded. For any particular test special care was taken to have cultural conditions of the six experimental series as homogeneous as possible. The two sets of data of the 1949 tests, on the other hand, are taken from an experiment in which the main purpose was to ascertain the weight of emerging flies. For reasons to be discussed below, the number of eggs per vial had to be different in each strain and population. The numbers of eggs per vial for the January 1949 experiment are to be found in table 10 ; the numbers of eggs per vial in the March 1949 experiment were as follows : Oregon-R : 45 ; *w-B* : 51 ; Population 1 : 34 ; Population 2 : 35 ; Population 3 : 34 ; Population 4 : 33.

Table 4 shows the results of fertility measurements on a total of 26,900 eggs. While in the Oregon-R strain a noticeable improvement took place in the course of almost two years, the fertility of the *white-Bar* strain remained stationary. All of the populations tested were clearly superior to both parental strains. No clear cut trend in the improvement in fertility with the progress of the selection is noticeable. This, however, can be related to the fact that the conditions of measuring

TABLE 5

Analysis of variance of fertility data.   Transformed p = *sin²* φ.

Data of June and November 1947 and of March 1949

	d.f.	Sum of squares	Mean squares
Total	31	2218	...
Tests	2	365	182·5**
Populations	5	1532	306·4**
Error	24	321	13·37

fertility were not identical in successive tests. In order to test the significance of differences in fertility, two separate analyses of variance were made on the transformed values. The first (table 5) refers to the data of June and November 1947 and of March 1949, derived from vials not dissimilar in the number of eggs ; the second (table 6) to the January 1949 data, for which a preliminary analysis of covariance had to be made in order to eliminate variability due to considerable differences in egg densities within each strain or population. In every case the data have been transformed to the sin^2 of the observed percentage. This statistical treatment confirmed the conclusions already noted regarding the differences between the fertilities of the two strains and of the four populations. If we now take the average viability as measured in terms of fertility of the two original strains at their first test as equal to 1·00, the average viability of the four populations at their last test has improved by a factor of 1·37.

(d) Developmental rate

Groups of 10 females and 20 males taken from strains and populations were transferred to 300 c.c. bottles having a paper spoon medium heavily seeded with baker's yeast. The size of the spoon was such that it could be easily removed from and introduced back into the bottle without disturbing the flies. Collection of eggs for determining the developmental rate was made only on the second day after the flies had been transferred to the egg laying vials when the females had recovered from the shock of transfer and were laying eggs regularly. This technique made certain that the fertilised eggs had not stayed for a long period in the oviduct, and had therefore just started their development at the time of laying. The eggs were collected every four hours and transferred in groups of 20 into vials with equal amounts of food. The collecting took place at the same time for the strains and populations in order to insure the maximum of homogeneity in feeding and environmental conditions. Development took place at $25° \pm 0.5°$C. After pupæ had been formed in the vials they were

TABLE 6

Analysis of covariance and test of significance of differences between adjusted means in January 1949 data of fertility. Transformed values $p = sin^2 \phi$

Source of variation	Sums of squares and products				Errors of estimate		
	d.f.	Sx^2	Sxy	Sy^2	Sum of squares	d.f.	Mean square
Total . .	35	1,280,889	240,336	67,769	22,676	34	...
Populations .	5	176,002	236,344	67,341			
Error . .	*30*	*1,104,867*	*4,092*	*428*	*413*	*29*	*14·2*
					22,263	5	4452

For test of significance of adjusted means

$$Sy^2 - \frac{(Sxy)^2}{Sx^2} = 413 \qquad F = 4452/14.2 = 313 \text{ **}$$

removed and placed singly in 30 c.c. glass test tubes containing a strip of filter paper which had been soaked in water to provide high humidity. Water was added each day to the test tubes until the flies emerged. Beginning with the seventh day after the eggs had been collected, the test tubes were inspected at 2.00 a.m., 8.00 a.m., noon, 4.00 p.m., 8.00 p.m. and midnight, and the number of emerged flies recorded. Thus the time of egg laying was known within ± 2 hours, and the time of emergence of the imago was determined within ± 1, 2 or 3 hours. The schedule chosen was not the best possible one because the time intervals were not constant, but in view of the large number of records to be kept at the same time for the six experimental series, no other choice was available. The test was performed on Populations 1 and 2 at their 53rd generation and on Populations 3 and 4 at their 27th generation. A total of 862 flies was used. The mean times of development expressed in days and hours, together with the number of flies in each sample are given in table 7. In view of the fact that the time intervals were not constant no standard errors are given. In order to reach a more complete evaluation of the data, they are presented in graphical form in fig. 5, with time intervals of one day.

TABLE 7

Average time of development of samples of flies taken from the two strains and the four populations

Strain or population	Days	Hours	No. of flies
Oregon-R	10	6	123
white-Bar	9	11	100
Population no. 1 . . .	9	0	163
Population no. 2 . . .	8	19	170
Population no. 3 . . .	8	19	147
Population no. 4 . . .	9	12	159

A comparison of the distributions of developmental times of the four populations with those of the two strains indicates that the former are skewed towards lower values and that this is more marked in the

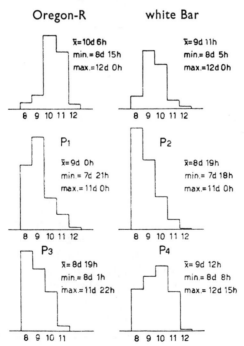

FIG. 5.—Distributions of the times of development for the two original strains and for the four populations. On the abscissa the days, on the ordinates the number of flies.

older populations (1 and 2) than in the younger ones (3 and 4). Furthermore, it is worthwhile pointing out that the extreme values of the distribution ranges shown on the figure are smaller in three out of four populations. A comparison between the six distributions carried out with the chi-square test shows that they are highly statistically different ($\chi^2 = 245 \cdot 91$; d.f. $= 23$; P$\ll$0·001). Also, a chi-square test between the pooled values of the two original strains on the one hand and of the four populations on the other hand shows that they are different ($\chi^2 = 109 \cdot 76$; d.f. $= 7$; P$\ll$0·001), and even a comparison of the developmental rates of the fastest growing of the two strains, *white-Bar*, with the population having the skewest distribution, P_2, shows that the lower values of the latter are significantly different from the former ($\chi^2 = 50 \cdot 39$; d.f. $= 7$; P$\ll$0·001). It therefore seems fair to conclude that in the experimental populations natural selection favoured those genotypes which led to a faster rate of development. If one compares the mean time of development of the two original strains (9 days, $20\frac{1}{2}$ hours) with that of the four

TABLE 8

Mean life of adult flies (in days)

	Oregon	*w-B*	P_1	P_2	P_3	P_4
No. of flies .	466	473	443	464	462	448
Average life .	30·37	22·50	36·90	30·24	37·81	40·41

	Analysis of variance		
	DF	SS	MS
Total . . .	2755	506,025	
Populations . .	5	98,278	19,655
	2750	407,747	148
	F = 132·5**		

populations (9 days, 3 hours), one finds a difference of 17·5 hours, or about 7·4 per cent. of the whole period of development. Thus, assuming that under the optimal conditions of this test time of development equals generation length, it is possible to compute that over a period of 100 days the two original strains would have produced 10·15 generations as against 10·96 generations produced by the average population. Thus, if we take the average viability as measured in terms of developmental rate of the two strains as equal to 1·00, the average viability of the four populations at the time of the test has improved by a factor of 1·08.

(e) *Adult longevity*

Ten groups of 50 newly emerged flies which were the progeny of samples taken from the strains and populations were placed in

3·5×12 cm. vials with standard food. They were transferred every five days without etherisation into a new vial with fresh food and record was kept of the deaths which had occurred during the interval. The flies were kept at 25°±0·5° C. throughout the experiment.

Populations 1 and 2 had reached the 73rd generations, and Populations 3 and 4 had reached the 47th when the samples were taken. Table 8 summarises the observed results. The actual numbers of flies of each group were somewhat less than the original 500 because some escaped in the process of transfer and some died of accident. The length of life has a normal distribution and the analysis of variance can accordingly be calculated on the actual figures. The differences between the observed means are highly significant, as shown in the table. Populations 1, 3 and 4 show mean life length values which are considerably greater than either of the two parental strains ; only Population 2 has a length of life equal to that of the Oregon-R strain.

As has been noted earlier, the mean life of the flies in the population under experimental conditions was about nine days. It seems hard to explain how a life span beyond the 22nd or 30th day under optimal environment could be of advantage under conditions of very great overcrowding. The data concerning fecundity and longevity in *Drosophila melanogaster* appear to be contradictory. Alpatov (1932) found that they are negatively correlated, and Hadorn and Zeller (1943) found that they are positively correlated. Our data indicate that there is no particular parallelism between them. Thus, it may be that they are products of independent genetic and physiological processes.

Longevity does not therefore appear to be selected for either directly or as a correlated response of the improvement in fecundity. It seems likely that it is the product of some general factor for increased resistance and hardiness which has been favoured during the period of selection. If this is the case, and if we take the average viability as measured in terms of longevity of the two original strains as equal to 1·00, the average viability of the four populations improved by a factor of 1·37.

5. CHANGE IN MORPHOLOGICAL CHARACTERS

The evidence so far discussed indicates that natural selection has operated at the level of quantitative physiological characters and that the genotypes of the four populations after several generations differ from those of the two parental strains. In view of these facts a new question can be raised : do these quantitative physiological changes find a counterpart in some quantitative change at the morphological level? If this is the case, we might understand better the changes in size and shape which have occurred in many organisms in the course of evolution. Two sets of experiments were started in order to bring some evidence on this point ; the object of the first was to ascertain whether any changes had occurred in the size and shape of the wing, and of the second to see whether the body weight and size had changed appreciably.

(a) Wing size

In order to make sure that larval competition did not influence the size of the characters to be measured, batches of 20 eggs, obtained from females hatched from samples taken from the strains and populations, were placed in 3.5×12 cm. vials with a constant amount of food and kept at $25° \pm 0.5°$ C. The left wings of about 50 males were removed and dry mounted between two glass slides. They were then enlarged 133 times by projection with a Bush Metaphot microscope and measured on millimetre paper.

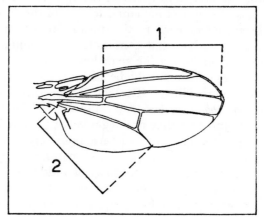

Fig. 6.—The two characters measured on the wings of the flies.

Table 9 records the results of the measurements and of the analysis of variance. The differences between the six means are highly significant, and the values of t for the differences between means taken two at a time show that (a) Oregon-R has wings longer than those of any other group; the statistical significance is at the 0.05 level for Population 4 and at the 0.01 level for the other four; (b) only Populations 2 and 3 have wings shorter than the *white-Bar* strain; (c) Oregon-R and *white-Bar* both have wider wings than any of the populations, but only Populations 2 and 4 show a statistically significant difference from the latter strain.

On the basis of such data we reach the general conclusion that under the experimental conditions genotypes with shorter and narrower wings were favoured and that the intensity of size decrease does not seem to be strictly correlated with the number of generations. Smaller wings were probably advantageous for the flies which lived under the more crowded conditions of the populations but the response to selection was not equally rapid in parallel populations.

(b) Body weight

It seemed particularly interesting to find out whether the action of natural selection for several generations had had any effect on body size. To measure this with satisfactory precision in *Drosophila melanogaster* is difficult, but an indirect estimate could be obtained from body weight.

In order to make significant comparisons between the body weights of samples of adult flies derived from the strains and populations it seemed necessary to make the feeding conditions as similar

TABLE 9

Values of wing characters no. 1 and 2 (wing length and width)

Strain	No. wings	$\bar{x} \pm e_s$	Analysis of variance
Character no. 1 (wing length)			
+Oregon-R	37	163·6±0·594	F = 6·38**
w-B	44	159·8±0·787	d.f. = 270 and 5
P₁	45	161·0±1·012	
P₂	50	157·7±0·726	t.₀₅ = 1·720
P₃	50	158·0±0·903	t.₀₁ = 2·268
P₄	50	161·6±1·126	
Character no. 2 (wing width)			
+Oregon-R	37	123·7±0·575	
w-B	44	118·8±0·571	F = 28·55**
P₁	45	118·0±0·706	
P₂	50	117·3±0·584	
P₃	50	116·7±0·828	t.₀₅ = 1·108
P₄	50	117·9±0·592	t.₀₁ = 1·146

Wing length		Wing width	
Oregon	163·6 ⎤ * ⎤ **	Oregon	123·7 ⎤ **
P₄	161·6 ⎦	w-B	118·8 ⎦
P₁	161·0 ⎦	P₁	118·0
w-B	159·8 ⎤ **	P₄	117·9 ⎤ **
P₃	158·0 ⎦	P₂	117·3 ⎦
P₂	157·7	P₃	116·7

as possible. In view of the different degrees of fertility shown by the strains and populations (see section 4c) it did not seem valid to let equal numbers of eggs develop on a constant amount of food. In order to take this factor into account, a first experiment was carried out, by using six different egg densities for each strain and population. The actual densities were calculated on the basis of the fertility data in such a way as to produce similar larval and pupal densities. It was hoped that by this procedure one could perform the analysis of covariance of the observed data, and calculate the F on the adjusted means after elimination of the density variable. The general results, which can be seen in table 10, however, were not suitable for this treatment, because it turned out that the regression between egg density and weight was linear for the Oregon-R and the *white-Bar*

TABLE 10

Mean living and dry weight of samples of 100 adults (50 ♀♀ and 50 ♂♂) expressed in
10^{-2} *gr., hatching from different egg densities (indicated in parentheses)*

	Oregon		white-Bar		P_1		P_2		P_3		P_4	
Adults and eggs per vial	256	(40)	160	(40)	204	(30)	217	(30)	212	(30)	213	(30)
Samples weighed	2		1		2		2		2		2	
Mean living weight ($\bar{x}$).		9·19		9·79		11·42		11·78		11·63		11·14	
Mean dry weight ($\bar{x}$)		2·48		2·56		2·91		3·17		3·02		2·92	
Adults and eggs per vial	240	(120)	200	(120)	246	(90)	230	(90)	244	(90)	241	(90)
Samples weighed	2		2		2		2		2		2	
Mean living weight ($\bar{x}$).		8·75		9·23		8·45		8·45		9·52		8·82	
Mean dry weight ($\bar{x}$)		2·37		2·52		2·19		2·30		2·68		2·41	
Adults and eggs per vial	261	(200)	266	(200)	260	(150)	244	(150)	259	(150)	282	(150)
Samples weighed	2		2		2		2		2		2	
Mean living weight ($\bar{x}$).		7·46		8·30		7·80		7·92		8·70		7·70	
Mean dry weight ($\bar{x}$)		1·85		2·31		2·10		2·17		2·41		1·95	
Adults and eggs per vial	411	(300)	361	(300)	382	(210)	344	(210)	395	(210)	392	(210)
Samples weighed	3		2		3		3		3		3	
Mean living weight ($\bar{x}$).		6·47		7·27		6·72		7·33		7·38		7·54	
Mean dry weight ($\bar{x}$)		1·86		2·08		1·78		1·88		1·97		1·96	
Adults and eggs per vial	463	(370)	459	(370)	482	(270)	477	(270)	472	(270)	509	(270)
Samples weighed	4		4		4		4		4		4	
Mean living weight ($\bar{x}$).		6·66		7·82		8·36		8·17		8·24		8·09	
Mean dry weight ($\bar{x}$)		1·75		2·35		2·55		2·52		2·52		2·58	
Adults and eggs per vial	511	(450)	552	(450)	588	(330)	593	(330)	565	(330)	617	(330)
Samples weighed	5		5		5		5		5		5	
Mean living weight ($\bar{x}$).		5·70		7·14		6·68		6·71		6·93		6·72	
Mean dry weight ($\bar{x}$)		1·55		1·95		1·71		1·77		1·74		1·68	
Total adults	933		903		963		931		951		1005	
Mean living weight (100 flies)		7·371		8·258		8·201		8·393		8·733		8·335	
Mean dry weight (100 flies)		1·976		2·295		2·206		2·302		2·381		2·250	

strains, but not for the four populations. If a transformation was used for all the values which made the regression of the populations linear, then the regression of the two strains became curvilinear. From a direct inspection of the data, however, it appears again that every population gave weight values which were greater than those of the Oregon-R strain and equal or slightly superior to those of the *white-Bar* stock.

236

In view of this difficulty, a second experiment was carried out using just one egg density per strain or population, as indicated by the numbers in parentheses in table 11 (experiment 2), which also summarises the data of the first experiment. A total of 8940 eggs was used, and besides weighing the sample groups of males and 50 females and comparing their mean weights, the total weight of adults produced in an average culture of each strain and population was calculated, by multiplying the mean weight by the actual mean number of adults obtained per culture. The two sets of data are in good agreement, in that they both show that the flies derived from

TABLE 11

Weight of Drosophila expressed in 10^{-2} *gr. For explanation see text*

	Oregon-R	white-Bar	P_1	P_2	P_3	P_4
Experiment 1						
Mean weight (100 flies)—						
Fresh	7·371	8·258	8·201	8·393	8·733	8·335
Dry	1·976	2·295	2·206	2·302	2·381	2·250
Total weight—						
Fresh	4·127	4·743	4·739	4·688	4·983	5·026
Dry	1·106	1·243	1·275	1·285	1·359	1·357
Experiment 2						
Mean weight (100 flies)—	(45)	(51)	(34)	(35)	(34)	(33)
Fresh	11·111	12·550	12·585	12·841	12·533	12·344
Total weight—						
Fresh	3·270	3·488	4·019	3·794	3·598	3·667

	♀ Oregon-R × ♂ white-Bar	♀ white-Bar × ♂ Oregon-R
Mean weight (100 flies) .	(33)	(33)
Fresh	12·643	12·688
Total weight—		
Fresh	3·709	3·869

the four populations have produced more " Drosophila material " per culture than flies obtained from either of the parental strains. The actual values are lower in the second experiment than in the first because of the smaller number of eggs present in the culture vials. The data from the crosses between the strains in table 11 will be considered later.

It seems therefore safe to conclude that under the experimental conditions those genotypes were favoured that allowed the flies to make a better use of the available food, assimilating it and transforming it into " Drosophila material," and thereby reaching a greater weight and thus, presumably, a larger size.

6. THE NEW GENOTYPE

The evidence thus far presented shows that in the course of these experiments every tested character in each of the four populations has undergone a certain change.   The degree of change was different in each population, but the trend was the same in all.   For some characters, as was the case for the fecundity of females, the values finally reached were much higher than those of either of the two parental strains, while in others, such as wing length, they were very close to one or the other of the two original stocks.   Furthermore it has been shown that these changes continued after the mutant genes had disappeared, and the members of the populations all had a wild-type phenotype.

The physiological characters tested can be regarded as measures of fitness and because of this consistent change toward a greater total fitness the inference seems justified that the observed changes clearly had a selective value and were the product of natural selection.   The viability factors which were calculated with respect to the average values of both parental strains for each tested character, and were presented at the close of subsections of section 4, can be used to estimate the total improvement in fitness of the populations.   If the factors computed for sterility, fecundity, fertility and developmental rate are multiplied together one gets a compound factor of 5·84. And if the improvement in longevity can also be considered, as an index of an increase in viability, then the total factor of fitness increase becomes equal to 8·00.   In other words, the total fitness improved in the course of about 80 generations by about 800 per cent.   This value may represent a potential which would not actually be realised in the population bottles because all of the measurements were made on flies which developed under optimal conditions, which certainly did not exist in the population bottles.   But since the improvement in each of the tested factors was certainly of an hereditary nature, the factor of 8 may be viewed as a valid estimate of the amount of evolutionary change in fitness between the beginning and the end of the experiment.   The change in wing size was also probably adaptive, since it can be surmised that under conditions of extreme overcrowding such as prevailed in the population bottles, smaller wings must have favoured survival.   It is not as easy, at first, to account for the associated increase of body weight and therefore presumably of size, because smaller individuals might be expected to have a better chance of survival in competition, under conditions of great density.   But this change was accompanied by, or was the product of, a better ability of the flies to exploit the available food and to convert it into " Drosophila material."   In view of this fact, one is led to conclude that the increase in weight, too, had a positive selective value.   We shall discuss its significance later.

It would appear, therefore, that new polygenic systems have arisen from the genotypes of the two original strains which have conferred on their carriers a remarkably higher viability and have thus increased substantially the fitness of the populations to the conditions in which they existed.

That new and better adapted genotypes were produced seems beyond any possible doubt, but they need not necessarily have been the product of a long continued selection. If this had been operating on the products of genetic recombination resulting from the mixture of the two sets of genes present in the Oregon-R and the *white-Bar* strains, in each of the four populations a new gene constellation would have been synthesised through a progressive process of casting off the less adapted and preserving the most favourable polygenic combinations. But the observed higher adaptive level could have been the result of a different process, namely that complementary-acting genes were brought into combination at the F_1 and stayed in the populations without selection at the F_1 gametic frequency, plus or minus sampling fluctuations. In this latter case the higher fitness

TABLE 12

Heterosis in the crosses between the two original strains

	Fecundity of females				
Cross	No. ♀♀ tested	Mean 10 d	No. eggs/day 15 d	Total 10 d	No. eggs 15 d
♀ w-B × ♂ +	12	49·67	*59·93*	5961	8942
♀ + × ♂ w-B	12	39·05	*40·54*	4686	7229

	Fertility		
Cross	No. eggs	No. adults	Percentage
♀ w-B × ♂ +	1000	906	*90·6*
♀ + × ♂ w-B	1000	900	*90·0*

of the populations would have been produced by a sort of heterotic response due to the complementary action of the genes, and it would have been achieved in one step, at the first generation, rather than through a steady progress extending over several generations. Viability factors such as those measured in this investigation do in fact often show heterosis when two unrelated strains are crossed.

Two tests on viability factors and one on body weight were accordingly performed on the two reciprocal F_1 hybrids of the original strains to see whether this alternative interpretation was plausible. The pertinent data were collected following the previously described techniques. As can be seen in tables 11 and 12, the hybrid values show a clear-cut heterosis reaching values similar and sometimes higher than those of the samples derived from the populations after many generations. This being the case, the previously discussed

239

interpretation attributing the higher adaptive level of the populations to the action of a long continued selection should be rejected.

7. COMPETITIVE ABILITY OF THE NEW GENOTYPE

If indeed no selection for quantitative traits had occurred and the populations had just been maintained in hybrid condition over the whole experiment, other questions arise. Thus, in view of the fact that, except for the May 1948 test for fecundity, all the measurements of viability factors and of morphological traits were performed on the progenies of samples taken from the populations, and were cultured under optimal conditions allowing both heterotic and non-heterotic individuals to survive, how could the reported higher fitness obtain? Similarly, how could the indication of progressive change in fecundity be explained? No wing measurements were performed on the heterotic hybrids, but it was hard to believe that they could have had wings smaller than the parental strains, as it is known that wing length is positively correlated with body size (Zarapkin, 1934 ; Buzzati-Traverso, 1947*b*). This being true, how could the data presented in table 9 be accounted for? And, finally, how could the increase in population size to be discussed in the following section (8) be expounded?

Because of these questions an experiment was required which might discriminate between the two alternative interpretations and explain the causes of the observed changes. If the observed change in viability had been due to the effects of natural selection, which had produced a new genotype better adapted to the culture conditions, it follows as a necessary consequence that this new combination of genes would have a better survival value in population bottles than strains which had not been subjected to similarly stringent selection. This supposition could be tested if the wild-type flies derived from the experimental populations were put in competition with the original *white-Bar* strain, using the same technique of breeding that had been followed previously. Should the greater viability be the result of a new combination of genes selected over many generations then one would expect that the rate of elimination of the *Bar* and *white* alleles would be faster than in the four original populations. If, on the contrary, the greater viability was due to some sort of complementary action of genes maintained at their F_1 frequency, then no such difference between the results of the old and the new selection experiments could be observed. Two new populations, referred to as Selected 1 and 2 (PS1, PS2), were therefore started with 10 virgin females and 10 males taken from Population 1, and 10 virgin females and 10 males taken from the *white-Bar* strain.

Table 13 and fig. 7 give the results obtained in the course of the first fifteen generations. The comparison with similar data of the four original populations shows beyond doubt that in the Selected populations the rate of elimination of the *white* and *Bar* alleles was much greater than in the first experiment. After 15 generations the mutant alleles were still present with a frequency of about 15 per cent. in the four old populations, but had already practically disappeared in the new ones. These data seem therefore sufficient to warrant the interpretation that the change in physiological and morphological characters was due to the action of natural selection which in the

TABLE 13

Selection rate in two of the original four populations and in the two new (Selected) populations

Generation	P_3		P_4		PS1		PS2	
	q_B	q_w	q_B	q_w	q_B	q_w	q_B	q_w
1	0·500	0·500	0·500	0·500	0·500	0·500	0·500	0·500
3	0·625	0·625	0·330	0·340	0·132	0·132	0·031	0·031
5	0·399	0·366	0·383	0·390	0·043	0·043	0·030	0·022
7	0·276	0·352	0·163	0·179	0·014	0·029	0·014	0·032
9	0·242	0·283	0·181	0·179	0·023	0·025	0·049	0·041
12	0·201	0·229	0·130	0·160	0·015	0·027	0·029	0·018
15	0·148	0·156	0·080	0·117	0·027	0·034	0·035	...

course of several generations has produced from the combination of the two original genotypes new polygenic constellations which ensured a better viability to their carriers and thereby made the populations progressively better adapted to their environments.

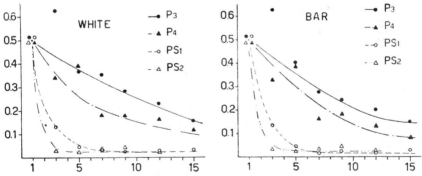

FIG. 7.—Elimination of the mutants *white* and *Bar* in Populations 3 and 4 and in the two Selected Populations. On the abscissa the number of generations, on the ordinate the gene frequencies.

8. NATURAL SELECTION MECHANISMS IN EXPERIMENTAL POPULATIONS

The growth of a population, whether natural or experimental, is known to be the result of the interaction of two groups of factors ; the " biotic potential " of the species and the "environmental resistance " (Chapman, 1928).

" The biotic potential represents the potential rate of increase of the species under given conditions. It is realised if there are no restrictions of food, no toxic waste products, etc. Environmental resistance can be measured by the difference between the potential number of organisms which can appear during a fixed time in consequence of the potential rate of increase, and the actual number of organisms observed in a given microcosm at a determined time. Environmental resistance is thus expressed in terms of the reduction of some potential rate of increase, character-istic for the given organism under given conditions " (Gause, 1934).

The increase in number of organisms per unit time depends in the first place on the potential number of offspring (b) which the organism can produce per unit time ; the total potential number of organisms present at a given time in a given environment will be given by the product of such potential increase by the number (N) of organisms present at the time considered. If there were unlimited food supply and no other limiting factors the population would grow according to an equation of geometric increase, where the constant b is the rate of potential increase of the organism. Under experimental conditions, as well as in nature, food is limited and other factors may further interfere with the growth of the population ; therefore the potential geometrical rate of population growth is not realised, and its limitation is due to a complex of factors which are described under the general term " environmental resistance." In a limited environ-ment with a constant supply of food, such as our population bottles, the potential geometric increase at every moment will be only partially realised, depending on how near the already existing size of the population reaches the maximum number (K) of individuals that can live within the limits of the chosen biotope or its numerical equilibrium. The difference between the maximal population possible and that already realised, expressed in terms relative to the maximal population, shows the number of " still vacant spaces " at a given time in a given microcosm ($K\text{-}N/K$). In accordance with this formula-tion, in populations like the ones of *Drosophila melanogaster* here con-sidered, which were started with a number of adults much smaller than that of the population at numerical equilibrium :

(1) The rate of growth will increase rapidly at first, will reach a maximum and then decline until attainment of the numerical equilibrium.

(2) The environmental resistance will be very small at the beginning and then will increase to a constant maximum value when the population has reached its maximal number, and correspondingly :

(3) The intensity of the struggle for existence, measurable by the ratio of the unrealised part of the potential increase over the realised part of the potential increase, is very little at the beginning of the experiment, but later increases considerably and very rapidly.

The quantitative treatment of the interaction between the biotic potential and the environmental resistance has been expressed by

Verhulst and by Pearl and Reed by means of the logistic curve :
$\dfrac{dN}{dt} = bN\dfrac{K-N}{K}$. A general discussion of this conception can be
found in Gause (1934).

Pearl and his co-workers (see Pearl, 1927) demonstrated that the growth of genetically homogeneous populations of *Drosophila melanogaster* follows the logistic curve. This interpretation is borne out by the data of L'Héritier and Teissier (1933), Bodenheimer (1938) and of the writer so far as homogeneous populations are concerned. The experiments reported here, however, are concerned with populations

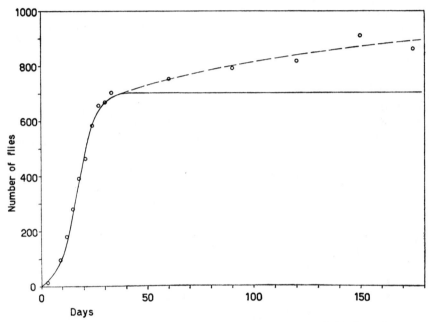

Fig. 8.—Comparison between the observed population growth (circles and broken line) and the calculated logistic curve (solid line).

which are changing genetically rather than with purely demographic phenomena. The experimental populations were started with equal numbers of two genotypes. While numerical equilibrium was being reached and later, a struggle for existence took place between the various genetic combinations present. The end result was a change in the biotic potential itself, which led to a further increase in the number of flies present in the bottles, beyond a first equilibrium value, as can be seen in fig. 8. This shows that the classical logistic curve is not realised in genetically heterogeneous populations. It accordingly seems worthwhile to analyse how this may occur.

The two groups of flies originally present in the first bottle differed in the shape and colour of the eyes and, we can now say, in fitness or biotic potential. This original population was accordingly genetically heterogeneous.   At the beginning there were two genotypes which had to face only a small environmental resistance.   From the second generation on, however, the struggle for existence became much more complicated because of genetic recombination, which led to an increase in the number of genotypes present.   How large this increase was is unknown.   It must have produced phenotypic variability in the considered components of fitness beyond the range of variation of the original strains ; but more important for the present discussion, it must also have produced a range of biotic potentials sufficient to permit the operation of natural selection within the conditions prevailing in the bottles.   This range must also have changed continuously during four years.

The ways in which different genotypes became represented by different average numbers in the next generation are certainly numerous and we can only attempt to list a few, with particular reference to the factors which have been measured in this investigation.

In the first place, adult flies having different genetic constitutions may show different percentages of sterility, as was the case for our Oregon-R and *white-Bar* stocks.   In the second place, flies of one sex can be differentially attracted by flies of the opposite sex having other genotypes ; this seems to be at least in part the cause for the elimination of *white* gene reported by Reed and Reed (1950) and by Merrell (1953), who showed that both red- and white-eyed females discriminate against white males in mating.   In the third place, flies genetically different can have different average fecundities, as was shown above.   In the fourth place, selective fertilisation might occur.   Certain types of sperm might fertilise certain types of eggs more easily than others ; there is no satisfactory experimental evidence on this point, but the possibility cannot be excluded.   In the fifth place, different genotypes may differ in fertility as was shown above, and this in turn may depend on a series of factors such as presence of lethals or semilethals, the ability to grab food, capacity to assimilate it, etc.   In the sixth place, developmental periods may be different, as shown above.   In the seventh place, hardiness in the adult stage can be different, as was found in our experiments in terms of longevity. In the eighth place, resistance against diseases at various life stages can be different.   Different values of each of these and similar factors will contribute to the differential success of any genotype in competition, provided that they are genetically determined and extend beyond the range of environmental variation.

While discussing the new adaptation level reached during the experiment (Section 6) it was pointed out that the total potential viability of the populations had increased by a factor of 8.   The intensity of the struggle for existence under the experimental conditions employed can be evaluated by the ratio of the unrealised part of the potential increase to the realised part.   The four populations reached their first numerical equilibrium after 33 days at an average value of 704 flies per bottle. The integrated differential equation of the logistic curve best fitting the experimental data is :

$$\frac{704}{1+e^{4\cdot03-0\cdot2344t}}.$$

From this expression the values shown in table 14 can be obtained. The lowermost figures of this table give an index of the struggle for existence. It will be noted that this has increased over 1000 times from the outset of the growth of the population to the 33rd day. Is it possible to evaluate the magnitude of competition in the population bottles in a more direct way? Using Pearl's data (1932) on the influence of density of population upon egg production in *Drosophila melanogaster*

TABLE 14

Growth of populations of Drosophila melanogaster. *The observed values are the average of the four parallel experiments.* b *(biotic potential)* $= 0\cdot2344$; K *(maximum population)* $= 704$

Day	N observed	N calculated	$bN-\dfrac{dN}{dt}$
3	16	24·40	0·036
6	51	47·63	0·073
9	94	90·02	0·141
12	179	160·73	0·297
15	281	263·67	0·600
18	392	385·46	1·212
21	465	499·29	2·448
24	583	586·66	5·024
27	657	639·44	9·989
30	669	670·77	20·278
33	704	687·16	42·481

one can estimate the number of eggs actually laid in conditions like the ones prevailing in our experiment. Using this estimate and the average viability data presented above, one can compute the number of zygotes that did not reach the adult stage for every one that did. The figure thus obtained, 554, shows again how intense selective processes were under the experimental conditions.

It should be mentioned, furthermore, that with the progress of the experiment it was noticed that the four experimental populations did not remain at the original equilibrium of 700 flies but slowly approached and later exceeded the average number of 900 flies per bottle (fig. 8). At the same time it was noted that the number of adults emerging from each bottle was positively correlated with the number of individuals present in the population when eggs were being laid in that particular bottle. The correlation was curvilinear, as one would expect, in view of the fact that the maximum number of adults which can be recovered from a certain amount of food is practically constant beyond a certain number of fertilised eggs present in the original culture bottle. Buzzati-Traverso (1947*b*) has shown

245

that it is not possible to obtain more than an average of about 140 adult flies from between 300 and 1000 eggs in experiments in which the same type of vial and an inbred strain of *Drosophila melanogaster* were used and the eggs were placed on the medium all at the same time. It seems safe to conclude that the increased viability and ability to exploit the available food made the populations better adapted to the environmental condition in the sense that they became more numerous. If it were possible to calculate from our data the value of the biotic potential at the end of the experiment it is certain that we would find a figure larger than the original 0·2344.

The consequence of these results for problems of demography will not be discussed here (Buzzati-Traverso, 1954) ; but a conclusion seems ineluctable : that the intensity of natural selection increased during the experiment, even though the environmental conditions were constant. This conclusion pertains only to the action of natural selection on traits determined by polygenes, for no such increase in the intensity of the struggle for existence is considered by the current mathematical theories of evolution in which the effects of selection on the frequencies of genes primarily affecting a single trait have been analysed. A new theoretical treatment of natural selection in polygenic systems therefore becomes necessary.

One more comment seems pertinent. Most discussions of evolution from the standpoint of genetics consider the selective value of a certain gene, or chromosome type alone, and, so to say, *in vacuo*. The fact is that the change in frequency of a single gene (or chromosome) during a number of generations means that the individuals carrying its allele will produce more or fewer adult offspring in the next generation than the individuals not carrying it. The factor which is decisive for changing frequency is a *productivity differential* involving of necessity the whole genotype and not one gene alone, for the latter will have different survival values in different genetic milieus. Some extreme mutants, like those mostly used in laboratory experiments, may affect specifically the productivity of its carriers to such an extent as to make the effects of the rest of the genotype and of the interactions of the mutant with it insignificant. But under natural conditions the commonest case is very likely that of " small " mutants where the natural selection mechanism probably involves many genes at one time. Thus, a continuous increase in the intensity of natural selection fostering both productivity and change in polygenic traits may be of cardinal significance in evolutionary events.

Finally, I have shown that a given physiological or morphological trait may differ in degree in parallel experiments, and that, as a consequence, the improvement in fitness realised in the four populations described above was not identical after a certain number of generations. In view of the fact that we are dealing with characters which are controlled by many genes this is not surprising. The very exacting sieve of natural selection acts throughout the whole life cycle of an organism and it is well possible that the same results, namely an increased total productivity or an adaptive change in morphological characters, can be reached in various ways through the action of various constellations of genes. For example, one of these may guarantee success during larval development, another may insure a hardier adult life. Each of two individuals carrying either of these constellations may show an identical total productivity value and yet the constituent factors, taken separately, can be very different. The complex genetic conditions which underlie the observed changes in fitness need not be the same in the four populations, nor indeed in all of their members. The only fact of significance is that one end result was achieved : higher productivity.

9. EVOLUTIONARY SIGNIFICANCE OF CHANGE IN POLYGENIC TRAITS

J. B. S. Haldane has pointed out (1949), that in view of the arbitrariness of distinctions between systematic categories, the most reliable measure of evolutionary rate is one which relates changes in the dimensions of the body of an organism or its parts, to time, whether expressed in units of geological time or in generations. It is generally accepted, however (see, *e.g.*, Fisher, 1930 ; Timoféeff-Ressovsky, 1939 ; and Simpson, 1944 and 1954) that mutations important for evolution are small, as measured in terms of structural change, and therefore that evolution can be explained in terms of the accumulation of small mutants affecting quantitative traits. This opinion seems substantiated by two considerations, that (*a*) differences between subspecies, species and higher systematic categories are ordinarily of a quantitative nature and accordingly fall under the control of polygenic systems, and that (*b*) a great majority of characters used by the taxonomist are in terms of measurements or ratios between measurements.

The data presented above bring evidence to show that evolutionary changes of the same degree as those observed by the paleontologist and the morphologist which may have taken millions of years to produce, can be observed within the limited span of a few dozens of generations. The variation in the size, and therefore shape, of the wings, as well as that concerning the size of the body are of this type. Furthermore, the correlation of reduction in wing size and increase in body size demonstrates that a change must also have occurred in the values of the coefficients of relative growth. These changes are significant for an understanding of evolutionary events not only from the viewpoint of qualitative differences but of quantitative ones also. If, in the case of the shortening of the wings, we take the values derived from Population No. 2 at its 55th generation ($157 \cdot 7 \pm 0 \cdot 726$) and compare it with that of the smaller of the two parental strains namely *white-Bar* ($159 \cdot 8 \pm 0 \cdot 787$), we can calculate that the average rate of change per generation is 0·00024 per cent. This change corresponds to a little less than one-twenty-thousandth of the standard deviation of the value of Population 3. This means that the observed rate was of the same order of magnitude of the fastest evolutionary change, heretofore recorded, namely the length height index of the human skull. This fact brings further evidence to indicate that known genetic processes are quite adequate to account for the evolutionary changes observed in the fossil record.

The analysis presented above brings still other evidence which may be of significance for an understanding of historical evolution. Paleontologists have found many examples of progressive increases in size within phyla. This seems to be a general trend among terrestrial vertebrates, and similar evidence is accumulating for other animal groups (see *e.g.* Stenzel, 1949). Castle (1932) argued that phylogenetic increases in size of this sort may be caused by competition among individuals in a given population of the same species and that the larger individuals or those attaining a large size earlier in life than others would be at an advantage over the smaller ones. Competitions *in utero* between mammalian embryos would be favoured by genetic conditions which would result in a more rapid rate of development, and thus a larger size at birth and maturity. It is quite possible that a similar phenomenon has actually occurred in our populations, where, as it has been shown, genotypes producing a faster development have been favoured.

My material also illustrates another evolutionary process. When the wild-type flies from the first natural selection experiment were put in competition with the original *white-Bar* strain, the two mutant alleles were eliminated at a much faster rate than in the four original populations, as a result of the greater fitness which had been attained by the " selected " wild type. Let us now consider a condition in nature in which there is a steady migration from Population A to Population B. As a result of this accretion of new variability by the latter, natural selection may produce genotypes better adapted to the environmental conditions of Population B by incorporating the favourable migrating genes and discarding the less favourable ones. In the course of time the pressure of selection against the latter would increase and they would accordingly be eliminated more and more rapidly, as was the case in our " new experiment " (see section 7). In this way a very elementary sort of isolating mechanism may arise.

New experimental data always raise new questions and broaden the scope of our investigations, and this attempt to analyse the action of natural selection on polygenic characters has accordingly proved to be quite rewarding. Its main significance lies in the fact that it may encourage the use of similar techniques in order to reach a deeper insight into the factors responsible for the " advancement of all organic beings, namely, multiply, vary, let the strongest live and the weakest die."

248

10. SUMMARY

1. Four parallel populations of *Drosophila melanogaster* were maintained in approximate numerical equilibrium for a period of about 4 years (100 generations) using Pearl's technique.

2. The foundation stock of each of the four populations consisted of equal numbers of males and females of a wild-type Oregon-R strain and of another strain homozygous for *white* and *Bar*. About 2,000,000 flies were classified for sex and phenotype. After about 30 generations the mutants were completely replaced by their normal alleles.

3. Samples of the two original strains and of the four populations were tested at different times for a series of physiological and morphological traits.

4. The following changes occurred in the experimental populations : (i) Sterility of females of the two original strains disappeared. (ii) A very marked and progressive increase in the average fecundity of females took place. (iii) The rate of development of the flies increased. (iv) The adult longevity of the flies increased. (v) Length and width of the wings become smaller. (vi) The average body weight of the flies increased.

5. The observed improvement in fitness by a factor of 8 over a period of about 80 generations as well as the morphological changes are interpreted as being due to the action of natural selection which, making use of the genotypes of the two original strains, has produced new polygenic systems better adapted to the conditions of the experiment.

6. To test the validity of this interpretation two new populations were started in which the wild-type flies derived from the previous experiment were put in competition with the original *white-Bar* strain. The rate of elimination of the mutant alleles was in this case much faster.

7. The mechanisms of natural selection in experimental populations are discussed and it is shown how the genetic heterogeneity of a population may affect its growth. This will follow a curve different from the logistic derived from the assumption of a constant value for the biotic potential of an organism which, on the contrary, falls under the control of natural selection. In fact the average number of adults in the four populations departed from the logistic curve calculated from a constant biotic potential. It is further concluded that the intensity of natural selection is bound to increase under constant environmental conditions if one takes into consideration polygenic systems.

8. The evolutionary significance of changes in polygenic traits is discussed. The observed rate of change in wing size is shown to be of the same order of magnitude as the fastest known rate of evolution as revealed by the fossil record. The increase in body size, too, is in agreement with progressive increase in the dimensions of animals observed by paleontologists for many phyla.

Acknowledgments.—The author is greatly indebted to Mr Giordano Peschiera for his precious help as technical assistant throughout the duration of these experiments ; to him he wishes to express his deep appreciation. The author wishes to thank : Dr L. L. Cavalli-Sforza for advice on the statistical treatment of the data ; Dr Renzo Scossiroli for the preparation of some of the drawings and both of them together with Professors Carl Epling and I. Michael Lerner for reading of the manuscript.

11. REFERENCES

ALPATOV, W. W. 1932. Egg production in *Drosophila melanogaster* and some factors which influence it. *J. exp. Zool.*, *63*, 85-111.

BODENHEIMER, F. S. 1938. *Problems of Animal Ecology.* Oxford : Oxford University Press.

BUZZATI-TRAVERSO, A. 1947a. Genetica di popolazioni in Drosophila. VII. Selezione naturale in popolazioni artificiali di *Drosophila melanogaster.* *Mem. Ist. ital. Idrobiol.*, *4*, 65-86.

BUZZATI-TRAVERSO, A. 1947b. Genetica di popolazioni in Drosophila. VIII. Sovrapopolamento in *Drosophila melanogaster.* *Mem. Ist. ital. Idrobiol.*, *4*, 87-106.

BUZZATI-TRAVERSO, A. A. 1954. On the growth of populations. *Proc. 18th Inter. Zool. Congress*, Copenhagen (in press).

CASTLE, W. E. 1932. Body size and body proportions in relation to growth rates and natural selection. *Science, 76*, 365.

CHAPMAN, R. N. 1928. The quantitative analysis of environmental factors. *Ecology, 9*, 111-122.

FISHER, R. A. 1930. *The Genetical Theory of Natural Selection.* Oxford : Clarendon Press.

GAUSE, G. F. 1934. *The Struggle for Existence.* Baltimore : Williams and Wilkins.

HADORN, E., AND ZELLER, H. 1943. Fertilitätsstudien an *Drosophila melanogaster.* I. Untersuchungen zum altersbedingten Fertilitätsabfall. *Roux Arch. Entw Mech. Organ., 142*, 276-300.

HALDANE, J. B. S. 1949. Suggestions as to the quantitative measurement of rates of evolution. *Evolution, 3*, 51-56.

KALMUS, H. 1945. Adaptive and selective responses of a population of *Drosophila melanogaster* containing e and e^+ to differences in temperature, humidity, and to selection for developmental speed. *J. Genet., 47*, 58-63.

L'HÉRITIER, P., AND TEISSIER, G. 1933. Étude d'une population de Drosophiles en équilibre. *C. R. Acad. Sci. (Paris), 197*, 1765-1767.

L'HÉRITIER, P., AND TEISSIER, G. 1934. Une expérience de sélection naturelle. Courbe d'élimination du gène " bar " dans une population de Drosophiles en équilibre. *C. R. Soc. Biol. Paris, 117*, 1049-1051.

L'HÉRITIER, P., AND TEISSIER, G. 1937. Élimination des formes mutantes dans les populations de Drosophiles. Cas des Drosophiles " bar." *C. R. Soc. Biol. Paris, 124*, 880-882.

MATHER, K. 1943. Polygenic inheritance and natural selection. *Biol. Revs., 18*, 32-64.

MERRELL, D. J. 1953a. Gene frequency changes in small laboratory populations of *Drosophila melanogaster. Evolution, 7*, 95-101.

MERRELL, D. J. 1953b. Selective mating as a cause of gene frequency changes in laboratory populations of *Drosophila melanogaster. Evolution, 7*, 287-296.

NIKORO, Z. S., AND GUSEV, S. N. 1938. Experimental analysis of the action of the automatic genetic processes. *Biol. Zh. (Mosc.), 7*, 197-216.

PEARL, R. 1927. The growth of populations. *Quart. Rev. Biol., 2*, 532-548.

PEARL, R. 1932. The influence of density of population upon egg production in *Drosophila melanogaster. J. exp. Zool., 63*, 57-84.

REED, S. C., AND REED, E. W. 1948. Natural selection in laboratory populations of Drosophila. *Evolution, 2*, 176-186.

REED, S. C., AND REED, E. W. 1950. Natural selection in laboratory populations of Drosophila. II. Competition between a white-eye gene and its wild-type allele. *Evolution, 4,* 34-42.

SIMPSON, G. G. 1944. *Tempo and Mode in Evolution.* New York : Columbia University Press.

SIMPSON, G. G. 1954. *The Major Features of Evolution.* New York : Columbia University Press.

STENZEL, H. B. 1949. Successional speciation in Paleontology : the case of the oysters of the Sellæformis stock. *Evolution, 3,* 34-50.

TIMOFÉEFF-RESSOVSKY, N. W. 1939. Genetik und Evolutionsforschung. *Z.I.A.V., 76,* 158-218.

WIEDEMANN, G. 1936. Modellversuche zur Selektionswirkung von Faktormutationen bei *Drosophila melanogaster. Genetica, 18,* 277-290.

ZARAPKIN, S. R. 1934. Analyse der genotypisch und durch Aussenfaktoren bedingten Grössenunterschiede bei *Drosophila funebris. Z.I.A.V., 67,* 374-388 ; *68,* 163-184.

251

HETEROSIS AND FITNESS IN EXPERIMENTAL POPULATIONS OF DROSOPHILA MELANOGASTER

Hampton L. Carson

Department of Zoology, Washington University, St. Louis, Missouri

Received October 3, 1960

Evolution is a process which results in the genetic adjustment of an interbreeding group of organisms to its environment. The pervading principle in this adjustment is natural selection. Operating under the conditions imposed by the prevailing mutation rates, population sizes and recombination patterns, natural selection builds a gene pool which copes with the particular environmental vicissitudes that the population encounters.

The present paper reports the results of laboratory experiments in which the kinetics of genetic adjustment are subjected to direct study at the level of integration of the sexual population. A set of environmental parameters is arbitrarily chosen, gene pools of various compositions are prepared and then are tested for performance under these conditions. The average size that the population maintains, when equilibrated over many generations by natural selection, is used as the measure of the performance of the group. A control or standard population is always maintained under identical conditions and is measured simultaneously with the experimental population being tested. That population which maintains the larger relative size is judged to be performing better from the overall biological point of view. Such a collective measure is referred to as the relative population fitness.

These experiments, of which preliminary reports have been made in Susman and Carson (1958), Carson (1958 a and b), Bert (1960) and Smathers (1961), show that natural selection in certain populations of Drosophila melanogaster favors balanced polymorphism due to autosomal heterosis. This polymorphism develops rapidly and is associated with a pronounced and sudden rise in fitness. Fitness levels are greatest soon after genetic alteration of the base populations, suggesting that simple luxuriant heterosis rather than coadaptive integration is serving fitness. Decline rather than increase of fitness with time further indicates that coadaptation is not involved.

MATERIAL AND METHODS

The material consists of three well-known laboratory stocks of Drosophila melanogaster. These are: 1. an ordinary wild-type Oregon-R (No. a4 of Indiana University); 2. a stock (hereafter for convenience called "sesro" which is homozygous for five third-chromosome genes: sepia (se), spineless (ss), kidney (k), sooty (e^s) and rough (ro) and 3. a third chromosome stock, Dichaete Stubble claret (D_3 Sb ca_2) balanced over the 3L and 3R Payne inversions.

The system of maintaining populations in vials is modified from that of Buzzati-Traverso (1955). The adult flies of each experimental population ("standing crop") are maintained in a chamber made of an ordinary glass shell vial (95 × 25 mm) which is extended in length by attaching a tube of cellulose acetate of the same dimensions ("supervial") to the mouth of the glass vial by drafting tape. The chamber of the supervial contains a small platform of blotting paper which serves as an additional area in the chamber for flies to rest upon and provides some moisture control. The unit is closed tightly at the end with cotton. The glass vial ("population vial") contains 9.5 cc of a carefully prepared, uniform, cornmeal-Karo-Agar medium prepared exactly according to the directions in Carson (1958b). The surface of the medium is yeasted with 10 mg of Fleishmann's fresh dry yeast, moistened with one drop of distilled water. A strip of absorbent toweling (15 × 75 mm) is doubled and pushed

Reprinted by permission of the author from Evolution, **15**, 496–509 (1961).

TABLE 1. *Example of cyclic weekly maintenance and measurement schedule for an experimental population*

Day of week[1]	Operations performed
Saturday	1. Open the population chamber and tape a FRESH POPULATION VIAL (No. 1) in position onto the supervial containing the population.
	2. Set aside the population vial which was removed from the population. This is the weekly "extra" or "egg sample" vial which is discarded or used for samples.
	3. COLLECT NEWLY-EMERGED FLIES from all old population vials onto unyeasted medium.
Monday	1. Etherize, WEIGH AND COUNT YOUNG FLIES which have been on unyeasted medium. Set aside momentarily.
	2. Open the population chamber, ADD the young flies from (1) above directly into the population and tape a FRESH POPULATION VIAL (No. 2) in position onto the supervial containing the population.
	3. Plug population vial No. 1 tightly and set into a vial rack. It is not opened again until F_1 flies appear, at which time collections from it begin.
	4. COLLECT NEWLY EMERGED FLIES from all old population vials onto unyeasted medium.
Wednesday	1. Open the population chamber and tape a FRESH POPULATION VIAL (No. 3) in position onto the supervial containing the population.
	2. Plug population vial No. 2 tightly and set into a vial rack. It is not opened again until F_1 flies appear, at which time collections from it begin.
	3. COLLECT NEWLY EMERGED FLIES from all old population vials onto unyeasted medium.
Friday	1. Open the population chamber, remove population, etherize lightly and WEIGH AND COUNT ENTIRE POPULATION. Set aside momentarily.
	2. Etherize, WEIGH AND COUNT YOUNG FLIES which have been on unyeasted medium.
	3. ADD flies from (2) above to the population and place in a clean supervial.
	4. Tape a FRESH POPULATION VIAL ("extra") in position onto the supervial containing the population.
	5. Plug population vial No. 3 tightly and set with other two from same week in a vial rack. These vials are not opened until F_1 flies appear, at which time collections from them begin.
	6. COLLECT NEWLY EMERGED FLIES from all old population vials onto unyeasted medium.

[1] Operations are always completed before noon.

down into the food cake to the bottom of the vial.

The founder individuals of a population, consisting of at least 50 flies of each sex, are placed in such a chamber. A new population vial is substituted for the old on a strictly regular change cycle. The vials removed from contact with the adult flies are plugged and set aside until F_1 flies appear. As soon as emergence begins, the young flies are collected and added directly into the chamber together with the older flies. Under these circumstances, the adult population builds up rapidly to a maximum size. After an initial tendency to oscillate, the population comes into equilibrium with the food source in such a way that the weekly additions from the old vials approximately equals the weekly accumulation of dead flies in the chamber. The details of the weekly cycle of operations of an exemplary population are given in table 1. Population vials are always retained until all flies have emerged; thus no artificial selection is made for genes favoring rapid development.

The experiments to be reported here were all begun by first establishing a base pop-

TABLE 2. *List and description of experiments reported in this paper, several forthcoming papers and in Carson 1958b. For derivation of populations and further details, see fig. 1 and text.*
$C = control;\ E = experimental$

Experimental population No.	Period No.[1]	Designation in Carson 1958b	Base population	Infected with single autosome sets from:
C-1a	1	C-1	se ss k e^s ro	none, control
C-1b	1	–	se ss k e^s ro	none, control
C-1c	1	C-2	se ss k e^s ro	none, control
C-1d	1	C-3	se ss k e^s ro	none, control
C-1e	2	–	se ss k e^s ro	none, control
C-1f	2	–	se ss k e^s ro	none, control
C-1g	3	–	se ss k e^s ro	none, control
C-1h	3	–	se ss k e^s ro	none, control
C-4a	1	C-4	Oregon-R	none, control
C-4b	2	–	Oregon-R	none, control
C-5	1	C-5	Oregon-R	none, control
E-1a	1	E-1	se ss k e^s ro	Oregon-R
E-1b	2	–	se ss k e^s ro	Oregon-R
E-1c	3	–	se ss k e^s ro	Oregon-R
E-1d	3	–	se ss k e^s ro	Oregon-R
E-1e	3	–	se ss k e^s ro	Oregon-R[2]
E-2a	1	E-2	se ss k e^s ro	Oregon-R
E-2b	2	–	se ss k e^s ro	Oregon-R
E-3	2, 3	–	se ss k e^s ro	none[3]
E-4	2, 3	–	se ss k e^s ro	none[3]
E-5	2	–	se ss k e^s ro	⎧Oregon-R, followed
E-6	2	–	se ss k e^s ro	⎩by D$_3$ Sb ca$_2$
E-7	2	–	Oregon-R	se ss k e^s ro
E-8	2	–	Oregon-R	se ss k e^s ro
E-9a	2	–	Oregon-R	se ss k e^s ro
E-9b	3	–	Oregon-R	se ss k e^s ro
E-9c	3	–	Oregon-R	se ss k e^s ro
E-9d	3	–	Oregon-R	se ss k e^s ro[2]

[1] Period No. 1: January 1957–April 1958
Period No. 2: May 1958–February 1959
Period No. 3: March 1959–October 1959

[2] Back selection experiments, reported in Smathers, 1961

[3] X-ray experiments, not reported in this paper

ulation of flies from either the sesro or Oregon stocks. After a stated interval, foreign genetic material was introduced into these populations in minimal amounts. Ordinarily this was done by adding to the population in question a single male individual which was an F_1 from a cross between a female chosen at random from the population and a male from the donor stock.

A list of the populations formed in the course of this study is given in table 2, and the derivation of each population with respect to ancestral populations is given in figure 1. The course of the experiments is divided into three time periods: No. 1, January 1957–April 1958; No. 2, May 1958–February 1959; No. 3, March 1959– October 1959. Certain of the populations, e.g. the control population C-1 (fig. 1; table 2), have run continuously throughout the three periods covered by this paper. The same designation number has been retained throughout for a given population but a lower-case letter has been affixed to the number to apply to the various replicates or direct descendents of this population which have not been purposely changed genetically. When a genetic change is made in a population, that population is given an "E" (experimental) number. Replicates or linear descendents of it bear the same number but are distinguished by lower-case letters.

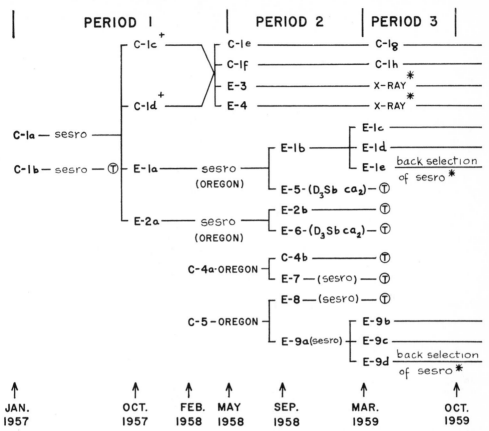

Fig. 1. Derivation of various experimental populations of *Drosophila melanogaster*. The genetic nature of the base population is given: "sesro," "Oregon," etc. Introduced autosome sets are in parentheses. Populations marked by asterisks (*) have been reported in Smathers (1961) or in a forthcoming paper.

Populations were duplicated, when desired, in the following manner. For example, the two control sesro populations C-1a and C-1b were established from stock in January of 1957. In October of 1957, C-1b was terminated and C-1a divided into four parts, C-1e, C-1d, E-1a and E-2a. The flies from the adult population were divided equally among the four new populations. The population vials from which flies were hatching were distributed as evenly as possible among the four replicates. Under these circumstances it takes about seven or eight weeks before the new equilibrium is reached and measurements can be recommenced. Ordinarily, populations were split into two rather than four new populations. On one occasion, two populations were combined and then split into four replicates (C-1d and C-1e, May, 1958: see figure 1.)

As indicated in table 1 (Friday, No. 1) data on the size of adult populations were obtained once a week by etherizing, weighing and counting the adults present in the population chamber. At approximately four-week intervals, the phenotypes of the adult flies in the populations were also recorded.

Two times a week, the young emerging flies were weighed, counted, and added to the population. The phenotypes of these were recorded at approximately 4-week intervals. The total weight (or number) of flies emerging in any one calendar week is referred to as the "production" of the population. In tables 3 and 4, for example,

TABLE 3. *Size and production of experimental populations of* Drosophila melanogaster *during 20 consecutive weeks at equilibrium. Period No. 2: 1958–59 (see fig. 1)*

Population No.	Base population	Single autosome sets introduced from	Population size		Production	
			Mean No. individuals per week	Mean wet weight (mg per week)	Mean No. individuals per week	Mean wet weight (mg per week)
C-1b[1]	se ss ro	none (control)	161.3 ∓ 7.3	94.4 ± 3.3	92.7 ± 7.2	47.2 ± 4.5
C-1e	se ss ro	none (control)	169.0 ± 8.8	104.0 ± 5.5	83.3 ± 5.3	42.3 ± 2.4
C-1f	se ss ro	none (control)	157.7 ± 8.3	99.8 ± 5.7	78.7 ± 5.5	41.3 ± 2.9
E-1b	se ss ro	Oregon-R	478.4 ± 17.4	279.0 ± 9.4	239.4 ± 14.5	128.7 ± 8.2
E-2b	se ss ro	Oregon-R	477.3 ± 11.7	280.5 ± 7.3	239.9 ± 14.7	128.6 ± 7.3
E-5	se ss ro	Oregon-R, then D³ Sb ca²	471.5 ± 18.6	263.6 ± 9.4	224.6 ± 16.4	119.3 ± 8.7
E-6	se ss ro	Oregon-R, then D³ Sb ca²	496.5 ± 21.6	283.5 ± 10.4	233.9 ± 19.3	122.4 ± 10.0
C-4b	Oregon-R	none (control)	348.4 ± 8.8	202.3 ± 5.9	162.2 ± 11.6	87.0 ± 5.5
E-7	Oregon-R	se ss ro	376.6 ± 16.6	215.5 ± 8.4	183.2 ± 13.8	98.6 ± 6.9
E-8	Oregon-R	se ss ro	476.5 ± 16.2	278.6 ± 7.1	253.0 ± 13.3	140.5 ± 7.3
E-9a	Oregon-R	se ss ro	467.0 ± 12.0	281.4 ± 7.1	258.7 ± 16.6	145.4 ± 9.5

[1] Based on 17 consecutive weeks at equilibrium; Period No. 1: 1957–58 (see fig. 1).

the mean production is given for a number of consecutive weeks, usually 20.

The weekly population size measurements upon which the 20-week means shown in tables 3 and 4 are based were obtained by taking the total starting population size (e.g., table 1, Friday, No. 3) and adding to this the size of the population which is surviving seven days later (e.g., table 1, Friday, No. 1). This sum was then divided by two.

THE EXPERIMENTS

a. *sesro (Oregon) Populations*

Populations so designated are composed of base populations of sesro into which a haploid set of autosomes from Oregon-R were introduced. These populations are designated as E-1 and E-2. They were started on December 23, 1957, when two of four replicate populations of sesro, which had been running at equilibrium, were infected with single males carrying one set of autosomes from Oregon-R. The results observed over the ensuing 30 weeks (period 1) were given in tabular and graphic form in Carson (1958b) and are shown also in fig. 2. This experiment was continued for a total of about 95 weeks. Data on population size and production of these populations, as well as controls running simultaneously, are given in tables 3 and 4 (E-1, E-2 and their controls C-1e to C-1h).

Population sizes in milligrams wet weight of these two populations, relative to their sesro controls, are summarized graphically

TABLE 4. *Size and production of experimental populations of* Drosophila melanogaster *during 20 consecutive weeks at equilibrium. Period No. 3: 1959 (see fig. 1)*

Population No.	Base population	Single autosome sets introduced from	Population Size		Production	
			Mean No. individuals per week	Mean wet weight (mg per week)	Mean No. individuals per week	Mean wet weight (mg per week)
C-1g	se ss ro	none (control)	132.1 ∓ 3.1	77.6 ∓ 1.7	87.1 ∓ 2.7	49.5 ∓ 1.8
C-1h	se ss ro	none (control)	123.0 ∓ 2.4	70.4 ∓ 1.4	84.7 ∓ 3.9	46.7 ∓ 2.0
E-1c	se ss ro	Oregon-R	342.0 ∓ 11.8	177.9 ∓ 6.7	171.8 ∓ 8.0	84.0 ∓ 3.7
E-1d	se ss ro	Oregon-R	346.6 ∓ 17.8	186.7 ∓ 9.1	170.7 ∓ 10.0	86.0 ∓ 4.5
E-9b	Oregon-R	se ss ro	425.6 ∓ 10.6	234.4 ∓ 5.7	220.9 ∓ 8.1	114.7 ∓ 3.9
E-9c	Oregon-R	se ss ro	446.1 ∓ 12.9	243.4 ∓ 6.7	234.6 ∓ 10.6	122.0 ∓ 4.9

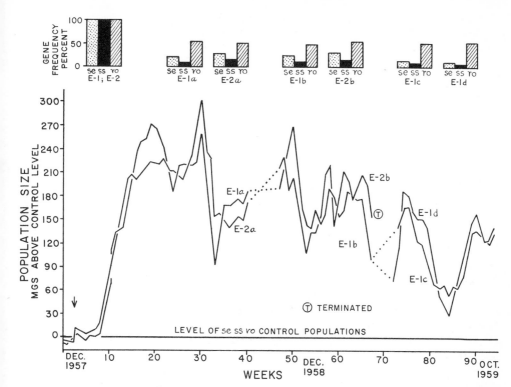

FIG. 2. Size of two sesro (Oregon) populations. These are *se ss ro* base populations to each of which a single set of autosomes from Oregon-R was added (arrow). The histograms show the frequencies of the genes before (extreme left) and during (right) the course of the experiments (see tables 2, 3, and 4).

in fig. 2. In this figure, the mean weekly size levels of the two control populations are represented along a horizontal line parallel to the abscissa and the level of each experimental is represented in terms of the milligrams difference from this control level. After introduction (arrow, fig. 2), population size rises steeply to a level which, in period 1, is 3.45 times that of the control. After about 30 weeks the size of both populations falls to an intermediate level, which, during period 2, is 2.75 times the control. During the third period, approximately weeks 70–90 (fig. 2), the population size falls to a new low level which is 2.47 times that of the control. This means that after 90 weeks the populations had lost about one-quarter of the new size gained following introduction of foreign genes.

Following introduction of the males,

there was an immediate drop in the frequency of the marker genes observed in the population. Free recombination was observed. Frequencies of phenotypes of *se*, *ss*, and *ro* have been recorded at regular intervals throughout the experiments; the results of these counts are given in table 5 and are summarized in the histograms given along the top of fig. 2. Estimates of gene frequency have been made by taking the square root of the frequency of homozygous phenotypes.

In general, after the initial rapid adjustment (see Carson, 1958b), frequencies of the marker genes have been quite stable throughout the course of the experiment. Not only were *se*, *ss*, and *ro* present after 95 weeks but *k* and e^s were also still present in substantial frequencies. Detailed analysis, however, did not encompass these latter two genes. Rough, for instance, fell

TABLE 5. *Gene frequencies in experimental populations of the composition "sesro (Oregon),"*
that is, ones in which a base population of se ss ro flies was infected with one set of auto-
somes from Oregon-R. Gene frequencies have been calculated by taking the square root of
the zygotic frequencies of observed homozygotes. See also histograms in fig. 2

Population No.	Period No.[1]	No. of samples	Total flies counted	Sepia		Spineless		Rough	
				%se/se	%se	%ss/ss	%ss	%ro/ro	%ro
E-1a	1	12	4,376	4.04	20.11	0.94	9.67	27.99	52.91
E-2a	1	12	4,532	6.53	25.55	2.30	15.16	26.96	51.92
E-1b	2	5	2,501	5.12	22.62	1.39	11.81	21.07	45.90
E-5	2	5	2,562	4.76	21.82	0.47	6.86	22.21	47.13
E-2b	2	5	2,801	10.99	33.15	2.14	14.63	25.06	50.06
E-6	2	5	2,582	9.99	31.62	2.59	16.09	30.75	55.45
E-1c	3	5	1,757	1.99	14.11	0.91	9.54	26.41	51.39
E-1d	3	5	1,823	1.37	11.71	0.55	7.41	26.77	51.74

[1] See fig. 1.

to approximately 50% and has remained close to this level thereafter (table 5; fig. 2).

Although both *se* and *ss* declined somewhat from their high points, both were still present in substantial frequency when the experiment was terminated (*se* was a little above 10% and *ss* a little under 10%; see table 5).

b. *Oregon (sesro) Populations*

Populations so designated are the reciprocal of the former. They are composed of Oregon-R base populations into which a haploid set of autosomes from sesro was introduced. The data for one control and three experimentals are given in tables 3 and 4 (C-4, E-7, E-8, and E-9). Control populations C-4 and C-5 have been previously reported on in Carson (1958b). The population sizes of all these populations are shown graphically in fig. 3. Single males carrying one set of autosomes from sesro were added to populations E-7, E-8 and, E-9a at week 43, in September 1958 (arrow, fig. 3). As this operation consisted of adding a wild-type fly to a wild-type population, it was not possible to see immediately if the infection of the three populations was successful. In populations E-8 and E-9a, however, mutant individuals appeared about three weeks later (see "X" marks in week 46, fig. 3). In population E-7, however, mutant individuals did not

appear until after a long lag period of about 10 weeks (see "X" mark in week 63, fig. 3).

Reference to table 3 shows that the control Oregon population (C-4b) maintains a size approximately twice the size of the sesro controls (2.03 in period 2; this is somewhat less than period 1, when the comparable figure was 2.34). In the two experiments where the sesro chromosomes became immediately established (E-8 and E-9a), the population sizes rapidly increased until they were 2.80 (E-8) and 2.83 (E-9a) times the sesro controls. Both of these populations thus well surpass the control Oregon population. Population E-9, carried into period 3 in two replicates (E-9b and E-9c, table 4) showed a slight increase over this original level. E-9b is 3.18 and E-9c is 3.29 times the size of the control sesro populations in period 3. Thus, the introduction of sesro autosomes into Oregon stock produces a population with a relative population fitness about the same as the reciprocal experiment, sesro (Oregon). The Oregon (sesro) experiments were not carried for a long time as the reciprocals were. Therefore, it is not possible to see if a long-term breakdown in relative fitness comparable to that observed in the sesro (Oregon) occurred.

Population E-7, fig. 3, showed a lag period before the marker genes appeared. During this lag, the population showed no

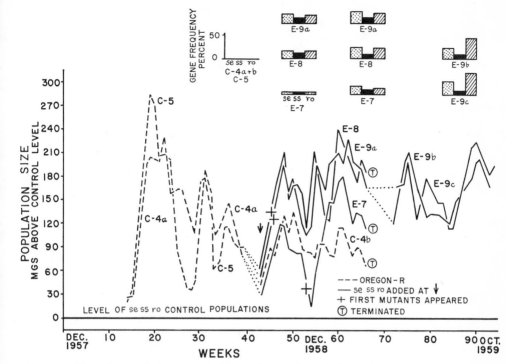

FIG. 3. Size of control Oregon populations (– – – –) and three Oregon (sesro) populations (————). The latter are Oregon base populations into each of which a single set of autosomes from *se ss ro* has been added (arrow). The histograms show the frequencies of the genes during the course of the experiments (see tables 2, 3, and 5).

increase in size, but was, in fact, somewhat below the control. Coincident with the appearance of the mutants, however, a sudden rise in size occurred (weeks 54 to 60, fig. 3) and the average size of the population during period 2, as given in table 3, does not reflect this late change. Although this experiment was terminated in March of 1959, a sample of the population was placed in ordinary laboratory culture in bottles. All five marker genes were still present in this stock at the time of discard at the end of December, 1959.

Once introduction of the marker genes into the Oregon base populations was accomplished, the frequency of each of the three genes *se*, *ss*, and *ro* rose to levels which are very similar to those observed in the reciprocal experiments (table 6 and the histograms in fig. 3). Rough, which reached a frequency of about 50% in experiments E-1 and E-2, was again the most

frequent of the markers, but was somewhat less frequent, reaching a level of about 43%. Sepia is next in frequency and spineless is the least frequent; this is the same order as observed in the reciprocal experiments.

c. *sesro (Oregon)* (*D^3 Sb ca^2*) *Populations*

Populations so designated began as sesro base populations to which were added successively (1) an autosome set from Oregon-R and (2) an autosome set from a laboratory stock having a third chromosome marked with dichaete, stubble, and claret. This latter chromosome included the inversion In3LD. Both dichaete and stubble are homozygous lethal.

Four replicates of sesro (Oregon) populations were established in September, 1958 by dividing populations E-1a and E-2a (see fig. 1). Immediately after division, and before the populations had risen

TABLE 6. *Gene frequencies in experimental populations of the composition "Oregon (sesro),"
that is, ones in which a base population of Oregon-R flies was infected with one set of autosomes from se ss ro stock. Gene frequencies have been calculated by taking the square root of
the zygotic frequency of observed homozygotes. See also histograms in fig. 3*

Population No.	Period No.	No. of samples	Total flies counted	Sepia		Spineless		Rough	
				%se/se	%se	%ss/ss	%ss	%ro/ro	%ro
E-7	2-early	4	1,584	0.19	4.35	0.19	4.35	0.19	4.35
E-7	2-later	4	1,942	2.63	16.22	1.03	10.15	1.65	12.84
E-8	2-early	4	2,146	2.70	16.43	1.44	12.00	2.47	15.72
E-8	2-later	4	2,353	5.14	22.67	1.02	10.09	5.27	22.96
E-9a	2-early	4	2,015	4.12	20.30	1.34	11.58	3.28	18.11
E-9a	2-later	4	2,387	6.24	24.98	1.42	11.92	5.03	22.43
E-9b	3	5	2,269	5.38	23.19	0.97	9.85	17.85	42.25
E-9c	3	4	1,599	7.63	27.62	0.63	7.94	20.14	44.88

again to equilibrium size, individual males carrying a set of autosomes from the D^3 stock and the rest of their chromosomes from the population concerned, were introduced into two of the replicates (populations E-5 and E-6). In both cases, although these males lived for about five days in each population, no D^3 Sb offspring were observed. Accordingly, a second introduction was attempted a month later. Ten virgin females hatching from each population were placed with a single male of the same composition as the above and left for five days in an ordinary culture tube. As soon as many larvae appeared, these ten females and the male were introduced into the respective populations.

Following this procedure, flies showing both dominants appeared in both populations in small numbers. In population E-5, two D^3 Sb flies hatched in the population about 2 weeks after introduction; presumably these were F_1's from the introduced flies. About a month later, one individual carrying D^3 Sb and two carrying D^3 alone hatched, but subsequently no further flies carrying either mutant were seen, and it appears that the genes were eliminated. Attempts to introduce the genes into population E-6 met with greater success. Ten F_1 individuals were observed and subsequently individuals carrying either D^3 or Sb or both were observed regularly. Both genes remained in the population at about 1% until termination of the experiment in March of 1959, a total of about six months.

Laboratory cultures derived from this latter population were examined periodically until discarded in December, 1959, and no D^3 or Sb were observed. They were thus apparently eliminated soon after the population was placed in stock.

Reference to table 3 will show that the introduction of these genes and the chromosomes carrying them into the population is not accompanied by any further rise in the relative population fitness.

d. *Survival of Mutant Phenotypes in the Adult Population*

Most of the above populations were regularly examined and the phenotypes counted under the binocular microscope. These counts were made both on flies recently eclosed from the pupa and flies existing in the adult population. In both cases the flies were under continual strong natural selection. Tables 7 and 8 show the frequencies of the three mutant phenotypes in the different populations at eclosion and in the adult population. In almost every case sepia phenotypes are less frequent in the adult populations than at eclosion. In four cases these differences are statistically significant at the levels shown in the tables. Spineless shows the same tendency; the totals for the reciprocal experiments are significant at the 1% level.

On the other hand, flies of a rough phenotype show the opposite tendency, that is, they tend to be more frequent in the adult population than at hatching. It will

TABLE 7. *Survival of mutant homozygotes in sesro (Oregon) populations. Frequency of each phenotype at eclosion from the pupa is compared with the frequency in the adult population*

Population	Total	Per cent se/se	Difference, adult minus eclosion	Per cent ss/ss	Difference, adult minus eclosion	Per cent ro/ro	Difference, adult minus eclosion
E-1a							
eclosion	1,352	4.51		1.26		27.81	
adult	2,848	3.76	−0.75	0.77	−0.49	28.16	+0.35
E-1b							
eclosion	722	4.85		1.39		16.48	
adult	1,779	5.23	+0.38	1.29	−0.10	22.93	+6.45[2]
E-1c							
eclosion	542	2.03		1.11		21.40	
adult	1,215	1.98	−0.05	0.82	−0.29	28.64	+7.24[2]
E-1d							
eclosion	520	2.31		0.77		23.85	
adult	1,303	1.00	−1.31[1]	0.46	−0.31	27.94	+4.09
E-5							
eclosion	597	5.70		0.50		20.27	
adult	1,965	4.48	−1.22[1]	0.46	−0.04	22.80	+2.53
E-2a							
eclosion	1,026	7.12		4.19		29.92	
adult	2,024	6.97	−0.15	1.83	−2.36[2]	29.30	−0.62
E-2b							
eclosion	655	11.6		2.75		22.60	
adult	2,146	10.8	−0.8	1.96	−0.79	25.82	+3.22
E-6							
ecolsion	701	10.98		4.85		27.10	
adult	2,191	9.68	−1.30	1.87	−2.98[2]	31.36	+4.26[1]
Total							
eclosion	6,115	6.20		2.21		24.55	
adult	15,471	5.88	−0.32	1.23	−0.98[2]	27.17	+2.62[2]

[1] χ^2 for the difference indicates a p value less than 0.05 .
[2] χ^2 for the difference indicates a p value less than 0.01 .

be noted, however, that in some individual cases the differences are not very great.

e. *Associations of linked Mutant Markers in the Populations*

All sesro (Oregon) and Oregon (sesro) populations show occasional individuals hatching which are phenotypically sepia-spineless, sepia-rough, or spineless-rough. The question arises whether any of the five linkage markers introduced (*se, ss, k, e^s* and *ro*) have remained in these populations in non-random association. To test this, over 100 wild-type males were taken from each of four populations (E-1c, E-1d, E-9b, E-9c) and their two third chromosomes tested by crossing to sesro virgin females. Analysis of these and comparable data from a number of other experimental pop-

ulations will be presented in a later publication.

DISCUSSION

When two genetically different cross-fertilizing populations of the same species are subjected to identical controlled laboratory conditions under natural selection, the population which maintains the larger size may be said to be performing better, from the biological point of view, than the smaller one. The larger population thus may be said to have a collective genetic endowment, or gene pool, which enables it to exploit the substrate provided by the investigator in such a way as to produce a greater biomass than the smaller population. Population size, then, may be used as a measure of the fitness of the mendelian population as a whole. The term *relative*

TABLE 8. *Survival of mutant homozygotes in Oregon (sesro) populations. Frequency of each phenotype at eclosion from the pupa is compared with the frequency in the adult population*

Population	Total	Per cent se/se	Difference, adult minus eclosion	Per cent ss/ss	Difference, adult minus eclosion	Per cent ro/ro	Difference, adult minus eclosion
E-7							
eclosion	685	2.63		1.02		1.72	
adult	1,690	2.13	−0.50	0.89	−0.13	1.30	−0.45
E-8							
eclosion	1,196	5.35		1.84		4.26	
adult	3,303	3.48	−1.87[2]	1.00	−0.84[1]	3.82	−0.44
E-9a							
eclosion	1,242	6.92		2.50		4.99	
adult	3,160	4.62	−2.30[2]	0.95	−1.55[2]	3.99	−1.00
E-9b							
eclosion	709	5.36		0.99		15.37	
adult	1,560	5.38	+0.02	0.96	−0.03	18.97	+3.60[1]
E-9c							
eclosion	538	8.74		0.74		15.61	
adult	1,061	7.07	−1.67	0.57	−0.17	22.43	+6.82[2]
Total							
eclosion	4,370	5.79		1.63		7.28	
adult	10,774	4.23	−1.56[2]	0.92	−0.71[2]	7.48	+0.20

[1] χ^2 for the difference indicates a p value less than 0.05 .
[2] χ^2 for the difference indicates a p value less than 0.01 .

population fitness is suggested for this attribute. The genetic adjustment of different gene pools may be compared in this manner.

Both number of individuals and biomass wet weight have been used in this study as measures of the relative population fitness. The data show, however, that the two modes of measurement are about equally useful because the mean weight per fly does not show sharp reduction as the population increases in number following hybridization. In fact, a slight change of the opposite sort is observed. In most of the experiments, number and weight of flies hatching each week ("production") was also recorded separately. This measure, however, is essentially a part of the overall population size; its usefulness is further limited by the fact that considerable week-to-week variance is encountered.

The relative population fitness bears no relationship to the fitness in the sense of the adaptive value, W (see Dobzhansky, 1951). The latter is a property of an individual genotype and refers to its relative capacity to transmit its genes to the next generation. The relative population fitness is an attribute of a mendelian population measured in laboratory tests under controlled conditions. The measure cannot be applied to natural populations because equilibration of the environment is not possible.

In the present experiments, it has been shown that when a mutant population is infected with a limited amount of genetic material from a wild-type stock, the size of the new hybrid population rises within a few generations to a level well above that of either donor population. This high fitness was maintained for about fifteen generations, after which periodic slight declines were observed. The reciprocal experiment, in which genetic material from the mutant stock is introduced into a wild-type population, a similar result is obtained, although the new population size level is reached more slowly. Nevertheless, populations derived in the two ways ultimately show closely similar properties.

Accompanying the change in size in each population in which third chromosome marker genes have been used, a balanced polymorphism for these genes has developed. In all experiments, furthermore, each of the five marker genes has been retained in relatively high frequency under the continual, severe natural selection which obtains in these populations. This condition indicates the presence of heterozygous advantage for these gene loci or at least for chromosome sections marked by these genes. The data further suggest that the principal object of selection has been a generally beneficial heterosis.

That this heterosis does not depend to a significant degree on heterotic effects of the precise marker loci themselves is indicated by the work of Smathers (1961). Using replicates of polymorphic populations E-1 and E-9 (E-1e and E-9d, fig. 1), Smathers performed back selection for a monomorphic mutant phenotype while maintaining large numbers of flies so as to minimize the effect of random drift. When the performance of these rederived monomorphic populations was tested simultaneously with the polymorphic and original monomorphic controls, their performance was close to that of the polymorphic populations. Evidently, heterozygosity at these particular loci contributes little, if any, to population fitness. Smathers suggests that polygene blocks of unknown size, closely linked to the markers, may be responsible for the heterosis observed in these experiments.

Heterosis is observed almost immediately and the effect is strongest at the beginning of the experiments, shortly after introduction. Thus, the heterosis functioning here appears to be simple luxuriance rather than populational heterosis (coadaptation) which would require a time-consuming developmental process involving recombination and subsequent selection of recombinant types. This conclusion is further borne out by the results of the experiments of Bert (1960). When inversions were introduced in such a way that recombination is effecively prevented in the population, the heterosis observed is not greatly different from that seen in experiments in which recombination is freely permitted by the cytogenetic situation.

That luxuriant heterosis appears to serve fitness at the beginning of the experiments does not necessarily mean that coadaptation could not follow in later generations. There is, in fact, ample opportunity for the development of coadaptation, especially within populations E-1 and E-2, which ran for nearly two years under conditions of free recombination. During this time, however, the fitness level has declined rather than increased. Thus, if coadaptation did occur in the later generations it must have been effective only in preventing an even greater loss of fitness due to drift in these small populations. It seems likely to the writer, however, that only luxuriant heterosis is operative in these experimental populations.

The slow breakdown of fitness may be explained as due to the loss of heterozygosity because of the effect of inbreeding and random drift in these relatively small populations. According to this idea, first generation hybrids would be expected to display the greatest luxuriance, and as recombination proceeds in the population it may be expected that it will slowly destroy the integrity of blocks of genes having heterotic effects. Thus heterozygosity for a number of chromosome regions would be lost by random drift. In this sense, recombination is destructive of population fitness in relatively small, inbred populations which are exploiting the advantages of luxuriant heterosis.

An experimental population to which foreign genetic material has already been added appears to be easily saturated. The evidence for this comes from those experiments in which attempts were made to introduce genes from the dichaete-stubble stock into a population already carrying a series of mutant genes. These experiments, however, should be looked upon more as pilot experiments than as constituting a fair study of the process of building up of multiple heteroses.

The present experiments permit no decision as to whether the heterosis effects observed are due to dominance, overdominance or to some combination of the two (Crow, 1952). Whatever the most important type of gene action turns out to be, however, these experiments demonstrate that the fitness of the mendelian population under natural selection may be directly served by the condition of heterozygote superiority. This superiority is not a characteristic of F_1 generation individuals only but, if the proper conditions of population size are maintained, can be held by selection over a number of generations. This suggests that luxuriance can indeed function in the adjustment of organisms to their environments and is not confined to the F_1 of artificially-made crosses.

In a recent general article (Carson, 1959), the writer has contrasted two types of genetic adjustment: that in which selection favors the homozygous condition at most loci (homoselection) and that in which selection for heterozygotes (heteroselection) predominates. In the current experiments, heteroselection, with resulting balanced polymorphism, appears to be the major mode of genetic adjustment. This does not appear to represent the acquiring by the population of specific genetically determined features which adapt its members to the special niches presented within the experimental population. Rather, natural selection seems to favor the heterozygous condition because of the superior general vigor with which the heterozygous individuals are endowed.

Phenomena similar to those studied in these experiments apparently occur often in natural populations. Whenever two relatively inbred populations which have been historically separate come into contact without full sexual isolation, events similar to those studied here may follow. Thus local increase in population size and performance may result. The population may spread in a radial fashion, often moving against ecological gradients. A number of examples from natural populations have been cited by Carson (1959), including

cases of both intra- and interspecific hybridization. One case may be cited here which may serve as a further example. Wilson and Brown (1958) state that in approximately 1918, a "dark phase" of the fire ant, *Solenopsis saevissima* was introduced into the United States, apparently from southern South America. During the first ten years or so following its introduction it was apparently unable to spread outside of the limits of Mobile, Alabama, where the introduction occurred. About 1930, however, there began a population expansion throughout the southeastern United States which has reached colossal proportions. This event is correlated with an apparent second introduction of a "light phase" of the same species from central South America. It is tempting to suggest that this spread has amounted to an example of adjustment through heteroselection of the type studied experimentally in this paper.

Changes of this kind, however, do not represent major evolutionary adjustment in the sense that the organism acquires and fixes the genetic basis for the conquering of a new ecological niche or niches. If the basis for adjustment is luxuriance with an underlying unfixed genetic condition characterized by balanced polymorphism, this is a type of evolutionary adjustment that may be progressively improved only to a certain point. The population cannot go beyond this by vigor selection alone. New niches may indeed be entered but these are conquered only by virtue of the general adaptability of heterotically buffered organisms, not because an adaptive novelty has been acquired.

SUMMARY

1. A procedure is described for maintaining experimental populations of *Drosophila melanogaster* in vials in such a way that the amount of food and the change cycle is strictly uniform.

2. Measurements were made of the size of various genetically different populations maintained under the same conditions

while under natural selection in the laboratory.

3. Each of two populations homozygous for five third chromosome recessives (ses-ro) were infected with a single autosome set from Oregon-R stock. Population sizes were measured thereafter for 94 successive weeks. The size of both populations increased nearly three and a half times within about three generations. At the termination of the experiment, the experimentals had declined somewhat, falling to about two and a half times the control size. Reciprocal experiments gave similar increases in population size but the effect occurred more slowly.

4. Correlated with the rise in population size the mutant genes became balanced in the populations. Although the gene frequencies vary somewhat from population to population, rough is always the most frequent (average: 51.4%) sepia next (average: 24.4%) and spineless the least frequent (average: 12.3%). Kidney and sooty were likewise retained in all populations. Attempts to superimpose more third chromosome genes were not successful.

5. When two genetically different populations are tested under these uniform population conditions in the laboratory the one which is able to maintain the greater size, or biomass, is deemed to be performing better biologically under the given conditions. Size thus may be used as a measure of the relative population fitness.

6. High relative fitness appears to be directly correlated with heterozygosity; thus heterosis appears to contribute directly to fitness.

7. The experiments provide no evidence that coadaptation of chromosomes is involved in any of the adjustments that the population makes, although this possibility cannot be excluded. Rather, the evidence supports the view that heterosis is of the simple luxuriant sort. This luxuriance is not confined to the early generations but is persistent over many generations.

ACKNOWLEDGMENTS

I am especially grateful to Miss Janette Corn for painstaking and unfailing assistance in the handling of these populations on the very arduous schedule required by the experimental design. I wish also to thank Mrs. Marion Stalker for preparing the figures. The work has been supported by Grant G-7441 from the National Science Foundation.

LITERATURE CITED

BERT, G. R. 1960. Fixed heterozygosity and fitness in *Drosophila melanogaster* populations under strong natural selection. Rec. Gen. Soc. Amer., **29**: 57.

BUZZATI-TRAVERSO, A. A. 1955. Evolutionary changes in components of fitness and other polygenic traits in *Drosophila melanogaster* populations. Heredity, **9**: 153–186.

CARSON, H. L. 1958a. Increase of fitness in experimental populations following introduction of one haploid set of autosomes. Proc. Xth Intern. Congr. Genet., **II**: 44–45.

——. 1958b. Increase in fitness in experimental populations resulting from heterosis. Proc. Nat. Acad. Sci., **44**: 1,136–1,141.

——. 1959. Genetic conditions which promote or retard the formation of species. Cold Spr.ng Harb. Symp. Quant. Biol., **24**: 87–105.

CROW, J. F. 1952. Dominance and overdominance. *In*: Heterosis, Ed. by J. W. Gowen, Iowa State College Press, Ames. 552 pp.

DOBZHANSKY, TH. 1951. Genetics and the Origin of Species. 3rd ed. Columbia University Press, New York. 364 pp.

SMATHERS, KATRINA M. 1961. The contribution of heterozygosity at certain gene loci to fitness of laboratory populations of *Drosophila melanogaster*. Am. Nat., **95**: 27–37.

SUSMAN, M., AND H. L. CARSON. 1958. Development of balanced polymorphism in laboratory populations of *Drosophila melanogaster*. Am. Nat., **92**: 359–364.

WILSON, E. O., AND W. L. BROWN, JR. 1958. Recent changes in the introduced population of the fire ant *Solenopsis saevissima* (Fr. Smith). EVOLUTION, **12**: 211–218.

AN ATTEMPT TO COMPARE THE FITNESS OF POLYMORPHIC AND MONOMORPHIC EXPERIMENTAL POPULATIONS OF *DROSOPHILA PSEUDOOBSCURA*

J. A. BEARDMORE,* TH. DOBZHANSKY,† and O. A. PAVLOVSKY †

Department of Zoology, Columbia University, New York

Received 18.ii.59

1. INTRODUCTION

CHROMOSOMAL polymorphism, due to inversions of blocks of genes, is widespread in natural populations of many species of Drosophila. The polymorphism is probably almost always adaptive and usually balanced. Experimental populations which contain mixtures of karyotypes as a rule reach stable equilibria; this indicates that the structural heterozygotes are heterotic. The adaptive values of the karyotypes are, however, quite sensitive to environmental variations; the superior fitness of the heterozygotes may be more pronounced in some environments than in others, and it may even be absent altogether. It appears, however, that the heterozygotes possess net adaptive advantages over the range of the environments to which the population is exposed in its natural habitats.

Direct comparisons of the fitnesses of polymorphic and monomorphic populations have, however, seldom been attempted. This is the problem to which we address ourselves in the pages that follow. Third chromosomes with AR and with CH gene arrangements are common in many populations of *Drosophila pseudoobscura* in California and elsewhere. Dobzhansky (1948, 1957), Levine (1955), and Levene, Pavlovsky, and Dobzhansky (1958) have shown that experimental populations which contain these chromosomes are subject to strong selection which at 25° C. conduces to an equilibrium of about 70-75 percent AR and 25-30 percent CH. Taking the fitness of AR/CH heterozygotes to be unity, that of AR/AR homozygotes turns out to lie, in different experiments, between 0·65 and 0·85, and that of CH/CH homozygotes between 0·42 and 0·60. We have accordingly set up several experimental populations with AR and CH chromosomes in laboratory population cages. Three of these were polymorphic populations containing AR and CH chromosomes, two monomorphic populations with only AR, and two monomorphic populations with CH chromosomes. After several generations during which the populations might have undergone selection for adaptation to the environments of the population cages, attempts were made to obtain estimates of certain parameters which we believe to be significant for evaluation of the fitness of the populations.

* Commonwealth Fund Fellow; present address, Department of Genetics, The University, Sheffield, England.

† The work under Contract No. AT-(30-1)-1151, U.S. Atomic Energy Commission.

2. MATERIAL AND TECHNIQUES

The foundation stocks of the experimental populations were prepared using 16 strains homozygous for AR, and 13 strains homozygous for CH, all derived from flies collected in the locality of Pinon Flats, Mount San Jacinto, in California. The foundation stocks of the monomorphic AR and CH populations consisted of about 2000 flies each, obtained by intercrossing about equal numbers of flies from all the AR or CH strains respectively. The polymorphic populations were also descended from 2000 founders each, but were obtained by intercrosses of all the available AR and CH strains ; the foundation stocks were so contrived that the initial gametic frequencies of AR and CH chromosomes were 0·2 and 0·8 respectively. The experimental populations were started on the following dates (all in 1957) :

Population no.	Chromosomes	Date
173	AR+CH	January 10
174	CH	January 11
175	AR	February 1
176	AR+CH	February 5
180	AR	May 11
181	AR+CH	May 11
182	CH	May 11

All the populations were kept in wooden cages containing 15 food cups each, a fresh cup being inserted generally on alternate days. Nos. 174-182 were kept at 25° C. in well-regulated incubators provided with electric fans, and No. 173 at 25° but in a constant temperature room with poor ventilation. From time to time a cup with food in which pupæ were beginning to form was withdrawn from each of a series of cages (Nos. 173-176 or Nos. 180-182), attached by adhesive tape to a glass " chimney " having a diameter equal to that of the cup, provided with a cotton stopper and placed in an incubator at 25° C. When the adults began hatching in the cups, they were collected daily (including Sundays), etherised, counted, and weighed individually on a Misco Quartz Helix Balance, on which a load of 5 mg. caused an extension of 67 mm. from zero (read to one-half of a mm.). Only flies with fully expanded and hardened wings were weighed. It is important for the evaluation of the data in tables 2-6 to note that the samples from the different cages were not taken simultaneously. The series of populations Nos. 173-176 were sampled between 5th November 1957 and 9th January 1958, and again between 8th and 16th June 1958. The series of populations Nos. 180-182 were sampled between 30th January and 30th May, and again between 27th June and 15th July 1958. It will be seen that during most of 1958 the populations were in better condition than during 1957, as a consequence of which the cups yielded more flies in 1958 than in 1957.

The two series of populations are, thus, not necessarily comparable, while the populations within a series are, with the possible exception of No. 173 (see above).

At approximately the same time as each cup to be used for the determination of the biomass was taken from each of the populations, another similar cup was removed for the purpose of measuring wing length. All the flies were allowed to emerge from such a cup and a random sample taken from the total emergence in each cup. Ten samples (cups) were taken from each of populations 173, 176, 175 and 177 and five samples from populations 180-2. The number per sample was fifty flies of each sex, or the total emergence if this was less than fifty flies ; no fly was rejected for any reason other than torn or crumpled wings. Both wings were then removed from each fly and mounted in paraffin oil under cover-glasses, ten pairs of wings to a slide, with the left wings forming a lower row and the right wings an upper row. The measurement of wing length was accomplished using a widefield binocular microscope at a magnification of 60×, with a standard eyepiece micrometer, divided into 100 divisions ; wing lengths were estimated to one-tenth of a scale division. The distance chosen to represent wing length was from a point near the posterior end of the humeral cross-vein to the tip of the wing near the end of the third vein, such distance in an average wing corresponding to about 85 units of the micrometer scale.

3. RESULTS

(i) *The selection process in the polymorphic populations*

The changes which took place in the three polymorphic populations are shown in table 1. The foundation stocks had 20 percent of AR and 80 percent of CH chromosomes. Control samples taken in two populations fourteen days after the start (*i.e.*, eggs from the surviving individuals of the foundation stocks) had, as expected, the initial

TABLE 1

Changes in the frequencies of AR and CH chromosomes in the polymorphic populations (in percent)

Days	173		176		181	
	AR	CH	AR	CH	AR	CH
0	20·0	80·0	20·0	80·0	20·0	80·0
14	22·7	77·3	20·7	79·3	...	...
35	39·3	60·7	40·0	60·0	40·7	59·3
70	45·0	55·0	48·3	51·7	41·3	58·7
105	50·0	50·0	50·3	49·7	55·3	44·7
140	60·7	39·3	56·7	43·4	...	...
175	57·3	42·7	...	...	...	...
264-275	66·3	33·7	66·3	33·7	67·7	32·3
302	64·3	35·7	...	...	...	...
365	64·3	35·7	71·3	28·7	67·7	32·3
488	...	...	...	...	69·0	31·0
583	...	...	78·3	21·7	...	...
610	72·7	27·3	...	...	...	...

frequencies unchanged. In the first generation developing in the cages, the frequency of AR chromosomes about doubled (see the 35th day sample in table 1; the mean generation length in these populations is estimated to be about 25 days). In about four generations from the start, the AR and CH chromosomes became equally frequent (the 105th day samples). A year after the start an equilibrium was approached but apparently not yet fully attained. The samples in which the flies were counted, weighed, and measured were, thus, taken during the period in the life of the polymorphic populations when the latter consisted of about 45-50 percent of AR/CH structural hetero-zygotes, and when the incidence of AR homozygotes was greater than that of CH homozygotes.

(ii) *Number of flies produced*

The means and variances of the numbers of the flies which hatched from the cups taken from the different population cages are reported in table 2. The amounts of the food medium placed in the different cups were, of course, as uniform as practicable (about 25 cc.). The number of the eggs which the flies in the population cages deposit on each cup is probably always greater, and frequently greater by at least one order of magnitude, than the number of adult flies which eventually hatches. The number of the adults that hatch is, thus, an indication of the ability of the genotypes in a given population to utilise successfully the environmental opportunities at their disposal.

It can be seen at a glance that the first series of populations (Nos. 173-177) was less productive than the second series (Nos. 180-182). As stated above, this is ascribable to environmental conditions during the year 1958 being better than during 1957. What interests us are

TABLE 2

Number of flies hatching per cup in different populations

Population	Sex	Mean	Variance	Variation coefficient	Cups examined
173, AR+CH	Female	99·93	1629	40·4	33
176, AR+CH	Female	131·50	2265	36·2	33
175, AR	Female	86·24	1985	51·7	33
177, CH	Female	97·88	2781	53·9	33
181, AR+CH	Female	188·35	3383	30·8	20
180, AR	Female	139·75	4218	46·4	20
182, CH	Female	119·80	2487	41·6	20
173, AR+CH	Male	70·27	877	42·1	33
176, AR+CH	Male	85·27	1072	38·4	33
175, AR	Male	60·82	806	46·7	33
177, CH	Male	65·09	1284	55·1	33
181, AR+CH	Male	138·90	2523	36·2	20
180, AR	Male	90·65	2082	50·4	20
182, CH	Male	82·45	1736	50·5	20

comparisons of the polymorphic and monomorphic populations sampled simultaneously. The polymorphic populations Nos. 173 and 176 produced respectively $99·9 \pm 7·1$ and $131·5 \pm 8·4$ females and $70·3 \pm 5·2$ and $85·3 \pm 5·8$ males per cup. The differences between Nos. 173 and 176 are again ascribable to the environment (see above). The monomorphic populations, Nos. 175 and 177, yielded respectively $86·2 \pm 7·9$ and $97·9 \pm 9·3$ females and $60·8 \pm 5·0$ and $65·1 \pm 6·3$ males. The productivity of the monomorphic populations is thus not significantly lower than No. 176, both for females and for males. Since the populations Nos. 175, 176, 177 were kept in identical environments, they are fully comparable, while No. 173 is not quite so.

In the second series, the polymorphic population No. 181 produced $188·3 \pm 13·3$ females and $138·9 \pm 11·5$ males per cup. The monomorphic populations Nos. 180 and 182 yielded only $139·8 \pm 14·9$ and $119·8 \pm 11·4$ females and $90·7 \pm 10·5$ and $82·5 \pm 9·6$ males per cup. The productivity of the polymorphic population is again significantly greater.

Table 2 also shows the variances and the coefficients of variation of the productivity in the different populations. The productivity of the polymorphic populations is consistently less variable than that of the monomorphic ones. The six variation coefficients for the polymorphic populations range from 30·8 to 42·1, and for the monomorphic ones from 41·6 to 53·9. The first series of populations

TABLE 3

Weight (in mg.) of flies in polymorphic populations

No. 173			No. 176			No. 181		
Mean	s^2	Flies	Mean	s^2	Flies	Mean	s^2	Flies
Females			Females			Females		
0·804	0·0120	80	0·889	0·0291	110	0·912	0·0140	127
0·897	0·0234	65	0·845	0·0206	160	0·786	0·0223	164
0·783	0·0116	83	0·949	0·0153	117	0·737	0·0150	143
0·738	0·0112	96	0·910	0·0133	115	0·873	0·0153	132
0·845	0·0177	100	0·659	0·0161	134	0·816	0·0228	247
0·929	0·0199	91	0·776	0·0209	143	0·730	0·0354	261
0·975	0·0298	93	0·754	0·0291	87	0·678	0·0218	265
1·026	0·0133	99	0·752	0·0158	148	0·691	0·0293	204
0·765	0·0309	215	0·688	0·0247	226	1·108	0·0245	162
0·727	0·0201	140	0·741	0·0300	150	1·037	0·0148	125
Males			Males			Males		
0·721	0·0108	39	0·769	0·0119	53	0·803	0·0138	59
0·796	0·0131	45	0·729	0·0099	90	0·665	0·0211	124
0·686	0·0084	34	0·789	0·0101	77	0·660	0·0145	92
0·636	0·0104	79	0·770	0·0054	41	0·762	0·0096	70
0·679	0·0148	70	0·601	0·0100	69	0·709	0·0157	145
0·846	0·0103	59	0·700	0·0117	111	0·635	0·0253	217
0·803	0·0145	68	0·696	0·0150	57	0·656	0·0159	197
0·866	0·0069	55	0·687	0·0140	84	0·633	0·0142	157
0·674	0·0206	139	0·604	0·0138	169	1·041	0·0165	124
0·665	0·0120	115	0·673	0·0141	145	0·892	0·0137	84

seems to be more variable than the second, but the difference is not significant.

Note should be taken of the deviation from the normal ratio of sexes observed regularly in all populations. The male sex is deficient, forming only 39 per cent. to 41 per cent. of the total. Such a scarcity of males is usual in overpopulated cultures, the male being obviously the weaker sex.

(iii) Weight of the flies

The mean weights of the female and male flies in the different populations are reported in tables 3 and 4. For each population all the flies hatching in each of ten cups were weighed individually, as stated above in the section on Material and Techniques. The number of flies in each cup, the mean weights, and the variances of the individual weights (s^2) are given. The data are further summarised in table 5, which shows the unweighted averages of the mean weights of the flies from each of the ten cups in each population. Table 5 shows also the variance of the individual weights of the flies and the variances of the mean weights in the different cups. The variances of " individuals " are unweighted means of the variances reported in

TABLE 4

Weight (in mg.) of flies in monomorphic populations

No. 175—AR			No. 177—CH			No. 180—AR			No. 182—CH		
Mean	s^2	Flies	Mean	s^2	Flies	Mean	s^2	Flies	Mean	s^2	Flies
Females			Females			Females			Females		
0·786	0·0571	141	0·894	0·0222	70	0·932	0·0331	98	0·837	0·0269	150
0·940	0·0325	141	0·669	0·0176	133	0·915	0·0292	81	0·875	0·0315	100
0·808	0·0278	53	0·786	0·0176	71	1·047	0·0312	58	0·719	0·0248	174
0·954	0·0382	59	0·892	0·0171	76	0·858	0·0218	47	0·762	0·0161	111
0·760	0·0332	99	0·848	0·0334	119	0·706	0·0173	180	0·564	0·0175	134
0·962	0·0324	36	0·852	0·0261	103	0·773	0·0330	258	0·806	0·0282	150
0·762	0·0279	57	0·729	0·0422	64	0·754	0·0271	276	0·874	0·0184	150
0·892	0·0319	119	1·023	0·0317	91	0·925	0·0489	176	1·032	0·0419	45
0·680	0·0348	134	0·726	0·0262	213	1·060	0·0240	84	1·072	0·0124	54
0·742	0·0155	187	0·653	0·0207	331	1·071	0·0125	116	1·085	0·0222	42
Males			Males			Males			Males		
0·682	0·0317	104	0·720	0·0169	53	0·761	0·0196	53	0·728	0·0175	128
0·760	0·0207	86	0·618	0·0142	78	0·876	0·0243	57	0·699	0·0235	81
0·641	0·0175	35	0·738	0·0152	49	0·912	0·0119	36	0·634	0·0157	91
0·773	0·0146	34	0·750	0·0150	30	0·756	0·0141	30	0·649	0·0081	60
0·696	0·0192	83	0·746	0·0122	71	0·703	0·0208	184	0·674	0·0192	96
0·762	0·0154	24	0·759	0·0171	79	0·641	0·0154	97	0·533	0·0063	85
0·724	0·0160	36	0·634	0·0197	44	0·665	0·0142	181	0·768	0·0124	83
0·779	0·0153	66	0·905	0·0237	87	0·826	0·0302	112	0·811	0·0218	15
0·581	0·0178	90	0·611	0·0144	136	0·904	0·0168	65	0·890	0·0106	33
0·650	0·0136	145	0·551	0·0144	212	0·889	0·0126	49	0·919	0·0132	27

tables 3 and 4; these are, then, the average variances of the individual fly weights emerging in the same cup. The variances of " means " are computed from the ten average weights shown, for each population and sex, in tables 3 and 4; these variances characterise the reactions of the flies to the differences in the environmental conditions found in the different cups.

Flies from the polymorphic populations are neither consistently heavier nor lighter than those from the monomorphic ones. Examination of the tables and of fig. 1 shows, however, that there exists, as expected, a rather weak but significant negative correlation between the numbers of the flies emerging per cup and their weights. This only means that when fewer flies develop in a given amount of food they are bigger flies. The heterosis in polymorphic populations does not make the flies large. Average weights of female flies exceeding 1 mg. have been observed only among samples taken during spring and summer of 1958, both in monomorphic and in polymorphic populations. Examination of fig. 1 suggests, however, that, with equal population

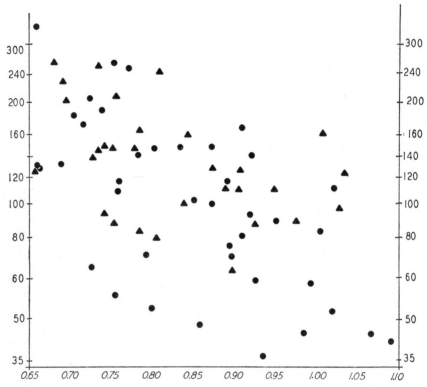

Fig. 1.—Mean weight (in mg.) of a female (abscissæ) plotted against the log. of the number of flies hatching in a cup (ordinates).
Circles—monomorphic populations. Triangles—polymorphic populations.

densities, the flies tend to be slightly heavier in polymorphic than in monomorphic populations.

The data on the variability of the body weight are more informative. Table 5 reports the variances of the weights of individuals emerging from the same food cup; consider these data separately for the two sexes and for the two series of the experimental populations (Nos. 173-177 and Nos. 180-182). With the sole exception of males in population 182, the polymorphic populations show smaller variances than the comparable monomorphic ones. To eliminate the possible disturbing effects of the differences in the average weights, we have computed the coefficients of variation for individuals emerging from the same cup. Females are more variable in weight than males; the variation coefficients range from 16·2 to 18·4 in polymorphic, and 18·0 to 21·7 in monomorphic populations for females, from 15·0 to 17·0 in polymorphic and 16·7 to 19·1 in monomorphic populations for males. No consistent trend is shown by the variances of the mean weights; it may, or may not, be significant that in three of the four possible comparisons the monomorphic CH populations are the most variable ones.

TABLE 5

Mean weight (in mg.) of a fly, and variances of individual (intra-cup) and of mean (inter-cup) weights in polymorphic and monomorphic populations

Population	Sex	Mean	Variance of individuals	Variance of means
173, AR+CH	Female	0·8485	0·01897	0·0107
176, AR+CH	Female	0·7963	0·02148	0·0094
175, AR	Female	0·8286	0·03312	0·0101
177, CH	Female	0·8072	0·02415	0·0134
181, AR+CH	Female	0·8368	0·02151	0·0213
180, AR	Female	0·9039	0·02780	0·0173
182, CH	Female	0·8626	0·02399	0·0273
173, AR+CH	Male	0·7371	0·01217	0·0069
176, AR+CH	Male	0·7018	0·01159	0·0043
175, AR	Male	0·7047	0·01817	0·0044
177, CH	Male	0·7031	0·01626	0·0103
181, AR+CH	Male	0·7456	0·01603	0·0178
180, AR	Male	0·7842	0·01799	0·0096
182, CH	Male	0·7305	0·01483	0·0142

(iv) Biomass

Multiplying the number of the flies hatching in the different cups by their mean weights, we obtain the total weights of the flies emerging in the different populations per unit of food (the nutrient medium in the cup). The figures so obtained are shown in table 6. The results

TABLE 6

Total weights (biomass) in mg. produced per cup in different populations

Sex	Polymorphic populations			Monomorphic populations			
	No. 173	No. 176	No. 181	No. 175	No. 177	No. 180	No. 182
♀	84·82	104·71	157·61	72·17	78·15	126·32	103·33
♂	51·80	59·87	103·52	42·86	45·76	63·88	60·23
Total	136·62	164·58	261·13	115·03	123·91	190·20	163·56

are clear and consistent if comparable populations are compared. Consider the Nos. 173-177 series first. In the polymorphic populations, a cup produced from 85 to 105 mg. of females and from 52 to 60 mg. of males, *i.e.* from 137 to 165 mg. of flies. In the monomorphic populations a cup yielded from 72 to 78 mg. of females and from 43 to 46 mg.

of males, *i.e.* from 115 to 124 mg. of flies. In the Nos. 180-182 series, the polymorphic population yielded 158 mg. of females and 104 mg. of males, *i.e.* about 261 mg. of flies per cup. The comparable mono-morphic populations yielded 103 to 126 mg. of females and 60 to 64 mg. of males, *i.e.* 164 to 190 mg. of flies. The polymorphic popu-lations are clearly more efficient producers of the living substance of the species *Drosophila pseudoobscura*.

(v) Wing length

The mean wing lengths characterising the different populations are shown in table 7 together with the variances attached to these

TABLE 7

Mean wing length (in mm.) and intra-cup (individual) variance and variance of means (inter-cup) in different populations studied

Population	Sex	Mean	Intra-cup variance	Inter-cup variance
173, AR+CH	Female	2·225	0·01169	0·00268
176, AR+CH	Female	2·236	0·00915	0·00207
175, AR	Female	2·252	0·01674	0·00452
177, CH	Female	2·197	0·01833	0·00419
181, AR+CH	Female	2·249	0·01016	0·00126
180, AR	Female	2·157	0·01099	0·00277
182, CH	Female	2·156	0·01217	0·00335
173, AR+CH	Male	2·020	0·00846	0·00216
176, AR+CH	Male	2·041	0·00622	0·00153
175, AR	Male	2·039	0·00945	0·00243
177, CH	Male	2·013	0·00703	0·00212
181, AR+CH	Male	2·062	0·00739	0·00093
180, AR	Male	2·034	0·01099	0·00377
182, CH	Male	1·969	0·01296	0·00139

values. In the 170 series of populations it seems that the AR flies from population 175 have the longest wings and CH flies from popu-lation 177 have the shortest wings, the flies from the polymorphic populations being of intermediate wing length. In the 180 series on the other hand, the mean wing length in the polymorphic population is greater than in both of the monomorphic populations. There is thus an indication that polymorphic populations *may* produce larger individuals than monomorphic populations but this is not inevitable and presumably depends largely upon external factors and upon the relative numbers of individuals produced in the two types of popu-lations. It is to be expected that where more individuals are produced in a culture these will be smaller than when there are fewer. In fact the polymorphic populations produce more flies whose mean wing length is usually as great as, or greater than, those from monomorphic populations.

Comparison of the variances of wing length in the different popu-lations gives, with a single exception, a quite consistent picture, namely that the polymorphic populations are less variable than the monomorphic ones. Let us consider the intra-cup (individual) variances first. In the 170 series of populations, the females in polymorphic populations show variances of 0·0117 and 0·0092, and in monomorphic ones 0·0167 and 0·0183; the males in polymorphic populations, 0·0085 and 0·0062, and monomorphic ones, 0·0094 and 0·0070 (the population No. 177 being exceptional). In the 180 series, the females in the polymorphic population have the variance of 0·0102 and in the monomorphic ones, 0·0110 and 0·0122; the males show 0·0074 in the polymorphic and 0·0110 and 0·0130 in the monomorphic ones. The variances of means (intra-cup) behave similarly. In the 170 series, the females of the polymorphic populations give 0·0027 and 0·0021, and of the monomorphic ones 0·0045 and 0·0042; the males in the polymorphic, 0·0015 and 0·0022, and in the monomorphic ones, 0·0024 and 0·0021 (the population No. 177 is again exceptional). In the 180 series, the polymorphic population gives 0·0013 and the monomorphic ones, 0·0028 and 0·0033 for females; and for males, 0·0009 in the polymorphic and 0·0038 and 0·0014 in the monomorphic populations.

The inescapable conclusion is that populations segregating for large genetic units are in general showing less phenotypic variation than populations pure breeding for these same units of inheritance.

(vi) Asymmetry

The mean intra-fly difference between right and left wings, *i.e.* wing asymmetry, calculated for each population is shown in table 8.

TABLE 8

Mean asymmetry of wings in microns in flies in different populations

Sex	Polymorphic populations			Monomorphic populations			
	No. 173	No. 176	No. 181	No. 175	No. 177	No. 180	No. 182
♀	8·287	8·999	8·906	10·174	10·548	10·153	8·916
♂	7·913	8·459	7·971	9·831	9·659	9·259	8·542

It can readily be seen that, restricting comparisons to within the 170 and 180 groups of populations respectively, flies from monomorphic populations are characterised by higher average values of wing asymmetry than flies from polymorphic populations. In fact, an analysis of variance shows that the apparent differences are statistically highly significant (table 9) in all except one of the informative comparisons (181 < 182). In this connection it is worth noting that the flies from population 182 are here considerably shorter in wing length than those from 181 (see table 7 for mean wing lengths) and the asymmetry value is therefore correspondingly lower than it would have been had the mean wing length of flies from 182 been more nearly equal to that of the 181 flies. This is because the amount of asymmetry of bilaterally paired organs or structures appears to depend partly upon the absolute size of the organs themselves (Thoday, 1958). Thus, all other things being equal, flies with shorter wings have more symmetrical wings than flies with longer wings. In this case, population 182 flies have significantly shorter wings than population 181 flies but the same level of quantitative asymmetry; it seems reasonable to suppose that the homeostatic mechanisms of development are less efficient in the 182 flies than in 181 flies. This is, then, in general

TABLE 9

Comparisons of mean values of wing asymmetry in polymorphic and monomorphic populations

Females			Males		
Polym.	Monom.	P	Polym.	Monom.	P
173	<175	<0·001	173	<175	<0·001
173	<177	<0·001	173	<177	<0·001
176	<175	<0·001	176	<175	<0·001
176	<177	<0·001	176	<177	<0·001
181	<180	<0·01	181	<180	<0·01
181	<182	<0·05	181	<182	<0·05

agreement with the conclusion to be drawn from the other comparisons in table 9, that is, that in the polymorphic populations development is on average more homeostatic or better canalised than in the monomorphic populations.

4. DISCUSSION

Among the seven experimental populations which we have studied, four were monomorphic and three were polymorphic. Among the monomorphic ones, two were homozygous for third chromosomes with the AR gene arrangement and two homozygous for the CH arrangement. The polymorphic populations contained both AR and CH chromosomes, their frequencies approaching equilibrium values, *i.e.* AR being about twice as frequent as CH. Among the zygotes formed in the polymorphic populations, slightly fewer than half were the heterokaryotype AR/CH, about one-third were the homozygotes AR/AR, and the remainder belonged to the homokaryotype CH/CH. Slightly more than half of the flies in the polymorphic population were, therefore, chromosomally identical with the flies in the monomorphic populations AR/AR and CH/CH, respectively.

The findings described on the preceding pages must be interpreted in the light of the known composition of the experimental populations. We have found that the polymorphic populations differ in a number of respects from the monomorphic ones.   The simplest explanation of this would seem to be that the properties of the polymorphic populations which distinguish them from the monomorphic ones are due to the presence in the former of the AR/CH karyotype.   The greater numbers of flies and the greater biomass produced in the polymorphic populations may, thus, be due to greatly superior survival rates of the AR/CH class compared to the homozygotes.   It is less easy to interpret similarly the lower variances found in the polymorphic populations, for this would mean that the AR/CH heterozygotes show a quite remarkably low variability.   After all, the genetic component of the variance should be, if anything, greater in the polymorphic populations. Consideration should therefore be given to a possible alternative. Levene, Pavlovsky and Dobzhansky (1954, 1958) found that the adaptive values of the karyotypes in experimental populations may be quite appreciably modified by the presence or absence of other karyotypes in the same medium.   The fitness and other properties of, for example, AR/AR may, then, not be the same in a pure culture and in a culture in which AR/AR shares the environment with AR/CH and with CH/CH.   There may quite conceivably exist a kind of mutual facilitation between the karyotypes which normally live side by side in natural populations.   AR/AR and CH/CH may actually benefit by living in the vicinity of each other and of the AR/CH karyotype.

Regardless of whether the differences between the polymorphic and the monomorphic populations are due to a superiority of the heterozygotes or to mutual facilitation, it is important that these differences are of a kind which might be expected to confer a greater adaptedness on the former.   The ability to produce a greater number of individuals and a greater biomass from a given amount of food would certainly be advantageous under most natural conditions. The lack of heterosis expressed in a greater weight or a greater size of the flies in the polymorphic populations is certainly compatible with the above view.   In the first place, when a culture with a fixed amount of nutrients produces more flies these may well be smaller flies.   Secondly, examination of fig. 1 suggests that there is a tendency for the flies from polymorphic populations to be heavier than flies from monomorphic ones when they develop in cultures with similar degrees of crowding (the triangle symbols in fig. 1 tend to be grouped above and to the right of the circles).   And thirdly, it appears that flies from crowded cultures are as fecund as those from uncrowded ones if they are treated equally as adults (Spiess, 1958, see, however, Saveliev, 1928;   this matter needs reinvestigation).   Granted the unsatisfactory state of our understanding of Drosophila ecology, it would seem that a population which produces more flies is likely to have an advantage over one producing larger flies.

It is less easy to evaluate the adaptive significance of the lower variances of the productivity, of the weights of the individuals developing in the same cup, and of the lower degree of asymmetry of the wing length observed in the polymorphic populations. Dobzhansky and Wallace (1953), Dobzhansky, Pavlovsky, Spassky, and Spassky (1955), and Dobzhansky and Levene (1955) all found that the survival rates of heterozygous genotypes in Drosophila are less variable than those of the homozygotes. Furthermore, among the homozygotes, those less viable over a range of environments tend to be most variable (this is borne out also by unpublished data of Dobzhansky and Spassky). Interpretation of these findings has not been free from confusion; some writers alleged that other writers believed that the low variability of the survival rates caused these rates to be high. Perhaps the following comment may be helpful. Some genotypes endow their carriers with a superior developmental homeostasis, or, to use Waddington's (1957) terms, superior canalisation or superior homeorhesis, in a given range of environments. Other genotypes yield a less versatile developmental homeostasis. A superior homeostatic buffering should result in preservation of life and successful development, and consequently in a high viability, in a variable environment. But the same superior homeostatic capacity should make the survival rates over a certain range of environments more uniform, *i.e.* less variable. Uniformity of the survival rates is neither the cause nor the consequence of high viability; high survival and uniform survival are both conditioned by superior homeostasis (or canalisation, or homeorhesis).

Mather (1953) and Tebb and Thoday (1954) found that the numbers of sternopleural bristles on the two sides of the body in *Drosophila melanogaster* are more often asymmetrical in homozygotes than in heterozygotes. Although Thoday (1958) has shown that genetic imbalance rather than homozygosity as such is responsible for greater asymmetry in some cases, this agrees with our finding that the two wings of a fly are more often asymmetrical (different in length) in monomorphic than in polymorphic populations. Waddington (1957) ascribes asymmetries to "developmental noise", and draws a distinction between this phenomenon and the developmental instability resulting from imperfect homeostatic buffering. We feel that these phenomena are likely to be rather closely related; anyway, it is hardly an accident that heterozygous genotypes, at least those heterozygous for coadapted gene complexes derived from the same population, show both low variance in traits concerned with fitness and low asymmetry (see also Lerner, 1954).

We conclude that experimental populations of *Drosophila pseudoobscura* polymorphic for AR and CH chromosomes are superior in fitness to populations monomorphic for AR or for CH. This assuredly does not mean that monomorphic populations of this kind cannot be maintained; at least under laboratory conditions they are reasonably prosperous. But as Li (1955) has justly remarked: "Should man become a one-legged animal, we cannot be sure that mankind will perish from earth when raised in pure cultures", *i.e.* if all men should be one-legged animals. Polymorphic populations in Drosophila are superior to monomorphic ones in the same sense in which populations of two-legged men are superior to one-legged ones.

5. SUMMARY

Seven experimental populations of *Drosophila pseudoobscura* have been studied in laboratory population cages. Three of them were polymorphic for the AR and CH gene arrangements in the third chromosomes, two were monomorphic for AR, and two for CH chromosomes. The polymorphism is balanced owing to heterosis in the AR/CH heterozygotes. After the polymorphic populations had approached the equilibrium frequencies of AR and CH, samples were taken from all the populations. The samples consisted of cups with the nutrient medium, withdrawn from the cages at a rate of, at most, one cup per week, during the period of mass pupation of the larvæ in the cups. The following data were obtained from the samples: (1) numbers of female and male flies hatching, (2) weights of individual flies, (3) length of the wings, (4) asymmetry of the lengths of the two wings of the same individual, and (5) total weight (biomass) of the flies hatching from a cup.

The results obtained show that (*a*) the polymorphic populations produce more individuals than do the monomorphic ones (*cf.* table 2), (*b*) the numbers of individuals hatching per cup are less variable in the polymorphic than in the monomorphic populations (table 2), (*c*) the mean weights of a fly are about the same in comparable polymorphic and monomorphic populations (tables 3-5), (*d*) the variances of weights of individuals hatching in the same cup are smaller in polymorphic than in monomorphic populations (tables 3-5), (*e*) the biomass produced is greater in polymorphic than in monomorphic populations (table 6), (*f*) the mean length of the wings is about the same in polymorphic and monomorphic populations (table 7), (*g*) the variance in wing length is generally greater in the monomorphic populations (table 7), (*h*) the asymmetry of the wings is greater in monomorphic than in polymorphic populations (tables 8 and 9).

We conclude that the polymorphic populations which we have studied are superior in Darwinian fitness to the monomorphic ones. It is conjectured that this superior fitness may be due not only to high adaptive value of the heterokaryotype AR/CH, but also to favourable interaction (mutual facilitation) between the carriers of the different karyotypes.

6. REFERENCES

DOBZHANSKY, TH. 1948. Genetics of natural populations XVIII. *Genetics, 33*, 588-602.

DOBZHANSKY, TH. 1957. Mendelian populations as genetic systems. *Cold Spring Harbor Symp. Quant. Biol., 22*, 385-393.

DOBZHANSKY, TH., AND LEVENE, H. 1955. Genetics of natural populations. XXIV. *Genetics, 40*, 797-808.

DOBZHANSKY, TH., PAVLOVSKY, O., SPASSKY, B., AND SPASSKY, N. 1955. Genetics of natural populations. XXIII. *Genetics, 40,* 781-796.

DOBZHANSKY, TH., AND WALLACE, B. 1953. The genetics of homeostasis in Drosophila. *Proc. Nat. Acad. Sci., 39,* 162-171.

LERNER, I. M. 1954. *Genetic Homeostasis.* John Wiley, New York.

LEVENE, H., PAVLOVSKY, O., AND DOBZHANSKY, TH. 1954. Interaction of the adaptive values in polymorphic experimental populations of *Drosophila pseudo-obscura. Evolution, 8,* 335-349.

LEVENE, H., PAVLOVSKY, O., DOBZHANSKY, TH. 1958. Dependence of the adaptive values of certain genotypes in *Drosophila pseudoobscura* on the composition of the gene pool. *Evolution, 12,* 18-23.

LEVINE, L. 1955. Genotypic background and heterosis in *Drosophila pseudoobscura. Genetics, 40,* 832-849.

LI, C. C. 1955. The stability of an equilibrium and the average fitness of a population. *Amer. Naturalist, 89,* 281-295.

MATHER, K. 1953. Genetical control of stability in development. *Heredity, 7,* 297-336.

SAVELIEV, V. 1928. On the manifold effect of the gene vestigial in *Drosophila melanogaster. Tr. Soc. Natur. Leningrad, 63,* 65-88.

SPIESS, E. 1958. Chromosomal adaptive polymorphism in *Drosophila persimilis. Evolution, 12,* 234-245.

TEBB, G., AND THODAY, J. M. 1954. Stability in development and relational balance of X-chromosomes in *Drosophila melanogaster. Nature, 174,* 1109.

THODAY, J. M. 1958. Homeostasis in a selection experiment. *Heredity, 12,* 401-415.

WADDINGTON, C. H. 1957. *The Strategy of the genes.* Allen & Unwin, London.

THE ORGANISATION OF POLYGENIC ACTIVITY WITHIN A CHROMOSOME IN *DROSOPHILA*

II. VIABILITY

E. L. BREESE * and K. MATHER

*Agricultural Research Council Unit of Biometrical Genetics,
Department of Genetics, University of Birmingham*

Received 1.x.59

1. INTRODUCTION

IN an earlier paper (Breese and Mather, 1957) we have described an investigation into the distribution, along chromosome III of *Drosophila melanogaster*, of genetic activity affecting the numbers of abdominal and sternopleural chaetae. The starting material comprised chromosomes III from two lines, H and L, selected respectively for high and low numbers of abdominal chaetae. From these were constructed a variety of recombinant chromosomes, each of which included known combinations of segments from the H and L chromosomes III. This was achieved by the use of the so-called " rucuca " marker stock, but as finally produced the recombinant chromosomes themselves contained no marker genes, though they may have contained short segments of material from between the marker genes of the " rucuca " chromosome. The chromosomes built up and the segments of which they were constructed are listed in table 1 and fig. 1 respectively, which are reproduced from the earlier paper. The legends to table and figure provide further information about the recombinant chromosomes, and a full account of the technique of construction is to be found in the earlier paper.

Once constructed, a recombinant chromosome was maintained against *Me Sb* in the male line, and was thus protected from disruption by further recombination and also in large measure from the action of selection. It could, of course, accumulate variation by mutation during its maintenance, and we have evidence that this in fact occurred.

The recombinant chromosomes were tested for their effects chiefly in diallel sets of crosses. The crosses used were always of the types $\dfrac{I}{Me\ Sb} \times \dfrac{J}{H}$ where I and J indicate any two of the recombinant chromosomes. The *Me Sb* chromosome largely reduces, even if it does not wholly suppress, recombination in the mothers so that the identity of chromosome I is in the main preserved. A cross of this kind yields four types of progeny : $\dfrac{Me\ Sb}{H}$; $\dfrac{J}{Me\ Sb}$; $\dfrac{I}{H}$; $\dfrac{I}{J}$. The last class is of course wild type and provides the material for assessing the joint effect

---

* Now at Welsh Plant Breeding Station, Aberystwyth.

Reprinted by permission of Oliver & Boyd, Ltd. from HEREDITY,
14, 375-399 (1960).

of I and J on the chaeta characters. It will be observed, however, that the first class is constant over all crosses and so may be used as a

TABLE 1

The recombinant wild-type chromosomes constructed and used in the experiments. Capital and small letters indicate segments derived from chromosome III of the H and L lines respectively. The limits of the segments denoted by A-a, B-b, etc. are shown in fig. 1. In Group (c) the constitution in respect of segment D-d is not fully certain as the gene ca was omitted from the marked chromosome used in the process of construction

Group	(a)	(b)	(c)	
Parental chromosomes	(1) ABCD = (2) abcd =	APQRD = apqrd =	AXYZRD axyzrd	
Recombinant chromosomes	(3) aBCD (4) abCD (5) abcD (6) ABCd (7) ABcd (8) Abcd	(9) APqrd (10) APQrd (11) apQRD (12) apqRD	(13) AxyZR(D) (14) AxYZR(D) (15) AXYzR(D) (16) AXyzR(D) (17) AxyzR(D)	(18) axyZr(d) (19) axYZr(d) (20) zXYZr(d) (21) aXYzr(d) (22) aXyzr(d)

basis for comparing the effects of the recombinant chromosomes on the viabilities of their carriers. The crosses which provided the information about chaeta number described in the earlier paper, also yielded

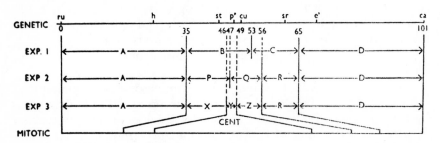

FIG. 1.—The genes used in constructing the wild-type chromosomes and the segments of which, in consequence, these chromosomes were constructed (see in the text).

The extent of each segment is indicated by the arrows, the limits being shown in their average positions. Apart, however, from the left of A and the right of D, the limits might fall by the vagaries of recombination anywhere between the straddling genes (*e.g.* the right limit of A might come anywhere between *h* and *st*) the average position being midway between them on the genetical map. This variation in position of recombination could also lead to a small piece of the marked chromosome being inserted in the region of the limit.

The average positions of all the limits are indicated in relation to the genetical map (above) and some of them also in relation to the mitotic cytological map (below). The general position of the centromere (Cent.) is shown on the mitotic map, though it may well be nearer to the left limit of region Y than is indicated. All positions on this map are very approximate.

From Breese and Mather (1957).

the data on viability now to be described. The various sets of crosses and experiments will be referred to in this paper in the same way as in the earlier report.

2. THE MEASURE OF VIABILITY

In all crosses, the parents were mated for 2-3 days in tubes and then transferred to half-pint milk bottles in which their progeny were raised for counting and recording.

In the first set of crosses made (M1 in the first experiment) the parents remained in the bottles until their early offspring began to emerge. The result was numbers of flies too large for complete classification to be undertaken. Samples of 130-150 were therefore classified from these cultures. In all later crosses, the parents were restricted to 48-60 hours in the bottle, and all the progeny emerging were classified.

At first, in the M1 and M2 sets of crosses in the first experiment, no regard was paid to sex in estimating viability, which was measured as

$$100 \left[\frac{I}{J}\right] \bigg/ \left(\left[\frac{I}{J}\right] + \left[\frac{Me\ Sb}{H}\right]\right)$$ where $\left[\dfrac{I}{J}\right]$ is the number of wild-type

flies of both sexes and $\left[\dfrac{Me\ Sb}{H}\right]$ the number of flies of both sexes carrying the two marked chromosomes. Equal viabilities of the two classes will then be indicated by a value of 50 per cent. The H and $Me\ Sb$ flies were disregarded. These classes could affect the viability as we measured it by affecting the level and outcome of competition among the four classes within the bottle, but any such effect would seem unlikely to be great in the experiments as conducted and its consequences negligible.

A different — and unexpected — complication was, however, revealed by these early sets of crosses. It became clear that the male and female wild-type flies were showing different effects of the recombinant chromosomes III on their viabilities. In all later crosses, therefore, the viability of the wild-type flies was measured separately for males and females. In each case the measure

taken was $100 \left[\dfrac{I}{J}\right]^* \bigg/ \left(\left[\dfrac{I}{J}\right]^* + \left[\dfrac{Me\ Sb}{H}\right]\right)$ where $\left[\dfrac{I}{J}\right]^*$ is the number of

wild-type males *or* females, according to which viability was being measured. Males and females were, however, pooled in the $\dfrac{Me\ Sb}{H}$

class as although there was often a slight shortage of females, in no case was this significant and the ratio borne by the two sexes to one another did not vary significantly over the whole set of experiments. Equal viabilities of the two classes will thus be indicated by a value of $33\frac{1}{3}$ per cent. In every experiment but two where viabilities were measured separately the female proved to vary from cross to cross, as tested by contingency χ^2's measuring the variation in relative numbers of these females and the marked flies (table 2). Further, there was always a significant shortage of the wild-type females when compared with either the wild-type males or the marked flies. As measured by these

χ^2's the viability of males on the other hand failed to show any sign of variation in any experiment, and there was no shortage of these males by comparison with the marked flies. Thus genetic differences in chromosome III are revealed by changes in viability of the females; but these same differences failed to produce comparable changes in the viabilities of the males. Further evidence of this difference between

TABLE 2

Contingency χ^2's testing variation of numbers of wild-type flies relative to Me Sb/H flies in the various experiments. Males and females were not recorded separately in M1 and M2 of the first experiment so that the test is of variation in the pooled numbers of the two sexes. In all other cases the test is of variation in the numbers of wild-type males and females separately. In all cases the males and females are pooled in the Me Sb/H class, as the sex ratio did not vary significantly among these flies

Experiment	Variation relative to *Me Sb/H* class of numbers of wild-type					
	Females and Males					
	χ^2		N		P (in per cent.)	
1. M1 . .	87·9		48		<0·1	
M2 . .	62·0		48		8	
	Females			Males		
	χ^2	N	P (in per cent.)	χ^2	N	P (in per cent.)
1. O1 . .	106·4	48	0·1	40·3	48	78
O2 . .	45·1	47	56	35·1	47	90
2. Set 1 .	80·8	58	3	70·7	58	14
2 .	71·2	46	1·3	51·7	46	32
3. Set 1 .	58·3	34	0·6	41·0	34	23
2 .	38·9	35	35	43·9	35	17
4. . .	55·1	27	0·1	36·7	27	10
Total .	455·8	295	v. small	319·4	295	16

the sexes will be found in the later sections dealing with the individual experiments, though as will be seen it was not so great in the last as in the earlier experiments.

3. THE FIRST EXPERIMENT

In this experiment all the chromosomes (1)-(8) (see table 1), with the exception of (2), were used in a diallel set of crosses, every chromosome being brought from the mother into combination with every chromosome from the father. With 7 chromosomes there were thus 49 combinations including the 7 homozygotes. The 42 heterozygous combinations fall into 21 pairs, the members of a pair differing only in the way in which the two chromosomes were brought in from the two parents.

The diallel set was made up four times, giving all combinations of two genetic backgrounds (M, the background of the *Me Sb/H* stock, and O, the Oregon background) and the two groups of recombinant chromosomes (1 and 2), these being formally alike but constructed on different occasions so that they may differ as a result of the normal variation in position of crossing-over between the marker genes. One heterozygous combination failed in one of the four replicates. The consequent missing value was replaced by the viability from its reciprocal cross, and the corresponding adjustment made in the degrees of freedom available in the analysis of variance.

In the first two diallel sets (M_1 and M_2) no distinction was drawn between male and female wild-type flies, but in the O_1 and O_2 diallel sets of this, and in all later experiments, males and females were counted separated. Pooling males and females in O_1 and O_2 as well as in M_1 and M_2, the average viability percentages as defined in section 2 above, were found to be M_1-47·4, M_2-49·5, O_1-46·6 and O_2-48·7 in the four diallel sets with a grand average of 48·0, where, of course, 50 per cent. indicates a viability equal to that of the *Me Sb/H* class which was used as the yardstick. When the sexes are taken separately in the O_1 and O_2 sets $33\frac{1}{3}$ per cent. indicates viability equal to that of the *Me Sb/H* class (see section 2) and the average percentages actually found were O_1 females 28·8, O_2 females 30·6, O_1 males 31·9 and O_2 males 33·8. Thus overall viabilities are reasonably high: we are not dealing with sub-lethal combinations of genes. The range of viabilities encountered in the females of the O_1 and O_2 diallel sets is illustrated in fig. 4.

The viability percentages were all transformed into angles (see Fisher and Yates, 1957) before analysis in this and all the other experiments. These viability results were analysed in two ways, as were the chaeta numbers of the earlier paper. This first analysis was by means of the W/V and W/W′ relations of the diallel tables (see Hayman, 1954; Jinks, 1954; and Breese and Mather, 1957). The W/V and W/W′ graphs are shown in fig. 2 for the sexes pooled in the combined M and O replicates, and for the sexes separately in the combined O_1 and O_2 replicates. The corresponding graph for the abdominal chaetae is also repeated from fig. 2 of the earlier paper for comparison. Each point on the various graphs is numbered to show the recurrent chromosome in the diallel array from which that point is derived. This was also done in fig. 2 of the earlier paper, but unfortunately an incorrect set of numbers was assigned to the points in that figure. The error has been rectified in the present fig. 2, which in this respect therefore corrects and replaces the earlier graph.

Several points emerge from these graphs. In the first place, in contrast to the females, the males of O_1 and O_2 show little more than

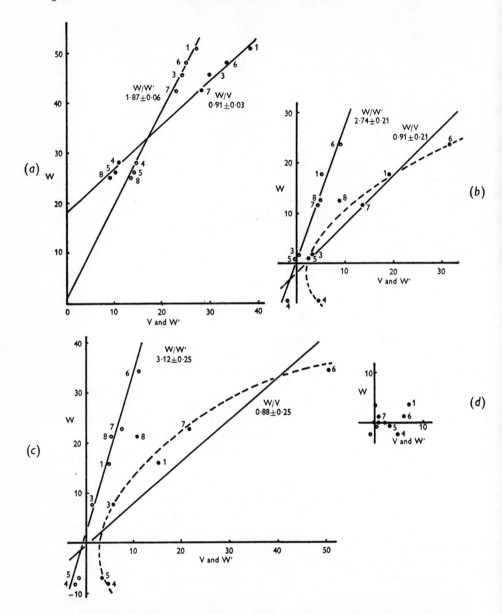

Fɪɢ. 2.—The W/V (solid circles) and W/W′ (open circles) graphs from the diallel analyses of the first experiment for (a) abdominal chaeta number and (b)-(d) viability. For (b) the data are from the combined sexes in the complete experiment, for (c) from females in O1 and O2, and for (d) from the corresponding males. The numbers indicate the chromosomes to which the points relate. The straight lines are the best fitting linear regressions, for which the calculated slopes are shown. The dotted curves in (b) and (c) have no special significance, being included only to bring out the curvilinear nature of the W/V relation in these graphs. For the sake of clarity no regression lines are shown in (d), and some of the chromosome numbers are omitted.

Note. (a) is from Breese and Mather (1957) where, however, the points were numbered incorrectly in respect of the chromosomes to which they relate. This numbering is now corrected.

random scatter about the point (O, O) in both W/V and W/W' relations. Completely random scattering round (O, O) would imply a total absence of genetic difference among the seven chromosomes in their effects on viability of the males. The small departure from random scatter shows that this is not fully the case, and indeed we shall see further indications of effects in male viability in other experiments; but the graphs of fig. 2 show that any effect on males is very small as compared with effects on females.

The second point to emerge from the graphs is not only that the females (and, of course, correspondingly the pooled sexes) show striking genetic differences among the seven chromosomes, but also that the genes responsible display both dominance and interaction among themselves. The action of dominance is revealed by the spacing of the array points along the lines in the graphs; and the action of interaction by the curvilinearity of the W/V relation and also by the departure of the W/W' line from a slope of 2. Slight departures of both kinds were detected in the graphs from chaeta numbers and were ascribed in the earlier paper to causes other than genic interaction. Those in the viability graphs are, however, so much larger and more striking as to leave no doubt that interaction is present and is, to say the least, a much more important feature of the gene system in chromosome III affecting viability than of that affecting chaeta number. We may note, too, that, in so far as the intercept of the best fitting W/V line on the y-axis can still be used to measure dominance where the relation is basically curvilinear, its proximity to the origin indicates complete or virtually complete dominance of the operative combinations of genes for viability as compared with the partial dominance indicated in the case of the chaeta. We shall see further evidence of high dominance later.

The third and last feature to be noted about these graphs is that the seriation of the points relating to the seven individual chromosomes is different in the case of viability from that shown with the chaeta numbers. The place of a point in this seriation reflects the overall dominance, or potence, of the combination of genes carried by the chromosome it represents, the farther down towards the left of the line the greater being the potence. In the case of chaeta number, the main division of the points is between (4), (5) and (8) carrying the more dominant b segment and (1), (3), (6) and (7) carrying the more recessive B segment. The wholly H chromosome, (1), is the most recessive. With viability, however, the B-b segment is no longer outstanding in determining the potence properties and the most recessive and most dominant chromosomes are (6), ABCd, and (4), abCD, respectively. The significance of this observation will be examined in more detail later: the point to note for the moment is that in respect of their contributions to dominance and potence the segments do not behave in the same way for viability as for chaeta number.

The second analysis of the data was by fitting constants to represent the contribution of the various segments to the additive and dominance variation in viability, just as was done for chaeta number. These constants can be used as the basis for arriving at an analysis of variance which allows the contributions of the different possible sources of variation in viability to be tested for significance (see Breese and Mather, *loc. cit.*). If all four diallel sets are to be brought into a single analysis, the results from the pooled sexes must be used as only these

TABLE 3

Analyses of variance of results of first experiment

Item	N	Mean squares		
		All sets— sexes pooled	O_1 and O_2	
			Females	Males
Additive effects (A) .	4	120·12*	145·50*	9·89
Dominance (D) . .	4	108·85*	122·26*	33·36†
Res. interaction (I) .	19	17·56	28·16*	7·99
Backgrounds (B) . .	1	10·42	...	...
Groups (G) . . .	1	72·01*	33·39	29·96
B×A B×D	8	20·79	...	...
B×I	19	9·16	...	...
G×A	4	15·54	2·55	15·89
G×D	4	34·58†	22·00	7·79
G×I	19	13·16	15·21	15·91
Remaining interactions .	28	7·13	...	...
Reciprocals . . .	84/41‡	12·77	11·27	8·81
Theoretical error . .	...	11·47	12·01	11·76

* P < 0·01.
† 0·05 > P > 0·01.
‡ 84 for " All sets " and 41 for the two " O_1 and O_2 " columns. Note that both these values are reduced by 1 owing to a missing cross.
All tests of significance were carried out by means of χ^2's as described in the text.

are available from M_1 and M_2. For O_1 and O_2, however, the sexes may be analysed separately. The three analyses of variance, for pooled sexes over all four diallel sets and for the females and males respectively in O_1 and O_2, are given in table 3 and the average value of the eight constants, a " d " measuring the additive contribution and an " h " measuring the dominance contribution from each segment, are given again for the three different sets of data in table 4.

In contrast with the earlier analyses of chaeta number, no items appear for the sex difference and its interactions in the present analyses. The sexes were not separately recorded in M_1 and M_2 so that the sex difference cannot be introduced into the analysis of the complete experiment, and where it could be introduced in the analysis of O_1 and O_2 the position is in fact made clearer by dealing with the sexes quite separately. A slightly different break-down has further been adopted for a number of items in the present analyses in order to bring out certain special features of the viability results. The tests of significance were also carried out differently. With the chaeta numbers these had to be based on comparisons with error variances estimated from the reciprocal differences and high order interactions. A different possibility is open with the viabilities since these are measured as proportions. When transformed into angles, proportions have a theoretical variance of $\dfrac{820 \cdot 7}{n}$ (Fisher and Yates, 1957), where n is the total number of individuals from which the proportion is estimated. This number varies, though not too widely, from culture to culture, but a theoretical variance can still be found for use in the analysis by

TABLE 4

The constants measuring the additive and dominance contributions of the four regions in the first experiment. For d a positive value indicates higher viability given by the H segment, and a negative sign higher viability given by the L segment. For h a positive sign indicate dominance in the direction of higher viability

	d_a	d_b	d_c	d_d	h_a	h_b	h_c	h_d	s.e.
All sets—sexes pooled	−0·53	−1·21	−0·48	0·86	1·85*	0·45	0·50	1·38†	0·64
O1 and O2 Females	−0·74	−1·39	−0·16	2·04†	2·17†	2·16†	−0·05	2·12†	} 0·82
Males	1·13	−0·89	0·37	0·77	1·62	1·17	−0·08	0·47	

* P<0·01.   † 0·05>P>0·01.

taking the harmonic mean of the different numbers of individuals counted in the various crosses and using this as the value for n in the formula. The error variances so obtained are given in the bottom line of table 3. Where such a theoretical variance is available, the ratio borne by any sum of squares in the analysis to the theoretical error is distributed as a χ^2 for the number of degrees of freedom appropriate to the sum of squares. All the tests of significance of table 3 have been carried out in this way.

It is encouraging to see in table 3 that the differences between reciprocal crosses and the high order interactions nowhere significantly exceed the theoretical sampling variation and indeed in most cases are slightly, though again not significantly, sub-normal. Evidently there is no unexpected or unaccounted major source of variation in the experiments. Taking first the analysis of the complete experiment, there is no doubt of the genetic effect of chromosome III on viability in respect of both additive and dominance components. The effect of residual non-allelic interactions among the segments is not fully significant. The probability for this item is, however, very little above 5 per cent. ($\chi^2_{[19]} = 29 \cdot 09$ as compared with $\chi^2_{[19]} = 30 \cdot 14$ at P $= 0 \cdot 05$)

and taking this in conjunction with the graphs of fig. 2, there can be little doubt that interactions are having their effects. The difference between backgrounds (M *versus* O) appears to be without importance but the differences between the formally similar recombinant chromosomes of the two groups, 1 and 2, are significant. Evidently the precise positions of the points of recombination are important in respect of viability. Furthermore there is an indication that the effect on dominance varies differently with groups, though that of the additive components does not.

The female viabilities in sets O1 and O2 can obviously give no information about the effects of background or its interactions. In other respects, however, these females not only test the same effects but confirm the complete analysis in a remarkable way. The residual genetic interactions now emerge as fully significant, and while the effects of groups and the $G \times D$ interaction are sub-significant their mean squares are both large and, again in conformity with the full analysis, that for $G \times A$ is small.

The male viabilities are in striking contrast. No item is significant except for the dominance effects and that has a probability higher than 2 per cent. With eight items tested it would not be unduly surprising to find one of them showing by chance a probability of just below 5 per cent. Thus no great weight can be placed on this single significant item. Indeed if we sum the χ^2's for all eight items in this male analysis we find $\chi^2_{[96]} = 94 \cdot 04$ with a probability of $0 \cdot 48$. The sex difference in the expression of the genetic effects of chromosome III on viability in this experiment is clear from the analysis of variance which completely confirms the conclusion reached from the diallel graphs of fig. 2, *c* and *d*.

One further point remains to be noted about the genetic interactions among the segments as shown by the analysis of females. This gives a mean square of $28 \cdot 16$ as compared with $145 \cdot 50$ for additive effects—

a ratio of $\dfrac{1}{5 \cdot 17}$ or $\dfrac{1}{8 \cdot 27}$ if both mean squares are reduced by the theoretical error variance. This compares with corresponding ratios of

$\dfrac{1}{225}$ and $\dfrac{1}{310}$ for abdominal chaeta. Relative to additive effects interactions loom larger in respect of their contribution to the variation in viability than they do in respect of variability in chaeta number, as indeed does dominance also.

The importance of dominance emerges also from the eight constants, the four d's and four h's attributable to the four segments, shown in table 4. Here again the males of O1 and O2 show no significant genetic effects. Tested against their empirical standard error, by no means all of the constants are individually significant in the O1 and O2 females or the pooled sexes of all four diallel sets. There can be little doubt of the additive effect exerted by segment D-d (constant d_d)

and it will be observed that in both sets of results this is of sign opposite to d_a, d_b and d_c. The D segment from the H line evidently makes for higher viability than does its counterpart from the L line, whereas in all the other three segments the L line appears to make for a higher viability than does the H. Significant dominance is indicated by h_a, h_b and h_d in three of the four segments, it being in every case in the direction of dominance for higher viability. Furthermore the h's are on the whole higher in value than the d's suggesting what, for want of a better term, might be described as " over-dominance " in these three segments; though we must note that even where demonstrated such " over-dominance " of a segment carries no implication of over-dominance at any single gene locus in the chromosome.

These findings about the distribution of the additive effects between H and L chromosomes and about dominance again agree, at least broadly, with the conclusions to be drawn from the diallel graphs in fig. 2 *b* and *c*. The chromosome ABCd (No. 6) is farthest up to the right in both diallel graphs, showing that it is the most recessive of the seven. This is to be expected since dominance is for high viability and the A, B and C segments from the H line and the d segment from the L line all give lower viabilities than do their counterparts. Similarly the chromosome abcD (No. 5) is at the other end of the line as would be expected. It is more difficult to sort out the effects of the individual segments from the remaining points in the figure as the structure of the diallel sets is not orthogonal in respect of the segments, but so far as can be judged they are in full agreement with the expectations from table 4.

4. THE REMAINING EXPERIMENTS

The remaining three experiments undertaken for the analysis of the control of chaeta number are less informative than the first one about viability. The fourth experiment is of a different type and as we shall see yields somewhat disparate results. The second experiment ran into such difficulties from missing cultures that its full analysis was impossible even in respect of chaeta number, while both it and the third experiment were undertaken to analyse further the B-b segment which had proved to be of prime importance in the mediation of chaeta number but is of less dominating significance for viability.

(i) The chromosomes used in the second experiment were (3), (5), (6), (8), (9), (10), (11) and (12) of table 1. They confound the effects of segments A-a and D-d, A always being present with d and a with D. At the same time they break segments B-b and C-c down into three new segments P-p, Q-q and R-r (fig. 1). The diallel set of crosses among the eight chromosomes was attempted twice, different groups of recombinant chromosomes being used on the two occasions. As we have noted, so many combinations failed as to make diallel analysis impossible. A partial analysis of variance was, however, attempted from each set of crosses, by fitting constants. The results are shown in table 5, which sets out the analyses of variance, and table 6, which sets out the constants themselves and compares these with the corresponding groups of constants obtained from the first

TABLE 5

Analyses of variance of results of second experiment. The entries under " Females " and " Males " in the body of the table are mean squares

Item	1st diallel			2nd diallel		
	N	Females	Males	N	Females	Males
Components . .	8	43·8*	15·2	8	38·4*	17·9
Res. Interaction .	26	12·3	9·7	18	18·4	16·8
Reciprocals . .	24	8·3	19·1*	20	11·3	13·9
Theoretical error .	...	10·7	10·7	...	12·2	11·9

* P<0·01. † 0·05>P>0·01.

experiment. The d and h components were not fitted separately in these analyses, so that in table 5 the item for components covers both additive and dominance effects.

TABLE 6

A. *Additive and dominance components of variation in the second experiment. The figures given are averages over the two diallels*

	d_{a-d}	d_p	d_q	d_r	h_{a+d}	h_p	h_q	h_r	s.e.
Females .	−0·95	0·02	−2·23†	0·66	2·32†	−0·12	0·61	0·16	⎫ 0·84
Males .	0·23	0·72	−0·04	−0·74	1·32	0·31	0·28	−1·37	⎭

† 0·01<P<0·05.

B. *Comparison of components from first and second experiments*

	d_{a-d}	h_{a+d}	d_b+d_c*	h_b+h_c
Females				
1st experiment .	−2·78	4·29	−1·55	2·10
2nd experiment .	0·95	2·32	1·55	0·65
Males				
1st experiment .	0·37	2·10	−0·52	1·09
2nd experiment .	0·23	1·32	−0·06	−0·78

* Regions B+C in first experiment = P+Q+R in second experiment.

Results are presented separately for males and females in both tables. The analyses of variance for the males reveal no item significant against the theoretical error variance except that for reciprocal differences in the first diallel. This could easily be due to the vagaries of sampling, and indeed if we take all four " reciprocals " mean squares together there is little to suggest anything beyond sampling variation. The main effects for components are significant in females in both diallels. In this they differ from the males just as in the first experiment. No good evidence of residual interaction appears from either set of crosses.

Again in conformity with the first experiment, the only significant constants in table 6A are from the females, though the high standard errors (denoted s.e. in the table) render their individual values rather uninformative. The components are compared for the two experiments in table 6B, where the summed actions of regions B and C are set against those of P, Q and R to which they correspond when taken together.

TABLE 7

Analysis of variance of third experiment. The entries in the main body of the table are mean squares

Item	N	Females	Males
Components (C) . .	6	85·2*	13·2
Res. interactions (I) . .	14	15·2	37·6*
Diallels (D) . . .	1	26·6	90·0*
D × C . . .	6	49·3*	25·8
D × I . . .	14	14·3	18·4
Reciprocals . . .	29	11·9	19·1
Theoretical error . .	...	16·2	15·8

* P < 0·01.

Again agreement is as good as could be expected in view of the large standard errors attaching to all entries in the table.

(ii) The third experiment consisted of two diallels, one including chromosomes (1) and (13)-(17) and the other chromosomes (2) and (18)-(20) of table 1. Both of them provide information about the effects of regions X-x, Y-y and Z-z into which regions P-p and Q-q have been jointly broken down (see fig. 1). The two diallels differ, however, in the ways they incorporate the effects of regions A-a, D-d and R-r, so that their overall contrast with one another cannot be interpreted unambiguously. Two combinations (one for each sex) which failed to yield results in this experiment have been given the value of their reciprocals. The numbers of degrees of freedom (N) have been correspondingly adjusted. Four other cultures also failed but were replaced by corresponding cultures raised on a later occasion. The analysis of variance and values of the components are shown for the sexes separately in tables 7 and 8.

The analysis of variance shows the contributions of the three regions, X, Y and Z, to be significant in females and their effects would appear to vary between the two diallels. There is no significant evidence of interaction in this sex. Curiously enough, however, the item for interaction is significant in the males as is also that for the difference between the diallels. The interpretation of especially the former item is not, however, obvious in the absence of any significant effect of components.

No single component is significant in table 8A. This is not surprising in view of the large standard error attaching to the estimates and in view of the restricted range of the segments under examination as compared with those of the first experiment. Nevertheless, so far as they go, the components of variation set out in table 6A agree with

TABLE 8

A. *Additive and dominance components of variation in the third experiment.*
The figures given are averages over the two diallels

	d_x	d_y	d_z	h_x	h_y	h_z	s.e.
Females .	−2·34	−1·56	−1·04	1·15	1·99	0·77	⎱ 1·56
Males .	0·41	0·06	0·58	−0·05	1·50	−1·15	⎰

B. *Comparison of components from second and third experiments*

	d_{p+q}	h_{p+q}	d_{x+y+z}	h_{x+y+z}
Females . .	−2·21	0·49	−4·94	3·91
Males . . .	0·68	0·59	−0·11	−0·15

Regions P+Q in 2nd experiment = X+Y+Z in 3rd experiment.

expectation. The female components are in general larger and more consistent that the male. Thus all the female d components are negative and all the h's positive. Furthermore the results from this third experiment agree as well as might be expected with those from the second experiment (table 8B).

(iii) The fourth experiment was of a different kind from the second and third. Eight homozygotes were raised and compared, the eight comprising every combination of the compound regions A-a, PQ-pq and RD-rd. The experiment was carried out in quadruplicate but a few cultures failed in some replicates, none, however, failing in all replicates. This is reflected in the degrees of freedom for variation between like cultures being fewer than the basis design of the experiment would lead one to expect. Since all genic combinations were homozygous in this experiment, no h components are involved—only d components and interactions between these additive components. The four replicates or groups were carried out at the same time and were randomised together. There is thus no point in taking out an item for gross group or " block " effects. The groups differed in carrying similar but not identical recombinant chromosomes so that the variation of components and interactions over groups (item " replicates $\times$ (C+I) ") is of prospective interest.

The results are set out in tables 9 and 10. The most striking feature of table 9 is that, for the first time in these experiments, the effects of

TABLE 9

Analysis of variance of the fourth experiment. The entries in the body of the table are mean squares

Item	N	Females	Males
Components (C) . .	3	63·2†	96·0*
Res. interactions (I) .	4	9·8	26·5
Replicates $\times$ (C+I) . .	6	90·8*	55·8*
Between cultures of like genotype	14	35·6†	11·7
Theoretical error . .	...	19·9	18·9

* $P < 0.01$. † $0.01 < P < 0.05$.

the segments are as significant in males as in females. There is no clear evidence of interaction from either sex, but the components vary from group to group in both. The empirical error variance, measured by variation between replicates of the genotypes, is significantly higher than the theoretical error in the females but not in males. The individual components of variation set out in table 10 are uninformative,

TABLE 10

Additive components of variation in the fourth experiment. The figures given are averages over the four replicates

	d_a	d_{p+q}	d_{r+d}	s.e.
Females . .	−1·16	0·37	−0·06	1·68
Males . . .	−0·98	−0·33	−1·09	1·32
Mean . .	−1·07	0·02	−0·57	1·49

except for their being of much the same size in both sexes, thus confirming the analysis of variance of table 9.

In setting these results into relation with those of the earlier experiments we must bear in mind that earlier the comparisons were chiefly among at least partly heterozygous combinations whereas this time they are among homozygotes. It may be therefore that the sex difference is mainly to be found in the behaviour of heterozygotes, variation among homozygotes showing up in one sex as much as the other. Comparisons among the viabilities of the homozygous males of the first experiment, however, reveals no expression of the differences which

295

are detectable between their sisters, and so lends no support to this possibility. It is possible, too, that the contrast with earlier experiments springs in part from variation, newly arisen by mutation during the time the chromosomes were stored between their construction and their use in this last experiment. That mutation had occurred is testified by the appearance of lethal homozygotes in this last experiment though obviously no lethals could have been present when the recombinant chromosomes were first made up. Whatever the cause of the contrast, the different structure of the experiment or mutation, it is clear that this last experiment adds little to our earlier evidence, especially to that from the first experiment.

5. THE GENETICAL ARCHITECTURE OF VIABILITY

Our information about the genetical architecture of viability must come chiefly from the first experiment: failure of cultures, differences in design and the narrower range of genetic differences followed, combine to make the second, third and fourth experiments less informative. So far as they go, however, they agree with the first one in the results they give except that none of them reveals genic interaction in an unambiguous way and the fourth shows differences in viabilities among males where no such differences appeared from any other experiment. The failure of interaction to appear clearly in the later experiments should not be regarded too seriously. There is a hint of its occurrence in the second experiment, where the mean squares depending on it exceed error in the females of both diallels (table 5). The third experiment is concerned with genetic differences confined to a very narrow region of the chromosome, and the fourth experiment again gives a hint of interaction among the males which here are revealing the effects of genic differences even more strongly than the females. The appearance of differences in viability among the males of the fourth experiment is a more positive disagreement with the earlier results. The reason for this occurrence is, however, obscure and it need not prevent us from discussing the genetical properties of the differences among the females upon which the first experiment throws most light.

Perhaps the most striking result of the experiment is this difference in the extent to which the sexes reveal the effects of genes mediating viability. This would be worthy of further study as a problem in its own right. It is not, however, our chief concern at present. Rather we wish to consider the genetical causation and structure of the character as we have found it. The first experiment (table 4) gives evidence of genetical activity of every segment of chromosome III, except segment C-c, in determining the viability of females. Furthermore segment D-d would appear to be acting in the opposite direction to its fellows in the sense that higher viability is associated with D, derived from the H chromosome, whereas with the other segments it is associated with a, b and c from the L chromosome. Dominance is clear and, it would appear, complete. Also it is unidirectional towards high viability. Interaction occurs between the genes of different segments and the diallel analysis points to it being of a kind analogous to the " duplicate genes " of classical genetics with the dominant high viability genes of one segment tending to suppress, or at least reduce, the effects of low viability genes in the other segments.

One further point is made clear by this first experiment. The flies vary in the length of chromosome for which they are heterozygous. Some are homozygous for all of the four segments. Others are heterozygous for one segment, still others for two, three and even all four segments. The average viabilities of the different type of female are plotted against the number of segments for which they are heterozygous in fig. 4, the figures being obtained from the O1 and O2 diallels of the first experiment, in which the sexes were recorded separately. There is a tendency for viability to show a general rise as the number of heterozygous segments increases from one to three. But the flies heterozygous for all segments by no means show the greatest viability, nor do all the homozygous combinations show viabilities poorer than those of the majority of heterozygotes. In other words viability cannot be simply related to heterozygosity: gene content is the important consideration and not heterozygosity *per se.*

Now the genetical architecture of viability stands in sharp contrast to that of chaeta number as revealed by these same flies (Breese and Mather, 1957). Dominance was detectable in respect of chaeta number, but it was not so strong as with viability. Also it was ambidirectional and not unidirectional as with viability. There was evidence of interaction between the genes of different segments affecting chaeta number but again it was quite trivial in its effects as compared with the interaction of the genes affecting viability (fig. 2). The contrast of the additive or d, effects of the segments on chaeta number and viability is less instructive, since the uniformly greater chaeta producing activity of the H segments as compared with the L is to be attributed to the artificial selection applied for this character especially to the ancestors of the H line. We may note, however, that the relative magnitude of effect of the four segments are not the same for the two characters (fig. 3). Also it is perhaps significant, in view of the correlated response of fertility to selection for chaeta number observed by earlier authors (*e.g.* Mather and Harrison, 1949) that the segments from the L line gives higher viability in more cases than do segments from the H line which is descended from ancestors more heavily selected for chaeta number.

This contrast between the genetical architectures of chaeta number and viability is of interest in two respects. In the first place it shows us that the effects on the two characters cannot be attributed to any simple pleiotropic action of the same set of genes. The relative magnitudes and directions of the additive effects of the segments differ for the two characters, as do their properties in dominance and inter-action.   To take the analysis further we have investigated the corre-lation between chaeta number and viability among the 28 genetic combinations in the females of diallels O1 and O2.   The linear regres-sion of viability (measured in angles) on abdominal chaeta number is −0·235 which has a probability of almost exactly 0·05.   It is thus of marginal significance.   It accounts for 14 per cent. of the overall variation in viability; and if we use differences between the reciprocals

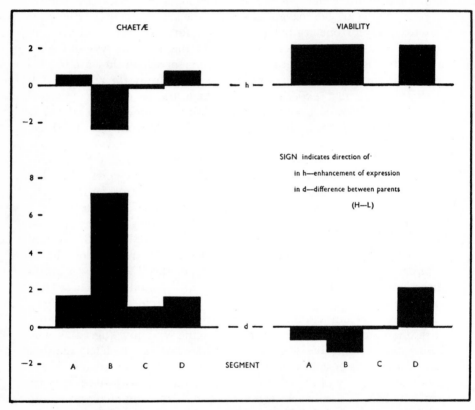

Fig. 3.—The contributions made by the four segments A-D (see fig. 1) to the additive (d) and dominance (h) variation in abdominal chaeta number and viability.   All data are from the first experiment, those for chaetae being from the combined sexes in the whole experiment and those for viability from females in O1 and O2 only.   The units of measurement are chaetae in the one case and angularly transformed percentage viabilities in the other.

of the crosses from which the 21 heterozygous combinations are derived as a measure of non-heritable variation, so arriving at an estimate of the heritable variation among the 28 genotypes we find that the correlation of chaeta number and viability still accounts for no more than 18·5 per cent. of the heritable variation in the latter. Thus even if we ascribe the whole of this relation between the characters to pleiotropic action of individual genes—an assumption which is by no means necessarily valid—we still have over $\frac{4}{5}$ of the heritable variability in viability to account for by reference to further genes. Evidently simple pleiotropy is of but little help to us in understanding the relations between the genetic control of characters such as chaeta number and viability.

This is not to say that the pleiotropic action of genes is never of significance in determining the relations between characters or their correlated reponses to selection. Where characters are related developmentally in a reasonably simple way we must expect pleiotropic

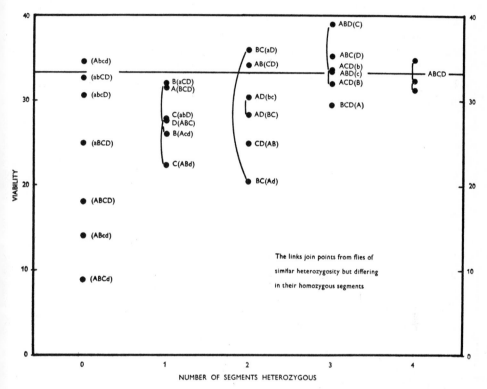

Fig. 4.—Viabilities of females in families from O1 and O2 of the first experiment plotted against the number of segments for which the flies were heterozygous. The segments for which the family was heterozygous are shown by unbracketed capital letters against each point and the homozygous segments by bracketed capital or small letters according to whether they came from H or L. All viabilities are in percentages, the horizontal line at 33⅓ per cent. marking the level at which the wild-type flies have a viability equal to their *Me Sb/H* sibs.

relations between them. Even in such cases, however, the pleiotropic tie may have far from simple consequences, as has been shown by Cocks (1954) in respect of the obviously relatable characters, abdominal and sternopleural chaeta numbers. When, therefore, we turn to such disparate characters as chaeta number and viability it is no surprise to find that pleiotropy of gene action is of little help in understanding their relations. Linkage of the members of the relevant polygenic systems is then the key to the determination of covariation within related groups and correlated responses to selection. Such linkage will ensure that chromosome segments, or effective factors to use the term of Mather (1949), will show pleiotropic action even where the individual genes do not; but it will be a stable pleiotropy only so long as the chromosome segment is unbroken by crossing-over, for recombination will result in a redistribution of the linked associations and hence in a reassociation of the characters themselves. This conclusion is not new. The significance of linkage as opposed to genic pleiotropy, and the distinction between the apparent and resolvable pleiotropy of a segment or effective factor, which springs from linkage, and the unresolvable basic pleiotropy of single genes, have often been discussed and emphasised (*e.g.* by Mather and Harrison, 1949). The subject is raised yet again only because the present results hammer home so firmly the distinction between genes and segment and the insufficiencies of genic pleiotropy as an explanation of the relations observable between characters in genetical experiments.

6. GENETICAL ARCHITECTURE AND NATURAL SELECTION

The second respect in which the contrast between chaeta number and viability is of interest lies in the relation it reveals between the genetical architecture of a character and the forces of natural selection to which that character has been subjected (Mather, 1960). Now chaeta number and viability must be acted on differently by natural selection. Chaeta number would appear to have a central optimum with both extremes at a disadvantage relative to the more central values.   In other words selection will be essentially stabilising. Viability on the other hand will obviously be subject more to directional selection, the advantage lying with the higher expression of the character.

It has been pointed out by Fisher (1930) that natural selection will tend to modify the phenotypic expression of heterozygotes towards closer resemblance to that of homozygotes carrying the more favourable allele. With unconditional advantage of one allele over another, such as would generally be the case where selection is essentially directional, this will mean unidirectional dominance as we have found with the viability genes. With stabilising selection, however, the more common allele will in the long run be the more favourable irrespective of the direction in which it pulls the character. Dominance should then tend to become ambidirectional (Fisher, *loc. cit.*) as is the case with the genes governing chaeta number. Thus the difference between the polygenic systems giving viability and chaeta number in respect of their properties of dominance is relatable to the difference in the impact of natural selection upon them.

The same difference might also be expected to arise in respect of non-allelic interaction. Directional selection would be expected to favour any interaction which tended to conceal the shortcomings in action of the individual genes, and this is achieved by a duplicate system of interaction where dominance and interaction pull together, as we find it in the case of viability. With stabilising selection towards a central optimum the advantage of a given type and direction of interaction would vary with the combination of genes, so that there would be a lower and less persistent pressure of selection towards interaction and even such as evolved would tend to be ambidirectional and self-cancelling. Interaction should thus be a less striking feature of the gene systems governing a character of this type, and indeed in the case of chaeta number they appear to be so.

Studies in *Drosophila pseudoobscura, persimilis* and *prosaltans* have shown that interaction is as much a feature of the genetical architecture of viability in these species as in *D. melanogaster* (Spiess, 1958). And indeed we should expect it to be so as natural selection must be directional in its impact on viability in one species as much as in another. Spiess goes on further to point out the relation of the occurrence of so-called synthetic lethals to genic interactions. Such recombinational lethals would be expected with a duplicate type of interaction of the kind we have found, though we may note that complementary inter-actions, where homozygosity for one recessive gene produces the effect irrespective of the constitution at other loci, would not give them. This complementary relation is characteristic of the classical point mutation lethals, which serves again to emphasise the distinction between lethality springing from mutational and balance effects. Both types of lethal have been found in chromosome II of *D. melano-gaster* (Misro, 1949), but surprisingly enough Hildreth (1956) has not been able to obtain evidence of synthetic or balance lethals in chromo-some III. Spiess seeks to relate this to a difference in the properties of interaction in the polygenic systems of the two chromosomes as they affect viability, citing our own evidence that interaction of the genes in chromosome III is of little significance in the control of chaeta number. Even leaving aside the problem then raised of why the properties in interaction should differ between the gene systems of the two chromo-somes, it is now clear that the difference in interaction is a feature not of the two chromosomes but of the two characters. Indeed certain of our observations positively suggest that such balance lethals do arise. In building up stocks for experiment 3 some 23 chromosomes were selected as showing recombination between st and p^b and 19 as showing recombination between p^b and cu. Two chromosomes for each set proved to be lethal when homozygous and, what is more, the lethals in the two $st-p^b$ recombinants appeared to be allelic as did the two in the p^b-cu recombinants. The suggestion of a link between recombina-tion and the appearance of lethals is clear. Our present data thus suggest that synthetic lethals are capable of production by recombina-tion in chromosome III. So Hildreth's results are still unexplained and it would indeed appear worthwhile to repeat his experiments with other examples of chromosome III to discover whether his findings were characteristic of this chromosome in general or merely specific to the sample of it that he happened to employ.

Differences in the genetical architecture of characters may be expected to show up when crosses are made between individuals from different populations, that is to say when combinations of genes are brought together which do not normally meet and which have therefore not been subjected to co-adaptation by the action of natural selection (Mather, 1943). With a relatively simple genetic system showing ambidirectional dominance such as is to be expected from the past action of stabilising selection and which has been found in the case of chaeta number, the relative unbalance of heterozygous genotypes resulting from crosses between individuals from different populations should show itself merely by increased average departure from the optimum. This departure is as likely to be towards lesser as towards greater manifestation of the character. In other words, inter-population hybrids should show a greater spread round their overall mean which itself need not depart from the mean of intra-population families. This spread must of course be measured as the variance of mean of families raised from inter-population crosses, since the variance within such families will chiefly reflect the degree of heterozygosity of the parents and so is largely irrelevant to the measurement of unbalance.

No data are available for chaeta number in crosses between wild populations of *D. melanogaster*, but the frequency of chiasma formation has been followed in such crosses of the campion plant *Lychnis dioica* by Dr C. W. Lawrence (see Mather, 1959). Chiasma frequency is a character with a central optimum and therefore subject to stabilising selection. Mr Lawrence has found an overall mean number of 14·07 chiasmata in the pollen mother cells of families raised from crosses within populations and an overall mean of 14·22 from crosses between populations. These two averages do not differ significantly. When, however, the variances were calculated among the family means, a figure of 3·6 was found for crosses between populations as against 1·15 for crosses within populations. This difference is in the expected direction and is significant. These figures differ a little from those quoted by Mather (1959) as a result of the addition of further material.

Observations are available on the viability of flies from inter-population crosses in a number of species of *Drosophila* (Vetukhiv, 1954, Wallace and Vetukhiv, 1955). The remarkable fact has emerged that viability is commonly higher in the F_1 of such crosses than in crosses made within populations, though in the F_2 it falls very much below the intra-population level. This result becomes much less surprising, however, when we consider the architecture of viability as we have found it. Dominance is unidirectional towards high viability, and in that it will be selected for in every population where the genes are segregating, we might expect it to be displayed as strongly or virtually as strongly in heterozygotes from crosses between populations as in those from crosses within. Interactions will be selected only among genes occurring together and we might therefore expect them to be a less marked feature of genotypes obtained by crosses between, as opposed to within, populations. No clear information is available on this point. The mere occurrence of unidirectional dominance will, however, ensure that if the viability is maintained at its normal level by different polygenic combinations in different populations, the F_1 hybrids will enjoy the advantage of the genes from both populations and this will display itself as an even higher manifestation of the character. On this view the inter-population F_1's should be heterozygous for more viability genes than individuals within populations, and indeed would owe their greater viability to this higher heterozygosity. That they are in fact more highly heterozygous is attested by the great fall of viability in F_2, where the wider segregation and the lower effect of interaction between genes from different populations in maintaining viability will be making themselves felt.

The problem therefore resolves itself into the question of why populations should differ in the genes which maintain viability at its normal level. We should expect the genes varying and segregating in any one population to be but a sample of the full range of member genes of the polygenic system affecting viability, the rest of the genes being homozygous in that population. We should expect, too, that the genes varying in one population, or to put it the other way, the genes homozygous in one population, not to be the same as those in the other, if only for reasons of sampling. But why should the homozygous genes sometimes be the recessives making for lower viability, which will frequently be covered in inter-population F_1's, rather than always the dominant genes making for higher viability? The effects of any recessive genes tending to lower viability will of course be mitigated by their interactions, but they cannot have been wholly removed or the population flies would not be of lower viability than the inter-population hybrids. We must suppose, therefore, that even though viability within populations is not the highest that can be achieved, it is nevertheless adequate. While it would seem obviously to be true that higher viability will always have an advantage, it might well be that above a certain level the selective advantage does not rise correspondingly with the increase in viability as measured in experiment. Viability might then be stabilised at a level below the maximum by the operation of other factors within the population. Random fixation, such as must tend to occur within polygenic systems, would tend to result in at least some of the less advantageous genes becoming fixed and if the selective disadvantage were not great it could fail fully to counteract this tendency. In any case one thing is certain: the higher viability of the inter-population hybrids could not itself be stabilised within a population, for we have seen that it breaks down in F_2 as a result of segregation and recombination. High viability in one generation is not itself sufficient: it must be maintainable over the generations. The behaviour of inter-population hybrids shows us that there can be a conflict between these requirements, for the genetic combination which gives the high expression of the character contains within its wide heterozygosity the seeds of its own breakdown. We must not be surprised, therefore, if we find the expression of a directionally selected character within a population to be not the maximum achievable but the maximum maintainable, and these are by no means necessarily the same thing.

7. SUMMARY

In the experiments described by Breese and Mather (1957) for investigating the distribution along chromosome III of polygenic activity affecting chaeta number, the wild-type flies whose chaeta were counted were obtained as parts of segregating families all of which contained $\frac{Me\ Sb}{H}$ flies. The proportion of wild-type flies relative to this constant marked class provides, therefore, a measure of the effect on viability of the various recombinant chromosomes that the wild-type flies carry.

In all but one of the experiments the females alone showed clear effects of the various recombinant chromosomes III on viability, the males showing little if any variation. For various technical reasons only the first of the experiments provides useful information about the genetical architecture of viability; and this shows dominance to be marked and unidirectional towards high viability. Non-allelic interactions of a kind relatable to the classical " duplicate gene " type are present and strong. Viability is not directly relatable to degree of heterozygosity.

The genetical architecture of viability is markedly different from that of chaeta number as revealed by the same flies in the same experiments. The simultaneous effects of the chromosomes on the two characters cannot be ascribed, except perhaps to a very small extent, to simple pleiotropy in action of the individual genes. Rather the pleiotropic effects of the chromosome segments are due to linkage within them of different polygenic systems affecting the two characters.

The differences in genetical architecture of the two characters are relatable to the different impacts of natural selection on them, selection for chaeta number being stabilising towards a central optimum and that for viability being directional towards an extreme value. The different expressions in inter-population crosses of characters showing the different architectures are reviewed and the occurrence in such F_1 hybrids of viabilities exceeding the levels found within populations is discussed. Viability within populations must be related to the maximum level maintainable which is by no means necessarily the maximum level achievable in any one generation.

8. REFERENCES

BREESE, E. L., AND MATHER, K. 1957. The organisation of polygenic activity within a chromosome in *Drosophila* I. Hair characters. *Heredity, 11,* 373-395.

COCKS, B. 1954. Polygenic systems controlling the expression of major mutant genes which affect chaeta number in *Drosophila melanogaster. Heredity, 8,* 13-34.

FISHER, R. A. 1930. *The Genetical Theory of Natural Selection.* Clarendon Press, Oxford.

FISHER, R. A., AND YATES, F. 1957. *Statistical Tables for Biological, Agricultural and Medical Research.* 5th ed. Oliver and Boyd, Edinburgh.

HAYMAN, B. I. 1954. The theory and analysis of diallel crosses. *Genetics, 39,* 789-809.

HILDRETH, P. E. 1956. The problem of synthetic lethals in *D. melanogaster. Genetics, 41,* 729-742.

JINKS, J. L. 1954. The analysis of continuous variation in a diallel cross of *Nicotiana, rustica* varieties. *Genetics, 39,* 767-788.

MATHER, K. 1943. Polygenic inheritance and natural selection. *Biol. Revs., 18,* 32-64.

MATHER, K. 1949. *Biometrical Genetics.* Methuen, London.

MATHER, K. 1960. Evolution of polygenic systems (in the press).

MATHER, K., AND HARRISON, B. J. 1949. The manifold effect of selection. *Heredity 3,* 1-52 and 131-162.

MISRO, B. 1949. Crossing-over as a source of new variation. *Proc. 8th Int. Congr. Genetics. Hereditas Suppl. Vol.,* pp. 629-630.

SPIESS, E. B. 1958. Effects of recombination on viability in *Drosophila. Cold Spr. Harb. Symp. Quant. Biol., 23,* 239-250.

VETUKHIV, M. 1954. Integration of the genotype in local populations of three species of *Drosophila. Evolution, 8,* 241-251.

WALLACE, B., AND VETUKHIV, M. 1955. Adaptive organisation of the gene pools of *Drosophila* populations. *Cold Spr. Harb. Symp. Quant. Biol., 20,* 303-309.

RELATIVE FITNESS OF GENETICALLY OPEN AND CLOSED EXPERIMENTAL POPULATIONS OF DROSOPHILA ROBUSTA

HAMPTON L. CARSON

Department of Zoology, Washington University, St. Louis, Missouri

Received December 16, 1960

W HEN a genetically variable gene pool faces a new environmental challenge, microevolutionary change may be expected to occur. To understand this change, it would be ideal to know the details of the structure and integration of the gene pool both before and after the change. Although such conditions can hardly be met in any study of natural populations, an approach, at least, can be made in laboratory experiments.

In a number of species of Drosophila, genetic control is now such that the artificial construction of various kinds of gene pools presents no particular difficulty. The classical methods for the experimental study of gene pools in the laboratory (L'HÉRITIER, NEEFS and TEISSIER 1937; WRIGHT and DOBZHANSKY 1946; REED and REED 1948; BUZZATI-TRAVERSO 1955) provide an opportunity for the application of stringent natural selection and afford some control of population size. These experimental designs, however, provide no means for comparing the over-all biological performance of one gene pool with another when both are maintained under similar environmental conditions. By providing exact amounts of food and space and exact change intervals to various genetically different experimental populations of D. melanogaster, CARSON (1958c; 1961), BERT (1960) and SMATHERS (1961) developed methods for making weekly population size measurements under the arbitrarily imposed conditions. CARSON (1961) has proposed that population size, measured for comparable gene pools under these conditions, may be used as a measure of the performance of the population, or, in short, its relative population fitness. The gene pool which maintains the larger size is judged the relatively more fit.

The present paper concerns itself with the extension of this method to laboratory populations of *Drosophila robusta*. This species is a common native faunal element of the deciduous forest of the eastern United States, having a large number of different gene arrangements which generally show clinal distributions and a strong tendency towards marginal homozygosity (CARSON 1955, 1958a, 1959).

Data are presented in this paper on laboratory populations derived from various geographic sources, both marginal and central. Some of the populations studied are genetically "closed" throughout the course of the experiment. Others have been kept genetically "open" by maintaining a continual inflow of genes; still others have been subjected to mass hybridization. The performance of these various populations and their controls has been compared, and the fate of chromosome polymorphism carried by them has been followed.

Reprinted by permission of Genetics, Inc. from GENETICS, 46, 553–567 (1961).

MATERIAL AND METHODS

Samples of *Drosophila robusta* were obtained from natural populations according to the usual methods of fruit baiting. This procedure is now known to provide a truly representative sample of the adult wild feeding population of this species (see CARSON 1958b, p. 28). Immediately upon collection of the wild samples from the natural population, males and females were separated and each female placed individually or with a single wild male into a separate culture vial. Salivary gland smears were made from her offspring using acetolactoorcein. In some cases wild females can be shown to have previously mated to two or possibly more different wild males in nature. One has no assurance, therefore, that a culture established from a single wild-caught female is descended from a single pair of wild flies. A newly caught female, however, may be rendered free of sperm from wild males by placing her individually in a culture tube and changing to a fresh vial often (every one or two days) until the eggs laid by the female no longer hatch. The female concerned may then be mated to a single wild male caught at the same time and place. This procedure has been used in those cases where it is desirable to know the precise number of wild homologs entering into a laboratory strain by way of the founders (see also CARSON 1958a).

A method for establishing and maintaining an experimental population in vials has been described in detail by CARSON (1961). With only minor modifications, this method was employed in the present work. Basically, the adult flies are maintained in a chamber made of an ordinary 25 × 95 mm shell vial to which is taped a cellulose acetate tube of the same size ("supervial"). The latter contains a platform of blotting paper and is plugged with cotton at the free end. The shell vial, which contains the food, is replaced at exact intervals by opening the chamber, holding the adult flies in the supervial, removing the old vial and taping a new one in position. In most of the populations to be reported on in this paper, four changes a week were made. Each food vial contained 9.5 cc of a specially prepared uniform corn meal-Karo-agar medium, to which has been added ten mg of dry Fleishmann's yeast moistened with one drop of distilled water.

Each time the population chamber was opened, flies which had emerged in vials which were previously in contact with the population were added to the adult population. Under these conditions, the size of the population eventually comes to equilibrium with the space and food available. In the experiments to be described, the handling schedule varied in minor ways from one set of experiments to the next; the details of the procedure used will be given in each particular case. Under these conditions, the average time from egg to adult is greatly attenuated and averages about 32 days. Allowing approximately ten days for attainment of sexual maturity, the generation time may be estimated at six weeks. All weighings of flies were made on a Roller-Smith microtorsion balance which had a capacity of 500 mg.

THE EXPERIMENTS

Laboratory populations having marginal or central geographical origins

Population size and production of the Steelville and Chadron populations: In the experiments reported on in this section, two strains of *D. robusta* have been used, each of which was ultimately derived from a single pair of wild flies collected at Steelville, Missouri, (Sv), a central location in the range of the species, and Chadron, Nebraska, (C) which is geographically and ecologically marginal. These strains were maintained as two of the controls used in the experiments described in CARSON 1958a and were there designated as Sv-135 and C-66 respectively. In January, 1957, four experimental populations were established, two from Sv-135, hereafter referred to as S-1 and S-2 and two from C-66, referred to as C-1 and C-2.

The gene arrangement frequencies present in both of these strains were determined at the time of establishment of the laboratory strains from the F_1 produced by the pair of wild founders and at intervals thereafter (Tables 1 and 2). It will be noted on Table 1 that at the time that S-1 and S-2 were established (early in 1957) gene arrangement 2L-2 had already been lost, leaving 2L and 2L-3 as the two alternative arrangements in the left arm of chromosome 2. The X chromosome is homozygous for gene arrangement; the alternative gene arrangements present in the right arm of the second chromosome are 2R-1 and, in the right arm

TABLE 1

Gene arrangement frequencies (in percent) in the control laboratory populations (S-1; S-2) originally derived from a single pair of wild flies (Sv-135) captured at Steelville, Missouri

Gene arrangement	Aug. 1955 (F_1 from Sv-135)	Dec. 1955	Feb. 1956 (from culture)	July 1956	Jan. 1957 (S-1)	Feb. 1957 (S-2)	Aug. 1957 (S-2)	Nov. 1957 (S-2)	Aug. 1958 (S-2)
XL:XR-1	100.0	100.0	100.0	100.0	100.0	100.0	100.0	100.0	100.0
2L	35.0	55.0	70.0	65.0	62.2	80.0	67.3	80.0	70.3
2L-2	25.0	10.0	. . .	. . .	. . .	. . .	. . .	. . .	. . .
2L-3	40.0	40.0	30.0	35.0	37.8	20.0	33.7	20.0	29.7
2R (2R-1)	75.0	85.0	55.0	45.0	87.9	80.0	50.0	46.7	57.4
3R (3R-1)	45.0	50.0	55.0	65.0	36.5	55.0	30.8	16.7	8.1
Number of chromosomes examined	20	20	20	20	74*	20	52	30	148

* 57 X chromosomes.

TABLE 2

Gene arrangement frequencies (in percent) in the control laboratory populations (C-1; C-2) originally derived from a single pair of wild flies (C-66) captured at Chadron, Nebraska

Gene arrangement	Aug. 1955 F_1 from pair C-66	Jan. 1957 (from culture)	Dec. 1957 (C-2)	Aug. 1958 (C-2)
XL-1:XR	100.0	100.0	100.0	100.0
2L-3:2R	100.0	100.0	100.0	100.0
3R	100.0	100.0	100.0	100.0
N^x	20	19	42	77
N^a	20	20	42	78

N^x=Number of X chromosomes examined.
N^a=Number of autosomes examined.

of the third chromosome, 3R-1. The founder strain and populations C-1 and C-2 have been homozygous for gene arrangement since their inception (Table 2).

Each population was founded from 50 females and 50 males taken at random from the stocks. The change and yeast cycle was precisely as described in CARSON 1961 for *Drosophila melanogaster*. After approximately 12 weeks the populations showed signs of reaching a maximum size and weekly measurements of the size of the adult population (number and weight of individuals present) were begun (see Week 1, Table 3). The figures in Table 3 represent the average of two measurements each week. The starting size (including new additions made on that day) is added to the finishing size seven days later and the sum divided by two (see CARSON 1961). These measurements were carried out for 20 consecutive weeks, during which time each population was handled in identical fashion. The data show that the mean number and weight are higher in S-1 and S-2 than in C-1 and C-2. In only one instance, however, is the difference between two of these means significant at the five percent level. Thus the mean number of flies

TABLE 3

Population size of four experimental populations of Drosophila robusta. *Chadron-1 and -2 (C-1, C-2) are replicates which are homozygous for gene arrangement; Steelville-1 and -2 (S-1, S-2) are replicates which carry a number of inversions*

Week number	Chadron-1 (C-1)			Chadron-2 (C-2)			Steelville-1 (S-1)			Steelville-2 (S-2)		
	No.	Wt. mg	Avg. fly size mg	No.	Wt. mg	Avg. fly size mg	No.	Wt. mg	Avg. fly size mg	No.	Wt. mg	Avg. fly size mg
1	273	498	1.82	261	477	1.83	298	484	1.63	263	462	1.76
2	293	528	1.80	365	609	1.67	305	491	1.61	383	609	1.59
3	354	620	1.75	424	678	1.60	345	558	1.62	446	694	1.56
4	385	651	1.69	469	750	1.60	388	626	1.62	490	766	1.57
5	383	659	1.72	456	711	1.56	405	659	1.63	441	674	1.53
6	367	643	1.75	346	563*	1.63	422	680	1.61	336	528*	1.57
7	365	646	1.77	230	388*	1.69	415	667	1.61	239	400*	1.67
8	369	645	1.75	283	460	1.63	372	613	1.65	322	532	1.65
9	303	529*	1.75	305	489	1.61	305	524*	1.72	345	544	1.58
10	231	413*	1.79	302	498	1.65	235	405*	1.72	320	520	1.63
11	230	392	1.74	284	482	1.70	253	403	1.59	326	536	1.64
12	256	443	1.73	266	456	1.71	253	425	1.68	360	578	1.61
13	340	541	1.59	274	456	1.66	354	544	1.54	367	583	1.59
14	296	452	1.53	330	506	1.53	352	510	1.45	377	594	1.58
15	250	416	1.66	408	585	1.43	332	510	1.54	398	596	1.50
16	336	466	1.39	411	589	1.44	380	598	1.57	394	548	1.39
17	335	517	1.54	337	497	1.48	406	626	1.54	340	465	1.36
18	364	559	1.54	280	419	1.49	386	585	1.52	314	437	1.39
19	322	481	1.50	307	456	1.45	346	534	1.51	291	434	1.49
20	272	411	1.51	326	501	1.54	263	417	1.59	289	472	1.63
Mean weekly number	316.2±11.4			333.2±15.3			340.8±13.1			352.1±14.0		
Mean weekly weight	525.5±20.6			528.5±21.8			542.5±19.8			548.6±20.8		

* Population arbitrarily reduced at one point during the week to exactly 400 mg.

in C-1 differs from S-2, giving a t value of 1.98 with 38 degrees of freedom. The means and their standard errors, however, are affected by the following events. At one point in its 20-week history, each population was reduced artificially to exactly 400 mg wet weight for two consecutive weeks, after which it was again allowed to seek its maximum under natural selection. Furthermore, all populations show a progressive decline in size over the 20-week period, a fact which affects the usefulness of the mean value.

The total number and weight of flies hatched each week ("production") from each of the four populations is given on Table 4. Again, populations S-1 and S-2 outperform C-1 and C-2. The means for weight produced by C-1 and C-2 are very close, a fact which correlates with their closeness in population size. The higher of these two, C-1, differs from the lower Steelville population, S-1, (t = 2.73; P is less than .01). It is noteworthy also that S-2 is higher than S-1 (t = 3.76; P is less than .001). Differences in number of flies produced are not

TABLE 4

Weekly production of four experimental populations of Drosophila robusta. *Chadron-1 and -2 (C-1, C-2) are replicates which are homozygous for gene arrangement; Steelville-1 and -2 (S-1, S-2) are replicates which carry a number of inversions*

Week number	C-1 No.	C-1 Wt. mg	C-2 No.	C-2 Wt. mg	S-1 No.	S-1 Wt. mg	S-2 No.	S-2 Wt. mg
1	94	151	125	187	106	165	154	232
2	80	128	121	173	100	164	169	256
3	77	127	101	153	104	168	115	188
4	83	137	70	111	96	163	81	136
5	77	139	60	101	105	160	95	157
6	83	135	116	171	115	187	108	186
7	80	127	85	128	46	110	117	205
8	51	90	67	112	53	90	133	220
9	55	105	69	120	55	93	122	216
10	59	99	60	103	92	143	123	211
11	79	133	27	47	83	146	130	211
12	104	174	51	81	113	184	92	164
13	86	129	95	107	109	174	134	224
14	81	137	164	223	115	185	191	301
15	105	165	122	179	151	232	162	238
16	92	145	80	123	131	204	102	157
17	131	201	82	132	120	215	130	218
18	123	172	113	166	138	204	126	206
19	116	158	83	137	121	174	123	212
20	94	131	111	188	114	179	105	191
Total number	1750		1802		2067		2152	
Mean weekly number	87.5±4.8		90.1±7.2		103.4±19.3		107.6±16.1	
Total weight	2783		2743		3340		4129	
Mean weekly weight	139.2±5.9		137.2±9.5		167.0±8.3		206.5±8.3	

statistically significant at the five percent level of probability. It therefore appears that the Steelville populations, especially replicate S-2, are both larger and more productive than the Chadron populations.

Mass hybridization of a Steelville and a Chadron population: In August, 1957, the adult populations of C-1 and S-1 were discarded and two new hybrid adult populations built up by combining hatching flies from C-1 equally with hatching flies from S-1 continually over a period of about six weeks. These new populations were designated C1S1-A and C1S1-B. C-2 and S-2 were retained as controls.

The production of these populations was measured for 55 consecutive weeks following the completion of hybridization (Table 5). Various population conditions were maintained throughout this period but each of the four populations was treated in identical fashion. For the first 13 weeks, the size of the adult populations was allowed to be determined strictly by natural selection, as in the experiments prior to hybridization (except for one two-week trial period of artificial reduction to 400 mg). During weeks 14–27, however, a ceiling of 425 mg was artificially imposed on the size of each of the four populations. This was accomplished by adding hatching flies to the population twice a week as usual, but adding each time only enough young flies to bring the total weight of the adult population to exactly 425 mg. It was soon found, however, that this level was rather high and that several populations (e.g. C-2 and C1S1-A) usually remained below it. Accordingly, from week 28–55, all populations were artificially held to 300 mg. Under this system, at only one point during the final 20-week period did any population fall naturally below 300 mg during an entire week. This population, C-2, during week 48, fell to a low point of 274 mg even after all additions were made. During all other weeks in all populations, discards were necessary to keep the populations down to 300 mg.

TABLE 5

Production (in mg wet weight/week) of populations of Drosophila robusta *before and after mass hybridization of two populations. After the first 20 weeks, C-1 and S-1 were halved and recombined to make populations C1S1-A and C1S1-B*

Population number	Before hybridization		After hybridization			
	Period 1 Feb. to July 1957 (free population size)		Period 2 Aug. 1957 to Apr. 1958 (various population sizes)		Period 3 Apr. 1958 to Sept. 1958 (pop. size held to 300 mg.)	
	Total weight produced (mg)	Mean weekly weight (mg)	Total weight produced (mg)	Mean weekly weight (mg)	Total weight produced (mg)	Mean weekly weight (mg)
C-1	2783	139.2±5.9	....	....	....	....
C-2	2743	137.2±9.5	4000	114.2± 8.9	2112	105.6±15.3
S-1	3340	163.8±8.7	....	....	....	....
S-2	4129	206.5±8.3	6137	175.3±10.7	3930	196.5± 8.6
C1S1-A	....	....	5361	153.2± 9.9	3249	162.5± 7.9
C1S1-B	....	....	5373	153.5± 9.9	3491	174.6± 7.4
Number of weeks at equilibrium	20		35		20	

Table 5 gives the mean production of the four populations after hybridization; the first two columns in the body of the table repeat the means from Table 4 for comparison. It will be noted that during both periods 2 and 3 (after hybridization), C-2 is the lowest and S-2 is the highest. The hybrid populations are intermediate in value and in one instance, C1S1-A is significantly lower than S-2 at the five percent level or below (S-2 *vs.* C1S1-A, Period 3: t = 2.912, P is less than .01).

When populations C-1 and S-1 were combined to form the new hybrid populations C1S1-A and C1S1-B, the question arises whether the gene arrangements introduced from the two sources become balanced or whether one set will replace the other. The results of two tests for the presence of chromosome arrangements in each of these populations one year after the hybridization (approximately nine generations) are given in Table 6. From these data it will be noted that whereas the parental populations are homozygous for different gene arrangements on both arms of the X chromosome (Tables 1 and 2), the hybrid populations display a condition in which X chromosome gene arrangements from both geographical sources have remained in substantial frequency. XL and XR-1 from Steelville are close to 66 percent in each population; this reflects, apparently, a strong tendency for these two right and left arm arrangements to remain associated. Conversely, arrangements XL-1:XR from the Chadron population are similarly associated. Heterozygosity in 2L, 2R and 3R is maintained despite the admixture of homozygous Chadron flies. It is not possible to tell if any intergeographic heterozygotes for these autosomes are maintained in the populations in a manner comparable to that found in the X chromosome.

The facts brought out by the above experiments may be summarized in the following statement. Steelville populations from the center of the range of the species, and carrying a number of inversions, significantly outproduce structurally homozygous Chadron populations from the margin of the range. The sizes of the Steelville populations, furthermore, are likewise somewhat greater. Populations formed by mass hybridization of two of the replicates show a performance

TABLE 6

Gene arrangement frequencies (in percent) in two experimental laboratory populations (C1S1-A; C1S1-B) one year after they were formed by mass hybridization of Chadron population C-1 and Steelville population S-1

Gene arrangement	C1S1-A Aug. 1958	C1S1-B Aug. 1958
XL	68.1	67.3
XL-1	31.9	32.7
XR	34.8	35.5
XR-1	65.2	64.5
2L	26.2	45.2
2R	75.4	69.2
3R	55.0	52.8
N	104	69

close to that of the Steelville control population and in no case surpass it, whereas the Chadron control population continues to be the lowest. Despite their failure to exceed the performance of the Steelville populations, however, the hybrid populations have considerably more chromosomal polymorphism than the Steelville control because in these populations both left and right arms of the X chromosome carry intergeographical polymorphism.

Performance in "open" and "closed" populations

In August, 1956, a large sample of *Drosophila robusta* was obtained from Plainwell, Michigan (CARSON 1958b). Gene arrangement frequencies were obtained by studying the chromosomes of larvae which were F_1's from the wild individuals. The results of this study are shown in the first column in the body of Table 7. Individual pairs nos. 1 through 18 were chosen and an experimental population (PW) started using all 36 adults and their F_1's. This population came to equilibrium and was handled in an identical manner to the populations in the previous experiment (S-1, S-2, C-1 and C-2). Size and production measurements made over a 20-week period in early 1957 are given in Table 8. It will be noted that this performance is very similar to the performance of the Steelville populations previously described (Tables 3 and 4). During this time all polymorphism present at the beginning of the experiment was retained except for 3R-1 and 3L-R which were apparently eliminated (Table 7, 3rd column).

In July of 1957, PW was divided into two populations (PW-A and PW-B) and each replicate was allowed to come to equilibrium. Beginning immediately at the time that the split was made, and continuing thereafter for 31 consecutive

TABLE 7

Gene arrangement frequencies (in percent) in samples from a natural population of D. robusta from Plainwell, Michigan (PW) and in open (PW-A received 82 wild males over a 31-week period) and closed (PW-B) laboratory populations derived from it

Gene arrangement	F_1 from wild population		Experimental laboratory populations				
	Total sample Aug. 1956	Pairs 1–18 Aug. 1956	(closed) PW Mar. 1957	(open) PW-A Aug. 1957	(closed) PW-B Aug. 1957	(open) PW-A Dec. 1957	(closed) PW-B Dec. 1957
XL	44.9	38.9	52.6	72.5	50.0	56.1	45.9
XL-1	55.1	61.1	47.4	27.5	50.0	43.9	54.1
XR	21.2	19.4	49.6	51.7	64.7	31.8	26.2
XR-1	76.3	75.0	50.4	48.3	35.3	68.2	73.8
2L	57.6	52.8	45.6	20.7	11.4	29.8	5.2
2L-1	5.9	5.5	30.9	47.9	63.6	41.7	57.1
2L-2	8.5	16.7	8.1	17.1	13.6	10.7	29.9
2L-3	28.0	25.0	15.4	14.3	11.4	17.8	7.8
2R	89.8	80.6	94.0	87.1	86.3	85.7	89.8
3R	94.1	91.7	100.0	95.0	100.0	86.9	100.0
3R-1	4.2	5.5	...	5.0	...	13.1	...
3L-R	1.7	2.8	...	...	...	...	...
N^x	118	36	133	120	34	66	61
N^a	118	36	136	140	44	84	77

TABLE 8

Population size and production of experimental populations derived from Plainwell, Michigan.
PW and PW-B are closed populations, whereas PW-A received 82 wild
males over a 31-week period

Population designation	Period	Population size mg wet wt./week	Production Total	mg wet wt./week
PW	20 weeks Feb.-July 1957	548.0±16.5	2989	149.6±12.0
PW-A (open)	26 weeks Aug. 1957-Feb. 1958	472.6±17.6	3899	150.0±11.2
PW-B (closed)	same as above	503.2±14.5	4094	157.5±12.3

weeks, wild-type males from various sources were added to PW-A. No additions were made to PW-B. The males were added to PW-A one at a time, usually each time the population was opened for weighing and counting. For the first six weeks, four males per week were added; from the seventh through the 31st weeks, five males per week were added. In order of addition, the number and source of the males was: Olivette, St. Louis County, Missouri (flies came directly from nature) 57; scarletoid net (laboratory mutants) 8; C1S1-A (see previous section) 2; Springfield, Ohio (directly from nature) 60; Webster Groves, Missouri (directly from nature) 22.

Over the 26-week period that the introductions were made into PW-A, population size and production were measured (Table 8). The differences between the means are not significant (e.g. population size of PW-B *vs.* PW-A gives a t value of 1.342; $P = 0.5$ to 0.10). Thus it is apparent that the introduction of foreign flies has not been associated with a corresponding increase in population size.

Gene arrangement frequencies in the original PW population and in the replicates derived from it are shown in Table 7. It will be noted that whereas PW and the closed derivative from it, PW-B, have 100 percent 3R, PW-A shows 3R-1 in substantial frequency. This gene arrangement clearly was introduced into this population with some of the wild males. As in the previous experiment, experimental populations of *D. robusta* seem to be highly tenacious of chromosomal polymorphism.

To summarize the facts: an experimental population with many gene arrangements from Plainwell, Michigan, is very similar in performance to populations from Steelville, Missouri. This performance is not altered by the introduction of a continual flow of males from different sources and geographical areas despite the fact that at least some of these introductions have been proved to be successful.

Gene arrangement frequencies in closed populations
under strong natural selection

In July and August, 1957, collections were made at Bridgewater, Vermont, and Olivette, Missouri, respectively. The results of the analyses of the chromosomes from the wild females are given in the first and fourth columns in the body of Table 9. The Vermont sample shows typical marginal characteristics, as has been pointed out in CARSON (1958a,b). The Olivette sample came from Olivette Woods (CARSON 1958b) and shows, 11 years after the first study of this locality, the same equilibria which have been observed throughout the period of study. The only apparent difference is the high level of 2L relative to 2L-1. These two gene arrangements, however, have made noteworthy fluctuations in the past but have always returned later to intermediate levels.

Immediately following capture of the wild flies, two Bridgewater (B-1 and B-2) and two Olivette (O-1 and O-2) populations were established. Each Bridgewater population was begun in August, 1957 using two females and two males from each of 48 F_1's from wild females. Thus a total of 192 founder flies were used for each replicate. The Olivette populations were also begun in August using two females and two males from each of 50 F_1's from wild females. A total of 200 founder flies were thus used for each replicate.

All four of these populations were maintained on a schedule identical to that described previously until equilibrium size of approximately 500 mg or more was achieved. At this point, in November of 1957, a new cycle of change was instituted and measurements of size and production were abandoned. A new vial with food and 10 mg yeast was added only once a week; at the same time, collection of hatching flies was made from all vials which had previously been in contact with the population and these flies added to the adult population. Under these

TABLE 9

Gene arrangement frequencies (in percent) in samples from various natural populations of D. robusta *and in experimental populations derived from them after 30 generations of strong natural selection*

Gene arrangement	Bridgewater, Vermont, F_1 from wild population July 1957	Laboratory populations		Olivette, Missouri, F_1 from wild population Aug. 1957	Laboratory populations	
		B-1 May 1960	B-2 Apr. 1960		O-1 May 1960	O-2 May 1960
XL	2.9	31.3	48.6	99.5	100.0	100.0
XL-1	97.1	68.7	51.4	...	...	...
XL-2	...	...	...	0.5	...	...
XR	95.4	100.0	100.0	40.3	53.3	36.7
XR-1	...	...	...	56.0	46.7	63.3
XR-2	4.6	...	...	3.7	...	...
2L	26.1	18.6	30.9	70.8	31.9	50.6
2L-1	8.9	35.1	53.0	21.3	57.5	22.8
2L-2	...	...	...	6.9	10.0	21.5
2L-3	65.0	46.4	16.0	0.9	...	...
2L-8	...	...	...	...	...	5.1
2R	100.0	100.0	100.0	83.3	93.1	98.1
3R	98.8	100.0	100.0	77.8	59.4	85.4
3R-1	0.4	...	...	22.2	40.6	14.6
3L-R	0.8	...	...	...	...	...
N^x	174	83	142	216	160	158
N^a	257	97	181	216	120	120

conditions, the equilibrium size of the population was reduced to approximately 125 mg. This treatment was continued for approximately two and one half years, about 30 generations, after which time chromosome samples were taken by removing individuals or pairs of flies as they hatched under strong natural selection and testing them for the presence of chromosome aberrations. The results of these tests are given in Table 9.

There appears to be a tendency for loss of gene arrangements which were rather rare in the founders. Thus, XR-2 is lost from both Bridgewater and Olivette populations, 2L-3 is lost from the Olivette populations and 3R-1 and 3L-R are lost from the Bridgewater populations. Polymorphism is nonetheless retained tenaciously in a number of instances; the levels of polymorphism are in a number of cases different in the different replicates.

Of particular interest is the appearance of a new gene arrangement, 2L-8, in population O-2. This arrangement appears to have arisen within this population and has achieved a frequency of around five percent. The new inversion is a very short one. Its distal break is near the base of the arm, in the middle of region 23A (CARSON 1958b). This region consists of six bands and the break is between bands number three and four. The proximal break is in the heterochromatin, that is, its position is indistinguishable in the salivary gland chromosome from the position of the proximal breaks of 2L-2 and 2L-3. There is no evidence that the inversion is pericentric. Inversion 2L-8, furthermore, is associated with a gene arrangement which otherwise has the 2L-1 gene arrangement; it is probable, therefore, that it arose in and has remained associated with this arrangement.

DISCUSSION

The relatively high fitness of the Steelville and Plainwell populations under the test conditions appears to be correlated with the high degree of chromosomal polymorphism that they contain. In a discussion of this type of genetic adjustment, the writer (CARSON 1959) suggested that this polymorphism may permit the populations concerned to exploit the environment through "heterotic buffering", that is, the supergene heterozygotes are more fit than homozygotes because of their better general performance in all niches of the environment and all phases of the life of the individual. This interpretation applies particularly to large central rather than small marginal populations. The latter are considered to be inbred, rather closely adapted to a limited number of niches, specialized genetically and relatively homozygous. Experimental populations of marginal origin (e.g. Chadron, Nebraska) perform less well under the test conditions than populations of central origin.

When the relatively low-fitness marginal populations from Chadron, Nebraska were hybridized with the relatively high-fitness central populations from Steelville, Missouri, the resulting hybrid populations do not differ in relative fitness from the parental Steelville populations. In other words, heterosis is not observed on the populational level. A like result is obtained when attempts are made to improve the Plainwell, Michigan, population by opening it to a continual inflow of new genetic material.

The proposal may be made that in the two instances mentioned above the populations of central origin are already carrying a high degree of heterozygous balance and may be very nearly saturated in the sense that little improvement by increasing the amount of heterotic buffering is possible. The fact that further polymorphism is nonetheless accepted in chromosome X (for the Chadron-Steelville hybrid populations) and chromosome 3 (for the open Plainwell population) while no further increase in population size or production is observed may be explained as follows. We may assume that saturation is not complete but that the increment of change in population fitness is so small as not to be detectable under these circumstances and by the method used. Evidence for "saturation" of a heterotic system was presented by CARSON (1961) who showed that several populations of *D. melanogaster*, which were carrying considerable polymorphism would not readily accept more.

The Steelville populations ultimately were derived from a single pair of wild flies whereas the Plainwell populations were established from 18 pairs. This difference in genetic background, however, does not appear to affect the final performance of these two types of populations. They are almost identical in this regard. It is suggested that the considerable heterozygosity carried by the original pair of wild Steelville flies is correlated with the high performance of the populations derived from it. This may be regarded as indicative of the great storage capacity of the heterozygous karyotypes found in central populations.

Most of the gene arrangements present in experimental populations of *D. robusta* which are polymorphic are retained for long periods, perhaps indefinitely. This is true also of the Bridgewater and Olivette populations which were carried for about 30 generations under very severe selection. This persistence is considered to be due to the large role played by the heterotic buffering system of the organism which suddenly finds itself facing an uniquely new environment such as that provided by the experimenter in the laboratory. The data nevertheless show that in a number of instances gene arrangements which were originally rare in the sample when it was taken from nature are lost from the experimental populations derived from these samples. This may be due to the relatively small size of the experimental populations. This should permit chance fixation in the population by random drift of those gene sequences which have homozygotes which are very close in selective value to the pertinent heterozygote. The large size of natural populations would be expected to prevent such fixation in central populations. XL-2, XR-2 and 2L-3, for instance, have been present in the Olivette, Missouri, population for 11 consecutive years at frequencies which often fall below one percent, yet are consistently encountered in population samples (CARSON 1958b). Experimental populations established from this area, however, show loss of these "rare" arrangements.

The case where a new arrangement arose in an experimental population and increased in frequency therein requires comment. The small inversion involved was at the base of the second chromosome; specifically, the change occurred in arrangement 2L-1. This latter arrangement existed in the population in high frequency, apparently balanced there by heterosis, at the time of the occurrence of the new inversion. Because of the well-known suppressive effects of inversions on crossing over in *D. robusta* (Carson 1953; Levitan 1955) separation of this new inversion from the arrangement in which it arose would be expected to be rare and was, in fact, not observed.

The selective relationships between the various gene arrangements in this chromosome arm would be expected to be complex, as the addition of the new arrangement raises the number of coexisting gene arrangements to four and the number of competing karyotypes for this arm to ten, four homozygotes and six heterozygotes. This new gene arrangement could have increased in frequency either because it conferred some selective advantage on those individuals carrying it or because its increase was largely fortuitous due, at least partly, to linkage with a gene arrangement already participating in a major heterotic association. This latter possibility is further increased by the fact that the population was small throughout the experiment. In a more extensive analysis of a similar case Sperlich (1959) demonstrated that a new X-ray-induced inversion in *D. subobscura* behaved in a heterotic manner in three different population cages in which it was tested with different alternative sequences. In the absence of similar tests, no decision can be made concerning this new aberration in *D. robusta*.

There appears to be no general and progressive tendency for decrease in chromosomal polymorphism in the relatively uniform environment in which these laboratory populations were maintained. In these long-term experiments, and in previous ones (Levitan 1951; Carson 1958b) the reduction of variability observed by Lewontin (1958) was not observed. The writer feels that in *D. robusta* the sectional heterozygotes have some general physiological homeostasis which provides for heterotic buffering even in the relatively, but by no means absolutely, uniform conditions under which the populations are reared. Lewontin's hypothesis that polymorphism should be lost in a uniform environment, furthermore, would appear to hold only if each heterozygote is specially adapted in nature to some slightly different environmental variable which is not recapitulated in the laboratory conditions.

SUMMARY

1. Laboratory populations of *Drosophila robusta* have been maintained under continual strong natural selection with carefully controlled conditions of food and space in such a way as to provide an opportunity for weekly measurement of population size (weight and number of adult individuals) and production (weight and number of individuals hatched).

2. Experimental populations derived from the center of the species range tend to remain highly polymorphic for gene arrangement throughout the experiments. Their performance is better than structurally homozygous lines derived from marginal sites.

3. Populations derived from hybridization of marginal and central populations do not surpass the performance of the parental populations of central origin. They nevertheless retain much polymorphism, some of which is intergeographic.

4. Experimental populations kept genetically open by continual additions of foreign flies did not detectably surpass those to which no additions were made, although it was proved that at least one intergeographic polymorphism was added under natural selection.

5. These facts suggest that, within the limits of the sensitivity of the method for measuring population fitness, the original (central) polymorphic populations are close to saturation and cannot, at least under the conditions of population size obtaining in the experiments, be significantly improved by the addition of further polymorphism.

6. Experimental populations derived from one pair of flies from the center of the range and populations derived from many pairs of flies both showed a high degree of performance and were not different from one another. This suggests a high storage capacity in karyotypes from central populations.

7. Populations under extreme adverse conditions, wherein the food was very closely limited and population size remained small, nevertheless retain their polymorphism tenaciously over many generations. The frequencies of the various arrangements, however, achieve equilibria different from the wild populations from which they came. In some instances, furthermore, they are different from each other.

8. A new inversion arose within one population and under natural selection rose to a frequency of about five percent. It is suggested that this new aberration may be quasi-neutral and may have been carried along because it is closely linked to a gene arrangement which exists in the population in balanced condition.

9. These findings generally provide support for the hypothesis that chromosomal polymorphism, as found in central populations, provides heterozygotes which are superior to their corresponding homozygotes in all facies of the environment, that is, show heterotic buffering. In contrast to this, marginal populations appear to be rather more narrowly specialized and exploit the environment through fixation of genes or gene combinations in the homozygous state.

ACKNOWLEDGMENTS

I wish to thank Mrs. CAROLE KONRAD, Mrs KOYOKO KATO and Miss JANNETTE CORN for their painstaking assistance with the routine handling of the experimental populations. Collections of flies from Webster Groves, Missouri, Plainwell, Michigan, and Springfield, Ohio, were made by DR. H. D. STALKER, to whom I am greatly indebted not only for this but for many other kindnesses. This work was supported by grants G-421 and G-7441 from the National Science Foundation.

LITERATURE CITED

BERT, G. R., 1960 Fixed heterozygosity and fitness in *Drosophila melanogaster* populations under strong natural selection. Genetics **45**: 975.

BUZZATI-TRAVERSO, A. A., 1955 Evolutionary changes in components of fitness and other polygenic traits in *Drosophila melanogaster* populations. Heredity **9**: 153–186.

CARSON, H. L., 1953 The effects of inversions on crossing over in *Drosophila robusta*. Genetics **38**: 168–186.

1955 The genetic characteristics of marginal populations of Drosophila. Cold Spring Harbor Symposia Quant. Biol. **20**: 276–287.

1958a Response to selection under different conditions of recombination in Drosophila. Cold Spring Harbor Symposia Quant. Biol. **23**: 291–306.

1958b The population genetics of *Drosophila robusta*. Advances in Genet. **9**: 1–40.

1958c Increase in fitness in experimental populations resulting from heterosis. Proc. Natl. Acad. Sci. U.S. **44**: 1136–1141.

1959 Genetic conditions which promote or retard the formation of species. Cold Spring Harbor Symposia Quant. Biol. **24**: 87–105.

1961 Heterosis and fitness in experimental populations of *Drosophila melanogaster*. Evolution **14**: (in press).

LEVITAN, M., 1951 Experiments on chromosome variability in *Drosophila robusta*. Genetics **36**: 285–305.

1955 Studies of linkage in populations. I. Associations of second chromosome inversions in *Drosophila robusta*. Evolution **9**: 62–74.

LEWONTIN, R. C., 1958 Studies on heterozygosity and homeostasis. II. Loss of heterosis in a constant environment. Evolution **12**: 494–503.

L'HÉRITIER, P., Y. NEEFS, and G. TEISSIER, 1937 Aptérisme des insectes et sélection naturelle. Compt. rend. (Paris) **197**: 1765–1767.

REED, S. C., and E. W. REED, 1948 Natural selection in laboratory populations of Drosophila. Evolution **2**: 176–186.

SMATHERS, KATRINA M., 1961 The contribution of heterozygosity at certain gene loci to fitness of laboratory populations of *Drosophila melanogaster*. Am. Naturalist **95**: 27–38.

SPERLICH, D., 1959 Experimentelle Beitrage zum Problem des positiven Heterosiseffektes bei der Strukturpolymorphen Art *Drosophila subobscura*. Z. Vererb. **90**: 273–287.

WRIGHT, S., and TH. DOBZHANSKY, 1946 Genetics of natural populations. XII. Experimental reproduction of some of the changes caused by natural selection in certain populations of *Drosophila pseudoobscura*. Genetics **31**: 125–136.

Effects of Recombination on Viability in Drosophila[1]

ELIOT B. SPIESS

Department of Biological Sciences,
University of Pittsburgh, Pittsburgh, Pennsylvania

INTRODUCTION

To Charles Darwin the origin of variation was not only perplexing but a troublesome hindrance to a satisfactory completion of his natural selection theory. Darwin consistently confessed ignorance with respect to the causes of variation. At present, one hundred years after the Darwin-Wallace papers, we are sophisticated by our knowledge of the complex facts of mutation, Mendelian recombination and linkage, but when presented with the problem of extracting inherited variation from a population, wild or domesticated, and a tremendous spectrum of genotypes is laid out before us, we find it no small task to decide on the exact origin of specific differences (especially quantitative differences). Mendel's discovery gives us the advantage over Darwin; but how much of the spectrum of variation, that is, the free variability observed, comes directly from mutation, how much from segregation, how much from recombination is often difficult to measure. How much potential variability is stored in heterozygous condition, how much in linked complexes?

[1] The work reported in this article concerning *D. persimilis* recombination was supported in part under Contract No. AT-(30-1)-1775, United States Atomic Energy Commission.

Reprinted by permission of Long Island Biological Association from
COLD SPRING HARBOR SYMPOSIUM, 23, 239–250 (1958).

Well adapted, crossbreeding populations of organisms contain extensive genetic diversity. Much of that diversity is incorporated in heterozygosity; on inbreeding in the laboratory a vast array of segregants appears. Individuals reaching adulthood in wild populations are heterozygous far more commonly than they are homozygous for at least a few loci. But in addition to this well known fact (Timofeef-Ressovsky, 1940; Dobzhansky, 1951; Dobzhansky, 1955) it has been demonstrated that recombination between loci on chromosomes taken from a well adapted population releases an extensive array of variability also.

In 1946 Dobzhansky analyzed the viabilities of recombination products from three wild second chromosomes derived from a population of *Drosophila pseudoobscura*. Recombination between these chromosomes generated a diversity of viabilities extending from lethality to slightly supervital and also varying degrees of retardation in developmental rate. Of great interest was the production of lethality by recombination between "normal" chromosomes; such recombination products were called "synthetic lethals".

Misro (1949) tested three non-lethal second chromosomes of *D. melanogaster* for the effects of recombination on production of lethals. Females heterozygous for these chromosomes produced 2.12 % lethals out of 1200 recombinant chromosomes tested, of which nearly three-fourths (1.55 %) were attributed to recombination alone when the effects of mutation were subtracted. Homozygous females or males heterozygous for the original chromosomes produced an average of 0.52 % lethals out of 1300 chromosomes tests, or about one-third as great an effect.

Wallace *et al.* (1953) also tested recombinants of chromosome II from *D. melanogaster* but more extensively to include all viability classes and abdominal bristle number. Five non-lethal chromosomes from two different experimental populations were chosen and chromosomes tested following recombination. Homozygous recombinants displayed lethality and a wide distribution of viabilities. The results were less striking for bristle numbers but variance increased significantly. Some recombinants were uniform and others were highly variable.

The question arises as to how extensive the potential variability tied up in linked complexes may be and how much of the variability observed from inbreeding techniques in the laboratory can be attributed to release of variability by recombination within linked complexes. To make potential variability observable, we may employ techniques to reveal the effects of homozygosity for whole chromosomes or techniques to release variability by recombination from linked complexes or both; in either case the array of genotypes released or revealed depends on the amount of genetic heterogeneity existing in the population and, more important, on the functional nature of that heterogeneity as stressed by Dobzhansky (1946) and Wallace *et al.* (1953). The kinds of variability observable in a population must be largely a function of that population's genetic system, or structure, that is, the system of mating, the number, organization, and genetic architecture of the chromosomes in the population. As has recently been pointed out by Breese and Mather (1957) "the response of a population to the force of selection will depend on the genetical architecture of the character being selected and this genetical architecture in turn reflects those general properties which together constitute the genetic system of the population and species."

Two contrasting types of population genetic structure have been formally proposed by Dobzhansky (1955) as the "classical" and "balance" hypotheses of the adaptive norm. Briefly these hypotheses compare the nature of heterozygosity and its function towards the population's adaptive norm: in the classical hypothesis the adaptive genetic structure of the population "features" homozygotes, heterozygosity is transient though it may occur at considerable loci, and unfixed alleles are on the way to fixation in homozygotes of highest adaptive value; in the balance hypothesis heterozygosity is permanent, it will exist because heterozygotes have superior adaptive value, the highest adaptive norm which can be attained by the population will demand high frequency of heterozygosity, and most homozygotes which occur will have inferior adaptive value.

Wallace and his coworkers (1953) have discussed the consequences of these two population genetic structures in terms of what should be expected from recombination of linked loci. In the classical hypothesis, if loci A, B, and so forth are common while alleles a, b, and so forth are rare because of adaptive superiority of $\frac{A\ B\ \cdots}{A\ B\ \cdots}$ when a random sample of chromosomes from that population is crossed so that recombinants can be extracted from the F_1's, recombinants should be uniform for the most part.

In the balance hypothesis, if $\dfrac{A\ B\ \cdots}{a\ b\ \cdots}$ and/or $\dfrac{A\ b\ \cdots}{a\ B\ \cdots}$ are superior genotypes and the most common in the population, it would be expected that recombination would produce diversity.

In both the classical and balance populations selection should act to preserve linkage relations which determine good viability (good non-allelic interactions); but in the classical population all linkages should be similar and recombination between chromosomes of *good* viability should give *good* derived products, that is the average viability of any sample of chromosomes should be about the same before and after recombination.

In the balance population homozygotes derived from the recombination of good viability chromosomes may well show extremely non-adaptive effects. Selection acts to preserve good gene action at heterozygous loci but simultaneously also good interactions between loci (non-alleles). In addition, chromosomes in which crossing over is not suppressed by special cytogenetic mechanisms (like inversion heterozygotes) might be expected to evolve a multiple allelic system of high order to raise the probability of constant heterozygosity. If a multiple allelic system is developed, recombination should engender a great variety of linkages and consequently a variety of non-allelic interactions, most of which if kept in the heterozygous state would determine uniformly well adapted phenotypes but most of which in the homozygous condition might have a diversity of adaptive values from very low to high extremes. Different chromosomes of *good* adaptive value from a balanced population may be expected to engender recombinants which might be exceedingly diverse in homozygous condition and in most cases far from well adapted.

Undoubtedly these types of population genetic structure are not mutually exclusive. Real species may run a spectrum of genetic structure from one extreme to the other. If recombination products depend on the functional nature of the population's genetic heterogeneity, it is of interest to make comparisons between these products taken from different populations and from different species. Such comparisons will give us some basis for judgment about the spectrum of population genetic structures and chromosomal architectures.

Joint Experiments on Recombination in Various Species of Drosophila

Methods

Early in 1954, Th. Dobzhansky, C. Pavan, and I agreed to use a common plan to study the effects of recombination on viability in four species of Drosophila, namely, *D. pseudoobscura*, *D. willistoni*, *D. prosaltans*, and *D. persimilis*. The first two species are very widely distributed, quite abundant, and ecologically versatile. The second two species are more narrowly adapted and occur in much less extensive areas: *D. prosaltans* has thin population density, and *D. persimilis*, while it may become very abundant in favorable seasons and cool moist habitats, is certainly more specialized than its sibling species, *D. pseudoobscura*. Unfortunately the experiments on *D. willistoni* owing to a series of accidents were not completed.

From the standpoint of adaptive versatility and population size, it is tempting to postulate that the first two species would contain much greater genetic diversity and that their population genetic structure should approach that described by the "balance" hypothesis while that of the other two species should incline towards the status envisioned by the "classical" hypothesis.

In each species populations were sampled from two localities separated either by some distance or ecological conditions or both. The effect of homozygosity for whole chromosomes on viability was revealed by using a balanced marker technique in each species (for general technique, see Dobzhansky and Spassky, 1953). It was decided that chromosome II in all these species should be studied; homology of loci has been established between the chromosome II of *D. pseudoobscura* and *D. persimilis* (Dobzhansky and Epling, 1944) and between *D. willistoni* and *D. prosaltans* (Spassky and Dobzhansky, 1950). In all cases experimental stocks established for any species were identical in arrangement, that is, free of inversion differences.

Detailed techniques for these experiments are included in the following references: Spassky *et al.* (1958); Spiess (1958); Dobzhansky *et al.* (1958); and Levene (1958). Briefly they can be summarized as follows: Males collected in nature were mated to females homozygous for a recessive mutant on chromosome II. A single F_1 male is crossed to females possessing the same recessive plus a dominant homozygous-lethal marker and an inversion suppressing crossing over. In the following generation brothers and sisters showing the dominant marker but not the recessive are mated. Their progenies should consist of 67% dominant flies and 33% non-marker flies (homozygotes for the "wild" chromosome). Viability is then defined as a proportion of the total progeny: normal viability (33%); recessive lethal (zero wild type flies); and semilethals, subvitals, and supervitals are proportions greater than zero, defined according to certain limits within the viability distribution observed (see Dobzhansky and Spassky, 1953).

As expected some of the wild chromosomes were lethal or semilethal. Among those which were normal or subvital in homozygous condition, ten chromosomes were selected from each locality. Sharply deleterious chromosomes were avoided intentionally. In Dobzhansky's laboratory these strains in the homozygous condition for chromosome II were maintained by mass matings (*D. pseudoobscura* and *D. prosaltans*) while in our laboratory they were maintained in the balanced condition by mass matings at first and then by single pair matings (*D. persimilis*).

To produce recombinant chromosomes, the ten strains carrying normal or subvital chromosomes from each locality were intercrossed in all possible combinations, that is, with 10 chromosomes, 45 intralocality combinations are possible, and with 10 from two localities, 100 interlocality crosses are possible, or a total of 190 crosses. F_1 females heterozygous for two wild chromosomes were mated to recessive marker males. Their progeny then contained chromosomes the majority of which must have been crossovers between wild chromosomes now in heterozygous condition with the recessive marker. Ten progeny males selected as a sample in each cross were mated *singly* to females of the same dominant marker as in the original extraction crosses. Flies showing the dominant marker but not the recessive contained identical wild recombinant chromosomes. Of those, brothers and sisters were mated to produce a final generation in which exactly 100 flies were counted in each culture. For 190 crosses then, 1900 chromosomes were tested by counting 190,000 flies.

After more than three-fourths of the tests had been completed including at least half of the combinations of each strain, retests of the 20 original chromosomes were made to check on their viability and variance without the effect of recombination as well as to take note of mutation which might have occurred during the course of the experiment. Each retested strain was replicated in six cultures. In one case we found a lethal in a retest in *persimilis* which had presumably arisen by mutation. We then had to re-extract a "normal" chromosome from the wild stock and test it over again in all its combinations.

THE ARRAY OF VIABILITIES

The data comprising 1900 progenies for each species are ponderous. Some individual progenies (that is, chromosomes tested) may be highly correlated with the viability contributions of the parental chromosomes, some may be completely unique in viability or some may take some intermediate value between complete uniqueness and complete correlation with parental chromosome viabilities. To describe such a mixture of events, it will be useful to present first the general, or average, effects which recombination has upon viability; followed by the kinds of differences engendered by recombination (consideration of variances); the special problem of synthetic lethals; and finally possible schemes of gene action proposed to explain the effects observed.

General Effect of Recombination on Viability

For intralocality crosses each chromosome is tested by mating to nine others, producing a total of 90 recombinant chromosomes, with 10 chromosomes per cross. The mean viability of these 90 derived chromosomes represents the average effect of a particular chromosome on its recombination products, which might be termed for convenience the "recombinability" of that chromosome. In Table 1 the effect of recombination for all chromosomes within localities is calculated by averaging ten such recombinability effects (that is, 450 different cultures are averaged, but each culture is counted twice). The means for the original chromosome viabilities (controls) in each species are greater than these average effects of recombination.

With crosses between localities the recombinability of each chromosome is the mean viability of 100 cultures, and the average effect of recombination for all interlocality crosses is the mean viability of 1000 different cultures. In all three species these average effects for interlocality chromosomes are below their controls; and no greater change in viability means is created by recombination between chromosomes from different localities than by recombination between chromosomes from the same locality.

327

The consistency of this lowering of viability is evident from the data of Table 2. Each species is alike in the excess of lowered viabilities for average "recombinability" effects. (In general those few recombinabilities which were not lower

TABLE 1. THE GENERAL RESULTS OF RECOMBINATION IN TERMS OF VIABILITY ($\overline{M}$) AND VARIANCE ($\overline{V}$) MEANS

Data from Dobzhansky, Levene, Spassky and Spassky; and Spiess.

D. pseudoobscura

	Control $\overline{M}$ (Viability)	Recombination $\overline{M}$
Texas	27.96	24.43
California	28.96	21.58
Interlocality............	....	23.06

	Control $\overline{V}$ (Variance)	Recombination $\overline{V}$
Texas	7.85	70.3
California	2.36	60.3
Interlocality............	....	62.7

D. persimilis

	Control $\overline{M}$ (Viability)	Recombination $\overline{M}$
South Fork	32.1	27.99
White Wolf	31.7	28.74
Interlocality............	....	27.75

	Control $\overline{V}$ (Variance)	Recombination $\overline{V}$
South Fork	5.87	31.35
White Wolf	−1.40	20.89
Interlocality............	....	28.36

D. prosaltans

	Control $\overline{M}$ (Viability)	Recombination $\overline{M}$
Rio de Janeiro	33.11	28.12
Pirassununga	30.53	27.88
Interlocality............	....	28.27

	Control $\overline{V}$ (Variance)	Recombination $\overline{V}$
Rio de Janeiro	−3.6	67.7
Pirassununga	5.6	36.5
Interlocality............	....	53.4

than their corresponding control had parental chromosomes of below average viability.) To

examine this consistency further the number of
crosses (recombination products between any
two chromosomes) averaging less than the common parent control chromosome are also given.
Recombination products of similar and dissimilar
geographic origin again have consistently lower
viability than their "normal" viability controls.

The obvious question comes to mind: do these
results show that crossing over lowers viability?
Not at all. In the first place, stocks in Dobzhansky's laboratory were maintained in the
homozygous condition in which crossing over
was certainly not discontinued, yet in retests
of original chromosomes for the controls there

TABLE 2. PROPORTIONS OF RECOMBINATION PRODUCTS
COMPARED WITH CONTROLS

Average viability ($\overline{M}$) and average variance ($\overline{V}$) are
the average effects of one chromosome upon all its recombination products. Cross viabilities (CM) and cross
variances (CV) are the average effects of ten derived
chromosomes from two particlar original chromosomes.

	$\overline{M}$ less than con- trol M	$\overline{V}$ greater than con- trol V	CM less than common parent M control	CV greater than common parent V control
D. pseudoobscura				
Intral. Texas	7/10	10/10	63/90 = .70	78/90 = .85
Cal.	9/10	10/10	78/90 = .87	83/90 = .92
Interl. Texas	8/10	10/10	76/100 = .76	85/100 = .85
Cal.	9/10	10/10	88/100 = .88	90/100 = .90
D. persimilis				
Intral. S.F.	10/10	10/10	76/90 = .84	57/90 = .63
W.W.	8/10	7/10	69/90 = .77	59/90 = .66
Interl. S.F.	10/10	10/10	86/100 = .86	67/100 = .67
W.W.	8/10	9/10	77/100 = .77	78/100 = .78
D. prosaltans				
Intral. Rio	10/10	10/10	75/90 = .83	76/90 = .84
Pira	8/10	10/10	63/90 = .70	70/90 = .78
Interl. Rio	10/10	10/10	76/100 = .76	86/100 = .86
Pira	7/10	10/10	59/100 = .59	76/100 = .76

was no lowering of viability with respect to their
initial isolation viabilities. (In our laboratory
keeping stocks in the balanced condition prevented
crossing over in them and consequently a comparison of control retests with initial isolation
tests would not reveal an answer to the question.)
It is clear that crossing over does not lower viability within the control stocks.

Attention might be drawn to the fact mentioned
in connection with Table 2 that those chromo-

somes which did not produce lowered recombination products were in general those of subvital original viability. Of course if lowered viability were the result of crossing over, the effect should not be reserved for chromosomes of high viability only but should occur more universally.

The experimental chromosomes were not a random sample of the natural population from which they are derived but were selected for their good viability. It might be helpful in proposing an explanation for the lowering phenomenon to list the average viabilities of random second chromosomes from the three species, including all lethals:

	All Chromosome II's Average Viability
D. pseudoobscura (Dobzhansky, California, 1953):	19.82%
D. persimilis (Dobzhansky, California, 1954):	23.32%
(Spiess, California, 1953):	22.35%
D. prosaltans (numerous localities in Brazil, 1954):	21.30%

Average viability of second chromosomes in these species amounts to subvitality bordering on semi-lethality. A more logical interpretation of the drop in viability following recombination of "good" chromosomes is proposed by Dobzhansky: "the distribution of viabilities found in the natural population tends to be restored by recombination", or the average of the recombinants regresses toward the mean of the population from which the original chromosomes were selected. This outcome is far more likely if the genetic structure of the wild population is of the balanced type where homozygotes are expected to be inferior in adaptive value to heterozygotes. A sample of "good" chromosomes from the classical population would be expected on the contrary to average approximately the same both before and after recombination.

No more extreme drop in viability follows recombination of inter- than intralocality chromosomes. Presumably a population of hybrids containing mixed chromosomes from two localities would produce a distribution of viabilities with a mean intermediate between the means of the two parent populations. Recombination then could accomplish no greater change than to regress towards such an intermediate position.

Genes determining viability must act in nonadditive ways to satisfy these results. Minus modifiers cannot be added by recombination in excess of those already present in the two parents. Viability of homozygotes must be dependent largely upon epistatic interactions of genes which they contain. These points will be discussed in more detail later.

Differences Engendered by Recombination

For each pair of chromosomes crossed, ten recombinant chromosomes were tested. Our attention can first be directed at differences between these ten derived chromosomes within any cross. (A comprehensive model for the analysis of variances is given by Howard Levene (1958), to whom the author is completely indebted for any understanding of the statistical approach to this problem.) If the ten derived viabilities are distributed randomly around the mean for the cross, the observed variance ($\sum d^2/9$) should equal the binomial error variance obtained by counting 100 individuals in an average sample $\left(\dfrac{\bar{X}(100 - \bar{X})}{100}\right)$. If real differences exist between recombinant chromosomes of greater magnitude than random effects would produce, a positive difference would be obtained by subtraction of the binomial variance from the observed variance.

In Table 1 the average "real" variances ($\bar{V}$) are given for each population. None of the control $\bar{V}$'s are significantly greater than zero, except for one value in the Texas intralocality crosses of *D. pseudoobscura* which is only barely significantly greater than zero. These control $\bar{V}$'s measure a component of total variance brought about by environmental variables, residual genotype variables plus possible mutations.

But in marked contrast, recombination $\bar{V}$'s (average real variance for all crosses) are several times larger than their controls in every case. The consistency of increase in differences between derived chromosomes can be seen from inspection of Table 2. Not only are each of the ten chromosomes able to increase variance on the average by recombination (except for three chromosomes in *D. persimilis* White Wolf locality which had no measurable effect on variance, two of which had fairly high control variances of about 20), but also the majority of crosses with which a particular chromosome is involved as common parent (right column of Table 2).

Average real variances for interlocality crosses in every case are intermediate between the respective intralocality variances. Especially in *D. prosaltans* the two localities are quite diverse in creating differences between derived chromosomes; yet chromosomes of mixed geographic origin produce a very nearly exact intermediate variance when recombined. Comparing intra- with interlocality production of variability, we can say the potential variability stored in linked complexes will engender no greater variability by recombination *between* than ·already exists *within* any local population.

Differences in viability between crosses may be due to additive or non-additive (interaction) effects of parent chromosomes. For interlocality crosses the additive effect of any chromosome (a_i) is the difference between the grand mean viability ($\hat{m}$) and the mean of crosses ($\bar{y}_i$) in which that chromosome was a parent ($a_i = \bar{y}_i - \hat{m}$). For example, if the mean viability of crosses in which chromosome A is a parent = 35 % and the grand mean of all crosses = 30 %, chromosome A has a 5 % additive effect. For intralocality crosses the additive effect is $\frac{9}{8}$ of that difference. Theoretically the additive effect of any chromosome is constant for all its recombinants. Consequently if viability were determined completely by additive effect contributions, all cross means could be completely predicted if simply the grand mean and additive effects of chromosomes were known. The difference between this predicted value and the observed value measures a non-additive component, or interaction effect, of any two chromosomes upon their derived products. These specific effects of combinations would presumably be the same for any sample of derived chromosomes from a particular cross; (interaction effects were measured by subtracting the two additive effects of parent chromosomes and the grand mean from the average viability of a cross: g_{ij} (interaction) $= y_{ij} - a_i - a_j - \hat{m}$). It is clear that these additive and non-additive effects together in every case are intermediate between the respective intralocality variances. Especially in *D. prosaltans* the two localities are quite diverse in creating differences between derived chromosomes; yet chromosomes of mixed geographic origin produce a very nearly exact intermediate variance when recombined. Comparing intra- with interlocality production of variability, we can say the potential variability stored in linked complexes will engender no greater variability by recombination *between* than ·already exists *within* any local population.

Differences in viability between crosses may be due to additive or non-additive (interaction) effects of parent chromosomes. For interlocality crosses the additive effect of any chromosome

TABLE 3. PROBABILITIES IN % ON ANALYSIS OF VARIANCE F VALUES FOR VIABILITIES AND REAL VARIANCES
Within crosses variance on variances is theoretical and was used only for significance test. F values and degrees of freedom from Dobzhansky et al., Spassky et al., Levene, and Spiess, 1958.

Effects	D. pseudoobscura		D. persimilis		D. prosaltans	
	Viability	Variance	Viability	Variance	Viability	Variance
Additive Intralocal #1	0.05–0.10	0.10–0.50	40–50	75	50–75	50–75
Additive Intralocal #2	0.50–1.00	50–75	10–25	1.00–2.50	10–25	25–50
Additive Interlocal #1	0.10–0.50	50	0.10–1.00	1.00–2.50	50	75–90
Additive Interlocal #2	0.05–0.10	25–50	5–10	25–50	2.50–5.00	10–25
Non-additive Intralocal #1	<0.10	50	≪0.10	≪0.10	≪0.10	≪0.10
Non-additive Intralocal #2	≪0.10	<0.10	<0.10	≪0.10	≪0.10	≪0.10
Non-additive Interlocal	≪0.10	<0.10	≪0.10	≪0.10	≪0.10	≪0.10
Within Crosses Intralocal #1	≪0.10	—	<0.10	—	≪0.10	—
Within Crosses Intralocal #2	≪0.10	—	≪0.10	—	≪0.10	—
Within Crosses Interlocal	≪0.10	—	≪0.10	—	≪0.10	—

(a_i) is the difference between the grand mean viability ($\hat{m}$) and the mean of crosses ($\bar{y}_i$) in which that chromosome was a parent ($a_i = \bar{y}_i - \hat{m}$). For example, if the mean viability of crosses in which chromosome A is a parent = 35% and the grand mean of all crosses = 30%, chromosome A has a 5% additive effect. For intralocality crosses the additive effect is $\frac{9}{8}$ of that difference. Theoretically the additive effect of any chromosome is constant for all its recombinants. Consequently if viability were determined completely by additive effect contributions, all cross means could be completely predicted if simply the grand mean and additive effects of chromosomes were known. The difference between this predicted value and the observed value measures a non-additive component, or interaction effect, of any two chromosomes upon their derived products. These specific effects of combinations would presumably be the same for any sample of derived chromosomes from a particular cross; (interaction effects were measured by subtracting the two additive effects of parent chromosomes and the grand mean from the average viability of a cross: g_{ij} (interaction) = $y_{ij} - a_i - a_j - \hat{m}$). It is clear that these additive and non-additive effects together and the additive components of the viabilities for the crosses in which the same chromosomes were recombined (Dobzhansky *et al.*, 1958). The average correlation of means of all original chromosomes with their recombinabilities in intralocality crosses is 0.03 with confidence limits -0.24 and $+0.29$. The correlation for interlocality crosses is 0.26 with confidence limits of zero and 0.49. However, the correlation between additive effects of intra- and interlocality crosses is 0.57 with confidence limits of 0.37 and 0.73. In other words one cannot predict the recombinability of a chromosome from measuring it in a control before recombination, but when viability is raised or lowered by recombination with one chromosome, there is a slight tendency for the same raising or lowering when that chromosome recombines with other chromosomes of a larger sample. Since this correlation is significant only between recombination products, the raising or lowering must be dependent upon interaction after new linkages are formed.

The Problem Of Synthetic Lethals

A few crosses produced lethals, either by mutation or by recombination (see Table 4). These were left in the overall calculation. Out of the 190 crosses per species the largest number of crosses in which lethals occurred was 20 (*D. prosaltans*), and in many of those only one lethal occurred among the ten chromosomes tested; while omitting the lethals would tend to raise the viabilities and lower the variances slightly, the final effect is not altered significantly. If some lethals were produced by recombination, it would be a mistake to omit them from the calculations of course.

Dobzhansky (1946) in studying recombination products from certain wild chromosomes of *D. pseudoobscura* from Mt. San Jacinto found that two normal viability chromosomes (at 16.5°C) gave rise to lethal recombinant chromosomes apparently without mutation. He called this phenomenon a *synthetic lethal* arising through recombination of linked loci. Wallace (1953) obtained evidence for synthetic lethals in *D. melanogaster* chromosome II as did Misro (1949). Hildreth (1955, 1956), however, was not able to find evidence for such lethals in that species on chromosomes X and III. Making a very extensive survey of recombination chromosomes from both laboratory stocks and wild flies, Hildreth found that the number of lethals were not in excess of the lethals in the original stocks, and all of them could be accounted for by mutation. The X chromosome might be expected to give negative results since one third of a population's X chromosomes are in males in which a sex linked lethal would be eliminated. Any lethal condition, synthetic or point mutation, could not become established unless it had sex limited action. The X chromosome is not likely to be so favorable for the balance hypothesis and would have well adapted heterozygous combinations only in females. Non-adaptive homozygotes might occur in females only if genic action is limited to the female. Hildreth's negative findings for chromosome III is more difficult to explain. Either synthetic lethals are very rare or do not occur on that chromosome or Hildreth's sample was peculiar in some unaccountable way. That the first possibility might be the best explanation can be inferred from some recent evidence for polygenic activity on chromosome III described by Breese and Mather (1957). In *D. melanogaster* selected for high and low chaetae numbers these authors partitioned that chromosome with the "ru-cu-ca" markers and collected recombinants in order to find the relative contributions of the regions between markers to additive variation, dominance and interaction effects. They found genic activity for chaetae number in all chromosome regions but additive and dominance effects were preponderantly greater than interaction effects. It is possible that chromosome III's architecture is such that both for loci determining chaetae number and for loci determining viability interaction effects are low. If the two long chromosomes of *D. melanogaster* differ so markedly in their interaction effects and thus in their ability to synthesize lethals the explanation for such a difference is not yet in plain sight.

From the distribution of viabilities arising through recombination in the species *D. pseudoobscura*, *D. persimilis*, and *D. prosaltans* it should be apparent that some of the lethals could be considered extreme variants in an extensive array of viabilities. Undoubtedly some of them were also produced by mutation. Without a great deal of further testing it would be impossible to separate particular lethals into their respective origins. But from their distribution in crosses it can be shown that from a statistical standpoint not

TABLE 4. LETHAL CHROMOSOMES OBTAINED

| | Freq. | % | No. of crosses Producing | | Total Crosses |
			1 lethal	More than 1 lethal	
D. pseudoobscura					
Intraloc.	44/900	4.9	9	10	19
Interloc.	33/1000	3.3	12	7	19
D. persimilis					
Intraloc.	19/900	2.1	3	4	7
Interloc.	26/1000	2.6	4	5	9
D. prosaltans					
Intraloc.	45/900	5.0	5	10	15
Interloc.	64/1000	6.4	7	13	20

all can be mutants, at least in *pseudoobscura* and *prosaltans*.

Dobzhansky, Spassky, and Spassky (1954) found the average mutation rates of *D. pseudoobscura*, *D. persimilis*, and *D. prosaltans* at room temperature (22°C) to be respectively 0.56%, 1.31% and 0.47% lethals per generation. Stock cultures in the recombination experiments were kept at 16°C, and since it is known that cool temperature lowers the mutation rate, spontaneous mutation might be quite a bit lower. To be detected in the F_4 progeny in homozygous condition, a recessive lethal could originate in the heterozygous F_1 female (in which tested recombination occurs) or it could be formed by mutation in one of the single F_2 males, ten of which were tested in each cross. Attention can be directed first to those crosses in which just one chromosome out of the ten tested contained a lethal (see Table 4). It is more likely that if such single lethals arose by mutation they originated with the F_2 males or in single gametes of the F_1 females. (If the F_1 female is heterozygous for the mutation one-half of her sons should have the lethal; the probability that only $\frac{1}{10}$ carried such a lethal is $10(\frac{1}{2})^{10}$.) We can consider, then, nearly all of the crosses in which just one lethal occurred to be either from point mutation in an F_2 male or from some recombination interaction in the final homozygote stage. In *pseudoobscura* there were 21 such crosses, in *persimilis* 7, and in *prosaltans* 12. In the light of the mutation rates given above with 1900 chromosomes tested per species expected numbers of single lethal chromosomes would be in the same order: 11, 25, and 9. The mutation rates given can probably be considered the upper confidence limit since stocks were kept at cool temperature and only the last generation progeny in any cross was raised at 25°C. Consequently the value for *pseudoobscura* is nearly twice as great as expected, and *prosaltans* is slightly greater; so that in those two species mutation cannot easily account for all the lethals observed.

For those crosses in which more than one lethal occurred per cross, it may be assumed that if the F_1 female was heterozygous for a lethal, a distribution of tested chromosomes should be normal around a mean of 5 lethals per cross. (A Poisson distribution for origin in F_2 males in *pseudoobscura* gives expected 168 crosses with no lethals, 21 crosses with 1 lethal, 1.3 crosses with 2 lethals, and 0.5 with 3 or more lethals (Spassky *et al.*, 1958) if all 21 single lethals observed were to come from single mutations.) The distribution of crosses with two or more lethals in *pseudoobscura* is as follows:

No. Crosses	No. Lethals per Cross
6	2
6	3
1	4
3	5
0	6
1	7

Total 17 crosses

A chi-square test on the fit of these data to a symmetrical distribution around a mean of 5 gives $\chi^2 = 14.9$, and p about 1 %. The high number of crosses in which 2 or 3 lethals were found are not likely to be produced by mutation then. In *prosaltans* the distribution of crosses is symmetrical around a mean of 5, but the total number of such crosses comes to 23 out of 190, or 12.1 %. If all these were due to accumulation of point mutations over the duration of the experiment then the average number of generations (estimated at 6) times the known mutation rate per generation should estimate the total lethals expected to occur in F_1 females. According to Dobzhansky's estimates the 12.1 % figure is about 3.2 times too large to be accountable on the basis of mutation alone. For different reasons, then, these two species have either a distribution or an amount of lethality unaccountable by known lethal mutation rates; at least some considerable proportion of the observed lethals may have been produced by recombination.

Desynthesizing Lethals

Without access to numerous linkage markers in these species the proof of lethal synthesis or any other viability effects by recombination cannot be satisfactorily final. Nevertheless stronger evidence than the statistics presented above can be brought to bear on the problem by attempting to desynthesize such lethals. In our laboratory Mrs. Mary Rowan Capenos has pursued this matter in *D. persimilis*, which produced the least number of lethals of the three species used. Her experiments are still in progress but there is some evidence indicating that some recombination lethals might be desynthesized.

All crosses which produced lethals after recombination or non-lethal crosses which produced very high real variances (V > 50) and/or had low mean viabilities (M < 27 % wild type) were repeated on the assumption that synthetic production of lethals would be more probable from such crosses. The objectives were two fold: 1) if lethals were created by new linkages initially, recombining the same "good" chromosomes again and achieving the same result would tend to rule out mutation; and if those crosses which gave high variance or low means "just missed" synthesizing a lethal because of small sample size, enlarging the sample size by repetition of the cross might achieve such a synthesis. 2) If a lethal occurs after repeating a cross a desynthesis might be effected by outcrossing the new lethal to a "normal" stock which had never produced either low means or lethals in recombination experiments (this was our WW21 stock) and collecting derived chromosomes in the usual way.

Out of the 16 lethal producing crosses in the first experiment, 10 have been repeated to date with negative results. Crosses with initially high variances and low means have been more successful: from 12 crosses with variances >50, 8 have been repeated with production of 3 lethals in one cross and repetition of high variances in 4 other crosses; from 15 low viability crosses, 12 have been repeated with 7 giving similar low means on the second attempt and with 3 crosses producing lethals. Two of these have been outcrossed to "normal" and recombinants counted. Half the tested sons of an F_1 female should get the lethal if it is a point mutation; on the other hand, crossing over with a normal viability chromosome could restore better viability if loci interacting to produce lethality were not very closely linked. (Only loci of that sort are likely to enter into interaction differences by new linkages commonly enough to be detectable in our small sample sizes.) The main task of the desynthesis is to provide a large enough sample of tested chromosomes to effectively reduce the proportion of lethals below 50% to rule out a single pair of alleles in the F_1 female. Only if a measurable number of crossovers could restore better viability would the otherwise 50:50 ratio among noncrossovers be detected.

One cross (SF25 × WW13) which had a low mean (23.6%) in the first experiment produced 5 lethals out of ten chromosomes tested. Each lethal balanced over the dominant marker was outcrossed singly to "normal", and F_1 females were tested for recombinants. From 89 recombinant F_2 chromosomes so far analyzed, 35 (39%) had lethals. A homogeneity chi-square on the five tests was non-significant (p = .95). Two explanations are possible: 1) the lethal is a point mutation with incomplete penetrance, or 2) desynthesis has been accomplished, since 39% is significantly below 50% so that we can interpret the drop (11%) uniformly resulted in 22% new linkages which gave non-lethal viability (100% − 39% non-crossover lethals − 39% non-crossover normals).

Finally, while the statistical evidence for synthetic lethals in *D. persimilis* was not overwhelming, and while the assumption of point mutation was simplest in that species, we have now facts that are more easily interpreted as recombinational origin of certain lethals. The case for such extreme variants is more plausible.

In *D. prosaltans* Dobzhansky *et al.* (1958) have retested a certain strain which gave 7 lethals out of 10 chromosomes tested. The strain was out-crossed to the dominant marker stock and a new viable homozygous strain re-isolated. Out of ten retest crosses the new chromosome produced 19 lethals in 4 crosses. Since the retests were made immediately after the re-isolation of the homozygous viable chromosome, these lethals must have been synthetic.

General Scheme of Genic Action

Any scheme presented to account for the effects observed must satisfy these conditions: 1) the viability of both initial parent chromosomes must be near "normal" in the homozygous condition; 2) the average viability of homozygous derived chromosomes is lower (or extremely lower in the case of lethals) than their unrecombined parent chromosomes; and 3) variance must be greater among derived chromosome homozygotes.

Beginning with the last observation, variance will always increase if the parent chromosomes are genetically diverse. This result, so consistent in our data, emphasizes the genetic heterogeneity of the original parents and therefore points to a greater likelihood of balanced heterozygosity as the wild population's principal genetic structure.

To obtain consistent lowering of viability from parent to derived chromosomes, an additive scheme of gene action is not realistic irrespective of mathematical transformation of high excellence. For example, a simple additive scheme produces no average change:

$$P_1 \frac{+ - + - + -}{+ - + - + -}$$

$$\times \frac{- + - + - +}{- + - + - +} \quad \begin{array}{l} \text{Net increment} = +3 \\ -3 = 0 \text{ in each} \\ \text{parent} \end{array}$$

$$F_1 \frac{+ - + - + -}{- + - + - +} \times \frac{}{} \rightarrow$$

$$\left.\begin{array}{l} + - + + - + \\ - + - - + - \end{array}\right\} \begin{array}{l} 2 \\ -2 = 0 \end{array} \quad \begin{array}{l} \text{Average incre-} \\ \text{ment unchanged} \end{array}$$
$$\left.\begin{array}{l} + - + - + - \\ - + - + - + \end{array}\right\} \begin{array}{l} 0 \\ 0 = 0 \end{array} \quad \text{in recombinants.}$$

Crossing over increases the number of genotypes but does not alter the average increment. No elaboration of this additive scheme can change that fact.

Lewontin (personal communication) has suggested that if viability is a probability function (which it might not be) then the joint contributions of separate loci might be the product o their individual contributions. A logarithmic transformation would then reduce such a product system to an additive one but no consistent drop in viability could be demonstrated with such a transformation. If linked loci contribute to viability as the product of their individual viabilities, the geometric mean of their total contributions might be more appropriate:

Let $\dfrac{A}{A} = \dfrac{B}{B}$ produce an increment of 2

Let $\dfrac{a}{a} = \dfrac{b}{b}$ produce an increment of $\frac{1}{2}$

Let loci $A(a) - B(b)$ determine viability as the geometric mean of the two loci increments.

Then

$$P_1 \frac{AB}{AB} \times \frac{ab}{ab} \text{ Net increment average for } P_1$$

$$= \frac{2 + \frac{1}{2}}{2} = 1.25$$

$$F_1 \begin{array}{c} AB \\ \text{-}\times\text{-} \\ ab \end{array} \rightarrow$$

$$\left\{\begin{array}{ll} Ab & = \sqrt{2 \times \frac{1}{2}} = 1 \quad \text{Average progeny} \\ aB & = \sqrt{2 \times \frac{1}{2}} = 1 \quad \dfrac{1 + 1 + 2 + \frac{1}{2}}{4} \\ & \qquad\qquad\qquad = 1.125 \\ AB & = 2 \qquad\qquad \text{(assuming equal} \\ ab & = \frac{1}{2} \qquad\qquad \text{crossover and non-} \\ & \qquad\qquad\qquad \text{crossover classes)} \end{array}\right.$$

While the progeny average lower in this scheme, agreement with observed facts is lacking on two counts: 1) to reduce viability, one parent must have low viability, and 2) if parental loci are in repulsion the average of the progeny would be *raised*. There is no way of knowing which linkage exists in the observed crosses; we cannot assume all loci to be in coupling in order to make all routes downward from parent chromosomes to derived chromosomes.

If viability is largely dependent upon either the *sequence* of modifiers or the particular juxtaposition of such modifiers, a simple scheme of interaction satisfies the three observed conditions:

Let any x — y combination in either order = 1 increment in viability.

Let any x — x or y — y = 0 increment in viability.

$$P_1 \frac{x - y - x - y}{x - y - x - y}$$

$$(\times) \frac{y - x - y - x}{y - x - y - x}$$ Each parent has 3 $(x - y)$ combinations = 3 increments

$$F_1 \frac{x - y - x - y}{y - x - y - x} \times \frac{}{} \longrightarrow$$

$$\left.\begin{cases} x - y - y - x \\ y - x - x - y \end{cases}\right\} = 2 \atop = 2$$

$$\left.\begin{cases} x - y - x - y \\ y - x - y - x \end{cases}\right\} = 3 \atop = 3$$

Average = 2.5 (assuming equal crossover and non-crossover classes)

Particular interactions may be devised which would give very extreme changes (an x — x combination for example might be lethal). Epistatic interactions between linked loci are then vastly more important to viability determination in these natural populations than additive effects of such loci.

THE TOTAL VARIABILITY

If recombination determines a regression toward the mean and distribution of viabilities in the wild progenitor population, it can be inferred that a major portion of the variability usually observed by inbreeding wild organisms has been released by recombination of interacting loci. Undoubtedly these results fit the balanced population genetic structure better than the classical: if selection acts to preserve good gene action at heterozygous loci it must simultaneously act to preserve good interactions between such heterozygous loci. Homozygotes for chromosomes will be exceedingly rare in nature. All of which emphasizes the extreme complexity of the total genome and the urgency of knowing the population's genetic system before embarking on selection plans or drawing conclusions from a selection experiment.

How much variability observed by testing wild Drosophila for homozygote effects can be ascribed to recombination of linked complexes? Dobzhansky and his coworkers have collected extensive data on the total variability of chromosomes in wild populations. They have compared variances produced by recombination of these good viability chromosomes with the total variance observed between random chromosomes obtained in nature (Dobzhansky *et al.*, 1958). He has calculated that the amount of variance engendered by recombination within these normal chromosomes amounts to from 25 % to 43 % of the total variance observed in wild populations of these three species. *D. pseudoobscura* has the greatest potential variability in linked complexes with a minimum variance of 60 for derived chromosomes out of 140 total variance for all wild chromosomes (43 %), or for non-lethal derived chromosomes 48 out of 65 for all wild non-lethal chromosomes (74 %). *D. persimilis* and *D. prosaltans* have less potential variability apparently in this comparison of derived chromosome variances with original wild chromosome variances, namely about 25 % in both species when counting all chromosomes but about 28 % when omitting lethals from the comparison. It is impressive that these normal viability chromosomes should produce such a substantial portion of the genetic variability which a random sample of wild chromosomes would display.

When such a large proportion of the total variability can be manufactured by releasing the potential of linked complexes in an arbitary segment of the chromosome population, how much of the total variability could be produced by random recombination in the natural population? Undoubtedly a very large proportion, in fact nearly all variability in *D. pseudoobscura* homozygotes, might result from this source. The synthesizing and desynthesizing of new linkages which interact epistatically rather than new mutation becomes the chief immediate source of genetic diversity. As stated by Dobzhansky: "With a population structure of this sort a total suppression of the mutation process would probably fail to change the evolutionary plasticity of the species for very many generations."

Is this source of variation of equally high magnitude in all species? It does not seem so. *D. persimilis* releases less variability by recombination, yet in nature it has frequencies of lethals and semi-lethals about equal to *D. pseudoobscura* (25.5 % in *D. persimilis* to 33.0 % in *D. pseudoobscura* taken from the same locality in California.) If these two species differ in their ability to produce diversity by recombination, there are two likely explanations: 1) *D. persimilis* is more homozygous on the average and fits the classical population structure better than *D. pseudoobscura*; or 2) the species are nearly equal in heterozygosity as would appear from their lethal and semilethal frequencies but in order to maintain that heterozygosity, mutation rates in *persimilis* should be higher. Mutation rate is higher in *persimilis* by a factor of nearly two over that in *pseudoobscura* (Dobzhansky, Spassky, and Spassky, 1954). Consequently from the observation that *persimilis* shows a less drastic recombination effect, a decrease in heterozygosity in that species is not necessarily to be inferred. It is important to remember that epistatic interactions are selected for while loci are heterozygous and heterotic simultaneously. Less epistatic effects could mean either greater homozygosity or less heterotic heterozygosity. The latter could be the case if high mutation rate instead of allelic interaction maintains that heterozygosity.

D. prosaltans combines certain features of both other species: in one locality (Pirassunuga) recombination variance is low as in *persimilis*, while in the other locality (Rio) variance is high as in *pseudoobscura*. These differences are difficult to prove significant, but assuming that they are real, it would be still more difficult to prove that any two species are fundamentally different when only two localities have been sampled in each species. The two local populations chosen in *D. prosaltans* happen to give different results: if more localities in the other species were examined there is a question whether they would be more consistent or more variable than *D. prosaltans*. That tropical species is usually quite rare and it was expected that its recombination effects would be comparable with *D. persimilis*. Possibly if *D. willistoni* studies had been completed, a comparison of that species with *D. prosaltans* would have told us more about relative recombination effects between chromosomes from very heterozygous and less heterozygous species populations. At present we can only say that apparently one population of *D. prosaltans* seems to be more balanced and the other more classical.

It is worth being reminded perhaps that these results serve to remove the "independent genic locus" one further step from its old position of utility towards a more intricate design for the genetic material. These interactions between linked polygenes, if they *are* separable and can be called anything in the plural, and the interactions between alleles over long chromosomal distances demonstrated earlier for numerous naturally occurring inversion heterozygotes and now for these "supergenes" of linked complexes, all bring into focus a vast interdependency of genic actions in the total genome. Methods for analysis of such complexities are indispensable, yet the mere knowledge of their existence is useful.

Summary

The kinds of variability observable in a population are largely a function of that population's genetic system. For outcrossed populations, the functional nature of heterozygosity and the genetic combinations which have highest adaptive value serve to preserve beneficial linkage relationships simultaneously. Obligate heterozygosity may involve generation of a multiple allelic system which when recombined would engender a variety of linkages. Different chromosomes of good adaptive value from a population in which heterozygosity is obligate may be expected to engender homozygous recombinants of great diversity and of less adaptive value.

Experiments on these species of Drosophila (*D. pseudoobscura*, *D. persimilis*, and *D. prosaltans*) to test recombination products from 20 chosen good viability chromosomes in each species demonstrated a very extensive array of viabilities and a consistent lowering of viability among their homozygous recombined products. The total amount of variability released is greatest in *D. pseudoobscura* which is the most widely distributed and most versatile ecologically of the three species (amounting to 43% of the total variability observed for random chromosomes in nature). The other two species are not so spectacular but produce substantial variation (amounting to 25% of their total respective variabilities in nature). Most of the genetic diversity observed for these chromosomes in nature may well be produced by recombination of interacting linked genic complexes rather than by additively acting polygenes or by new mutations.

Addendum

In view of the considerable discussion in the following papers on recombinational effects of inversion heterozygotes on heterologous chromosomes, it seems pertinent to mention the following-ing difference between the experiments on *D. pseudoobscura* and *D. persimilis* and a personal communication from Professor Dobzhansky to the author concerning this difference.

In the *persimilis* experiments, chromosome III was made structurally homozygous for the Whitney arrangement. In *pseudoobscura* that chromosome was not made structurally homozygous (from Dobzhansky): "Although California strains have not been examined for chromosome III, the Texas strains are almost all Pikes Peak arrangement. This means that interpopulational hybrids are almost all heterozygotes while intrapopulational ones are mostly homozygotes. We would expect a greater recombinational effect in the inter- than in the intra- experiments and a greater variance in the former. Although a greater variance in the former was expected on other grounds, it is conspicuously absent in all three species."

References

BREESE, E. L. and MATHER, K., 1957, The organization of polygenic activity within a chromosome in Drosophila. I. Hair characters. Heredity *11:* 373–395.

DOBZHANSKY, Th., 1946, Genetics of natural populations. XIII. Recombination and variability in populations of *D. pseudoobscura*. Genetics *31:* 269–290.

—— 1951, Genetics and the Origin of Species. 3rd Edition, New York, Columbia Univ. Press.

—— 1955, A review of some fundamental concepts and problems of population genetics. Cold Spring Harbor Symposia Quant. Biol. *20:* 1–15.

DOBZHANSKY, Th., and EPLING, C., 1944, Contributions to the genetics, taxonomy, and ecology of *D. pseudoobscura* and its relatives. Carnegie Inst. Wash. Publ. *554,* pp. 183.

DOBZHANSKY, Th., LEVENE, H., SPASSKY, B., and SPASSKY, N., 1958, Release of genetic variability through recombination. III. *D. prosaltans*. Genetics: (in press).

DOBZHANSKY, Th., and SPASSKY, B., 1953, Genetics of natural populations. XXI. Concealed variability in two sympatric species of Drosophila. Genetics *38:* 471–484.

DOBZHANSKY, Th., SPASSKY, B., and SPASSKY, N., 1954, Rates of spontaneous mutation in the second chromosomes of the sibling species, *D. pseudoobscura* and *D. persimilis*. Genetics *39:* 899–907.

HILDRETH, P. E., 1955, A test for recombinational lethals in the X chromosome of *D. melanogaster*. Proc. Natl. Acad. Sci. U. S. *41:* 20–24.

—— 1956, The problem of synthetic lethals in *D. melanogaster*. Genetics *41:* 729–742.

LEVENE, H., 1958, Release of genetic variability through recombination. IV. Statistical theory. Genetics: (in press).

MISRO, B., 1949, Crossing over as a source of new variation. Proc. Intern. Congr. Genet., 8th Congr.: 629–630.

SPASSKY, B., and DOBZHANSKY, Th., 1950, Comparative genetics of *D. willistoni*. Heredity *4*: 201–215.

SPASSKY, B., SPASSKY, N., LEVENE, H., and DOBZHANSKY, Th., 1958, Release of genetic variability through recombination. I. *D. pseudoobscura*. Genetics: (in press).

SPIESS, E. B., 1958, Release of genetic variability through recombination. II. *D. persimilis*. Genetics: (in press).

TIMOFEEF-RESSOVSKY, N. W., 1940, Mutations and geographical variation. In "The New Systematics" ed. J. HUXLEY, Oxford Univ. Press, pp. 73–136.

WALLACE, B., KING, J. C., MADDEN, C. V., KAUFMANN, B., and McGUNNIGLE, E. C., 1953, An analysis of variability arising through recombination. Genetics *38*: 272–307.

WIGAN, L. G., 1949, Chromosome regions which give new variation by crossing over. Proc. Intern. Congr. Genet., 8th Congr.: 686–687.

DISCUSSION

LEVINS: The measurement of viability in a single environment could obscure the adaptive significance of genetic heterogeneity and in particular of recombination. Although it is true that intrapopulation heterozygotes often are more viable than homozygotes, it is unlikely that any one genotype in a population is superior to all others in all the environments naturally encountered.

Only by testing the effects of recombination in a series of environments can we decide whether the genetic heterogeneity observed is a result of mutation, the price of heterozygosity, or itself an adaptive character of the populations in question. Some at least of the recombinants may not be novelties but regularly recurring types adapted to particular aspects of the population's environment. If this were the case we might expect greater differences between intrapopulation and interpopulation recombinants, except that the use of the marker strains means that all recombinants are being tested against an alien genetic background.

SPIESS: While it would be very desirable to test particular recombinants in numerous environments to note their diversity of adaptabilities, I think we would lose sight of the main problem, namely the extent of potential variability tied up in linked complexes. It would certainly be a monumental task to assay the fitness of linked complexes to various environments.

I would favor the view that the intrapopulational recombinants are not novelties but that their action is utilized chiefly while heterozygous; so that unless heterozygosity on chromosome II is quite low, homozygous recombinants should be more likely to have reduced adaptive value in most environments. As Dr. Levins points out, interpopulational recombinants are more likely to be novelties and therefore have less fitness in the environments in which intrapopulational are adaptive.The results indicate no difference between intra- and inter- recombinants however, and I would hazard a guess that both kinds would show the drop in viability effect in most environments including the natural habitat.

PROUT: Your data show that certain linked complexes may be favorable and others unfavorable. Such a phenomenon brings up the question of possible mechanisms for maintaining certain linkage phases intact at the expense of others. Of course, one mechanism is a system of inversions which presumably reduces recombination between inversion gene pools to zero. Any other device which merely reduces crossing over (but not to zero) would act only to prolong eventual linkage equilibrium. I wonder if you have been able to visualize any new schemes which might provide the answer to this problem?

SPIESS: Apparently it must be stressed again that all variation released by the procedures described is homozygous variation. It is probably of only slight consequence to the net adaptive value in nature that homozygous complexes are favorable or unfavorable since identical linkages may be quite rare. Linkage equilibrium certainly has to be postulated for chromosomes lacking crossover suppressor mechanisms; but it is known that heterozygotic combinations of most wild chromosomes produce uniformly favorable phenotypes (Dobzhansky, Pavlovsky, Spassky, and Spassky, Genetics 40: 781–796; Cordeiro and Dobzhansky, Am. Nat. 88: 75–86). If heterozygosity of heterotic loci is to be maintained, a high order multiple allelic system and consequently a vast number of linkages must exist, any one of which seldom occurs in a homozygote in nature, and if it does, would be selected against unless it were preadapted for its environment by chance. For inversion systems heterozygosity could be maintained at fewer loci and/or with fewer alternative alleles than for systems lacking crossover suppressors.

Possible mechanisms for maintaining certain linkage phases intact at the expense of others cannot be postulated from our data; indeed we are attempting to find out the nature of systems lacking such mechanisms.

AN ESTIMATE OF THE MUTATIONAL DAMAGE IN MAN FROM DATA ON CONSANGUINEOUS MARRIAGES*

By Newton E. Morton, James F. Crow,

DEPARTMENT OF GENETICS, UNIVERSITY OF WISCONSIN

AND

H. J. Muller

DEPARTMENT OF ZOÖLOGY, UNIVERSITY OF INDIANA

Communicated August 28, 1956

In a diploid, outbreeding organism like man the deleterious mutants carried by the population are only partly expressed in each generation, being largely concealed by heterozygosis with more favorable alleles. However, the total hidden mutational damage carried by the population can be estimated indirectly from the detrimental effects of consanguineous marriage.

This method, applied to mortality data of Arner,[1] provided the basis for the statement that "a calculation from ... results of inbreeding in man ... leads to the conclusion that every person on the average contains heterozygously at least one lethal gene or group of genes which [homozygously would] ... kill an individual ... between birth and maturity."[2] The calculation itself was not given, however, and the stated figure of one lethal equivalent per person represents a conservative estimate, being a good deal lower than the most probable value (nearly two) actually indicated by the data. Recently Slatis[3] has used a similar procedure for estimating the number of heterozygous genes that, if homozygous, would cause detectable rare abnormalities and has arrived at a tentative estimate of eight such genes per person. His conclusions are qualified by the fact that the subjects were selected for having abnormalities, some of which may not have been simple recessives.

In this paper we shall present calculations whereby, using death rates both from Arner's and from two other published studies of consanguineous marriages, we have attempted to measure the total mutational damage. We shall also show how, by making some assumptions about the manner in which the mutations are expressed (and hence with less assurance), we have estimated the amount of mutational damage actually expressed each generation. Finally, we shall use the data to estimate the total mutation rate in man.

Human Consanguinity Data.—The selection of families on the basis of the consanguinity of the parents has both advantages and disadvantages. The disadvantages of this approach are that a large sample is required and that the sociological concomitants of consanguineous marriage (rural-urban differences, etc.) may be confounded with the genetic effects. The advantages are that it is not biased by selection of particular genetic entities and that homozygosity for two or more deleterious genes with possibly synergistic effects is unlikely at the low levels of inbreeding found in man.

Three published studies on consanguineous marriage fulfil the condition of a large sample. It is questionable whether they also meet the requirement for separation of genetic effects from the sociological correlates of inbreeding. The most recent and useful data (summarized in Table 1) were obtained by Sutter and Tabah[4] from

Reprinted by permission of the authors from PROCEEDINGS OF
NATIONAL ACADEMY OF SCIENCES, **42**, 855–863 (1956).

Catholic marriage dispensations issued during 1919–1925 in two French departments. These authors visited about two-thirds of the families and took histories of births and deaths, with notes on conspicuous abnormalities. The same information was obtained from town clerks for a control sample of unrelated parents married during the same period and selected without regard to fertility or medical history.

Arner[1] obtained his data by going through early American genealogies and recording, among other things, the number of deaths before age 20 in the children of consanguineous marriages. Nonconsanguineous marriages of the parents' siblings served as controls. He does not give the number of deaths for each kind of consanguineous marriage beyond first cousins, but only an average. However, elsewhere in his paper he gives data from which the approximate composition of this group may be inferred, and from this we have estimated the average inbreeding coefficient. The relevant data are given in Table 2.

TABLE 1

CHILD MORTALITY: DATA OF SUTTER AND TABAH

(Data Given as Deaths/Total, with Proportion of Deaths Below)

	First Cousins ($F = .0625$)	$1^1/_2$ Cousins ($F = .0312$)	Second Cousins ($F = .0156$)	Not Related ($F = 0$)
Morbihan:				
Stillbirths and neonatal deaths	51/461	3/78	23/309	72/1,628
	.111	.038	.074	.044
Infantile and juvenile deaths	64/410	17/25	32/286	138/1,556
	.156	.227	.112	.089
Loir et Cher:				
Stillbirths and neonatal deaths	18/282	6/105	11/240	36/1,117
	.064	.057	.046	.032
Infantile and juvenile deaths	32/264	1/99	17/229	60/1081
	.121	.010	.074	.056

TABLE 2

CHILDREN DYING UNDER THE AGE OF 20: DATA OF ARNER

First Cousins ($F = .0625$)	Other Cousins ($F = .0112$)	Not Related ($F = 0$)
113/672	211/1,417	370/3,184
.168	.149	.116

The third source of data is a very old study by Bemiss[5] based on correspondence with physicians, with consequent unintentional selection of families with conspicuous abnormalities. We have included his data on "children dying young" in Table 3. Although the abnormalities are undoubtedly selected, few of them were incompatible with life, and in fact the incestuous group (parent-child and sib matings, not included in Table 3), which recorded 29 of 31 as defective, included no

TABLE 3

CHILDREN DYING YOUNG: DATA OF BEMISS

Uncle-Niece ($F = .1250$)	Double First Cousins ($F = .1250$)	First Cousins ($F = .0625$)	Second Cousins ($F = .0156$)	Third Cousins ($F = .0039$)	Not Related ($F = 0$)
23/53	55/154	637/2,778	85/513	8/59	134/837
.434	.357	.229	.166	.136	.160

deaths. It is likely, therefore, that the data on deaths are not seriously biased by selection. Yet it is to be expected that these data would be less reliable than those from the other studies, especially the modern careful studies of Sutter and Tabah.

Definitions.—We wish to distinguish between *total* mutational damage and *expressed* mutational damage, both measured for the purposes of this paper in *lethal equivalents.*

A *lethal equivalent* is a group of mutant genes of such number that, if dispersed in different individuals, they would cause on the average one death, e.g., one lethal mutant, or two mutants each with 50 per cent probability of causing death, etc. The concept will be illustrated in a later section.

The *total mutational damage* per gamete is the average number of lethal equivalents in the zygote that would result from doubling the chromosomes of this gamete.

The *expressed mutational damage* per gamete is the average number of lethal equivalents in this gamete that would be expressed if it were combined with another gamete to form a zygote according to the mating system actually prevailing among the individuals being considered.

An Estimate of the Total Mutational Damage.—Considering a single locus, the probability of a particular zygote surviving the detrimental effects of mutants at this locus is[6]

$$1 \quad - \quad qFs \quad - \quad q^2(1 - F)s \quad - \quad 2q(1 - q)(1 - F)sh$$

| | Probability of death due to homozygosity from consanguinity | Probability of death due to homozygosity not from consanguinity | Probability of death in a heterozygote |

where s is the probability of death in the mutant homozygote and h is a measure of dominance, being 0 for a completely recessive factor and 1 for a gene causing the same probability of death in a heterozygote as in a homozygote. F is Wright's[7] coefficient of inbreeding and measures that fraction of loci that are homozygous as a result of consanguinity, being $1/16$ for children of first cousins, $1/32$ for those of first cousins once removed ($1\frac{1}{2}$ cousins), $1/64$ for those of second cousins, etc.

We make the assumption that different causes of death, genetic or environmental, are independent in action ("nonsynergistic" in the sense used by Muller[8]). On this model the fraction of survivors is

$$S = \Pi(1 - x)\{1 - qFs - q^2(1 - F)s - 2q(1 - q)(1 - F)sh\},$$

where x is the probability of a particular environmental cause of death, and the product is taken over all environmental causes and over all loci with mutant alleles. Since the number of causes is large and the separate probabilities are small, this is equivalent to

$$S = e^{-\Sigma x - F\Sigma qs - (1-F)\Sigma q^2 s - 2(1-F)\Sigma q(1-q)sh}$$
$$= e^{-(A+BF)},$$

or

$$-\log_e S = A + BF,$$

where $A = \Sigma x + \Sigma q^2 s + 2\Sigma q(1 - q)sh$ and $B = \Sigma qs - \Sigma q^2 s - 2\Sigma q(1 - q)sh$. The summation is over all environmental factors, or over all loci having mutant alleles.

In a randomly mating population ($F = 0$) the amount of expressed damage is measured by A. B is a measure of the hidden genetic damage that would be expressed fully only in a complete homozygote ($F = 1$). We take as a measure of total genetic damage per gamete the quantity Σqs, this being the amount expressed in a zygote formed by doubling the chromosomes of this gamete. This quantity is equal to the sum of B and the genetic component of A and hence lies between B and $B + A$.

Estimates of A and B were obtained from the weighted regression on F of the natural logarithm of the number of survivors. According to maximum-likelihood theory, the appropriate weights are $nS/(1 - S)$, where S is the expected fraction of survivors and n is the total number. The weights were obtained by iteration, starting with the observed value of S as a trial value. The values of A and B computed in this way are shown in Table 4. Because of the low levels of inbreeding found in man and the small number of deaths in the noninbred groups, virtually the same estimates of A and B are obtained from the simple approximation $S = 1 - A - BF$. Furthermore, since the effects of these factors as actually felt by future populations are dispersed over many individuals, the estimate of B is not greatly influenced by the way in which a large number of lethal effects (genetic and environmental) interact in an individual.

TABLE 4

ESTIMATES AND HOMOGENEITY TEST

	A	B	B/A	B_{FF}	B_{FO}	B_{CO}	χ^2_1
Sutter and Tabah (1953), Morbihan:							
Stillbirths and neonatal deaths	.0460	1.124	24.41	.901	1.233	1.163	.36
Infant and juvenile deaths	.0950	1.431	15.06	.937	1.665	1.222	.88
Total	.1410	2.555	18.12	...	...	...	..
Sutter and Tabah (1953), Loir et Cher:							
Stillbirths and neonatal deaths	.0335	.574	17.12	.398	.662	.538	.24
Infant and juvenile deaths	.0558	.908	16.26	1.201	.759	1.141	.36
Total	.0893	1.482	16.60	...	...	...	..
Arner (1908)	.1300	1.032	7.94	.446	1.803	.970	4.94*
Bemiss (1858)	.1612	1.734	10.75	2.193	1.392	1.371	2.73

It is possible that in any of these studies the consanguineous and nonconsanguineous groups are not comparable in some respect. For example, in the data of Sutter and Tabah the consanguineous group was interviewed by the authors, but the control data were gotten more indirectly. Also, especially in the Bemiss study, there is doubt about the accuracy of ascertainment of the more distant degrees of relationship. Further, there may be undetected environmental differences between the inbred and control groups. For these reasons we have made several tests for internal consistency of the data.

In Table 4 the regression coefficients B_{FF} were obtained from the different degrees of consanguinity, omitting the noninbred group entirely. This is to be compared with B_{FO}, which is based on the comparison of the noninbred group with the average of all the inbred groups. The χ^2 values are for the comparison of these two regression coefficients. The only data that show any evidence of inconsistency ($B_{FF} = .45$, $B_{FO} = 1.80$, $\chi^2_1 = 4.94$, $P \sim .03$) are Arner's, yet his material was collected with the greatest attention to an adequate control, and the computed values of A and B are in reasonable agreement with the other data. Possibly we have been misled in our indirect estimate of F for his "other cousins" group. An additional value is also given in the table, B_{CO}, based on comparisons of the outbred group with those from first-cousin marriages only. This is of special interest in the Bemiss study, since there is some doubt as to his definition of second and third cousins, and in the Arner study for the reason just given.

The Sutter and Tabah data include stillbirths and recorded late miscarriages, whereas the Arner and Bemiss data include mostly postnatal deaths. All these studies include deaths up to early adulthood. Making allowance for the incomplete stillbirth data in the Arner and Bemiss studies, we conclude that B for stillbirths plus juvenile deaths probably lies between 1.5 and 2.5, with $A + B$ only slightly larger. That is, the average gamete carries a group of detrimental factors that, if dispersed in separate individuals and made homozygous, would result in 1.5–2.5 deaths of that age group. Thus the total genetic damage here measured is 1.5–2.5 *lethal equivalents* per gamete, or 3–5 per zygote.

At loci with complete or partial dominance the genetic damage measured by this procedure is due to mutation. But overdominant loci where the heterozygote is fitter than either homozygote make a contribution to inbreeding decline, and hence to B, that is not related directly to mutational damage. It can be shown (Crow, unpublished) that if the two homozygous types have a selective disadvantage of s and t relative to the heterozygote, the genetic damage in a randomly mating population (i.e., the amount by which the population is less fit than if it were made up entirely of the optimum heterozygous type) is proportional to $st/(s + t)$, whereas if this population is made completely homozygous it is proportional to $2st/(s + t)$. Thus the contribution to B of such a locus is exactly equal to its contribution to A. In our data B is some fifteen times the value of A, and the latter includes nongenetic deaths, so we conclude that overdominant loci are not making any substantial contribution to B and that the genetic damage we are measuring is mutational.

These data omit abortions, early adult deaths, and cases of infecundity. Moreover, B would be still higher if genetic impairments that influenced the survival or reproduction of offspring or other relatives of inbred individuals were included. Thus the value of B taken to include these cases is probably at least twice as great as we have given. Furthermore, one lethal equivalent probably comprises several detrimental mutants. Therefore, every individual must be heterozygous for many genes which would be seriously deleterious if homozygous and which together probably produce an appreciable loss of fitness even in the heterozygote.

An Estimate of the Expressed Mutational Damage.—Given the observation that there are the equivalent of 3–5 lethals acting in late fetal to early adult stages per zygote, we can estimate the amount of damage expressed in a single generation. The probability of a particular mutant being eliminated by death due to homozygosity through inbreeding is $Fs;$ that of elimination due to the mutant meeting a preexisting allele is $(1 - F)qs;$ and that of elimination due to the mutant in a heterozygote is $(1 - F)(1 - q)sh$. Neglecting products of small quantities, the total probability of elimination is approximately $(F + q + h)s$. We shall designate $F + q + h$ by z.

The mutant genes actually found in the population will be determined in part by the number of generations that each mutant persists before elimination, and therefore the more completely recessive genes will contribute disproportionately to the inbreeding effect. The mean persistence of a mutant gene is the reciprocal of its probability of being eliminated in any particular generation and is therefore $1/zs$. Therefore, the number of mutant genes per gamete in the population is $\Sigma(\mu/zs)$, where μ is the mutation rate and the summation is over all relevant loci.

The total number of lethal equivalents per gamete is $\Sigma[(\mu/zs)s]$, or $\Sigma(\mu/z)$, whereas the number of expressed lethal equivalents per gamete is $\Sigma[(\mu/zs)zs]$, or simply $\Sigma\mu$. If z and μ are uncorrelated, $\Sigma(\mu/z)$ may be written as $(\Sigma\mu)(\overline{1/z})$. In that case, if estimates of $\overline{1/z}$ and of lethal equivalents are obtainable, this formula can be used to find $\Sigma\mu$, the total mutation rate. Now although q and μ are clearly correlated, the correlation between z and μ is not likely to be large. For q has probably comprised but a small part of z either in early times or at present, and although Muller[8] has suggested that selective processes might cause some correlation between h and μ, their effectiveness is not expected to be great. At any rate, to whatever extent z and μ may be positively correlated, this method will underestimate $\Sigma\mu$.

On the assumption that $\Sigma(\mu/z) = (\Sigma\mu)(\overline{1/z})$, the expressions for total lethal equivalents and for expressed lethal equivalents have a factor, $\Sigma\mu$, in common, which cancels out, leaving the following simple relationship: *The number of expressed lethal equivalents per gamete is the total number of lethal equivalents multiplied by the harmonic mean of z.*

There are several reasons for thinking that most elimination of deleterious genes is now in heterozygotes rather than in homozygotes. Direct measurements on *Drosophila* lethals and semilethals have shown a mean dominance of about 4–5 per cent.[9, 10] This was foreshadowed by Sturtevant's observation[11] that the number of lethals carried by wild populations of *Drosophila* is smaller than would be predicted with random mating (the occurrence of which was, however, questionable) and the observed rate of mutation. It was also indicated by the fact that most deletions of any magnitude have a depressing effect on viability as heterozygotes,[8, 9] by dosage compensation,[12] and by numerous observations of incomplete recessivity in various organisms, including especially those of Levit[13] on man.

To get the harmonic mean of z, which for the reasons just given we consider to be in large measure determined by the heterozygous effect of the mutants, we used the *Drosophila* data of Muller and Campbell (unpublished). Their values of h for 16 autosomal lethals range from .091 to $-.026$. The variance of these values (.00185) does not differ significantly from the variance of repeated observations on the same lethal (.00102), so it is possible that the values simply represent random deviations a true mean value of .042, constant for all lethals. In this case the harmonic mean of h would be the same as its arithmetic mean, or about .04. However, it seems more likely a priori as well as from the evidence given by visible mutants that the true value differs from mutant to mutant, but by less than the observed range would indicate because of measurement errors. We take the observed values and arbitrarily regress each toward the mean by the ratio of the "true" standard deviation (obtained by subtracting the variance of replications of tests on the same lethal from the variance among means of different lethals) to the observed standard deviation, compute for each gene the value of z, and take the harmonic mean. For this purpose the mutation rate per locus was assumed to be 10^{-5}, but it makes very little difference what value is chosen. With $F = 0$ the harmonic mean of z is .013, with $F = .001$ it is .014, with $F = .005$ it is .022, and with $F = .01$ it is .030.

There is a difficulty here in that the gene frequencies may have been largely determined at a time when F was large, but the present expressed damage is in populations with very little inbreeding. If we compute the equilibrium frequency of each mutants in a hypothetical population with $F = .01$, then compute the expressed damage in a population changed to $F = .001$, the result is .023 of the total damage.

It should be noted that mutants with nearly neutral or slightly favorable heterozygotes dominate this value out of all proportion to their initial rate of occurrence. For example, if only two mutants are omitted from the data of Muller and Campbell, the value is raised to nearly .04.

The data of Stern[10] and ten of the sixteen cases studied by Muller and Campbell were based on complete lethals, which, as pointed out by the latter workers, may be more dominant in their effect on survival than mildly deleterious genes, since the lethal homozygotes may be more than sufficient to kill the embryo. For example, Seto[14] showed that lethals that kill in the egg stage of *Drosophila*, which are presumably therefore more drastic, have a greater amount of heterozygous lethality than those killing at later stages. Muller and Campbell, however, do not show a conspicuously or significantly lower dominance for the near-lethals than for the complete ones (.039 versus .044). Moreover, there is some ground for the opposite inference that mutants at loci giving rise mainly to slight detrimentals would have a higher dominance than marked detrimentals because of a lower selective pressure acting to stabilize the expression of the loci.

We shall take the harmonic mean of z as .02. With 1.5–2.5 lethal equivalents per gamete, this corresponds to 3–5 per cent of expressed lethality per gamete, or nearly 6–10 per cent per zygote. The zygotic value is somewhat less than twice the gametic, since with homozygous deaths two lethals lead to only one zygotic death. However, this correction is small if most eliminations are in heterozygotes, as we judge them to be in modern populations. Synergism between different loci would also cause this estimated value to be too high, but for reasons given earlier this is not likely to introduce any sizable error.

Comparison with the values of A in Table 4 suggests that a substantial fraction of deaths in nonconsanguineous marriages may be attributed to heterozygous effects of the same factors that cause deaths as homozygotes in consanguineous marriages; that is, these deaths are in a large measure genetically selective.

An Estimate of the Rate of Occurrence of Detrimental Mutation.—From the relation given in the last section that the total number of lethal equivalents per gamete is $(\Sigma\mu)\overline{(1/z)}$, we can compute the mutation rate as the total number of lethal equivalents multiplied by the harmonic mean of z. Taking 1.5–2.5 as the total number per gamete and .02 as the harmonic mean of z, the total mutation rate of lethals and detrimentals causing deaths from late fetal to early adult states is .03–.05 per gamete per generation. This corresponds to an inbreeding coefficient of .005; if F in the past were as much as .01, the estimated mutation rate would be about 50 per cent greater.

If we assume that the total lethal and detrimental mutation rate, including that causing early embryonic deaths not detected in these studies, is 2–3 times the above values, we have a total mutation rate of .06–.15 per gamete. *Drosophila* data give 10^4 as the ratio of total detrimentals per gamete to single locus rate.[15] Using this value, we obtain a rate of $6\text{--}15 \times 10^{-6}$ detrimental mutations per locus per generation, a value in good agreement with the rates of visible mutations at selected loci.[16] Both types of estimates depend on a number of unverified assumptions and should therefore not be accepted uncritically. However, the agreement between the two essentially independent methods increases in some measure our confidence in each separately.

Discussion.—Besides the lethal effects considered here, there is mutational damage expressed as anatomical defect and nonlethal disease. Sutter and Tabah also give data on the increase of these in consanguineous marriages, from which it can be estimated that the average person carries about 4–5 genes which, if homozygous, could cause conspicuous abnormality. Such abnormality is likely to reduce reproductive potential. Other mutational damage affecting eventual reproductive potential has less conspicuous expression. For these reasons our figures probably underestimate the over-all mutational damage.

The data of Bemiss and Arner are for American populations a century or more ago, and those of Sutter and Tabah for rural French populations born about thirty-five years ago; yet the values of *A* and *B* are quite similar. Current United States rates for stillbirths (5 months' gestation or longer) are 0.016; for neonatal deaths (under one week), 0.017; and for deaths from 1 week to age 25, about 0.004. This total of .037 is about a third of that in the noninbred populations we have considered. Presumably the value of *B* would also be lower now, since many of the deaths in consanguineous families were known to be from infectious diseases that are now much rarer and for which genetic susceptibility is now less serious. In this connection it is noteworthy that Sutter and Tabah's data show a sharp rise in the incidence of tuberculosis with consanguinity. (A large body of carefully collected consanguinity data may be expected from the Japanese studies of the Atomic Bomb Casualty Commission.)

Provided that genetic selection is not suspended or reversed by improvements in environment, but merely attenuated, the mutational damage at equilibrium will be the same under mild or rigorous selection. However, recent improvements in the environment have taken place very rapidly relative to the time over which present gene frequencies were established. We believe, therefore, that mutational damage and mutation rates are more realistically measured in the data we have considered than from contemporary death rates, the genetic component of which is certainly not at equilibrium. For this reason it is of great importance that comparable studies be carried out on populations under primitive or rigorous conditions while they still exist. Such studies, by affording a comparison with those on modernized populations, would also provide a measure of the relaxation of selection under modern conditions.

Summary.—From studies of the increased mortality in children of consanguineous marriages it is estimated that the average person carries heterozygously the equivalent of 3–5 recessive lethals acting between late fetal and early adult stages. Assuming that the most important effect of detrimental "recessive" mutations in populations that undergo little present inbreeding is through heterozygous damage, and using *Drosophila* data to estimate the amount of this, the frequency of deaths in the populations studied due to the same factors as those causing the additional deaths in consanguineous marriages is estimated as 6–10 per cent. From this we estimate a total mutation rate of .03–.05 per gamete per generation to such genes. Since the total, including those causing early undetected embryonic deaths and detrimental effects after maturity, is probably 2–3 times as high as that accounted for here, the total mutation rate to lethals and detrimentals is estimated as

.06–.15 gamete per generation or, with 10^4 loci per gamete, $6–15 \times 10^{-6}$ per locus.

* Department of Genetics, University of Wisconsin, Paper No. 634.

[1] G. B. L. Arner, *Columbia Univ. Studies in History, Economics, and Public Law*, 31, No. 3, 1–99, 1908.

[2] H. J. Muller, *Bull. N.Y. Acad. Med.*, 24, 447–469, 1948.

[3] H. M. Slatis, *Am. J. Human Genet.*, 6, 412–418, 1954.

[4] J. Sutter and L. Tabah, *Population*, 7, 249–266, 1952; 8, 511–526, 1953.

[5] S. M. Bemiss, *Trans. Am. Med. Assoc.*, 11, 319–425, 1858.

[6] Here and later we are making the simplifying assumption that a pre-existing mutant allele has the same effect on viability as the new mutant.　This is justified as a first approximation by the observation that compounds of mutants are often near the average of the mutant homozygotes. This formula is given for only two alleles, but the extension to a larger number is obvious and the linearity in F remains.　In applying this to a real population, we assume $F = 0$ for all individuals not known to come from a consanguineous marriage.

[7] S. Wright, *Am. Naturalist*, 56, 330–338, 1922; *Ann. Eugen.*, 15, 323–354, 1951.

[8] H. J. Muller, *Am. J. Human Genet.*, 2, 111–176, 1950.

[9] H. J. Muller, *J. Cellular Comp. Physiol.*, 35, suppl. 1, 205–210, 1950, and unpublished data of Muller and Campbell.

[10] C. Stern, G. Carson, M. Kinst, E. Novitski, and D. Uphoff, *Genetics*, 37, 413–449, 1952.

[11] Referred to on p. 41 of Th. Dobzhansky and S. Wright, *Genetics*, 26, 23–51, 1941.

[12] H. J. Muller, *Harvey Lectures*, Ser. 43, pp. 165–229, 1947–1948.

[13] S. G. Levit, *J. Genetics*, 33, 411–434, 1936.

[14] F. Seto, *Am. Naturalist*, 88, 373–378, 1954.

[15] The "single locus" rate in *Drosophila* may, of course, be the total rate among a series of pseudoalleles.　In man there is not only this difficulty but the fact that mutants at different loci with phenotypically similar effects may be counted as mutants at a single locus.

[16] J. Neel and W. Schull, *Human Heredity* (Chicago: Univ. Chicago Press, 1954), p. 144.

MUTATION AND QUANTITATIVE VARIATION

G. CLAYTON AND ALAN ROBERTSON

Institute of Animal Genetics, Edinburgh

Almost all our knowledge of the origin of new variation by mutation comes from work on individual genes with lethal or visible effects. The extent to which new variation arises in continuously variable characters has received little attention. Gustafsson (1953) found that irradiation of barley produced variants of practical value though most of these may be simple Mendelian segregants. More recently, Scossiroli (1953) and Buzzati-Traverso (1953) have shown that new variation induced by radiation can be utilized by either natural or artificial selection to give striking changes in a population. The former was using two lines selected by Mather for the number of sterno-pleural chaetae until there was no further response. By irradiation and selection, he was able to change the mean of the up line from its previous plateau of 26 bristles to 44 bristles in 17 generations of radiation and selection. He was however unable to change the down line. It seemed possible to us that in the up line there had remained some unfixable genetic variation which had been released by the radiation perhaps by the production of chiasmata in unusual regions. Stimulated by this work, we decided to investigate on a small scale the effects of radiation in a strain in which genetic variation had been reduced to a low level by inbreeding.

In our other work on abdominal chaetae (Clayton, Morris and Robertson, in press) we have used as base population a stock which shortly after captivity in the wild has been kept in a population cage with average numbers around 5000. Mr. B. K. Sen, working on egg production in Drosophila, made several inbred lines from this by continued full-sib mating and one of these was chosen for the radiation work because, of the surviving lines, it had the least variance in the count of abdominal chaetae. It had then been inbred for 28 generations. Four selection lines were started in two groups. The two irradiated lines were given 1800 r of X-rays as adults each generation and the two control lines were not treated. Within each group, one line was selected upwards for the total number of chaetae on the fourth and fifth abdominal segments and the other downwards. The selection procedure was the same in all cases—25 ♂ and 25 ♀ were measured and the extreme 10 of each sex chosen as parents of the next generation. Culture was in half-pint bottles. The selection was continued for 17 generations.

The current effect of the radiation on lethals was not checked but at the end of the experiments, a sample of third chromosomes was made homozygous, by the usual technique, for each of the four lines. The numbers of chromosomes lethal and non-lethal when homozygous are given in table 1.

There is no doubt about the accumulation of lethals in the irradiated stocks. In a population of this small size, the equilibrium between mutation

Reprinted by permission of THE AMERICAN NATURALIST from THE AMERICAN NATURALIST, 89, 151–158 (1955).

TABLE 1

		Lethal	Non-lethal
Control	High (HC)	2	32
	Low (LC)	0	32
Irradiated	High (HR)	58	9
	Low (LR)	29	9

and selection is reached fairly quickly. If the heterozygotes are not at a disadvantage, Wright (1937) has shown that lethal recessives reach an equilibrium frequency of $\mu\sqrt{2\pi N}$ where μ is the mutation rate per generation and N the effective population size. If we take the actual size to be the effective size in our case (although the latter may in fact be less), the equilibrium frequency is about 11μ and should therefore have been reached during the experiment. The observed frequencies of lethal chromosomes are 3 per cent and 83 per cent in the control and irradiated lines respectively. Taking these as the equilibrium figures and allowing for chromosomes carrying more than one lethal, the mutation rate per generation works out at 0.3 per cent and 16 per cent, which is not unreasonable.

The effects of the selection are given in table 2 in which, to smooth out differences between generations due to the small numbers measured, the

TABLE 2

Generation	HC	LC	HR	LR
1–5	28.93	28.88	29.65	29.26
6–10	29.52	29.29	31.20	29.18
11–17	28.99	28.93	32.26	28.69
17A	29.02	28.72	31.64	28.30

generations are given in three groups 1-5, 6-10 and 11-17. The mean count of the two sexes has been taken. It had seemed possible in the early stages of the work that the radiation might be having a direct effect on the mean. This could arise because of the smaller number of eggs hatching in the radiation lines due to dominant lethals. For the last generation, 17A, there was therefore neither selection nor radiation and 50 flies of each sex were counted instead of 25.

The control lines change remarkably little during the course of the experiment. HC is higher than LC in the last two entries, the differences being 0.06 ± 0.36 and 0.30 ± 0.54 respectively. The radiated lines do show a slight drop of 0.50 bristles in 17A from the previous entry in agreement with the idea that the lower degree of crowding in these lines may have increased the mean count. Crowding is known to depress the count (Rasmusson, 1952) but it is a little surprising that our control conditions, which we had considered optimum, should have such an effect. LR is below the average of the two controls in gen. 17A (0.67 ± 0.39) and the value of the differences in the generations 11-17 of the experiment suggests that this difference may be real. HR does show a definite increase above the controls (2.77 ± 0.29) in gen. 17A. Our impression during the experiment was that this occurred in the early generations and the final figure was not as large as we expected earlier. Perhaps this is due to an isolated event rather than an accumulation of small effects.

The average variance of the two sexes calculated within generations is given in table 3. The two control lines have been averaged because of their similar behavior. The figures for each line are based on 48 d.f. per generation except for 17A where they are based on 98.

TABLE 3

Generation	Controls	HR	LR
1–5	5.03	6.39	5.72
6–10	4.60	7.55	5.44
11–17	4.43	8.91	4.62
17A	3.87	6.07	6.79

The trends are not as clear as they are for the means. The controls decline slightly but the effect is not significant. HR is more variable than the controls as might be expected from the response to selection. However, had all this extra variance been utilizable by selection, the response should have been greater. Our base outbred population has a mean variance of 12.2 and under this intensity of selection would respond at 1.5 chaetae per generation. LR is only slightly more variable than the controls except for generation 17A where the behavior of the two irradiated lines is surprising.

We had hoped to carry on selection for sterno-pleural chaetae simultaneously with this work but some of the lines were lost in the early generations. However, at generation 10 of LR, selection for sterno-pleurals was carried out for 5 generations in both directions under similar conditions to that described above for abdominal chaetae. There was no detectable divergence between the lines.

In experiments of this sort, it is essential to guard against the possibility of contamination. A response to selection may be due to a single contaminant. When this work was started no suitable inbred stocks were available in this laboratory though they have now been obtained. It was not realized until too late that our line was in fact marked. Examination of salivary chromosomes from LR at the end of the experiment, kindly made by Mr. G. R. Knight, showed that the line was homozygous for In(3R)K known to be present at low frequency in the base population. Unfortunately HR, the line with the greatest response, had by then been discarded. It may be noted that no new inversions were found in the 10 larvae examined in LR.

DISCUSSION

In mutation work on lethal or visible genes, the mutation rate can be simply stated as the proportion of chromosomes in each generation which gives rise to a change of a certain type. But for quantitative characters, we have no such absolute measurement and no way of bringing the results for the new variation on to the same plane of reference as those for "good" genes. Presumably our measurement of the effect of radiation in producing new continuous variation would be in terms of the increase in variance for a given dosage. One is still faced with the problem of comparing the new variation arising in different characters. A possible standard of comparison might be the genetic variance of the character usually observed in wild populations. This is perhaps vague, particularly for domestic animals, but it does have the merit of giving a figure which is also of evolutionary interest, i.e. the problem of how long it would take for a genetically invariant population to acquire as much variation as is usually found in the wild, solely by the accumulation of mutations.

In the character we used, the few observations on wild populations of *Drosophila melanogaster* suggest fortunately that the greater part of the genetic variance is additive and can therefore be measured from the response to selection. The latter can then be expressed as the product of the heritability of the character concerned and the selection differential. The heritability is equal to $\dfrac{\sigma^2 g}{\sigma^2 p}$ the ratio of the additive genetic variance $\sigma^2 g$, to the phenotypic variance $\sigma^2 p$ and, on the assumption of normality, the selection differential can be expressed as $\bar{i}\sigma p$, where $\bar{i}$, depending on the degree of selection, can be obtained from tables (Fisher and Yates 1938, table 20). We then have for the average response in each generation

$$\Delta G = \frac{\sigma^2 g}{\sigma^2 p} \cdot \bar{i}\sigma p; = \bar{i}\,\frac{\sigma^2 g}{\sigma p}$$

For the two control lines, the last two entries show HC higher than LC by 0.06 ± 0.36 and 0.30 ± 0.64. We may combine these to give a mean value of 0.12 ± 0.32. As an upper limit for this divergence, we can take the mean plus twice the standard error, i.e. 0.76 bristles, so that the response in each line would be 0.38. This would occur in about 14 generations giving an average response each generation of not more than 0.027. In the controls, $\bar{i} = 0.94$ (corresponding to 10 selected out of 25) and p = 2.1 (table 3). We have then

$$0.027 = 0.94 \times \frac{\sigma^2 g}{2.1}; \text{ i.e. } \sigma^2 g = 0.060$$

This is an average value over the 14 generations. The line had been continuously mated full-sib before the start of this experiment and assuming that equilibrium had been reached between the loss of variance due to the mating system (at a rate of 19.1 per cent per generation) and new variation arising per generation by mutation we would have for $\sigma^2 g(o)$ the genetic variance present at the start where

$$0.191\ \sigma^2 g(o) = \sigma^2 gm$$

where $\sigma^2 gm$ is the amount of new variation produced each generation. Thus $\sigma^2 g(o) = 5.2\sigma^2 gm$. During the experiment, the relative loss of variability will be $\dfrac{1}{2N}$, where N is the number of parents, in this case 20. Thus at generation $K : \sigma^2 g(K) = 0.975\sigma^2 g(K-1) + \sigma^2 gm$. This gives for the fourteenth generation $\sigma^2 g = 15\sigma^2 gm$ giving an average over the experiment of $10\sigma^2 gm$. The upper limit to $\sigma^2 gm$ is thus 0.006 units per generation. In the few wild populations that have been examined, the genetic variance has been about 5 units. The rate of spontaneous production of new variance in each generation is thus probably less than about .001 of that present in wild populations.

Two experiments bearing on the spontaneous origin of variation in this character have been carried out by Mather and Wigan (1942) and by Durrant and Mather (1954) both using the same Oregon stock, full-sib mated for 78 generations by 1942 and for over 300 generations by 1954. Mass selection for abdominal and sterno-pleural chaetae was done in the first experiment. The intensity of selection was higher than in our work (the extreme 1 in 20, corresponding to an $\bar{i}$ of 1.87) and the mating system involved slight inbreeding which would cause a loss of variance of about 5 per cent per generation. One might expect that the genetic variance would gradually increase until it stabilized at around 20 $\sigma^2 gm$. Progress was slow but definite in the first phase of the abdominal selection but increased in the later stages. The results in the last phase can be put into our framework as follows. The rate of divergence from generations 34–53 was roughly 0.2 bristles per generation, giving a rate of change in each line of 0.1. σp is given in table 3 of the paper as about 2.5. We have then

$$0.1 = 1.87 \times \frac{\sigma^2 g}{2.5}; \ \sigma^2 g = 0.13$$

If we assume this to be equal to 20 $\sigma^2 gm$, we obtain a value for the latter of 0.007 units per generation, of the same magnitude as our upper limit.

In the second experiment, a sample of 10 second chromosomes was taken from the inbred line and all possible zygotic combinations were formed. Significant differences between chromosomes were found in the bristle counts of zygotes containing them and the component of variance between chromosomes was 0.056. The rate of production of new variance between chromosomes is thus, by the argument presented earlier a fifth of this, 0.011, as the line had been mated full-sib. The new variance between diploid individuals is a half of this giving a value of $\sigma^2 gm$ for the second chromosome alone of 0.006 units per generation, again of the same order of magnitude.

Selection of sterno-pleurals was only done for 21 generations, producing in that time a divergence of one chaeta. This gives a value of 0.020 for the average value of $\sigma^2 g$ and of 0.002 units per generation for $\sigma^2 gm$. The chromosome assay gives 0.002 units for $\sigma^2 gm$ for the second chromosome only. In our outbred population, the genetic variance in sterno-pleurals is 1.7 units.

The experiments of Mather and his co-workers both suggest that the rate of production of new variance by mutation each generation is of the order of .002 to .001 of that present in wild populations both for abdominal and sterno-pleural chaetae. If rates of this magnitude are found for other characters and in other animals, the effect of mutation may in general be regarded as negligible in selection experiments in laboratory animals and, even more so, in domestic animals where such experiments rarely include even as many as five generations of selection. But from the evolutionary point of view, this rate must be considered as high. Many recent investigations have revealed a surprising amount of variability latent in wild populations which has in turn led to speculation as to the mechanisms preserving this variability in the population. It would seem from these results that, for characters such as numbers of sterno-pleural or abdominal chaetae, which are probably in themselves selectively neutral, the existing variation could well be maintained by the equilibrium between inbreeding and mutation, without the necessity of invoking mechanisms involving selection. In the absence of selection, equilibrium between mutation and inbreeding will be reached when the genetic variation in the population is equal to $2N \sigma^2 gm$ where N is Wright's effective population size. The variation found in our populations would thus only require that N should be of the order of hundreds. The only estimates of N for Drosophila, that of Wright, Dobzhansky and Hovanitz (1942) in *D. pseudoobscura*, were of the order of thousands or tens of thousands.

If we take the HR line, as that which showed the greatest response under selection, we find in generation 17A a deviation from the control means of 2.77 chaetae. Putting $\sigma p = 2.8$ in this case (table 2) we have $2.77/17 = 0.94 \times \sigma^2 g/2.8$ i.e. $\sigma^2 g = 0.49$. Taking this average value over all generations to be the actual value at the eighth generation, we get for the rate of accumulation of new variation a value of 0.06 units per generation or about 10 times the value calculated as the higher limit for spontaneous mutation. Thus at this rate it would need about 80 generations with a dose of 1800 r a generation to produce variance equal to that in wild populations.

However the observed increase in variance at the 6–10th generations was about 3 units compared with the calculation of the part utilizable by selection as 0.49. Perhaps the accumulation of lethals and steriles in the population may mask the utilization in selection of the new variation because many of the chromosomes will be unfixable, unless a crossover occurs at the right place. We propose to irradiate the random-bred base population and observe the effect on its utilizable variation. If this is important, it may be that other breeding programs, involving measures to reduce the frequency of recessive lethals, would be more successful than simple selection in making use of the new variation.

Apart from the experiments of Scossiroli and Buzzati-Traverso, referred to earlier, there are few other records of selection after irradiation. Lewis

(1949) reports work carried out by Harrison rather similar in design to our own. Males from an inbred line were given 4000 r each generation and selection was for abdominal chaeta number. Responses were obtained in the down lines but only in one of the up lines.

We are indebted to Dr. I. M. Lerner for drawing our attention to two papers by Russian workers who selected for sterno-pleural chaetae after irradiation. Serebrovsky (1935) started with a "Florida" stock of *Drosophila melanogaster*, which, judging by the variability at the start of the experiment, must have been inbred, though no mention is made of this. He gave 2000 r to males, 1000 r to females and used a mixture of family and individual selection with full-sib mating. After 8 generations the divergence between the control lines was greater than that between the irradiated lines. Using the four selected lines as starting material, he then changed to individual selection with much lower inbreeding. In the succeeding 10 generations, he obtained a divergence of 6 chaetae between the control lines and of only 2 between the irradiated lines. It is surprising that such variation should have remained in the control lines after 8 generations of full-sib matings.

Rokizky (1936), a pupil of Serebrovsky, then extended this work in more detail. In the first series he used the same Florida stock as Serebrovsky and a similar breeding and selection system as in the latter's first experiment. He only selected upwards with three lines, control, irradiated (3000 r in ♂) and temperature shocked (35-36°C in larvae). Selection for 12 generations produced little change in any of the lines. In his second series, starting this time from a Caucasus stock, he selected upwards 40 lines, 20 controls and 20 irradiated. Full-sib mating was carried out and selection was based on individual score for 25 generations. He again gave males 3000 r each generation. The results are summarized in table 4.

TABLE 4

Generation	Radiated		Control	
	Mean	S.D.	Mean	S.D.
1-5	20.01	2.11	19.80	1.96
20-25	20.61	2.63	19.96	2.17

The inbreeding system practiced severely reduces possible responses. The slight increase in the controls is not inconsistent with Mather's results. The radiated lines show a more definite increase and, as do our irradiated lines, an increase in variability. There was considerable heterogeneity of behavior amongst the irradiated lines. One gained 3.5 bristles with an average standard deviation in the later generations of 2.31 and another gained 1.4 bristles with an average increase in standard deviation to 3.26.

Our own results would suggest that the production of new variation in abdominal bristles by mutation is slow. Under irradiation, new variation can be detected but that utilizable by direct selection is small. The general tenor of the reports of similar experiments by other workers is in agreement, with the exception of those of Scossiroli (1953). In the latter case, the disagreement may be due to the fact that we started from an inbred line and he used a line which had ceased to respond to selection. Some of our results are not completely explainable and we regard this only as a pilot experiment leading to more detailed work with suitably marked stocks on both spontaneous and induced variation.

SUMMARY

Selection for abdominal chaetae has been carried out in an inbred line of D. melanogaster, both with and without irradiation of 1800 r of X-rays each generation. The response in the control stocks in 17 generations was not significant. The irradiated lines responded to selection but slowly compared with wild populations.

This is discussed in relation to the results of other workers. Two papers by Mather and co-workers are found to give consistent estimates of the rate of spontaneous production of new variance in abdominal chaetae of the order of 0.01 units each generation, which is not inconsistent with our results. The variance found in several wild populations is about 5 units. The evolutionary aspect of these results is discussed.

LITERATURE CITED

Buzzati-Traverso, A. A., 1953, On the role of mutation rate in evolution. Proc. IX Intern. Cong. Genetics, Bellagio.

Clayton, G., J. A. Morris, and A. Robertson, 1953, Selection for abdominal chaetae in a large population of Drosophila melanogaster. Proc. Symp. Genetics Pop. Struct., Pavia 7–15.

Durrant, A., and K. Mather, 1954, Heritable variation in a long inbred line of Drosophila. Genetica 27: 97–119.

Fisher, R. A., and F. Yates, 1938, Statistical Tables. Oliver and Boyd, Edinburgh.

Gustafsson, A., 1953, New genes and chromosomes in agricultural plants. Proc. IX Intern. Cong. Genetics, Bellagio.

Lewis, D., 1949, 40th Report of the John Innes Horticultural Institution, 30 pp.

Mather, K., and L. G. Wigan, 1942, The selection of invisible mutations. Proc. Roy. Soc., B, 131: 50–64.

Rasmusson, M., 1952, Variation in bristle number in D. melanogaster. Acta Zool. 33: 278–306.

Rokizky, P., 1936, Experimental analysis of the problems of selection by X-ray irradiation. Uspehi Zootehniceskih Nauk 2: 161–202.

Scossiroli, R. E., 1953a, Effectiveness of artificial selection under irradiation of plateaued populations of D. melanogaster. Proc. Symp. Genetics of Pop. Struct., Pavia 42–66.

    1953b, Artificial selection of a quantitative trait in D. melanogaster under increased mutation rate. Proc. IX Intern. Cong. Genetics, Bellagio.

Serebrovsky, R. E., 1935, Acceleration of the rate of selection of quantitative characters in D. melanogaster by the action of X-rays. Zoologiceskii Zurnal 14: 465–480.

Wright, S., 1937, The distribution of gene frequencies in populations. Proc. Nat. Acad. Sci. 23: 307–320.

Wright, S., Th. Dobzhansky, and W. Hovanitz, 1942, Genetics of natural populations VII. Genetics 27: 363–394.

On the relative role of mutation and recombination in responses to selection for polygenic traits in irradiated populations of D. melanogaster†

R. E. Scossiroli and S. Scossiroli
Istituto di Genetica, Università, Pavia, Italy

(*Received* 8 *December* 1958)

(1) X-ray treatments are a very efficient tool for inducing polygenic mutation and therefore additive genetic variability for polygenic traits in *Drosophila*.

(2) Artificial selection can make use of the new genetic variability.

(3) X-ray-induced increase in recombination rates does not seem to be an important factor in determining the observed effects, at least in the described experiments.

Information available on spontaneous and induced mutability of polygenes in animals and plants is very scanty. Polygenic mutants are indeed difficult to identify, quantitative traits being the result of the integrated action of many small units, the polygenes, and the effect of environment. As a consequence, the mutability estimates now available for some polygenic characters are indirect, obtained on the basis of changes in variability observed under experimental conditions.

Early information on spontaneous mutability of polygenic traits in plants is given by East (1935) for homozygous lines of tobacco. Recently Schuler and Sprague (1956) noticed that genetic variability developed spontaneously in mono-ploid lines of maize. In animals Castle (1951) may be quoted for high spontaneous mutation rate of modifiers of the hooded character in rats. In *Drosophila*, while Durrant and Mather (1954), Clayton and Robertson (1955), and Paxman (1957) give very low frequency of spontaneous mutability of polygenes for number of hairs; Buzzati-Traverso (1954, 1955) gave convincing evidence of genetic variability utilized by natural selection, originated by spontaneous mutation for polygenic traits.

Information available for polygenic mutations induced by ionizing radiations is also very limited. In plants the recent works reported by Gregory (1956) and by Oka *et al.* (1958) show clearly that x-ray treatments increased genetic variability useful for artificial selection in peanuts and rice, respectively. Estimates of mutation rate are given by Oka and co-workers in rice as $2 \cdot 4 \times 10^{-4}/\mathrm{Kr}$ for heading data, and $1 \cdot 7 \times 10^{-4}/\mathrm{Kr}$ for plant height, assuming 100 loci per character. In animals the only available evidence for increase of mutability of polygenes under irradiation is that given by Buzzati-Traverso (1955), Käfer (1952), Scossiroli (1954 a, 1954 b) and Timoféeff-Ressovsky (1934) in *Drosophila*. On the other hand, Clayton and Robertson (1955) were unable to obtain a clear-cut difference in response to selection between control and irradiated inbred strains of *Drosophila*. These workers believe that their data are discordant with

† This work was supported by the Comitato Nazionale per le Ricerche Nucleari, Divisione di Biologia, Roma.

respect to our own because their experiment was carried out on an inbred line, while in our 1954 experiments a line was used which had ceased to respond to selection. One may add, however, that their selection differential was fairly small and their method of selection was different.

Experiments have now been performed to discriminate between the relative role of mutation and recombination, two phenomena which can be affected by radiation and may influence the response to selection.

For these experiments isogenic populations were obtained from Oregon-*cd* and Samarkand-*cd* stocks, using the balanced lethals technique (the balanced stock used was ClB/+ ; al L⁴ Cy sp/Pm; Sb sr In (3R) Mé/H). Reciprocal crosses were also made between the two isogenic populations. Individual selection for high numbers of sternopleural hairs with a selection differential of $1·52\sigma$ (in practice, the 15 per cent highest individuals) was started on the two isogenic populations and on the two reciprocal crosses. Each population was divided into four lines selected independently for high numbers of sternopleural hairs with and without x-ray treatments, as follows:

A line: selected and treated every other generation with 3000 r applied to males and females;

B line: non-treated, but selected as line A;

C line: selected and treated as line A, but every generation;

D line: non-treated, but selected every generation as line C.

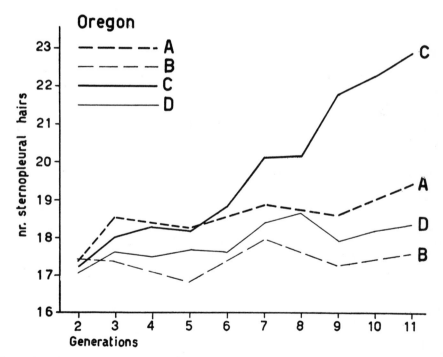

Figure 1.   Progress of selection for high number of sternopleural hairs in the isogenic population Oregon-*cd*. For explanation of A, B, C and D see text.

The comparison betweeen lines C and D in isogenic populations should reveal primarily induced mutation effects; while the same comparison in the hybrid populations (Samarkand-*cd* × Oregon-*cd* and reciprocal) should reveal the joint effects of induced mutation and recombination. On the other hand, in lines A and B, natural selection was allowed to play freely every other generation in order to make these experiments comparable, in part at least, with those previously described (Scossiroli 1954 a, 1954 b).

At the beginning of the experiment the two isogenic populations were tested for the presence of genetic variability for the selected trait. In contrast with Oregon-*cd*, the Samarkand-*cd* population showed a large amount of genetic variability ($h_D^2 = 0\cdot56 \pm 0\cdot12$; $h_S^2 = 0\cdot09 \pm 0\cdot05$). Therefore, assuming that the isogenization process on this population had not been efficient, the Samarkand-*cd* population was discarded. However, this does not affect the results of the comparisons between selections in hybrids and isogenic Oregon-*cd*, because it may alter merely moderately the amount of heterozygosity of the hybrid lines.

The progress of selection is shown in figures 1, 2 and 3. All the irradiated lines exhibit a higher response to selection than non-irradiated ones (controls). The progress shown by the non-irradiated lines of the Oregon-*cd* isogenic population is very limited (actually it is not significantly different from zero)

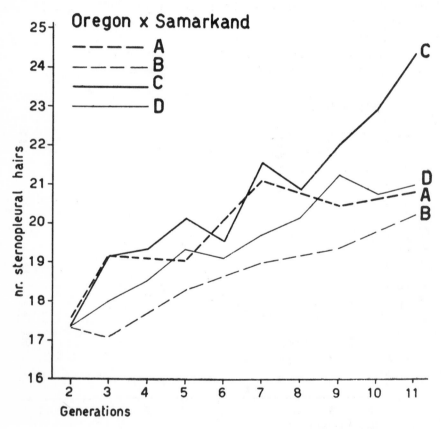

Figure 2. Progress of selection for high numbers of sternopleural hairs in the hybrid population Oregon-*cd* × Samarkand-*cd*. For the explanation see text.

and it may be interpreted as due to spontaneous mutations for polygenes concerning the selected trait, or to a limited amount of genetic variability still present in the population in spite of the isogenization process.

Populations	Lines	Treatments	Regression coefficients	
			For means	For standard deviation
Oregon-*cd* isogenic	A	3000 r	0·203 ± 0·108	0·098 ± 0·028
	B	control	0·084 ± 0·142	0·038 ± 0·030
	C	3000 r	0·637 ± 0·052	0·192 ± 0·026
	D	control	0·129 ± 0·035	− 0·001 ± 0·009
Average of the reciprocal crosses	A	3000 r	0·639 ± 0·168	0·356 ± 0·024
	B	control	0·492 ± 0·073	0·067 ± 0·007
	C	3000 r	0·836 ± 0·073	0·191 ± 0·019
	D	control	0·383 ± 0·039	0·056 ± 0·012

Table 1.   Regression coefficients of selection responses per generation
for means and for standard deviations.

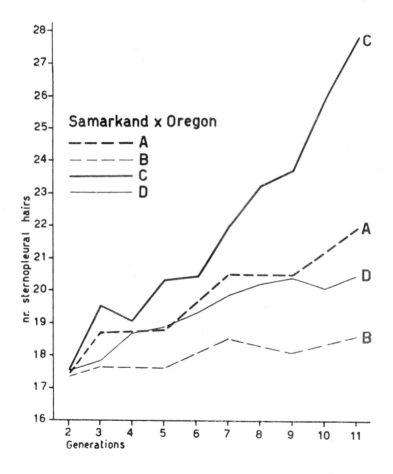

Figure 3.   Progress of selection for high number of sternopleural hairs in the hybrid
population Samarkand-*cd* × Oregon-*cd*.   For the explanation see text.

The response to selection is associated with an increase of variability, which is shown by figures 4, 5 and 6.

Figures 1 to 6 show a linear response to selection, both for means and standard deviation (with one only minor exception: line C, figure 4), suggesting that the simplest method to analyse differences between lines (at least to a first approximation) seems to be a comparison between the slopes of their selection responses. These slopes have been calculated as regression coefficients per generation of artificial selection and treatment, and therefore they are twice as large as those calculated on the basis of generation number for lines A and B, since in these lines selection and treatments were given every other generation.

Comparison	Populations	Selection method	Difference in regression coefficients of selection responses	
			For means	For variabilities
C–D	Isogenic	Every generation	0·508 ± 0·063	0·192 ± 0·027
A–B	Isogenic	Every other generation	0·119 ± 0·178	0·060 ± 0·041
C–D	Hybrid	Every generation	0·453 ± 0·082	0·135 ± 0·022
A–B	Hybrid	Every other generation	0·147 ± 0·183	0·289 ± 0·024

Table 2. Comparison between irradiated and not irradiated lines.

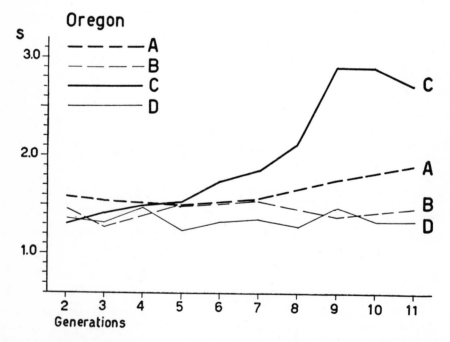

Figure 4. Standard deviation for number of sternopleural hairs in the course of selection on isogenic Oregon-*cd*. For explanation of A, B, C, and D see text.

In table 1 are presented the regression coefficients calculated for irradiated and non-irradiated lines under different methods of selection.

Let us first examine the effects of irradiation. This entails a comparison of line A with B, and C with D. A comparison between regressions of means and variabilities is presented in table 2.

According to these data one may infer that:

(*a*) Irradiation increases the response to selection, both in isogenic and hybrid lines; (*b*) the increase is marked and significant only with more stringent artificial selection (difference C–D compared with A–B), a finding to be further discussed later. In fact, the difference between 0·508 and 0·453 (0·055 ± 0·104) is not significant, nor is that between 0·119 and 0·147 (0·028 ± 0·256).

The responses of non-irradiated hybrid lines (0·492; 0·383) are significantly higher than those of the corresponding non-irradiated isogenic lines (0·084; 0·129); the differences are 0·408 ± 0·159 for B lines and 0·254 ± 0·052 for D lines. Such results appear justified, because in the latter only spontaneous mutation may contribute new variation available to selection, while in the former, recombination of already available genetic variation may be effective. Moreover, in non-irradiated isogenic lines B and D response is extremely weak (line D), or almost non-existent (line B). On the other hand, irradiated lines can be expected to show the effects of induced mutation, as well as induced intrachromosomal recombination.

A preliminary estimate, however rough and indirect, of the significance of x-ray-induced recombination could be obtained by comparing the effect of irradiation (C vs. D, or A vs. B) in isogenic and in hybrid lines. According to table 2 the irradiation effects in isogenic and hybrid lines are practically indistinguishable, for in the C vs. D comparison the regression coefficients are for means 0·508 and 0·453 (difference 0·055 ± 0·104), and for the A vs. B comparison the regression coefficients are 0·119 and 0·147 (difference 0·028 ± 0·256). Thus, the effect of induced intrachromosomal recombination cannot be a large one, if any. Some effect, however, is noticeable in terms of standard deviations for the A vs. B comparison. Table 3 points out the effect of different selection methods.

Populations	Treatment	Comparison	Differences between regressions	
			Of means	Of standard deviations
Isogenic	Controls	D–B	0·045 ± 0·146	0·158 ± 0·031
	3000 r	C–A	0·434 ± 0·119	0·099 ± 0·038
Hybrid	Controls	D–B	0·109 ± 0·082	0·011 ± 0·013
	3000 r	C–A	0·197 ± 0·183	0·165 ± 0·030

Table 3. Comparison between the two methods of selection.

While all comparisons show a similar trend, only one is markedly significant, namely that between isogenic lines. The comparison between lines selected every generation vs. lines selected every other generation shows, as expected, the greater response in the former, accompanied by a loss of fitness.

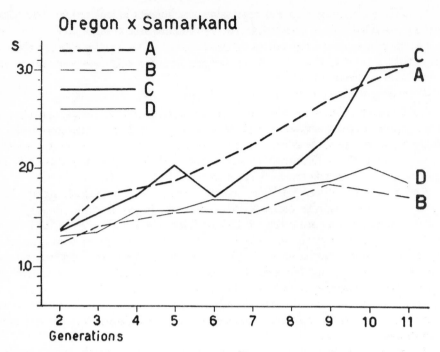

Figure 5. Standard deviation for number of sternopleural hairs in the course of selection on Oregon-*cd* × Samarkand-*cd*. For explanation of A, B, C and D see text.

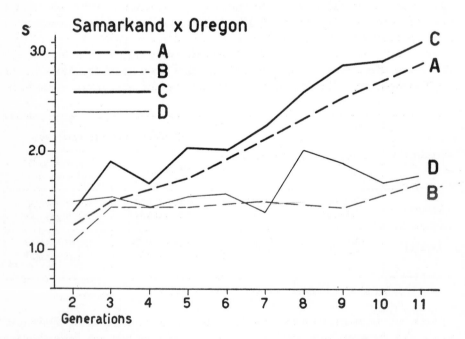

Figure 6. Standard deviation for number of sternopleural hairs in the course of selection on Samarkand-*cd* × Oregon-*cd*. For explanation of A, B, C and D see text.

Estimates of additive genetic variance present at the beginning of selection may be obtained on the basis of the selection pressure applied, and of the gain observed. From the relation:

$$\Delta_G = \frac{\sigma_g{}^2}{\sigma_p{}^2} \cdot \bar{i}\sigma_p$$

where $\sigma_g{}^2/\sigma_p{}^2 = h^2$ is the ratio of additive genetic variance to phenotypic variance, and $\bar{i}\sigma_p$ the selection differential, assuming normality of distribution, it is possible to estimate the additive genetic portion of variance and of heritability values:

$$\sigma_g{}^2 = \frac{\Delta \sigma_p}{\bar{i}} ; \quad h^2 \frac{\Delta_G}{\bar{i}\sigma_p} .$$

Estimates of additive genetic variance for the isogenic and for an average of the hybrid populations at generation one of the experiment are given in table 4 together with heritability values, taking $\bar{i} = 1 \cdot 52$ and σ_p as an average of the observed values for the two populations.

Populations	Methods of selection	Treatments	Lines	$s_G{}^2$	h^2
Isogenic	Every generation	3000 r	C	0·5046	0·35
		Control	D	0·1022	0·07
	Every other generation	3000 r	A	0·1608	0·11
		Control	B	0·0665	0·05
Hybrid	Every generation	3000 r	C	0·7821	0·39
		Control	D	0·3583	0·18
	Every other generation	3000 r	A	0·5978	0·30
		Control	B	0·4603	0·23

Table 4. Additive genetic variance ($s_G{}^2$) and heritability (h^2) for number of sternopleural hairs at the beginning of selection.

Since the estimates given in table 4 are related to the method of selection, it is not surprising that the values given for C lines are higher than those given for A lines.

(1) Des traitements par des rayons x sont des moyens très efficaces afin d'induire de la mutation polygénique et, par conséquence, une variabilité génétique additive pour les traits polygénique en la drosophile.

(2) La selection artificielle peut utiliser cette nouvelle variabilité.

(3) Une augmentation dans les taux de recombination induisée par des rayons x ne semblent pas d'être un facteur important pour la détermination des effets observés, au moins pas dans les expériments qui y ont été décrits.

(1) Röntgenbestrahlungen sind sehr wirksame Mittel zum Zwecke des Hervorrufens von polygenischen Transmutierungen und daher von zusätzlicher genetischer Variabilität für polygenische Züge in Drosophilie.

(2) Die künstliche Auswahl kann von der neuen, genetischen Variabilität Gebrauch machen.

(3) Die durch die Röntgenbestrahlung hervorgerufene Erhöhung der Rekombinationsziffern scheinen nicht einen wichtigen Faktor in der Bestimmung der beobachteten Wirkungen darzustellen, zumindest nicht in den beschriebenen Experimenten.

REFERENCES

BUZZATI-TRAVERSO, A. A., 1954, *Atti IX Congr. int. Genet.*, *Caryologia*, 4 (suppl.), 459; 1955, *Heredity*, **9**, 153.

CASTLE, W. E., 1951, *Genetics*, **36**, 254.

CLAYTON, G. A., and ROBERTSON, A., 1955, *Amer. Nat.*, **89**, 151.

DURRANT, A., and MATHER, K., 1954, *Genetica*, **27**, 97.

EAST, E. M., 1935, *Genetics*, **20**, 443.

GREGORY, W. C., 1956, *Brookhaven Nat. Lab. Symp. in Biology*, **9**, 117.

KÄFER, E., 1952, *ZIAV*, **84**, 508.

OKA, H. I., HAYASHI, J., and SHIOJIRI, I., 1958, *J. Hered.*, **49**, 11.

PAXMAN, G. J., 1957, *Genetica*, **29**, 39.

SCOSSIROLI, R. E., 1954 a, Symposium on Genetics of Population Structure, *U.I.S.B. Publ.*, Ser. B, **15**, 42; 1954 b, *Atti IX Congr. int. Genet.*, *Caryologia*, 4 (suppl.), 861.

SCHULER, J. F., and SPRAGUE, G. F., 1956, *Genetics*, **41**, 281.

TIMOFÉEF-RESSOVSKY, N. W., 1934, *Strahlentherapie*, **51**, 658.

STUDIES ON IRRADIATED POPULATIONS OF
*DROSOPHILA MELANOGASTER**

By BRUCE WALLACE

Biological Laboratory, Cold Spring Harbor, N.Y.

(With Five Text-figures)

(*Received* 28 *July* 1955)

INTRODUCTION

It is well known that the widespread use of ionizing radiations, because of their genetic effects, poses a problem regarding future generations. These radiations induce gene mutations. The vast majority of mutations have deleterious effects on individuals carrying them. Under the pressure of continued mutation, these deleterious mutations will accumulate in populations. Therefore, an irradiated population will, on the average, be harmed—have its 'fitness' reduced—by a continual exposure to irradiation.

The present article summarizes observations made on irradiated populations of *Drosophila melanogaster*. Some of the material presented here has been published previously (Wallace, 1950, 1951; Wallace & King, 1951, 1952). This summary, however, will introduce new material in addition to extending the original observations.

MATERIAL AND METHODS

The experimental populations. The experimental populations of *D. melanogaster* are kept in lucite and screen cages. The original flies were obtained from an Oregon-R strain kept by mass transfer for many years. Fourteen lethal- and semi-lethal-free second chromosomes were extracted from this strain through the use of a series of matings identical to those described later (Fig. 2). Flies carrying these second chromosomes and mixtures of Oregon-R and 'marked stock' chromosomes other than the second were the parental flies of the populations.

Brief descriptions of the populations are given in Table 1. The left-hand column gives the identifying number for each population. The second column indicates the origin of the population. 'Stocks' indicates populations whose original flies carried lethal-free second chromosomes of Oregon-R derivation. Three more recent populations are subpopulations of populations 5 and 6; the designation in the table gives the parental population and the generation during which eggs were removed to start the new populations. The third column indicates the number of adults in the population cages: 'large' refers to populations of about 10,000 individuals, 'small' to populations frequently with fewer than 1000 individuals. The last three columns of Table 1 give the type of exposure, the dose, and the date the population was started for each population. Chronic exposure refers to continuous exposure to radium 'bombs'. No exposure in the case of popula-

* This work was done under Contract No. AT-(30-1)-557, U.S. Atomic Energy Commission.

Reprinted by permission of A. K. Bhattacharyya from JOURNAL OF
GENETICS, **54**, 280–293 (1956).

tions 17, 18 and 19 means no exposure to radiation since they were taken from the original, irradiated populations. At the time the last three populations were started, the ancestral populations had been exposed to some 250,000 r. of γ-irradiation.

Table 1. *Details of the experimental populations*

Population	Origin	Size	Exposure	Dose	Date started
1	Stocks	Large	Acute	7000 r.♂♂ 1000 r.♀♀	25. vii. 49
3	Stocks	Large	None	—	25. vii. 49
5	Stocks	Small	Chronic	5·1 r./hr.	1. iv. 50
6	Stocks	Large	Chronic	5·1 r./hr.	15. iv. 50
7	Stocks	Large	Chronic	0·9 r./hr.	15. iv. 50
17	5–125	Small	None	—	27. iv. 54
18	5–125	Large	None	—	27. iv. 54
19	6–126	Large	None	—	15. v. 54

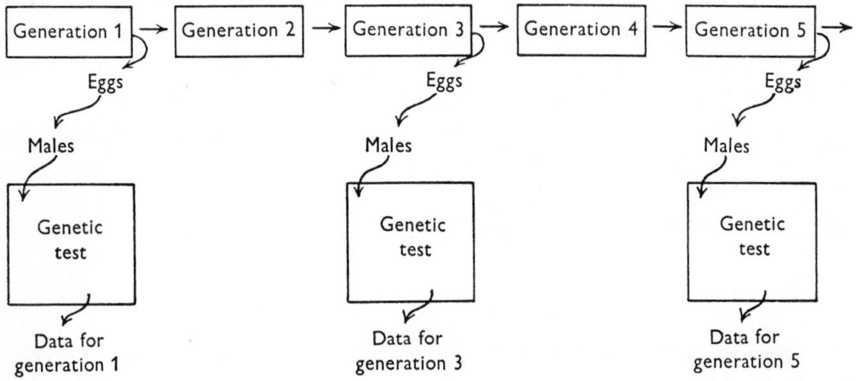

Fig. 1. Diagram showing the periodic removal of egg samples from the experimental population (top line) and the subsequent analysis of these samples by any one of the genetic tests shown in the following three figures.

A schematic representation of the analysis of the populations is shown in Fig. 1. Across the top of the figure, in an extremely simplified manner, are shown the successive generations of the population within its cage. Eggs are removed from the population at intervals, and these are allowed to develop under near-optimal conditions in half-pint culture bottles. Males hatching from these eggs are used to initiate a series of matings identified for the moment simply as 'genetic test'. The results of these tests, available only several generations after the removal of the egg samples, reveal the nature of the second chromosomes in the populations at the time the samples were taken.

The genetic tests are concerned solely with properties of second chromosomes. By the nature of the sampling technique the test yields information about those chromosomes capable of being transmitted from one generation to the next, the genetic endowment of the population. Dominant lethals, for instance, are not included in the analyses. Similarly, the nature of the test in the case of irradiated populations prevents the somatic effects of irradiation from influencing the results.

The genetic test. There are actually several genetic tests; these can be described according to their purpose or according to the nature of the parents of the F_3 generation. One question arising in connexion with the experimental populations concerns the behaviour of typical chromosomes when these are homozygous; the appropriate tests reveal the proportions of lethal, semi-lethal and subvital chromosomes within the populations. A second question concerns the behaviour of the same chromosomes in typical individuals of the various populations. Information is obtained here by bringing together different chromosomes from the same population in random, heterozygous combinations; presumably these are the types of combinations carried by individuals within a population.

The specific techniques used in the genetic tests are illustrated in Figs. 2–4. The matings by which a second chromosome is made homozygous are shown in Fig. 2. A wild-type

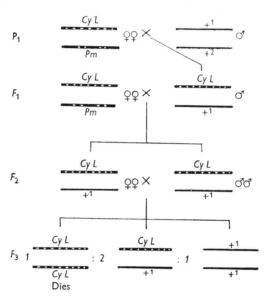

Fig. 2. System of matings (*CyL* technique) for testing second chromosomes in the homozygous condition (explanation in text).

male from the population (P_1) is mated to several *CyL/Pm* virgin females. (*Cy* (Curly), *L* (Lobe), and *Pm* (Plum) are three dominant, second-chromosome genes which are lethal when homozygous. The *CyL* chromosome, in addition to these mutant genes, carries two inversions that suppress crossing-over.) A single *CyL/*+ F_1 male is mated once more to several *CyL/Pm* females. Several pairs of *CyL/*+ males and females (F_2) are selected as parents of the following generation. The expected ratio of *CyL/*+ to +/+ (wild type) flies in the F_3 generation is 2:1; deviations from this ratio are ascribed to genes carried by the tested chromosome: a lethal is defined as a chromosome giving fewer than 3·1% wild-type flies (where $33\frac{1}{3}$% are expected); a semi-lethal, between 3·2% and 15·8%; and a 'quasi-normal', over 15·8%. Quasi-normal chromosomes are subject to further classification by appropriate statistical analyses (Wallace & Madden, 1953). The number of chromosomes of one population tested within a single sample has varied from over 400 in early samples of populations 1 and 3 to a routine 60–80 in current tests.

Fig. 3 shows the modification of the technique just described—the *CyL* technique— that is required to test random heterozygous combinations of chromosomes. Up to and including the F_2 generation, Fig. 3 differs from Fig. 2 only in showing the matings for three different original males (*a, b* and *c*). Each of these males is represented as having two second chromosomes differing from one another and from those of other males (1, 2, 3, 4, 5 and 6). Several males and virgin females are collected for each of the three F_2 cultures. At this time the natures of the chromosomes identified as 1, 4 and 5 are totally unknown. By crossing males of the first culture with females of the second, males of the second with females of the third, and so forth, a series of random combinations of second

Table 2. *A symbolic representation of the analysis possible with the CyL-Pm technique*

D indicates a lethal or semi-lethal chromosome; N, a normal chromosome; and +, a wild-type chromosome with undesignated effects on viability. Superscripts serve to distinguish between homozygous and heterozygous tests.

Homozygous

$$CyL/Pm: CyL/+^1 : Pm/+^1 : +^1/+^1$$
$$CyL/Pm : CyL/D^1 : Pm/D^1 : D^1/D^1$$
$$CyL/Pm : CyL/N^1 : Pm/N^1 : N^1/N^1$$

Heterozygous

$$CyL/Pm: CyL/+^1 : Pm/+^2 : +^1/+^2$$
$$CyL/Pm : CyL/D^1 : Pm/D^2 : D^1/D^2$$
$$CyL/Pm : CyL/N^1 : Pm/D^2 : N^1/D^2$$
$$CyL/Pm : CyL/D^1 : Pm/N^2 : N^2/D^1$$
$$CyL/Pm : CyL/N^1 : Pm/N^2 : N^1/N^2$$

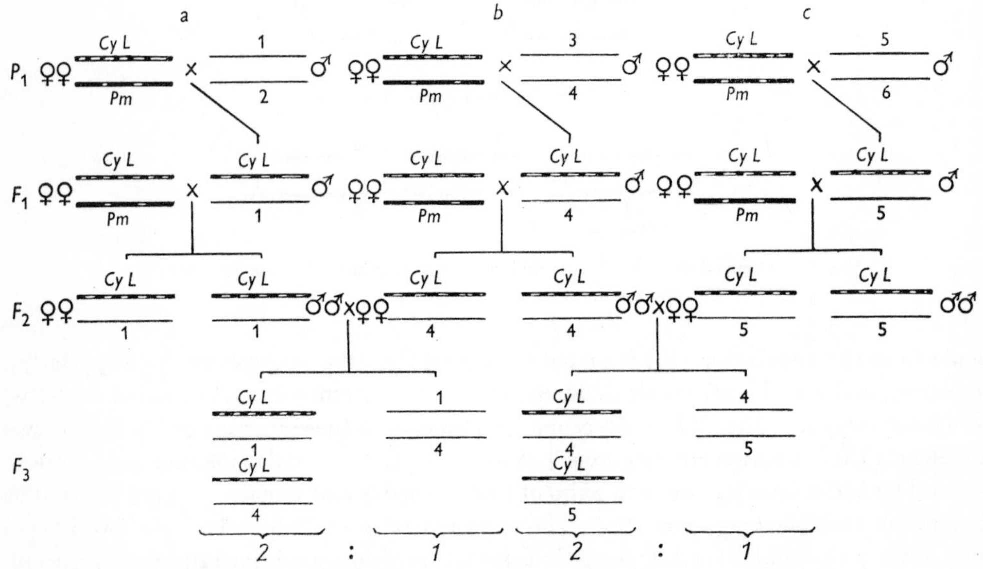

Fig. 3. System of mating (*CyL* technique) for testing random combinations of second chromosomes (explanation in text).

chromosomes is formed whose properties are reflected in the frequencies of wild-type flies in the F_3 cultures. These combinations are occasionally lethal; the frequency of these lethal combinations is a measure of the importance of the allelism of lethal genes within the populations. The average frequency of wild-type flies in a large series of F_3 cultures representing a sample of one population is a measure of the 'viability' of flies carrying these combinations—combinations, presumably, typical of that population. These tests are now made routinely so that each chromosome is tested in the homozygous condition as well as in the heterozygous condition with the chromosomes preceding and following it in the series of F_2 cultures; it is possible with this technique not only to determine the viability of a given heterozygous combination but also to identify the nature of each of the two chromosomes when these are homozygous.

The second technique—the *CyL-Pm* technique—yields the same basic information as the *CyL* technique described above; that is, it tells us how various chromosomes behave when homozygous and when in combination with other second chromosomes. However,

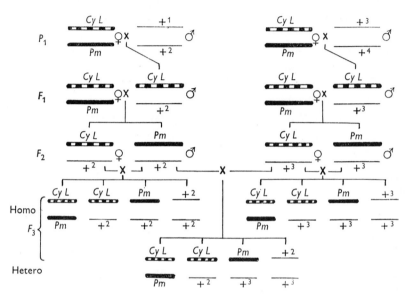

Fig. 4. System of mating (*CyL-Pm* technique) for testing second chromosomes either in the homozygous condition or in random combinations (explanation in text).

it has a marked advantage over the earlier technique; the standard class of flies used to compare the tested class is independent of the chromosome(s) being tested. In the matings illustrated in Figs. 2 and 3, conclusions regarding the wild-type flies are based on the relative frequencies of these flies to $CyL/+$ individuals. However, the $CyL/+$ flies carry the same second chromosome(s) as do the wild type. This lack of independence between the two classes impairs an otherwise elegant technique.

A rather simple change in the mating scheme assures the independence of the tested flies and their control standard. Instead of choosing $CyL/+$ F_2 males and females as parents, $CyL/+$ and $Pm/+$ males are now chosen (Fig. 4). To test chromosomes in the homozygous condition, brother-sister matings are used; to test chromosomes in heterozygous combinations, $Pm/+$ F_2 males of one line are outcrossed to $CyL/+$ females of another. In either case four classes of flies are expected in equal proportions: CyL/Pm, $CyL/+$, $Pm/+$ and $+/+$. If the relative viabilities (estimates of adaptive value) of these four classes of flies in any one test are actually 1, $1-s$, $1-t$ and $1-u$, it is easy to show that estimates of $1-s$, $1-t$ and $1-u$ are obtained by dividing the number of $CyL/+$, $Pm/+$ and $+/+$ flies by the number of CyL/Pm flies in that culture. (Haldane (1956) has pointed out that random variations in the number of CyL/Pm flies introduce a bias into these estimates; downward variations in this class increase the calculated ratios more than upward variations decrease them. He has suggested that the estimates of adaptive values be obtained by dividing the number of $CyL/+$, $Pm/+$ and $+/+$ flies by one more than the observed number of CyL/Pm individuals; the data reported below have been calculated on this basis.) Providing there are no specific interactions between larvae of different genotypes as they develop, alterations in the viability of one class should not interfere with the relative viabilities of other classes. Although the amount of data available at the moment is too limited to make the analysis worth while, it can be seen from Table 2 that there are a number of comparisons by which the existence of larval interactions can be detected. In the table, lethal and semi-lethal chromosomes are indicated by D (for 'drastic'), while quasi-normal chromosomes are indicated by N. If there are no interactions during development, comparable classes of flies should possess the same adaptive values regardless of their position in the table. For example, CyL/N flies should possess the same average adaptive value whether they are from the N^1/N^1 tests of homozygotes or from the N^1/N^2 or N^1/D^2 tests of heterozygotes. Finally, a comparison of the adaptive values of N/N, N/D and D/D heterozygotes gives a direct measure of the semidominance of lethal and semi-lethal chromosomes.

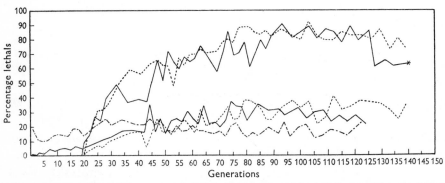

Fig. 5. The frequencies of second-chromosome lethals in five experimental populations as determined by samples taken periodically for nearly 150 generations. Three lower curves: —·—·, population 1; ———, population 3; – – – –, population 7. Two upper curves: ———, population 5; – – – – –, population 6 (descriptions of populations listed in Table 1).

Results of genetic tests

Homozygous tests. Our consideration of the homozygous tests will be limited to the frequencies of second-chromosome lethals in the different populations. The extensive information available for populations 1, 3, 5, 6 and 7 is presented in Fig. 5; the more limited information for populations 17, 18 and 19 is listed in Table 3.

The important fact brought out by Fig. 5 is that irradiation does alter the frequencies of second-chromosome lethals within the experimental populations. This is especially obvious in the cases of populations 5 and 6, less so in the case of population 7. The effect of the initial exposure of population 1 to X-rays is manifest in a higher frequency of lethals in that population than in the control during the first thirty-five or forty generations. Finally, the figure shows, too, that spontaneous mutations bring about a fairly rapid increase in the frequency of lethals in the control population, no. 3.

A second fact brought out by the figure is that the populations are probably at equilibrium as far as overall frequencies of lethals are concerned. Equilibria were established in populations 5 and 6 by the 60th or 70th generation following their origin. Both the control population and no. 7 seem to have reached equilibria by the 80th generation.

The data in Table 3 indicate the rates at which lethals are eliminated from irradiated populations following a cessation of irradiation. Populations 17 and 18, subpopulations of population 5, have lost lethals at a rapid rate; the frequency in population 18 after twenty-five generations seems to be about one-third the original frequency. Lethals in population 19 have been lost at a much slower rate; twenty-four generations after the cessation of irradiation the frequency of lethals in this population is more than 90 % of the original frequency.

Table 3. *Frequencies of lethals in various samples from populations* 17, 18, 19

Note that tests were not made during certain generations.

Generation	17 (%)	18 (%)	19 (%)
0	85·7	85·7	79·7
2	79·5	—	78·8
3	—	59·6	—
6	62·1	—	78·8
7	—	40·4	—
9	60·9	—	73·9
10	—	47·7	—
12	53·3	—	71·6
13	—	42·9	—
15	49·3	—	62·1
16	—	43·8	—
18	45·1	—	71·6
19	—	44·6	—
21	43·8	—	73·1
22	—	34·3	—
24	56·2	—	76·7
25	—	28·0	—

Heterozygous tests; CyL technique. Although it is of interest, a knowledge of the characteristics of typical chromosomes when homozygous need not be useful in predicting the role of these same chromosomes within a population. A better indication of the latter role can be obtained by a study of individuals heterozygous for random combinations of chromosomes of a given population. Presumably the individuals of the population itself are heterozygous individuals of this sort.

The data available for the eight experimental populations have been consolidated in Table 4. In this table are listed, too, data published in 1951 by Wallace & King. Three facts are especially noteworthy in this table: (1) The average frequency of wild-type flies in the tests of population 1 exceeds that of the control population; this has been true since the first test during generation 28. (2) Although populations 5, 6 and 7 have lower average frequencies of wild-type flies in the heterozygous tests than does the control population, the tendency has been for these frequencies to approach rather than to depart from that of the control. (3) After removal from irradiation, populations 17, 18 and 19 have continued to resemble the control population; the average frequency of wild flies in the tests of populations 17 and 18 is substantially higher than that of population 5.

Heterozygous tests; CyL-Pm technique. The first test utilizing the *CyL-Pm* technique was made with populations 1 and 3 during the 84th generation. The purpose of this test was to determine whether the consistently higher frequency of wild flies heterozygous for chromosomes of population 1 was the result of a higher viability of these wild-type individuals or of an unsuspected lower viability of $CyL/+$ individuals carrying chromosomes from this population. The results of this special test agreed with those of the routine technique: $CyL/+$ individuals of population 1 had an average adaptive value of 1.14 ± 0.02 ($CyL/Pm=1$); $CyL/+$ individuals of population 3, 1.17 ± 0.02; $+/+$ individuals of population 1, 1.32 ± 0.03; $+/+$ individuals of population 3, 1.17 ± 0.02. Clearly, the difference between the $CyL/+$ individuals was not significantly different, while that between wild-type flies was highly significant. The physical labour involved with this test was greater than that of the routine test, and so it was abandoned for more than fifty generations.

Table 4. *Average frequencies (percentage) of wild-type flies in heterozygous test cultures of experimental populations*

Data available in 1951 are listed for comparison with the more complete data available in 1954. Adaptive values are computed with population 3 as a standard (1·00). Number of tested combinations indicated by n.

Popula-tion	1951 (%)	1954 (%)	Adaptive value		n	
			1951	1954	1951	1954
1	35·02	34·80	1·04	1·03	994	3832
3	33·75	33·75	1·00	1·00	722	3762
5	31·07	31·97	0·92	0·95	390	3176
6	31·95	33·17	0·95	0·98	707	3318
7	32·83	33·26	0·97	0·99	730	3391
17	—	33·10	—	0·98	—	461
18	—	33·97	—	1·01	—	474
19	—	33·58	—	0·99	—	457

Table 5. *Estimates of the adaptive values of $CyL/+$, $Pm/+$ and $+/+$ (heterozygous) flies carrying chromosomes from different experimental populations*

These values are given directly by the CyL-Pm technique (Fig. 4). Number of tests indicated by n.

Population	$CyL/+$	$Pm/+$	$+/+$	n
3	1·04	1·18	1·09	86
5	1·06	1·16	1·06	221
6	1·07	1·16	1·14	144
7	1·10	1·21	1·17	149
17	1·10	1·22	1·18	148
18	1·07	1·15	1·10	235
19	1·05	1·18	1·13	232

The CyL-Pm technique was finally adopted as a semi-routine test at the 138th generation. The greater amount of labour entailed by this test is more than offset by the opportunity to determine directly the effects of given chromosomes in various types of combinations—with other chromosomes of the same population, with two different tester chromosomes (CyL and Pm), or even with normal chromosomes of other, isolated populations.

At the moment the data available are sufficient merely to introduce the type of results the test gives. These results are listed in Table 5. It appears from these limited data that the estimates of adaptive values obtained for the control population are substantially lower now than those obtained during the 84th generation; it remains to be seen whether future samples will continue to give these same results. The data for the other populations agree generally with those given in Table 4: populations 5, 6 and 7 occupy the same order as in the earlier table, and, at least in the case of 17 and 18, cessation of irradiation has brought about an increase in the estimated adaptive values.

Finally, it is of some interest to examine the effects of drastic (D) and normal (N) chromosomes from the populations on the relative viabilities of individuals of different genotypes. An analysis based on the available data is shown in Table 6. Because of the small number of observations per population, the data have been averaged through populations. Apparently the lethal and semi-lethal chromosomes from the populations have very little average effect in $CyL/+$, $Pm/+$ or $+/+$ heterozygous individuals. Random combinations of drastic chromosomes have a lower adaptive value, but this deficiency is largely eliminated by the exclusion from the calculations of those combinations that have fewer than one-half the expected frequency of wild-type flies. A more fruitful discussion of this type of data must await the accumulation of more information.

Table 6. *Estimates of the adaptive values of flies carrying various combinations of chromosomes as revealed by the CyL-Pm technique*

D represents lethal and semi-lethal chromosomes; N, normal chromosomes. In the column (D/D), combinations that were lethal or semi-lethal have been excluded from the D/D calculations.

Population	CyL/N	CyL/D	Pm/N	Pm/D	N/N	N/D	D/D	(D/D)
5	1·069	1·056	1·155	1·159	1·070	1·138	1·004	1·076
6	1·058	1·067	1·255	1·138	1·307	1·272	1·109	1·142
7	1·100	1·083	1·217	1·225	1·240	1·160	1·110	1·166
17	1·079	1·126	1·238	1·214	1·222	1·168	1·202	1·202
18	1·067	1·066	1·146	1·154	1·112	1·078	1·031	1·085
19	1·054	1·055	1·158	1·190	1·019	1·159	1·124	1·143
Av.	1·071	1·076	1·195	1·180	1·162	1·163	1·097	1·136
	1*	1·00	1*	0·99	1*	1·00	0·94	0·98

* Standard chosen for comparison.

ZYGOTIC CONSTITUTION OF ADULTS

The tests discussed above start with egg samples and end with cultures in which one notes deviations from expected Mendelian ratios. These studies have been supplemented by an analysis of adult males taken directly from population 6 at about the 130th generation of that population. Seventy males were tested by mating with CyL/Pm Ubx/Sb females. (Ubx is a third chromosome carrying a complicated series of inversions and the dominant gene Ultrabithorax; Sb is another third-chromosome marker, Stubble, a mutant affecting bristle shape.) Several $CyL/+$ $Ubx/+$ F_1 sons of each male were mated once more with CyL/Pm Ubx/Sb females. In a manner analogous to the technique described for Fig. 2, it was possible to determine for both the second and third chromosomes whether the sampled males carried two normal chromosomes, one normal and one lethal, or two lethals. That is, the test revealed for both the second and third chromosomes the types of males capable of escaping the rather severe larval mortality characteristic of an experimental population. Unfortunately, it was not possible to test seven or eight sons of each of the seventy males; if it had been possible to make tests of this sort we would have known the genotype of each male with near certainty. Nevertheless, for whatever number of F_1 sons tested for a group of males, there exists a technique for increasing the number of observed heterozygotes to adjust for those misclassified as homozygotes (N/N or L/L); each class of homozygote is then decreased by one-half of this correction.

The outcome of the test was as follows: 87 % of all second chromosomes ($n = 140$) and 92 % of all third chromosomes carried by the tested males were lethal when homozygous. These frequencies agree well with the frequencies of lethals among second chromosomes obtained through egg samples (Fig. 5). The distribution of zygotic types, extending from flies with only normal second and third chromosomes to those with all four of these autosomes lethal, fits the theoretical distribution predicted by the Hardy-Weinberg equation very well (Table 7). It is interesting to note, in spite of the small numbers of the test, that

Table 7. *The zygotic constitution of seventy adult males taken from population 6 during the* 130th *generation; both second and third chromosomes were analysed*

L indicates a lethal chromosome; N, a non-lethal. Negative observed values result from the correction made for N/L heterozygotes expected to be misclassified as N/N or L/L homozygotes.

Genotype		No. observed (adjusted)	No. expected	Difference (obs. − exp.)
N/N	N/N	− 0·040	0	−
N/L	N/N	− 0·347	0·070	−
L/L	N/N	− 1·202	0·350	−
N/N	N/L	− 0·343	0·140	−
N/L	N/L	5·680	2·310	+
L/L	N/L	9·437	7·770	+
N/N	L/L	− 0·033	0·980	−
N/L	L/L	14·043	13·370	+
L/L	L/L	42·805	45·080	−

those zygotic types, in which the observed (adjusted) numbers are smaller than the expected ones, include the five types carrying two normal homologous chromosomes (second, third, or both) and the class carrying four lethal autosomes. Excesses of observed over expected are found in the class heterozygous for both second- and third-chromosome lethals and in the two classes homozygous (L/L) for lethals on one pair of autosomes but heterozygous on the other. There exists, then, no evidence for strong synergistic interactions among the lethals of population 6 that lead to the elimination of individuals carrying two or more lethals.

CONCLUSIONS

The discussion of the above results will be limited to the role of deleterious mutations in these populations. At the risk of overstating the situation, this discussion will emphasize the possible importance of mutations in the heterozygous condition.

Several arguments can be advanced to disparage the role of heterozygosity in the genetic fabric of a species. First, it can be argued that a gene which is deleterious when homozygous is simply less deleterious when heterozygous. Secondly, should this happen not to be true in a given instance, it may be postulated that selection will eventually establish within the species an allele which, when homozygous, duplicates the action of the beneficial heterozygote. Thirdly, should a chance heterotic combination owe its selective superiority to slightly different functions of the two alleles, it is conceivable that selection will favour the establishment of a duplication at that locus and the fixation of one of the necessary alleles at one of these subloci and the other allele at the other.

Using Wright's (1931) analogy of 'peaks' and 'valleys', it would appear that the above three arguments are valid primarily in an evolutionary landscape of gentle undulations leading upward to a broad species peak. Regardless of its location on this sort of landscape, a population could eventually approach the ideal genotypic combination for the species. This type of landscape does not exist where there are strong selective forces because these transform the gentle hillocks into sharp peaks separated by deep valleys. In such a gullied terrain it may be unrealistic to contemplate what selection may be expected to do 'on the average' or 'in the long run'. Selection is opportunistic and, once a population is isolated on a given 'peak', the direction of selection must be to improve or add to that peak. Selection cannot drive a population into a sharply defined valley simply because a better peak exists somewhere beyond it.

There is no longer any question concerning the magnitude of some selective forces. The annual cycles of inversion frequencies in certain populations of *D. pseudoobscura* (Dobzhansky, 1943) or in frequencies of different body colours in ladybird beetles (Timofeeff-Ressovsky, 1940) require the postulation of sizable forces. Wright & Dobzhansky (1946) and Dobzhansky (1947) report adaptive values of inversion heterozygotes in experimental populations of *D. pseudoobscura* as great as 300% those of structural homozygotes. Allison (1955) calculates that persons heterozygous for the sickle-cell trait have a 25% selective superiority over 'normal' individuals in malaria-infected areas. The frequency of lethal *heterozygous combinations* in our experimental population 5 increased within two generations from a routine 1–2% to 10% or more; the increase in the estimated adaptive value shown in Table 4 occurred in spite of this increase in lethal combinations. There is ample reason, then, to suspect that the peaks and valleys of the genotypic landscape are somewhat more than mere undulations.

Objections can be raised against the view that a mutation which is deleterious when homozygous is simply less deleterious when heterozygous. Since the alleles found within a population are largely a *selected* series of genes, it is as reasonable to argue that the majority of these should be deleterious when homozygous. Selective forces, as we have seen, can be very powerful. Rapid changes within populations such as the establishment of equilibria for lethals within 60–80 generations indicate that selection is operating on genes largely in the heterozygous condition. The fact that a new allele is favoured within heterozygous individuals is no guarantee that it will be favoured in homozygotes as well. As adaptive changes at other loci occur relative to the presence of the heterotic combination, it becomes less probable that individuals homozygous for the new allele will, when finally formed, be selectively superior. The analogy of peaks and valleys is unable to describe this situation adequately. Rapid selection favouring a given heterozygous combination represents the discovery of a new peak. The top of this peak, however, immediately becomes the new landscape for the population with additional peaks and valleys whose very existence depends upon the newly formed heterotic combination.

One of the pitfalls confronting a genetically fluid scheme such as the one outlined here is the necessity for one genetic situation to be favoured in more than one combination. For instance, if A gives rise to A', and AA' individuals are heterotic, then the population will contain primarily AA and AA' individuals. If B now mutates to B', one wonders how BB' can be heterotic with both AA and AA' which, by definition, are different. The answer to this problem is not immediately apparent, but there is good reason to believe that the situation is not an impossible one. This problem is similar to that of the high adaptive values of inversion heterozygotes. In this case it is extremely common to find a number of alternative arrangements within a single population and, upon testing, to find that each heterozygote is selectively superior to the two corresponding types of structural homozygotes. In effect, this means that while A and A' must differ, A'' is heterotic with each in spite of this difference. The establishment of this type of genetic situation by natural selection must require a certain 'sophistication'; alleles or inversions giving the proper combinations are surely not a random collection of all alleles or inversions. Similarly, however, there is no reason to believe that selection cannot sort out mutations which are heterotic in a variety of gene combinations at other loci.

The argument that adaptively superior heterozygotes will eventually be replaced by homozygous systems faces three difficulties. In the first place, the possibility exists that one allele may not be able to substitute for the two alleles of the heterozygote. For instance, it would seem reasonable to assume that the selective advantage of sickle-cell heterozygotes lies in the possession of two types of haemoglobin; the normal haemoglobin serves to transport oxygen, while the sickle-cell haemoglobin seems to interfere with the establishment of malarial parasite populations.

A second and more difficult problem to be solved in replacing a heterotic system by a homozygous one lies in finding a basis upon which selection can operate to effect the replacement. Obviously, the initial selection cannot be on the still non-existent homozygous individuals. The allele to be favoured in homozygous individuals, then, must be favoured in heterozygous ones as well. In a world abounding with optimal amounts or concentrations of various substances, one wonders upon what the selection of heterozygotes will be based. Selection cannot be expected to favour the heterozygote that does almost the proper thing in anticipation of the coming homozygote. If, as they arise, selection favours mutations that improve the adaptive values of their carriers, one might expect the majority of these mutations to be beneficial in their actions when heterozygous and to be somewhat deleterious when homozygous.

The third problem confronting the replacement theory consists of speculations based on empirical observations. It seems quite likely (Wallace, 1953, 1954) that the high adaptive values of some inversion heterozygotes in $D.$ $pseudoobscura$ antedated the formation of the sibling species, $D.$ $persimilis$. In fact, it may not be wrong to say that speciation has frequently occurred as the outcome of forces involved with maintaining heterotic systems. Whether a species splits into two as a consequence of the heterotic system or whether the time required for the replacement of the heterotic system is so great that sibling species arise while waiting for the change to occur, it would seem that the grounds upon which the replacement of such systems is postulated are scarcely realistic.

This discussion can be concluded by considering the bearing of the above paragraphs upon problems facing an irradiated population. Because of the large number of subsidiary problems, many of which are moral and ethical rather than scientific, human populations are excluded from these considerations. It appears that within a species such as $D.$ $melanogaster$ an exposure that does not bring about an extinction of a population can give rise to artificial mutations that are incorporated into the genetic structure of the population. This can be illustrated in part by the failure of the average viabilities of heterozygotes to decrease as the frequencies of 'deleterious' genes increased in the chronically irradiated populations. It can be illustrated, too, by changes in semi-dominance of lethal and semi-lethal chromosomes. Wallace & King (1951) reported that in the F_3 cultures of the CyL tests the average frequency of individuals heterozygous for two 'drastic' chromosomes (lethal and semi-lethal combinations excluded from the calculations) was $3\cdot2\%$ below that of individuals heterozygous for two normal chromosomes.

The average frequency of individuals heterozygous for one drastic and one normal chromosome was 1·4 % less than that of individuals carrying two normals. Recalculation of the same figures for data now available gives 2·5 and 1·1 % as the decreases in these frequencies. The average semi-dominance of lethals and semi-lethals appears to have decreased slightly. The few data available for the *CyL-Pm* technique go even further; these indicate, when the data of all populations are combined (Table 6), an absence of semi-dominance of these 'drastic' chromosomes.

The decrease in semi-dominance of lethal and semi-lethal chromosomes, the increase in the adaptive value of the irradiated populations, and the further increases in adaptive values upon cessation of irradiation all emphasize the role of natural selection in consolidating gene pools which produce individuals with the highest possible adaptive values. One cannot deny that irradiation induces gene mutations nor that the majority of these are deleterious—especially when homozygous. Nor can one deny that deleterious mutations must be eliminated from populations. However, a sufficiently large proportion of the induced mutations are apparently capable of being incorporated into selectively favourable gene combinations to prevent not only the extinction of the exposed populations but also the continual decline of their adaptive values over a long period of time. The irradiated populations of *D. melanogaster* serve as excellent illustrations of isolated populations occupying separate genotypic peaks and, through the action of natural selection on available genetic variability, working easily demonstrable changes in the potentialities of these peaks.

SUMMARY

This paper summarizes the results obtained through analyses of irradiated, experimental populations of *Drosophila melanogaster*. Genetic techniques employed in these analyses are described in detail (see, too, Figs. 1–4).

In brief, the average viability of individuals carrying random combinations of chromosomes from each of two populations need not reflect the average effect of these chromosomes on the viability of homozygous individuals. Similarly, the accumulation within an irradiated population of chromosomes deleterious when homozygous need not result in a generation-by-generation decline in viability of heterozygous individuals characteristic of this population.

It is suggested that the seemingly deleterious chromosomes found within these populations are retained by virtue of their characteristics in heterozygous individuals. In general, it is suggested that any new mutation retained by a population is retained because it is favourable in its heterozygous carriers. There is no necessity that these mutations will be favourable as well when homozygous and, by definition, the majority of mutations found within a population should be heterotic within the genetic system of that population.

REFERENCES

ALLISON, A. C. (1955). Aspects of polymorphism in man. *Cold Spr. Harb. Symp. Quant. Biol.* **20** (in the Press).

DOBZHANSKY, TH. (1943). Genetics of natural populations. IX. Temporal changes in the composition of populations of *Drosophila pseudoobscura*. *Genetics*, **28**, 162–86.

DOBZHANSKY, TH. (1947). Genetics of natural populations. XIV. A response of certain gene arrangements in the third chromosome of *Drosophila pseudoobscura* to natural selection. *Genetics*, **32**, 142–60.

Haldane, J. B. S. (1956). The estimation of viabilities. *J. Genet.* **54**, 294–296.

Timofeeff-Ressovsky, N. W. (1940). Zur Analyse des Polymorphismus bei *Adalia bipunctata* L. *B.Z.* **60**, 130–7. (Quoted in Dobzhansky, Th. (1951). *Genetics and the Origin of Species*, 3rd ed. New York: Columbia University Press.)

Wallace, B. (1950). Autosomal lethals in experimental populations of *Drosophila melanogaster*. *Evolution*, **4**, 172–4.

Wallace, B. (1951). Genetic changes within populations after irradiation. *Genetics*, **36**, 612–28.

Wallace, B. (1953). On coadaptation in *Drosophila*. *Amer. Nat.* **87**, 343–58.

Wallace, B. (1954). Coadaptation and the gene arrangements of *Drosophila pseudoobscura*. *I.U.B.S. Symp. on Genetics of Population Structure*, I.U.B.S., series B, **15**, 67–94.

Wallace, B. & King, J. C. (1951). Genetic changes in populations under irradiation. *Amer. Nat.* **85** 209–22.

Wallace, B. & King, J. C. (1952). A genetic analysis of the adaptive values of populations. *Proc. Nat. Acad. Sci., Wash.*, **38**, 706–15.

Wallace, B. & Madden, C. V. (1953). The frequencies of sub- and supervitals in experimental populations of *Drosophila melanogaster*. *Genetics*, **38**, 456–70.

Wright, S. (1931). Evolution in Mendelian populations. *Genetics*, **16**, 97–159.

Wright, S. & Dobzhansky, Th. (1946). Genetics of natural populations. XII. Experimental reproduction of some of the changes caused by natural selection in certain populations of *Drosophila pseudoobscura*. *Genetics*, **31**, 125–56.

EXPERIMENTAL STUDIES OF THE DISTRIBUTION OF GENE FREQUENCIES IN VERY SMALL POPULATIONS OF *DROSOPHILA MELANOGASTER:* I. FORKED [1]

Warwick E. Kerr and Sewall Wright

Universidade di São Paulo and The University of Chicago

Received February 23, 1954 [2]

Introduction

For quantitative study of the sort of random drift due to inbreeding it is desirable to experiment with segregating genotypes that can be classified without risk of error and with populations that are all of a very small definitely known size.

With respect to the first condition, it is much the most satisfactory if *all* segregating genotypes can be distinguished accurately. This, however, limits severely the number of loci that can be studied. Something can be done where only dominants and recessives can be accurately classified.

Most pairs of alleles with such conspicuous difference in effect as to satisfy the first condition, turn out to be subject to such enormous differences in selection that the accumulation of random deviations, implied by the term random drift, is largely prevented. Selection pressure and the effects of random processes are roughly comparable in magnitude at a given gene frequency if the change in frequency in a generation which the former tends to bring about (Δq) and the variance increment due in a generation to the latter ($\sigma^2_{\delta q}$) are of the same order (Wright,

1931, 1948). Where the ratio ($\Delta q/\sigma^2_{\delta q}$) is as high as 10 in absolute value, there is not much accumulation of random deviations and hence little random drift. The size of experimental populations in studies of the latter, should be small enough to meet this condition. They should be constant for convenient comparison with theory.

The present experiments (all with *Drosophila melanogaster*) were designed to meet these conditions. Three series were performed. About 120 lines were started in each. In the first series, the sex-linked mutation forked (f) competed with its type allele. Four females (1 f/f, 2 f/+, 1 +/+) and 4 males (2 f/0, 2 +/0) were put in each vial. The second series involved the sex-linked semidominant mutation Bar (B) and its type allele. Each initial vial contained 4 B/+ females and 4 males (2 B/0, 2 +/0). The third series was with the autosomal alleles aristapedia, ss^a, and spineless ss; which produce a heterozygote that is close to type. Each initial vial contained 4 ss^a/ss females and 4ss^a/ss males. The alleles were thus equally frequent at the beginning of each experiment.

The cultures were allowed to develop until about 2 to 4 days after the offspring began to emerge. The flies hatched up to this time were discarded (in an evening). The flies which appeared next morning (if enough had emerged) were etherized and from among them 4 females and 4 males were taken at random and served as progenitors of the following generation. The etherized flies were put on a porcelain plate and the first 4 males and the first 4 females that happened to be closest to the

[1] Experimental data by W. E. Kerr, under a fellowship of the Rockefeller Foundation, mathematical analysis by S. Wright. Acknowledgment is made to Dr. Th. Dobzhansky for material and for his hospitality during the conduct of these experiments. Acknowledgment is also made to Dr. J. Crow for material and suggestions. Analysis was aided by a grant from the Wallace C. and Clara A. Abbott Memorial Fund of The University of Chicago.

[2] Editor's Note: This paper is the first of a series of three. The others will be published in successive issues of Evolution.

Reprinted by permission of the authors from Evolution, **8**, 172–177, 293–302 (1954).

right end of the plate were the flies taken. It was often, however, necessary to wait to the second and sometimes to the third day to obtain 4 of each sex. This procedure was repeated in every following generation in every line. The first series was carried 16 generations, the second 10 and the third 9 generations. In general, all 8 parents in each culture lived until their progeny started to emerge. In some instances one or more died a few days after the culture was started. No new flies were substituted. Lines were discontinued if fixation was attained. A few were discarded on account of mite infection and other accidents. These latter strains have not been included in the statistics presented here. The present paper will be confined to the experiments with the forked.

FORKED

Table 1 shows the most important results. Among the 96 lines with initial gene frequency (.50 f + .50 f⁺), 26 were still unfixed at the end of 16 generations. Wild type had become fixed in 41 and forked in 29. There is here only an insignificant suggestion that forked was at a selective disadvantage. There seems, however, to have been a shift toward increasing disadvantage of forked as the experiment proceeded. In the first 8 generations, wild type became fixed in 17 lines, forked in 23, while in the last 8 generations, wild type became fixed in 24 lines, forked in only 6, a difference with a probability from accidents of sampling of less than .01. Nevertheless it is clear that the selection against forked must have been slight to have permitted as much fixation as occurred against its pressure.

This result is in agreement with those of previous experiments. In Ludwin's (1951) experiments, the initial gene frequency of .50 in cultures which contained on the average about 44 males, 51 females

TABLE 1. *The amount of fixation of forked and its type allele in 96 lines, each consisting of 4♂'s and 4♀'s in each generation and carried 16 generations unless fixed earlier.* The amount of fixation from generation 4 to 16 is compared with the expected amount at a constant rate of 8.9% per generation.

	Type newly fixed	Not newly fixed	Forked newly fixed	Total	Observed (fixed) No.(o)	%	Calc. No.(c)	(o-c)	$\frac{(o-c)^2}{c}$
1	1	94	1	96	2	2.1			
2	0	92	2	94	2	2.1			
3	1	87	4	92	5	5.4			
4	5	79	3	87	8	9.2	7.7	+0.3	.01
5	3	70	6	79	9	11.4	7.0	+2.0	.57
6	1	66	3	70	4	5.7	6.2	−2.2	.78
7	5	59	2	66	7	10.6	5.9	+1.1	.21
8	1	56	2	59	3	5.1	5.3	−2.3	1.00
9	3	52	1	56	4	7.1	5.0	−1.0	.20
10	4	47	1	52	5	9.6	4.6	+0.4	.03
11	5	39	3	47	8	17.0	4.2	+3.8	3.44
12	2	37	0	39	2	5.1	3.5	−1.5	.64
13	3	34	0	37	3	8.1	3.3	−0.3	.03
14	3	30	1	34	4	11.8	3.0	+1.0	.33
15	1	29	0	30	1	3.3	2.7	−1.7	1.07
16	3	26	0	29	3	10.3	2.6	+0.4	.06
1–3	2	273	7	282	9	3.2			
4–8	15	330	16	361	31	8.6	32.1	−1.1	
9–16	24	294	6	324	30	9.3	28.9	+1.1	
4–16	39	624	22	685	61	8.9	61.0		8.37

but with enormous variations, fell to .30 in about 2 or 3 months and was still about the same at 6 months. In experiments by Merrill (1953) in populations that rarely exceeded 100 adults and in many cases were down to less than 10 flies, the frequency of forked similarly fell from .50 at the beginning to .30 by 99 days and averaged .33 in counts from 125 days to 270 days. There was no indication of increasing selection against forked in those experiments. Both authors found evidence of important differences in gene frequency among individual cultures which they attributed to random drift.

From inspection of table 1, it appears that the percentage of fixation (including both that of type and forked) rose to generation 4 but did not change consistently thereafter. The average rate for generations 4 to 16 was 8.91% (standard error 1.09%). Assuming theoretical constancy at this figure, the differences between observed and calculated numbers for unfixed and for newly fixed lines yields $\chi^2 = 8.4$, 12 degrees of freedom, probability .70–.80 of being exceeded by accidents of sampling.

The theoretical rate of fixation for a neutral sex-linked gene after a steady rate has been attained has been given as approximately $(2 N_M + N_F)/(9 N_M N_F)$ in which N_M is the effective number of males and N_F that of females. (Wright 1933). This approximation only applies, however, if N_M and N_F are moderately large. The panmictic index P ($= 1-F$ where F is the inbreeding coefficient) measures the amount of heterozygosis relative to that in a random bred stock. The exact recurrence formula derived by the method of path coefficients was given as follows in the paper cited. Primes refer to preceding generations.

$$P = P' - C_1 (2 P' - P'') + C_2 (2 P'' - P''')$$

where

$$C_1 = (N_F + 1)/(8 N_F),$$
$$C_2 = (N_M - 1)(N_F - 1)/(8 N_M N_F)$$

In the present case

$$C_1 = 5/32, \quad C_2 = 9/128.$$

$$P = .6875 \ P' + .296875 \ P'' - .0703125 \ P'''$$

TABLE 2. *The theoretical values of P ($=1-F$), P/P' and the proportional rate of change of P in a population consisting of 4 males and 4 females under sex linked inheritance and no selection*

Generation	P ($=1-F$)	P/P'	$\Delta P/P'$
0	1		
1	1	1	0
2	1	1	0
3	.914062500	.914062500	.085937
4	.854980469	.935363248	.064637
5	.788848877	.922651341	.077349
6	.731885910	.927789759	.072210
7	.677245259	.925342665	.074657
8	.627418808	.925427759	.073572
9	.580946889	.925931581	.074068
10	.538047138	.926155468	.073845
11	.498260630	.926053861	.073946
12	.461439099	.926099858	.073900
13	.427329066	.926079014	.073921
14	.395744515	.926088456	.073912
15	.366492734	.926084178	.073916
16	.339403833	.926086117	.073914
17	.314316879	.926085236	.073915
18	.291084347	.926085636	.073914
19	.269568980	.926085455	.073915
20	.249643934	.926085538	.0739145

The correlation $(1 - P_0)$ between the gametes that united to produce the foundation females was zero and the correlation $(1 - P_1)$ between the gametes that unite to produce their daughters is also zero. If there were no differential fecundity among the foundation flies there would be no correlation between mating males and females and hence $(1 - P_3) = 0$. From this point, however, the inbreeding coefficient rises. For calculation of P_3, $P'(= P_2)$, $P''(= P_1)$ and $P'''(= P_0)$ are all assigned the value 1. Table 2 shows the values of P, the ratio of successive values P/P' and the percentage change in P per generation $(100 (P - P')/(P')$ for 20 generations. It may be seen that P/P' oscillates about the value .9260855. This is approximated to 4 places by the 11th generation and to 7 places by the 19th. Values of P beyond this point can thus be calculated to 6 places by the formula $P = .9260855 P'$.

The rate of decrease of heterozygosis after it reaches stability can also be derived at once by equating P/P', P'/P'' and P''/P''' and expressing in terms of $x = \Delta P/P'$ (Wright 1933).

$$x^3 + x^2 (2 + 2 C_1) + x (1 + 3 C_1 - 2 C_2) + (C_1 - C_2) = 0$$

The solution is .0739145, the limit about which $\Delta P/P'$ oscillates in the successive generations.

The rate of fixation of lines approaches this same value although somewhat more slowly. Actually it has been noted that a practically constant rate 8.91% is attained by F_4. As this is 20.5% larger than the theoretical rate, it is implied that the actual variance due to random processes in each generation was 20.5% greater than expected. As the difference is only 1.5 times its standard error, it is not certainly significant. Taking it at face value, the excess might conceivably be due to fluctuating selection but as there is very little average selection it more probably means that the effective size of population

TABLE 3. *The distribution of unfixed classes after stability of form has been reached in a population in which $2N = 12$, no selection; and the distribution in the following generation, including newly fixed classes (each 1/24 of the total unfixed classes of the preceding generation). The frequency in each of the the unfixed classes is 11/12 of its value in the preceding generation, thus maintaining stability of form.*

	Unfixed classes	Following generation
0		.04167
1	.07881	.07224
2	.08985	.08236
3	.09317	.08541
4	.09475	.08685
5	.09554	.08758
6	.09576	.08778
7	.09554	.08758
8	.09475	.08685
9	.09317	.08541
10	.08985	.08236
11	.07881	.07224
12		.04167
	1.00000	1.00000

is about 83% of the theoretical value. In an autosomal diploid population the rate of decrease of heterozygosis is $\Delta P/P' = 1/(2N)$ (Wright, 1931). If effective size is defined as $P'/2 \Delta P$, the theoretical effective size with sex linkage and 4 females and 4 males per generation is 6.7646 while the effective size of the experimental population was 5.61. The difference if real can easily be accounted for if 1 or 2 of the 8 flies fail completely to reproduce in each generation.

The distribution of gene frequencies, during the period of constant rate of fixation, must have practically reached equilibrium of form. The actual distribution was not determined because of the lack of visible distinction between $+/+$ and $+/f$. It is of some interest, however, to consider what it must have been. It may suffice to give the distribution for an effective population of 6 and ignore the indicated slight selective differential (Wright, 1931). The standard is considered a population of 6 monoecious diploid individuals with completely random

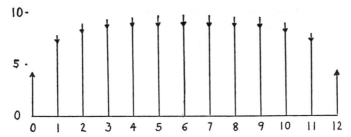

FIGURE 1. The theoretical distribution of gene frequencies (including newly fixed classes) after attainment of stability of form in a population in which $2N = 12$ and selection is absent. Rough estimates for the unfixed classes are given by the ordinates of the curve, $y = 1/12$, unit area (base 12) derived from indefinitely large $2N$. The frequencies (1/24) of the newly fixed classes are given exactly by half the terminal ordinates of this curve.

union of gametes, as it has been shown that the distribution is nearly the same for given N_e, irrespective of the system of mating (Wright, 1931).

Let $f(q)$ be the frequency of gene frequency q. The class with this gene frequency contributes to the classes of the next generation according to the expansion of $[(1 - q)(f^+) + q(f)]^{12} f(q)$ and thus to the class with gene frequency q_1 by

$$\frac{12!}{(2 Nq)! [2 N(1 - q)]!}$$

$$q^{2 Nq_1}(1 - q)^{2 N(1-q_1)} f(q).$$

The total frequency of q is the sum of all contributions from the 11 values of q from 1/12 to 11/12. This must be 11/12 of its value in the preceding generation if there is equilibrium of the form of the distribution. The equation can be solved algebraically as in a number of simple examples given in the reference cited [3] but it is

[3] We will note that one of these is incorrect as published, viz., that for irreversible mutation in populations of 3 monoecious individuals (p.

probably simplest in this case to start from a rough approximation and iterate, rating up each generation by 12/11, until stability is reached. The resulting distribution is shown in table 3 and figure 1.

While this solution applies to a situation with a slightly lower rate of fixation (1/24 for each allele) than that observed, the form of the distribution apart from the newly fixed classes is substantially correct for 4 ♀'s, 4 ♂'s (12 representative of the locus) for any effective size of parental population not too remote from 6. Indeed with an indefinitely large population in each generation, the form of the distribution is not very different, being approximately uniform for all gene frequencies (Wright, 1931).

118). The correct percentages are 42.40% for $q_a = 1/6$, 21.07% for $q_a = 2/6$, 15.54% for $q_a = 3/6$, 11.99% for $q_a = 4/6$, 9.00% for $q_a = 5/6$, total 100% for unfixed classes. The rate of fixation of A is 17.05% and of a, 4.53% of the unfixed classes.

TABLE 4. *The history of a line in which an eye color mutation appeared in generation 5 and drifted into fixation in generation 12*

	F_4		F_5		F_6		F_7		F_8		F_9		F_{10}		F_{11}		F_{12}	
	f	wᵃ	f	wᵃ	f	wᵃ	f	wᵃ	f	wᵃ	f	wᵃ	f	wᵃ	f	wᵃ	f	wᵃ
♀ recessive	2	—	1	1	0	0	1	3	0	0	0	2	0	4	0	3	0	4
dominant	2	—	3	3	4	4	3	1	4	4	4	2	4	0	4	1	4	0
♂ recessive	1	—	1	3	0	4	1	0	0	4	0	2	0	3	0	4	0	4
dominant	3	—	3	1	4	0	3	4	4	0	4	2	4	1	4	0	4	0

A situation that arose in one line (No. 109) in this series is interesting. In the 5th generation the flies taken to be parents of the 6th generation were found to be segregating for an eye color found to behave as an allele of white. This gene drifted in frequency until it became fixed in the 12th generation. The frequencies of f and this gene (apparently w^a) were as shown in table 4.

Thus this line had probably become fixed for the type allele of forked by the 9th generation and after the 12 generation for the new eye color mutant.

Discussion

Populations of 4 males and 4 females per generation are so exceedingly small that experiments such as the present may seem to have no implications for evolution in nature. It must be borne in mind, however, that changes in the underlying multifactorial genetic structure of species probably occur so slowly that an appreciable change in a thousand generations must be considered as an explosively rapid process.

Study in the laboratory of the factors that can contribute to such change is practicable only by stepping up the rates by at least one hundred fold. Thus the interaction between a weak selective advantage of one isoallele over another and a slight random drift, due to inbreeding, can be simulated by using alleles with selective differentials of ten percent or more instead of perhaps only one tenth of a percent or even one hundredth of a percent in populations of only one percent or even one tenth of one percent of the size of a typical natural deme.

In the case of forked, the selective differential is clearly much less than ten percent so that the results of the present paper illustrate random drift from inbreeding in an almost pure form. More complicated situations will be considered in the later papers of this series.

Summary

Ninety-six lines of flies (*Drosophila melanogaster*) were started, each from 4 females (1 f/f, 2 f/+, 1 +/+) and 4 males (2 f/0, 2 + /0), and continued to fixation or to the sixteenth generation by random selection of 4 females and 4 males as parents of each new generation. Type (f^+) became fixed in 41 lines, forked (f) in 29 lines, and 26 lines were still unfixed at the end. The amount of selection against forked was thus slight, although there was evidence that it was greater in the later generations than at first.

The rate of fixation (of both alleles combined) reached approximate constancy by the fourth generation at 8.9% per generation. This would imply an effective size of population 83 per cent of that expected under sex linkage with 4 females and 4 males per generation but the reduction is of doubtful significance.

In one line, an eye color mutation, probably apricot, appeared in F_7 and became fixed in F_{12}, three generations after fixation of the type allele of forked.

Literature Cited

Ludwin, I. 1951. Natural selection in *Drosophila melanogaster* under laboratory conditions. Evolution, **5**: 231–242.

Merrell, D. J. 1953. Gene frequency changes in small laboratory populations of *Drosophila melanogaster*. Evolution, **7**: 95–101.

Wright, S. 1931. Evolution in Mendelian populations. Genetics, **16**: 97–159.

——. 1933. Inbreeding and homozygosis. Proc. Nat. Acad. Sci., **19**: 411–420.

——. 1948. On the roles of directed and random changes in gene frequency in the genetics of populations. Evolution, **2**: 279–294.

EXPERIMENTAL STUDIES OF THE DISTRIBUTION OF GENE FREQUENCIES IN VERY SMALL POPULATIONS OF DROSOPHILA MELANOGASTER. III. ARISTAPEDIA AND SPINELESS

Warwick E. Kerr and Sewall Wright

Universidade de São Paulo and the University of Chicago

Received February 23, 1954

History by Generation

This experiment involves the histories of 113 lines, all started from groups of 4 s/a females and 4 s/a males (using s and a for the alleles spineless (ss) and aristapedia (ssᵃ) for simplicity). These were continued by random selection of 4 females and 4 males for 10 generations, except for 7 lines in which spineless became fixed. An additional line became fixed in this respect in the 10th generation. The distributions of number of aristapedia genes in each set of 8 flies is shown by generation in table 1, together with averages and variances of gene frequencies for each generation, excluding those previously fixed. The small number fixed is in marked contrast with the results with forked and Bar discussed in

Experimental data by W. E. Kerr under a fellowship of the Rockefeller Foundation, mathematical analysis by S. Wright. Acknowledgment is made to Dr. Th. Dobzhansky for material and for his hospitality during the conduct of these experiments. Acknowledgment is also made to Dr. J. F. Crow for material and suggestions. Analysis was aided by a grant from the Wallace C. and Clara A. Abbott Memorial Fund of the University of Chicago.

previous papers and is undoubtedly due to strong selection against both homozygous types, relative to the heterozygotes.

The mean gene frequency of aristapedia fell from initial .50 to .3544 in generation 5 among those in which fixation had not occurred but then rose somewhat to an average in the last 3 generations (.4032) which was substantially the same as that in generation 2 (.4043). The variance reached .0235 in 2 generations and fluctuated about this thereafter. A χ^2 test for homogeneity from generation 2 to 10 (excluding previously fixed lines, and grouping frequencies 0 and 1, and 11 to 14) gives $\chi^2 = 61.5$, n = 80, probability .94. Practically, we may consider that the distribution reached equilibrium of form in 2 generations with a mean gene frequency of $.3882 \pm .0049$ and a standard deviation of $.1536 \pm .0035$.

Selection Coefficients

If there were no differences in viability, generation 1 should consist of 25% a/a, 50% a/s and 25% s/s. The actual percentages (17.92 : 56.75 : 25.33) differ

TABLE 1. *The distribution of numbers of aristapedia genes, represented in each generation among 113 lines, consisting of 4 females, 4 males each.* Newly fixed spineless is distinguished from previously fixed spineless.

		Generation											Total 2–10
		0	1	2	3	4	5	6	7	8	9	10	
Old	0					(1)	(4)	(4)	(4)	(5)	(6)	(7)	
New	0				1	3			1	1	1	1	8
	1			2	3	1	2	2	3	1	3	1	18
	2		1	5	5	4	8	4	0	3	3	5	37
	3		1	6	9	9	10	6	8	6	8	10	72
	4		10	10	8	17	12	13	11	15	12	7	105
	5		11	15	17	13	19	19	17	15	10	13	138
	6		11	17	18	18	18	19	24	14	14	19	161
	7		22	22	21	18	16	16	14	17	18	12	154
	8	113	22	17	12	16	14	12	12	14	14	16	127
	9		20	8	10	6	7	12	9	7	10	10	79
	10		7	3	5	2	1	4	7	9	10	6	47
	11		6	6	3	3	2	1	2	2	2	3	24
	12		1	1	1	0		1	1	2	1	1	8
	13		1	0		1				2	1	2	6
	14			1		1							2
Total		113	113	113	113	112	109	109	109	108	107	106	986
$\bar{q}$		.5000	.4629	.4043	.3833	.3711	.3544	.3830	.3893	.4051	.4030	.4015	.3882
σ_q^2		0	.01707	.02351	.02333	.02515	.01896	.01932	.02095	.02603	.02677	.02693	.02350

significantly (probability <.001) and indicate viabilities of 63% for a/a and 89% for s/s relative to that for a/s. There is probably also a slight difference between males and females (probability about .04) in the viabilities of the homozygotes relative to the heterozygotes of the same sex. The present data give no indication of the true relative viabilities of males and females.

	a/a	a/s	s/s
Males	.525	1	.965
Females	.740	1	.819
Average	.632	1	.893

As these data are from a compact group which may not reflect accurately the situation in later generations, the ratios were obtained from all sets of 8 flies from generations 2 to 10, the parents of which consisted of 4 a/s females and 4 a/s males (table 2). These differed even more from expected 1:2:1 than did generation 1 (viability 47% for a/a and 57% for s/s relative to a:s). The differ-

ence from generation 1 is probably significant (probability .04). Table 2 also shows the ratios from other vials in which gene frequency was .50 in both sets of parents but in which one or both sets consisted of 1 a/a:2 a/s:1 s/s instead of 4 a/s in both sexes. In these cases, deviations from the 1:2:1 ratio among offspring may involve differential productivity of a/a and s/s relative to a/s as well as differential viability among the offspring. There is, however, no significant difference between (121–040) and (040–040) (females first in order a/a, a/s, s/s, males following in the same order) probability .80–.90, or between 121–121 and 040–121 (probability .10–.20) but these two groups differ significantly from each other (probability <.01). It appears that there can not be much difference between a/a and s/s females in productivity but that a/a males are much less productive than s/s males under the conditions of these experiments. When the fathers consisted of 1 a/a:2 a/s:1 s/s, the ratio among the offspring (19 a/a: 146 a/s:67 s/s) includes fewer a/a and more s/s than expected if a/a males were completely nonproductive and s/s males were as productive as a/s males (22.2 a/a:151.8 a/s:58.0 s/s if .50a:50s eggs). These data are not, however, numerous enough for reliable determinations of relative productivities.

The remaining data include so many types of mating with such entanglement of possible differences in productivity of a/a and s/s relative to a/s in both sexes that an analysis of the sort used in the much simpler sex-linked case of Bar did not seem practicable. We have, however, taken out 4 fairly large, moderately homogeneous groups to obtain rough estimates. In group E (table 3) 2 or 3 a/a female parents competed with at least one a/s female, but only one if any a/a male was present in the set of 4 males. Group F gives the same sort of test for an excess of a/a males. In group G, there were 2 or 3 s/s females competing with at least one a/s female while only one if any s/s male and only one if any a/a male were present. The last condition prevents overlap with group F. Group H is similar with reversal of the sexes and thus designed to test productivity with an excess of s/s males present.

The average gene frequency of aristapedia is naturally rather high among the parents in E and F (.590, .585 respectively) and much lower in G and H (.346, .345 respectively). The offspring regress strongly toward the population average in all cases (.470 in E, .432 in F, .360 in G, and .400 in H). Using unweighted averages, it appears that the parental difference between the two groups (.242) is reduced to only 29% of its value (.071) in the offspring, indicating an average selection of more than 70% against the homozygotes. The greatest deviation from the parental average is in F, again indicating complete or nearly complete failure of a/a males to produce in competition with a/s males, but the results in E indicate low productivity of a/a females also. The most nearly normal productivity of homozygotes seems to be that of s/s females, in excess in G.

With these indications as a starting point, sets of productivity coefficients were applied to the parental frequencies in E to H and constant viability coefficients were applied to the frequencies of the zygotes from random union of the

TABLE 2. *Offspring from vials in which the parents were of the types indicated at the tops of the columns*

	F₁ ♀ 040 ♂ 040		F₂–F₁₀ Total		A ♀ 040 ♂ 040		B ♀ 121 ♂ 040		C ♀ 040 ♂ 121		D ♀ 121 ♂ 121		A-D	
	no.	%	no.	%	no.	%	no.	%	no.	%	no.	%	no.	%
♀ a/a	94	20.8	434	11.0	19	18.3	12	13.6	6	9.4	4	7.7	41	13.3
a/s	254	56.2	2281	57.8	66	63.4	59	67.1	46	71.9	32	61.5	203	65.9
s/s	104	23.0	1229	31.2	19	18.3	17	19.3	12	18.7	16	30.8	64	20.8
♂ a/a	68	15.0	389	9.9	13	12.5	12	13.6	4	6.3	5	9.6	34	11.0
a/s	259	57.3	2198	55.7	71	68.3	59	67.1	42	65.6	26	50.0	198	64.3
s/s	125	27.7	1357	34.4	20	19.2	17	19.3	18	28.1	21	40.4	76	24.7
No.	904		7888		208		176		128		104		616	
q_a ♀		48.9		39.9		50.0		47.2		45.3		38.5		46.3
♂		43.7		37.7		46.6		47.2		39.1		34.6		43.2
Tot.		46.3		38.8		48.3		47.2		42.2		36.5		44.7

arrays of eggs and sperms estimated in each case. It appears that the viability coefficients (not distinguishing those of males and females) must be close to .50 for a/a and .75 for s/s to account for the percentages of heterozygotes. These are lower than indicated in F_1, but not so low as indicated by the progeny of a/s females with a/s males of later generations. The productivity coefficients are easily narrowed by trial to the nearest .05. These indicate relative productivities of a/a, a/s and s/s females of about .40:1: .75 respectively of a/a, a/s and s/s males of 0:1:.25 respectively under the conditions in these groups of parents.

The agreement with observed numbers of offspring (table 4) is not good ($\chi^2 = 13.3$) but from inspection of the differences, it is evident that no single set of productivity and viability coefficients can account well for the results in H and the others. H seems to require lower viability coefficients. Similarly application of the above set of coefficients to groups A to D also gives a poor fit ($\chi^2 = 13.9$) but this is considerably improved

by using .40:1:.60 for the viability coefficients of a/a, a/s and s/s respectively. If the single set of 6 coefficients based on E to H is applied to all 8 groups, $\chi^2 = 27.2$, n = 10, probability .001 to .01. This could no doubt be improved a little by deriving the coefficients with maximum probability from all of these data but it is obvious that there must be complications either in assortative mating or heterogeneity.

Possible sex differences in viability, indicated in the data from the first generation, have been ignored above. Groups A to D collectively do not show significant differences in the frequencies of the sexes and the same is true of E to H collectively. In both cases, however, there is a suggestion that aristapedia has somewhat lower viability and spineless somewhat higher viability in males than in females, relative to a/s in both, in agreement with the data from the first generation. Even on combining A to H the distributions of the sexes differ only enough to give $\chi^2 = 4.42$, probability .10 to .20. It is necessary to consider the

TABLE 3. *Offspring from vials in which the parents were in the categories indicated at the tops of the columns.* The exact composition of the parental as well as the offspring populations are shown in the columns.

	E				F				G				H			
	♀: 2,3 a/a, 1,2 a/s ♂: 0,1 a/a				♀: 0,1 a/a ♂: 2,3 a/a, 1,2 a/s				♀: 2,3 s/s, 1,2 a/s ♂: 0,1 s/s, 0,1 a/a				♀: 0,1 s/s, 0,1 a/a ♂: 2,3 s/s, 1,2 a/s			
	Parents		Offspring		Parents		Offspring		Parents		Offspring		Parents		Offspring	
	no.	%	no.	%	no.	%	no.	%	no.	%	no.	%	no.	%	no.	%
♀ a/a	171	54.1	57	18.0	21	11.9	29	16.5	24	4.5	38	7.2	45	7.2	57	9.1
a/s	118	37.3	190	60.1	117	66.5	105	59.7	210	39.8	304	57.6	474	76.0	396	63.5
s/s	27	8.6	69	21.8	38	21.6	42	23.9	294	55.7	186	35.2	105	16.8	171	27.4
♂ a/a	46	14.6	48	15.2	92	52.3	24	13.6	39	7.4	40	7.6	26	4.2	56	9.0
a/s	194	61.4	194	61.4	69	39.2	93	52.8	395	74.8	300	56.8	245	39.3	376	60.3
s/s	76	24.0	74	23.4	15	8.5	59	33.5	94	17.8	188	35.6	353	56.6	192	30.8
No.	632		632		352		352		1056		1056		1248		1248	
q_a ♀		72.8		48.1		45.2		46.3		24.4		36.0		45.2		40.9
♂		45.3		45.9		71.9		40.1		44.8		36.0		23.8		39.1
Tot.		59.0		47.0		58.5		43.2		34.6		36.0		34.5		40.0

TABLE 4. *The observed numbers of offspring of genotypes a/a, a/s and s/s in groups A to H and the expected number, assuming productivity in females of genotypes a/a, a/s and s/s in the ratio .40:1:.75 respectively, productivity of males of 0:1:.25 in the same order, and viability coefficients in both sexes of .50 for a/a:1 for a/s: .75 for s/s*

		o	c	o-c	$\frac{(o-c)^2}{c}$			o	c	o-c	$\frac{(o-c)^2}{c}$
E	a/a	105	109.9	− 4.9	.22	A	a/a	32	32.0	0	0
	a/s	384	399.5	−15.5	.60		a/s	137	128.0	+ 9.0	.63
	s/s	143	122.6	+20.4	3.39		s/s	39	48.0	− 9.0	1.69
F	a/a	53	44.1	+ 8.9	1.80	B	a/a	24	23.9	+ 0.1	0
	a/s	198	212.5	−14.5	.99		a/s	118	107.4	+10.6	1.05
	s/s	101	95.4	+ 5.6	.32		s/s	34	44.7	−10.7	2.56
G	a/a	78	77.2	+ 0.8	.01	C	a/a	10	17.4	− 7.4	3.15
	a/s	604	610.9	− 6.9	.08		a/s	88	78.1	+ 9.9	1.25
	s/s	374	367.9	+ 6.1	.10		s/s	30	32.5	− 2.5	.19
H	a/a	113	123.4	−10.4	.88	D	a/a	9	12.5	− 3.5	.98
	a/s	772	730.2	+41.8	2.39		a/s	58	62.3	− 4.3	.30
	s/s	363	394.4	−31.4	2.50		s/s	37	29.2	+ 7.8	2.08
Total			3288	3288.0	0	13.28	Total		616	616.0	0	13.88
Total	a/a	349	354.6	− 5.6	.09	Total	a/a	75	85.8	−10.8	1.36
	a/s	1958	1953.2	+ 4.8	.01		a/s	401	375.8	+25.2	1.69
	s/s	981	980.3	+ 0.7	0		s/s	140	154.4	−14.4	1.34

total distribution from generations 2 to 10 to obtain a significant difference (probability .01 to .02). These data are too heterogeneous for more than rough estimates. Assume that the zygotic frequencies $f_{aa(Z)}$, $f_{as(Z)}$ and $f_{ss(Z)}$ are the same in the sexes. Let $f_{aa(F)}$ and $f_{aa(M)}$ be the observed frequencies of a/a females and males respectively and similarly for a/s and s/s.

$$\frac{f_{aa(F)}}{f_{as(F)}} = \frac{f_{aa(Z)}V_{aa(F)}}{f_{as(Z)}}, \quad \frac{f_{aa(M)}}{f_{as(M)}} = \frac{f_{aa(Z)}V_{aa(M)}}{f_{as(Z)}}$$

The ratio $R_{aa} = V_{aa(M)}/V_{aa(F)}$ can now be obtained.

$$R_{aa} = \frac{V_{aa(M)}}{V_{aa(F)}} = \frac{f_{aa(M)}f_{as(F)}}{f_{as(M)}f_{aa(F)}}$$

$$R_{ss} = \frac{V_{ss(M)}}{V_{ss(F)}} = \frac{f_{ss(M)}f_{as(F)}}{f_{as(M)}f_{ss(F)}}$$

For F_2 to F_{10}, $R_{aa} = .930$, $R_{ss} = 1.146$. Letting

$$\bar{V}_{aa} = \tfrac{1}{2}(V_{aa(F)} + V_{aa(M)})$$
$$V_{aa(F)} = 2\bar{V}_{aa}/(1 + R_{aa})$$
$$V_{aa(M)} = 2\bar{V}_{aa} - V_{aa(F)}$$

Adopting

$$\bar{V}_{aa} = .50$$
$$V_{aa(F)} = .52, \quad V_{aa(M)} = .48$$

Similarly if

$$\bar{V}_{ss} = .75$$
$$V_{ss(F)} = .70, \quad V_{ss(M)} = .80$$

THE DISTRIBUTION OF GENE FREQUENCIES

In cases in which viability differences are small, in which the productivity coefficients of the various genotypes are sufficiently similar in males and females to be averaged without important errors, and in which mating is random, the average rate of change of gene frequency (Δq) can be expressed as a simple function of the gene frequency and the selection coefficients (Wright and Dobzhansky, 1946).

f(*frequency*) W (selection value)

a/a	q^2	$1 - s$	$\overline{W} = 1 - sq^2 - t(1 - q)^2$
a/s	$2q(1 - q)$	1	$\Delta q = \dfrac{q(1 - q)}{2\overline{W}} \dfrac{d\overline{W}}{dq} = -(s + t)q(1 - q)(q - \hat{q})/\overline{W}$
s/s	$(1 - q)^2$	$1 - t$	$\hat{q} = t/(s + t)$

The distribution of gene frequencies at equilibrium is (Wright, 1937):

$$\varphi(q) = (C/\sigma_{\delta q}^2) \exp\left[2\int (\Delta q/\sigma_{\delta q}^2)dq\right]$$

If random drift is due solely to accidents of sampling

$$\sigma_{\delta q}^2 = q(1 - q)/(2N)$$

$$\varphi(q) = C\overline{W}^{2N}/q(1-q)$$
$$= C[1 - sq^2 - t(1-q)^2]^{2N}/q(1-q)$$

In the present data, the situation is obviously much more complicated. The genetic arrays of the sexes differ systematically because of the differences in productivity and to a minor extent viability coefficients. Thus systematic departures from the binomial square law are to be expected among zygotic frequencies even if mating is assumed to be at random. These departures could be ignored in obtaining rough approximations by use of the averages of the coefficients for the sexes (cf. Wright and Dobzhansky, 1946) if it were possible to deal collectively with all populations of the same zygotic gene frequencies. The most serious difficulty arises from the fact that the frequencies of genotypes are determinable only after large but undoubtedly varying proportions of the homozygotes have died. Letting $W_{aa} = V_{aa}U_{aa}$, $W_{ss} = V_{ss}U_{ss}$, $s = 1 - W_{aa}$, $t = 1 - W_{ss}$, where the U's are productivity coefficients.

	Zygote	*Imago*	*Gamete*
a/a:	q^2	$V_{aa}q^2/D$	a: $(q - sq^2)/\overline{W}$
a/s:	$2q(1-q)$	$2q(1-q)/D$	s: $[1 - q - t(1-q)^2]/\overline{W}$
s/s:	$(1-q)^2$	$V_{ss}(1-q)^2/D$	

$$D = 1 - (1 - V_{aa})q^2 - (1 - V_{ss})(1 - q)^2 \qquad \overline{W} = 1 - sq^2 - t(1 - q)^2$$

The change of gene frequency from zygote to zygote and the distribution of zygotic gene frequencies are (approximately) as given above but the change of gene frequency from imago to imago and the distribution of the gene frequencies in imagoes can not be expressed in simple form. The zygotic q is here a quadratic function of the imaginal q.

We may, however, as in the case of Bar (Part II of this series), find an empirical relation between imaginal gene frequency and the change in the following generation. Table 5 shows the mean change in gene frequency in the offspring for each class of parental gene frequencies (generations 1 to 9), the variance of these changes ($\sigma_{\delta q}^2$) and the ratio $q(1 - q)/\sigma_{\delta q}^2$ which would indicate effective $2N_e$ if zygotic gene frequencies were in question and variability were due only to accidents of sampling.

Change of gene frequency is plotted against parental gene frequency in figure 1. From the form it appears that the formula, applicable to zygotic frequencies may give an adequate empirical fit. A rough evaluation of the coefficients can be obtained as described previously (Wright and Dobzhansky, 1946) from the regression of Δq on q in the nearly straight middle portion of the curve.

$$\frac{1}{\overline{W}} = 2\left(1 + \frac{\Delta q}{\bar{q}}\right)\left(1 - \frac{\Delta q}{1-\bar{q}}\right) - 1 - b_{\Delta q \cdot q}$$

$$s = \frac{1}{\bar{q}}\left[1 - \left(1 + \frac{\Delta q}{\bar{q}}\right)\overline{W}\right]$$

$$t = \frac{1}{1-\bar{q}}\left[1 - \left(1 - \frac{\Delta q}{1-\bar{q}}\right)\overline{W}\right]$$

In the present case, the entries from $q = 5/16$ to $q = 12/16$ yield $\bar{q} = .452$, $\Delta q = -.0331$, $b_{\Delta q \cdot q} = -.568$, $\overline{W} = .652$, $s = .875$, $t = .563$, $\hat{q} = .392$. If parental generation 1 is omitted, s comes out .878 and t .582.

The ratio $q(1-q)/\sigma_{\delta q}^2$ varies irregularly but there is no clear trend except perhaps for small values between $q = 1/16$ to $4/16$. The indicated estimate for $2N_e$ is 13.0 (instead of 16). Even this, however, is undoubtedly too high, since it is based on the variability after the frequencies of homozygotes have been cut down severely by selective viability (a complication that was absent or unimportant in the case of Bar).

If Δq and $\sigma_{\delta q}^2$ for imaginal gene frequencies may be taken as approximating empirically the same functions as for the zygotic frequencies, the distribution of imaginal gene frequencies should be approximated by the formula cited except

TABLE 5. *The observed changes per generation (Δq) in relation to gene frequency of parental populations of generations 1 to 9, the calculated values from the formula*

$$\Delta q = -(s+t)q(1-q)(q-\hat{q})/[1-sq^2 \\ -t(1-q)^2],\ s=.86,\ t=.60,\ \hat{q}=t/(s+t),$$

the variance of changes, $\sigma_{\delta q}^2$, and the ratio $q(1-q)/\sigma_{\delta q}^2$

16_q	f	q	Δq obs.	Δq calc.	$\sigma_{\delta q}^2$	$\dfrac{q(1-q)}{\sigma_{\delta q}^2}$
1	17	.0625	+.0882	+.0635	.0127	4.6
2	33	.1250	+.0511	+.0866	.0106	10.3
3	63	.1875	+.0972	+.0867	.0165	9.2
4	108	.2500	+.0689	+.0724	.0192	9.8
5	136	.3125	+.0533	+.0489	.0131	16.5
6	153	.3750	+.0049	+.0191	.0174	13.5
7	164	.4375	−.0312	−.0147	.0165	14.9
8	133	.5000	−.0536	−.0512	.0162	15.4
9	89	.5625	−.1088	−.0888	.0237	10.4
10	48	.6250	−.0950	−.1263	.0233	10.1
11	27	.6875	−.1574	−.1621	.0151	14.2
12	8	.7500	−.2969	−.1938	.0131	14.3
13	5	.8125	−.1750	−.2172	.0147	10.4
14	2	.8750	−.2500	−.2231	.0078	14.0
15	0	.9375	—	−.1863	—	—
	986					13.03

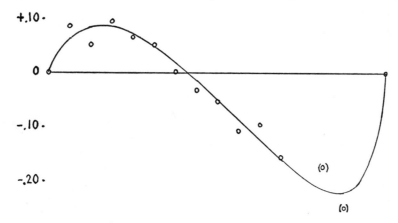

FIG. 1. Observed mean changes of gene frequency in relation to numbers of aristapedia genes in populations of eight flies (small circles) in comparison with those expected from the formula

$$\Delta q = -(s+t)q(1-q)(q-\hat{q})/[1-sq^2-t(1-q)^2];$$
$$s = .86,\ t = .60,\ \hat{q} = .411.$$

401

for the usual inaccuracy near the extremes in applying a formula based on large 2N to populations with small 2N. The low rate of fixation is ignored.

It turns out that the values s = .88, t = .58 give too small a mean and $2N_e$ = 13 gives, as expected, too small a variance. It was found by trial that the values s = .86, t = .60, $2N_e$ = 10.7 give the best fit without going to a larger number of decimal places. Figure 1 shows how well the values of Δq calculated from these estimates of s and t fit the observed values of Δq. Table 6 and figure 2 show the agreement between the observed and calculated frequencies of the gene frequencies. χ^2 = 5.38, n = 9 (on grouping the small classes 12 to 14), probability .80.

We take this opportunity to correct a typographical error and a confusion between two modes of presentation of certain equations in part II of this series (Evolution VIII, p. 235, right side)
In line 8:
 − 4Ns instead of − 4N at beginning

TABLE 6. *The observed frequencies of aristapedia genes in sets of 8 flies (generations 2 to 10) from unfixed parental populations, in comparison with frequencies calculated from* s = .86, t = .60, $2N_e$ = 10.7

	frequency			
16_q	o	c	(o −c)	$\frac{(o-c)^2}{c}$
0	8	10.4	−2.4	.55
1	18	20.9	−2.9	.40
2	37	38.8	−1.8	.08
3	72	68.9	+3.1	.14
4	105	105.7	−0.7	0
5	138	138.8	−0.8	0
6	161	156.3	+4.7	.14
7	154	151.0	+3.0	.06
8	127	124.6	+2.4	.05
9	79	86.9	−7.9	.72
10	47	50.1	−3.1	.19
11	24	23.2	+0.8	.03
12	8	8.1		
13	6	2.0		
14	2	0.3	+5.6	3.02
15	0	0		
16	0	0		
	986	986.0		5.38

In line 9:
$$q(1 − q)\varphi(q) = e^{2Ns}\chi(q)$$
In line 13:
$$\chi(q) = Cq(1 − q)[1 + C_1q(1 − q)$$

DISCUSSION

In natural panmictic populations of ordinary size, genes subject to such enormous selection, as that against Bar in the second paper of this series, would be eliminated too rapidly for random drift from inbreeding to be of appreciable importance. The same is probably true of forked (in the first paper) even though the selection against it was hardly detectible in the small experimental populations. In the case of aristapedia and spineless, the enormous selection against both homozygotes would keep a large population very close to the equilibrium point (about 40% ss^a). We may, however, consider the experimental populations as models, on exaggerated scales with respect to the effects of inbreeding and, in two cases, of selection, of situations that might occur in isolated local populations in nature with respect to a pair of isoalleles or of alleles with primary effects on multifactorial quantitative variability.

In arrays of such populations with effective size one thousand times as great as in the experimental populations, the random drift and ultimate fixation due to inbreeding would occur at only one-thousandth of the rates observed here. The forms of the distributions after approximate stability has been reached (in one thousand times the observed periods) would, however, be nearly the same as observed if selective disadvantage in all cases is only one-tenth of a percent of those in the experiments. Such coefficients are reasonable enough for isoalleles or alleles with primary effects on quantitative variability (Wright, 1952).

The experiments with forked may be considered as giving a model of the inbreeding effect in almost pure form. Those with Bar give a model of the case in which an allele tends toward fixation

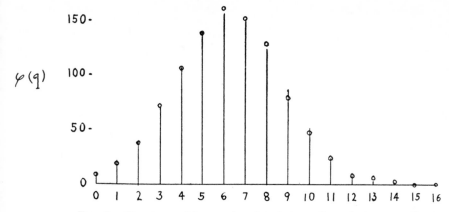

$\varphi(q)$

FIG. 2. The observed frequencies of each type of population according to number of aristapedia genes (small circles). These are compared with the theoretical frequencies in an array of populations in which a stable state has been reached with 86% selection against homozygous aristapedia, 60% against homozygous spineless, relative to heterozygotes, and with effective 2N of 10.7.

but not so decisively as to prevent the unfavorable allele from occasionally drifting into fixation against the pressure of selection. Those with aristapedia and spineless illustrate an approach to equilibrium between alleles because of selection against both homozygotes, but balancing of these selection pressures against random drift from inbreeding in such a way that gene frequency varies almost from one extreme to the other among the populations and one at least of the alleles may occasionally drift into fixation.

It should be recognized that in natural populations with effective size in the thousands, all other types of steady and random drift are likely to be present. Isolation from the rest of the species is not likely to be so complete that immigration can be neglected. Recurrent mutation may have to be considered. With respect to random drift it becomes necessary to take account of fluctuations in the coefficients pertaining to selection and amount and quality of immigration. In a broad sense, however, the experimental arrays may still be considered as exaggerated models of certain patterns of interplay of the directed and random processes which must be taken into account in the study of natural populations.

Summary

Among 113 lines, each starting from four ss^a/ss females and four ss^a/ss males and continued to fixation or to ten generations by random selection of four females and four males in each generation, there was rapid attainment of a nearly stable distribution of gene frequencies. Spineless, however, drifted into fixation in eight lines. Aristapedia reached a maximum gene frequency of 87.5%. The mean gene frequency of aristapedia came to be 38.8%.

Analysis indicated very strong selection against both homozygotes in both viability and productivity. The viability coefficients were approximately in the ratio .50:1:.75 for ss^a/ss^a, ss^a/ss and ss/ss respectively with only slight differences in the sexes. The productivity coefficients were approximately in the ratio .40:1:.75 for these genotypes in females and 0:1:.25 in males.

A relatively simple empirical formula was obtained for the net rate of change of gene frequency per generation (net selective values in the ratio .14:1:.40). The observed distribution of gene frequencies agreed closely with that expected from those values among populations with effective $2N_e$ of 10.7.

LITERATURE CITED

KERR, W. E., AND S. WRIGHT. 1954. Experimental studies of the distribution of gene frequencies in very small populations of *Drosophila melanogaster*. I. Forked. Evolution **8**: 172–177.

WRIGHT, S. 1937. The distribution of gene frequencies in populations. Proc. Nat. Acad. Sci., **23**: 307–320.

——. 1952. The genetics of quantitative variability. Quantitative Inheritance, p. 5–41,

edited by E. C. R. Reeve and C. H. Waddington. London. 151 p.

WRIGHT, S., AND TH. DOBZHANSKY. 1946. Genetics of natural populations. XII. Experimental reproduction of some of the changes caused by natural selection in certain populations of *Drosophila pseudoobscura*. Genetics, **31**: 125–156.

WRIGHT, S., AND W. E. KERR. 1954. Experimental studies of the distribution of gene frequencies in very small populations of *Drosophila melanogaster*. II. Bar. Evolution **8**: 225–240.

ON THE ROLES OF DIRECTED AND RANDOM CHANGES IN GENE FREQUENCY IN THE GENETICS OF POPULATIONS[1]

SEWALL WRIGHT

The University of Chicago, Chicago 37, Illinois

Received July 16, 1948

INTRODUCTION

Science has largely advanced by the analytic procedure of isolating the effects of single factors in carefully controlled experiments. The task of science is not complete, however, without synthesis: the attempt to interpret natural phenomena in which numerous factors are varying simultaneously. Studies of the genetics of populations, including their evolution, present problems of this sort of the greatest complexity. Many writers on evolution have been inclined to ignore this and discuss the subject as if it were merely a matter of choosing between single factors. My own studies on population genetics have been guided primarily by the belief that a mathematical model must be sought which permits simultaneous consideration of all possible factors. Such a model must be sufficiently simple to permit a rough grasp of the system of interactions as a whole and sufficiently flexible to permit elaboration of aspects of which a more complete account is desired.

On attempting to make such a formulation (Wright, 1931) it was at once apparent that any one of the factors

might play the dominating role, at least for a time, under specifiable conditions, but it was concluded that in the long run "evolution as a process of cumulative change depends on a proper balance of the conditions which at each level of organization—gene, chromosome, cell, individual, local race—make for genetic homogeneity or genetic heterogeneity of the species."

The purpose of the present paper is to reiterate this point of view in connection with certain misapprehensions which have arisen and in particular to analyze certain data which have been presented recently by R. A. Fisher and E. B. Ford (1947) as invalidating what they consider my point of view. This discussion leads to mathematical comparisons between the amount of random drifting of gene frequency expected in small populations merely from accidents of sampling and that expected in large ones from variations in degree and direction of selection or in amount and character of immigration.

SMALLNESS OF POPULATION SIZE AS A FACTOR

In spite of his repeated emphasis on dynamic equilibrium among all factors as the most favorable condition for

[1] This investigation was aided by a grant from the Wallace C. and Clara A. Abbott Memorial Fund of the University of Chicago.

evolution, the author has often been credited with advocating the all importance of a single factor, viz. sampling effects in very small populations. Thus in Goldschmidt's stimulating book "The Material Basis of Evolution" (1940) he states: "The adherents of such a view" (NeoDarwinism) "derive much comfort from the results of population mathematics, especially Wright's calculation (1931) showing that small isolated groups have the greatest chance of accumulating mutants even without favorable selection. . . . It is the contention that small isolated populations have the greatest chances from the standpoint of population mathematics." What I actually stated on this matter in the summary of the paper referred to was as follows: "In too small a population there is nearly complete fixation, little variation, little effect of selection and thus a static condition, modified occasionally by chance fixation of rare mutations, leading inevitably to degeneration and extinction." The same conclusion has been reiterated in all more recent general discussions.

POPULATION STRUCTURE AS A FACTOR

This misapprehension may have arisen from the emphasis put on population structure later in the same summary: "Finally in a large population, divided and subdivided into partially isolated local races of small size, there is a continually shifting differentiation among the latter, intensified by local differences in selection, but occurring under uniform and static conditions, which inevitably brings about an indefinitely continuing, irreversible, adaptive, and much more rapid evolution of the species" (than in a comparably large, random breeding population). It should be noted that a favorable population structure, under this view, may be prevented by excessive density of population, as well as by too small a total number (cf. Wright, 1943). The implied relation of size of population to rate of evolution is not a

simple one. I suspect that "inevitably" is too strong a word as used above, but otherwise this quotation still represents my position on the importance of population structure in evolution. The ways in which it is important were, of course, brought out more completely elsewhere in this paper and have been developed further in later papers.

This leads to consideration of a recent inaccurate statement of my views by R. A. Fisher and E. B. Ford. Their first reference is in the main an acceptable statement of the role which I have attributed to random shifts in gene frequencies, provided that the word "partially" is inserted before "isolated" and it is clearly understood that the primary significance of the process is as one of a number of adjuncts to intergroup selection. "Great evolutionary importance has been attached by Sewall Wright (1931, 1932, 1935, 1940) to the fact that small shifts in the gene ratios of all segregating factors will occur from generation to generation owing to the errors of random sampling in the process by which the gametes available in any one generation are chosen to constitute the next. Such chance deviations will, of course, be greater the smaller the isolated population concerned. Wright believes that such nonadaptive changes in gene ratio may serve an evolutionary purpose by permitting the occurrence of genotypes harmoniously adapted to their environment in ways not yet explored and so of opening up new evolutionary possibilities."

The next sentence indicates, however, that the authors have wholly missed the major point stressed in all of the cited papers. "Consequently he claims that subdivision into isolated groups of small size is favorable to evolutionary progress not as others have held through the variety of environmental conditions to which such colonies are exposed but even if the environment were the same for all, through nonadaptive and casual changes favored by small population size." Actually the point stressed most in these papers was the simultaneous treatment of all factors by the inclusion of coefficients measuring the effects of all of them on gene frequency in a single formula. Thus in the 1931 paper the formula for distribution of gene frequencies in a partially isolated local population included the coefficient N_1 for effective size of the local population, s_1 for selection due to local conditions, m_1 for rate of immigration and q_m for gene frequency among the immigrants (mutation pressure was here assumed to be the same throughout the species). This simultaneous treatment made it possible to specify the conditions under which one or another process would dominate with respect to a particular gene. Sampling fluctuations were treated as only one of a number of processes which lead to trial and error among local populations (Wright, 1931, p. 151). This has been reiterated in all later discussions. Thus in the 1940 paper (p. 175) it was noted that "in a large population, subdivided into numerous partially isolated groups, both adaptive and nonadaptive differentiation is to be expected" and it was concluded that conditions are most favorable for evolution when both processes are occurring. The 1935 paper dealt with quantitative variability, due to multiple factors, with the optimum near the mean. The principal conclusion was that slight oscillations in the position of the optimum in local populations provide an important mechanism by which all gene combinations with approximately the same effect in respect to the character under consideration come to be tried out with respect to secondary effects. It was recognized that such oscillations must be of considerable period to be important. Some significance in causing random changes in gene frequency had, however, been attributed to short time oscillations in severity of selection (Wright, 1931) but this effect was not then analyzed mathematically. This

question will be taken up later in this paper.

Fisher and Ford continue with an analysis of annual fluctuations of the frequency of a certain gene in an isolated population of the moth *Panaxia dominula*. They decide that the fluctuations are too great to have been due to accidents of sampling and hence conclude that they must have been due to fluctuations in the action of selection. They arrive at the following generalization.

"The conclusion that natural populations in general, like that to which this study is devoted, are affected by selective action, varying from time to time in direction and intensity and of sufficient magnitude to cause fluctuating variations in all gene frequencies is in good accordance with other studies of observable frequencies in wild populations. We do not think, however, that it has been sufficiently emphasized that this fact is fatal to the theory which ascribes particular evolutionary importance to such fluctuations in gene ratios as may occur by chance in very small isolated populations. . . . Thus our analysis, the first in which the relative parts played by random survival and selection in a wild population can be tested, does not support the view that chance fluctuations can be of any significance in evolution."

Thus Fisher and Ford insist on an either-or antithesis according to which one must either hold that the fluctuations of *all* gene frequencies that are of any evolutionary significance are due to accidents of sampling (attributed to me) or that they are *all* due to differences in selection, which tney adopt. As already noted, I have consistently rejected this antithesis and have consistently accepted both sorts as playing important, complementary, and interacting roles. According to the criteria developed in the 1931 paper and later, the genes in a population may be put into 3 classes with respect to the roles of selection and random sampling. One class of segregating genes in any population may be expected to be almost wholly dominated by selection in one way or another, another class almost wholly by accidents of sampling, while an intermediate class, to which special importance was attributed, will show important joint effects.

FLUCTUATIONS IN GENE FREQUENCY IN PANAXIA DOMINULA

To which of these classes the particular gene studied by Fisher and Ford belongs makes no difference from this standpoint. The use of criteria may, however, be illustrated by further analysis of the data.

A highly isolated population of the moth *Panaxia dominula* near Oxford, England, was studied. A rather conspicuous color variety, *medionigra*, has been present in this colony for at least 20 years but has not been found elsewhere. A more extreme variety, *bimacula*, which occurs in this colony much less frequently has been shown to be the

homozygote. The frequency of the medionigra gene is indicated by study of all available collections to have been less than 1.2% before 1929. The frequency had risen to 9.2% by 1939 when careful study was begun and reached its peak 11.1% in 1940. It dropped to 6.8% next year and since then has varied between 4.3% and 6.5%, without any well defined trend. From 1941 to 1946, the total number of imagines that emerge each season has been estimated from the proportions of captured and marked moths, recaptured after release. The most important data and estimates are shown in table I.

The authors make a statistical analysis of the data for the years 1939 to 1946 on the assumption that there are 1000 parents of each generation. They find that the chance that such great fluctuations could arise from accidents of sampling on this basis is less than 1% ($\chi^2 = 20.806$, 7 degrees of freedom, 1% value 18.475). They conclude that fluctuations in the action of natural selec-

TABLE I

	Estimates of Population Size N	Types of moth collected				q_m Frequency of m	δq_m Shift in q_m
		$+/+$	$+/m$	m/m	Total moths		
Up to 1928	—	164	4	—	168	.012	
							(+.080)
1939	—	184	37	2	223	.092	
							+.019
1940	—	92	24	1	117	.111	
							−.043
1941	2000–2500	400	59	2	461	.068	
							−.014
1942	1200–2000	183	22	—	205	.054	
							+.002
1943	1000	239	30	—	269	.056	
							−.011
1944	5000–6000	452	43	1	496	.045	
							+.020
1945	4000	326	44	2	372	.065	
							−.022
1946	6000–8000	905	78	3	986	.043	
							—

Estimated population size (N), numbers of each genotype and total moths captured, frequency (q_m) of medionigra gene (m) and shift in frequency (δq_m) to next generation (at least 11 generations in first case).

tion must therefore have been responsible for them.

In making these calculations, two years are included in which there are no estimates of population size. If the collections for the 6 years, 1941–1946, for which such estimates were made, are tested merely for heterogeneity, we find that χ^2 is 11.8 which, with 5 degrees of freedom, indicates a probability of about .04 that accidents of sampling, based merely on the limited size of the collections, could have given rise to as large deviations from the average. Thus there is no very compelling reason from the fluctuations themselves for assuming that there were any real fluctuations at all, during this period. It is necessary to include the two earlier years to get convincing evidence for real fluctuations. If this is done, χ^2 rises to 35.9, which, with 7 degrees of freedom, is far beyond even the 0.1% value, 24.3, leaving no doubt of the reality of a shift in gene frequency. The big shift is that between these two earlier years as a group (av. 9.8%) and the following 6 years (5.2%) for which the difference is 4.9 times its standard error, with a probability of about 10^{-6} of arising from accidents of sampling. The question thus largely resolves into what happened between summer 1940 and the next summer to cause such a marked drop in gene frequency and what happened at some undetermined time or times between 1928 when gene frequency was only 1.2% in collections and 1939 to cause a rise to 9.2%.

These changes may well have been due to shifts in the conditions of selection as supposed by the authors but there is nothing in the data as presented to rule out the alternative possibility of reduction to an exceptionally small effective population number on two (or more) occasions, an interpretation for such fluctuations that has long been urged by Elton. Nothing is stated of population size in the period 1928–1939 and all that is stated of the year 1940

is that the moths were not as common in this or later years as in 1939. The number actually collected in 1940 (117) was much less than in any other year.

The mean square of the 7 apparent shifts in gene frequency from 1939 to 1946 is .000488. The mean variance to be expected merely from the sizes of the samples collected is .000269. The difference, .000219, is an estimate of the variance of real shifts in gene frequency in the population.

The authors give no estimate of the amount of variation in selective value necessary to account for such fluctuations. Assume for mathematical simplicity that the heterozygote is intermediate between the two homozygotes. It may be noted that it makes no appreciable difference for this purpose what assumption is made about the rare homozygote bimacula. Assume that selective value is independent of gene frequency and has no trend but varies according to nonsecular fluctuations in conditions from year to year.

If medionigra has a selective advantage of s over type in a particular year, bimacula of $2s$, gene frequency tends to shift by the amount $\delta q = sq(1 - q)$.[2] The estimate for the variance of such shifts is thus $\sigma^2_{\delta q} = \sigma_s^2 \Sigma q^2 (1 - q)^2/n$, using σ_s^2 for the variance of fluctuations in the value of the selection coefficient s and n for the number of years used in calculating an average. For the 7 observed shifts in gene frequency, $\sigma^2_{\delta q} = .00453\sigma_s^2$. On equating this to the estimate of the real fluctuations (.000219) we find $\sigma_s^2 = .0483$, $\sigma_s = .22$. It is to be noted that this means an absolute standard deviation of 22%, not a mere 22% of the value of s (which in fact is here assumed to have an average value of zero). A standard deviation of .22 means that in the course of half a century the selective value of medionigra heterozygotes would vary between semilethality (or semisterility) ($s = -.50$) to a 50% advantage over type ($s = +.50$).

[2] See Appendix.

The homozygotes, on the hypothesis adopted, would range from complete lethality (or sterility) to a selective value twice that of type. This last aspect, however, is quite certainly not tenable since bimacula appeared as regularly when gene frequency dropped as when it rose. Its frequency in the total data was, as the authors note, very close to what would be expected in the absence of selection (11 observed, 10.2 expected).

It seems very probable that the heterozygotes actually have a slight net advantage over both homozygotes, as suggested by the authors. The major shifts in frequency are however so much greater than the possible systematic shifts that the latter can be ignored for the present purpose.

It is of interest to see how small the effective size of population (N) would have to have been to account in full for the estimated real variance of fluctuations. The variance for one generation is $q(1 - q)/2N$. For the period of years in question, we take $q(1 - q)/2N$ = .0648/2N as the mean variance to be expected from this cause. On equating to the estimated variance of real fluctuations, .000219, we find $N = 150$.

The effective size of population over a succession of generations is the harmonic mean of the effective sizes for the separate ones and thus may be very much smaller than the arithmetic mean. Its value is largely dominated by occasional very small values in particular years, if these occur. We come back to the conclusion that if the effective number of parents of the 1941 moths was very small (some 100 or less) it is possible to account for all fluctuations as those of small populations, even though the effective number from 1941 to 1946 were as much as 1000.

However, 117 moths were actually captured in the summer of 1940. The question of the relation between effective and apparent population size requires further consideration.

The harmonic mean of the authors' estimates of total number of imagines per year from 1941 is about 2000. The females are stated to lay some 200–300 eggs each. Thus the total number of eggs is typically more than 200,000. The females are described as not flying after emergence until they have laid a considerable proportion of their eggs, probably within the first 24 hours after fertilization. Thus the broods are largely concentrated in single spots, subject to the same environmental vicissitudes. The larvae are stated to winter in the 3rd instar. It is estimated that there may be over 50,000 well grown larvae in the spring to be reduced typically to a thousand or a few thousands by the time of emergence of the adults. The greatest menace to the late larvae is considered to be virus disease and to the pupae, mice.

The authors tacitly assume that this elimination of more than 99% of the individuals from egg to imago is random with respect to broods, unless some allowance is intended by using 1000 instead of 2000 as the population number in their calculations. The possibility of a much greater discrepancy between apparent and effective population number is a matter that would seem to require investigation. Thus analyses of some dozen pure breeds of live stock, including cattle, horses, sheep and swine by means of the inbreeding coefficient of hypothetical progeny from random parents (McPhee and Wright, 1925; Lush, 1943), have shown that in each the effective population number is of the order of 100 or at most a few hundred, a very small proportion of the total numbers registered per generation (tens of thousands in most cases). The special reasons responsible for the extreme smallness of N in these cases would not hold in nature. It is not, however, safe to assume without investigation that there are not other reasons for a considerable reduction of N. If, in the present case, there are any conditions of weather or disease that tend to destroy whole broods at any time in the annual cycle, the effective population number would be cut down accordingly. Again recent work by Dobzhansky and associates (1942, 1944) has revealed an extraordinary prevalence of segregating factors in *Drosophila pseudoobscura* in nature with high selection coefficients under some or all environmental conditions. At first sight this would seem to strengthen the view that selective differences are so important that fluctuations due to limitation in the number of parents would be negligible. This is certainly true for the genes or chromosome conditions in question but very heavy selective elimination in such respects would bring about a correlation between brood mates in fate and so automatically lower the effective population number for other more neutral segregating factors. In a sense, the ensuing shifts in the frequencies of these could be attributed to selection, but if the shifts in these neutral genes are equally likely to occur in either direction they must be credited to sampling variability. The situation is similar, except for the element of intent, to one that is familiar to livestock breeders. With very intensive selection for particular characters, others must be allowed to vary at random if numbers are to be maintained (cf. Wriedt, 1930). It would seem possible, a priori, that the causes of coincident elimination of broodmates (common environment, and common highly selective heredity) may be as important as causes of random elimination. If the former should produce an effect equivalent to elimination of 90% of the broods while the latter are causing random elimination of 90% within the favored broods, leaving the observed 1% to carry on, the effective population number would be only 10% of the apparent number and easily capable of accounting for the observed annual fluctuations.

The alternative is the hypothesis that variety medionigra had an average selective advantage of about 20% from 1928 to 1940 whatever fluctuations there may have been, and then shifted to approximate semisterility or semilethality in that year, followed by fluctuations without trend thereafter.

The present author is certainly in no position to decide between these hypotheses (or some combination of them). In a recent study of the frequency of lethals in nature in one of the chromosomes of *Drosophila pseudoobscura*, it was found that these were only about one fourth as numerous as they should have been on the basis of the adequately determined mutation rate and the necessary rate of elimination as recessive lethals in a large random breeding population (Wright, Dobzhansky and Hovanitz, 1942). On introducing all factors, that might shift gene frequency, into equations describing the observed results it appeared that the discrepancy could be accounted for either by a slight selection against heterozygotes (coefficient s) or by a slight excess tendency toward brother-sister mating (average inbreeding coefficient F) or a combination. In fact the coefficients entered the equation together (to the first order) as the sum ($s + F = .018$) so that it was impossible to separate them. Direct tests for selection (not included in the above statement) indicated no significant selection but the required amount was so slight that more extensive tests would have been necessary. This indeterminacy was unfortunate but it seems likely that more progress will be made in analyzing the difficult problems of the genetics of natural populations if all possibilities are treated symmetrically and any indeterminacy is brought clearly into view rather than concealed by an approach from the point of view of advocacy of any single factor, even one of such undoubted importance as selection.

COMPARISON OF DIVERSE TYPE OF FLUCTUATIONS

It is noted above that the observed annual fluctuations in the frequency of medionigra could be due to fluctuations in selective value above and below zero with a standard deviation of .22. Even if this is the correct interpretation for this gene, it does not follow that all segregating genes show comparable fluctuations. Genes with an average frequency of .05 in an indefinitely large population, and with no net selective advantage or disadvantage ($\hat{s} = 0$) but with fluctuations in selective value measured by a standard deviation $\sigma_s = .10$, would vary in gene frequency to about the same extent as would genes with the same average frequency but with no fluctuations in degree of selection in a population of effective size 1000. In the former case, $\sigma_{\delta q} = \sigma_s q(1-q)$ approximately, by the formula given earlier. With the values given above, $\sigma_{\delta q} = .10 \times .05 \times .95 = .0048$. In the case of neutral genes in a population of 1000,

$$\sigma_{\delta q} = \sqrt{q(1-q)/2N} = \sqrt{.05 \times .95/2000} = .0049.$$

If this sort of calculation is applied to genes with frequency .50, it would appear that fluctuating selective values with standard deviation of only .04 would be equivalent to the effect of sampling in a population of 1000. This, however, does not allow for the fact that the new values of gene frequency with q larger or smaller than .50, that result from the fluctuations, are subject to greater subsequent fluctuations from sampling than from selection, because of the relatively slow falling off of the term $\sqrt{q(1-q)}$ in comparison with $q(1-q)$ as q deviates from .50. A more thorough analysis of the effects of the two kinds of fluctuation is necessary.

In the long run, random fluctuations in gene frequency, whatever their cause, tend to result in a certain distribution of gene frequencies ($\varphi(q)$) about whatever equilibrium value ($\hat{q}$) is determined by the systematic pressures (Δq). The formula of these distribution curves may be found (see appendix). Figures 1 to 7 show such curves (formulae in appendix) under various postulated conditions. The abscissas are the possible gene frequencies from 0 to 1. The ordinates are the frequencies with which

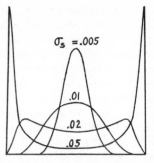

FIG. 1. The distribution of frequencies for genes with different amounts of random fluctuation of selection pressure ($\sigma_s = .005, .01, .02, .05$) in a population in which the only systematic pressure is that due to immigration ($\hat{s} = 0, m = .0001$) directed to a mean $\hat{q} = .50$. Size of population is assumed to be so great ($N > 10^6$) that fluctuations of gene frequency due to sampling are negligible.

these values may be expected to occur in the long run if the conditions remain the same. In figures 1 and 2 it is assumed that the frequency of a gene in a local population always tends to move toward .50 because of immigration from the rest of the species, in which this is the average gene frequency. The rate is assumed to be $m = .0001$ (one out of every 10,000 individuals in each generation has become a member of the population by immigration). In figure 1 the population is assumed to be very large, but gene frequency fluctuates about .50

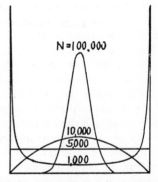

FIG. 2. The distribution of gene frequencies in small populations ($N = 1000, 5000, 10,000, 100,000$) in which the only systematic pressure is the same as in figure 1 ($\hat{s} = 0, m = .0001, q_I = .50$) but the only random changes in gene frequency are those due to sampling.

because of variations in the direction and severity of selection (mean selective differential zero ($\bar{s} = 0$), but standard deviation, σ_s, taking values .005, .01, .02 and .05 in the cases illustrated). The value $\sigma_s = .005$ means that the selective value of the heterozygote relative to type ranges from about 99% to 101% of type (deviations of about $2\sigma_s$ in each direction from 100%) and that the homozygotes have twice this range. In this case, the immigration pressure toward gene frequency .50 practically restricts gene frequency to the range .25 to .75. In the last case, however, the cumulative effects of the relatively violent fluctuations in selective value ($\sigma_s = .05$) keep the gene close to fixation or loss most of the time in spite of the continual return of both alleles by immigration. These curves may be compared with those in figure 2 in which no selective differentials are assumed at any time but the effective size of population is assumed to be so small ($N = 100,000$, $10,000$, $5,000$ or $1,000$ in the 4 cases illustrated) that the cumulative effects of accidents of sampling cause random drift about gene frequency .50, in spite of continual pressure toward this value from the immigration.

It may be seen that a standard deviation of .005 in selective value of heterozygotes (twice this in homozygotes) in a population of millions is only slightly more effective than mere accidents of sampling in a population of 100,000. A standard deviation of .01 in a population of millions is less effective than sampling in a population of 10,000. A standard deviation of .05 is roughly equivalent to sampling in a population of 1000. This is considerably greater than the value .0**4** reached by comparisons at $q = .50$.

If the immigration pressure were 10 times as great ($m = .001$) the same distribution curves would be obtained with values of σ_s that are 3.2 times as great and with values of N one-tenth as great. In the case of fluctuations in selection

the form of the curve depends merely on the value of the parameter m/σ_s^2 and in the case of sampling drift on the value of Nm.

It may be noted that even if m is as great as .01, the variations of gene frequency with $\sigma_s = .05$ in a very large population are only slightly greater than those due to sampling in a population of effective size 1000 (same distributions as those shown for $\sigma_s = .005$ in figure 1 and $N = 100,000$ in figure 2 with m assumed to be .0001 in both cases). Thus Fisher and Ford's contention that variations in the direction and intensity of selection cause much greater fluctuations in the frequencies of *all* genes than does sampling amounts to the contention that all segregating genes in a population such as that studied are subject to fluctuations in selective value with standard deviations much greater than .05.

Figures 3, 4 and 5 describe the situation where selection tends to increase gene frequency ($\bar{s} = .0002$) while this is opposed by immigration (rate $\bar{m} = .0001$) from populations which lack the gene. In figure 3 it is supposed that fluctuations are due wholly to ones in selective value. It requires a standard deviation

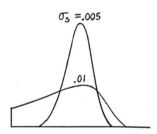

FIG. 3. The distribution of frequencies for genes with different amounts of random fluctuation of selection pressure ($\sigma_s = .005, .01$) where there is pressure of favorable selection $\bar{s} = .0002$ in heterozygotes, twice this in homozygotes, opposed by pressure of immigration ($m = .0001$) from populations in which the gene is absent ($q_I = 0$). Size of population is assumed to be so great ($N > 10^6$) that fluctuations of gene frequency due to sampling are negligible. Mutational origin at a very low rate is required to prevent permanent loss of the gene if $\sigma_s = .01$.

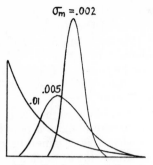

$\sigma_m = .002$

.005
.01

FIG. 4. The distribution of frequencies for genes where the systematic pressures are the same as in figure 3 ($s = .0002$, no dominance, $\bar{m} = .0001$, $q_I = 0$) but the amount of immigration fluctuates to different extents ($\sigma_m = .002, .005, .01$) and all other random fluctuations are negligible. Mutational origin at a very low rate is required to prevent permanent loss of the gene if $\sigma_m = .01$.

approaching $\sigma_s = .005$ to cause much departure from equilibrium ($\hat{q} = .50$). With $\sigma_s = .01$ there is wide departure in the direction of low frequencies and with still larger σ_s, the fluctuations in selective values tend to bring about complete and permanent loss of the gene under the postulated conditions. Figure 4 shows distribution of gene frequencies due to fluctuation in immigration rate (a factor which has no effect of this sort where immigration is responsible for the only systematic pressure as in figures 1 and 2). The standard deviation must again be relatively enormous ($\sigma_m = .002$, where

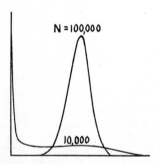

$N = 100,000$

10,000

FIG. 5. The distribution of gene frequencies in populations of 10,000 and 100,000 where the systematic pressures are the same as in figures 3 and 4 ($s = .0002$, no dominance, $m = .0001$, $q_I = 0$) except that mutation at the rate $v = 10^{-6}$ is assumed to prevent permanent loss. Random fluctuations of frequency are assumed to be due wholly to sampling.

$\bar{m} = .0001$) to cause much cumulative effect. There is a much greater effect and a lowering of mean gene frequency if $\sigma_m = .005$ and loss of the gene becomes inevitable if σ_m exceeds .01. It may be shown that fluctuations in the gene frequency of immigrants are even less effective. Figure 5 permits comparison with the effects of small population size, under like conditions, except that in this case it is assumed that complete loss is prevented by mutation at the rate of 10^{-6} per generation ($s = .0002$, $m = .0001$, $v = .000001$). It may be seen that the effect of sampling in a population of 100,000 is roughly comparable to that of fluctuation of selective value $\sigma_s = .005$ or of fluctuation in the amount of immigration $\sigma_m = .002$. In a population of 10,000 the gene would inevitably be lost unless restored by mutation. Even under the assumed conditions, the gene would be completely absent more than 50% of the time in this case.

It seems probable that there are many genes, especially those involved in quantitative variability, that have low net selective values (s less than .001 and even than .0001) and correspondingly small fluctuations in value. Fisher indeed has urged that an important phenomenon, the prevalence of dominance of type over deleterious major mutations, is due to genes that act solely as modifiers of dominance, the *maximum* selection pressure on which according to his calculation (Fisher, 1928, 1930) is of the same order as the mutation rate of the mutant gene in question, and thus of the order 10^{-6} per generation. While I have had qualms about accepting the existence of a large class of such nearly neutral genes (Wright, 1929a, b, 1934) [3]

[3] The efficacy of selection in modifying dominance where the heterozygote is the direct object of selection (a subject to which Fisher has devoted much attention (Fisher, 1935; Fisher and Holt, 1944)) does not require the existence of a class of genes with maximum selective differentials anything like as small as 10^{-6} and was explicitly accepted in my first discussion of this matter.

I have nevertheless been inclined to adopt the view that most evolutionary change is due to changes in frequencies of genes of the sorts of which Harland wrote "the modifiers really constitute the species." The "isoalleles" of Stern and Schaeffer (1943) belong in this category.

While annual fluctuations in selective value can have little significance with respect to such factors, variations in selective value of longer period (such as the writer had in mind in his 1935 paper) are, of course, more important. Still more important are the relations between net pressures on genes over very long periods and the effects of sampling. According to the criteria given in the 1931 paper, sampling variance is significant only when the net pressures are small. This is illustrated by changing the interpretations of figures 2 and 5 along the lines indicated earlier. On multiplication of the net pressures due to selection, immigration and mutation by any factor, the distribution curve for gene frequencies remains the same if the hypothetical size of population is divided by the same factor. Immigration pressure is not necessarily the same for all genes but is the same on the simplest model. Selection pressure (and mutation pressure) may, however, differ enormously among different genes and thus may put these in different classes with respect to the importance of sampling. Figure 6 deals with the case of genes which tend to persist at 50% frequency because of equal selection against both homozygotes and which are prevented from ever being permanently lost by mutation rates of 10^{-6} per generation in both directions. Effective population size is taken as 10,000. If the selective advantage of the heterozygote is 1% ($s = .01$), or more, there is very little variation of gene frequency about the equilibrium frequency, .50. If, however, the advantage is only 0.1% there is rather wide variation. Genes for which $\bar{s} = .0003$ vary in frequency from one extreme to the other and each homo-

zygote is fixed about 18% of the time. For genes for which $s = .0001$, each homozygote is fixed more than 30% of the time and frequencies between 10% and 90% are rare in spite of the pressure toward 50% due to both selection and mutation. Without the latter, indeed, one or the other phase would soon become permanently fixed even with genes for which $s = .0003$. It has sometimes

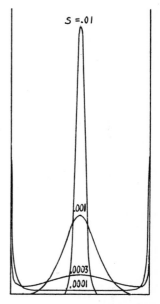

FIG. 6. The distributions of frequencies of 4 classes of genes in a population of effective size 10,000. Selection is assumed to favor the heterozygotes equally over both homozygotes but to different extents ($s = .01$, .001, .0003, .0001) in the 4 classes. Low rates of mutation equal in both directions ($v = u = 10^{-6}$) are assumed to prevent complete fixation of either homozygote.

been held that nonadaptive differentiation due to sampling can only occur in populations of a few hundred (cf. Lack, 1947) but given enough time and sufficiently neutral segregating genes, this can occur in completely isolated populations whenever $4Nv$ is less than 1, v being the mutation rate from the allele most likely to be fixed under the conditions. Thus with mutation rates of 10^{-6}, there can be random fixation up to a population size of 250,000.

Figure 7 deals with a more complex situation in a population of 10,000. Immigration at rate $m = .0001$, tending to establish a gene frequency of .10, is here supposed to be supplemented by selection in which the heterozygous mutant has advantages ranging from .00001 to .001 and homozygotes twice as much in each case. Those genes for which $s = .001$ are almost fixed by

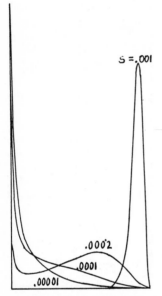

FIG. 7. The distributions of frequencies of 4 classes of genes in a population of effective size 10,000 as in figure 6. In this case, selection is assumed to favor the genes to different extents in the 4 classes ($s = .001, .0002, .0001, .00001$) with no dominance, but with opposition by immigration ($m = .0001$) from population in which gene frequency q_I is .10.

selection in spite of the adverse immigration pressure. Genes for which $s = .0001$ are, on the other hand, largely dominated by the immigration pressure but their frequencies vary over a wide range. At certain intermediate values (e.g. $s = .0002$) there are peak frequencies both above and below 50%. Genes for which $s = 10^{-5}$ are so much dominated by the sampling effect that their frequencies are below 0.5% more than 20% of the time and below 5% about half the time

in spite of the pressure of immigration toward a gene frequency of 10% and of selection toward complete fixation.

The importance of random fluctuations of gene frequency, whatever their cause, cannot be adequately evaluated by considering single pairs of alleles in a single population. What is important is simultaneous variation of gene frequencies at many loci, each with many alleles which differ only slightly in selective value, in each of many local populations. The significance is in contributing to the material for the selection of genetic systems as wholes, which may be expected to take place through the welling up of population growth and emigration from those centers in which at the moment the most adaptive systems happen to have been arrived at and the modification by immigration of those centers in which population growth has become relatively depressed because of less successful general adaptation.

It must be emphasized again that this contribution of random differentiation of local population with respect to the more neutral sets of alleles is only one aspect of the whole trial and error process. The great importance of the contribution of selective differentiation among such populations with respect to less neutral alleles is obvious. Moreover, the nonadaptive differentiation is obviously significant only as it ultimately creates adaptive differences.

SUMMARY

Evolution is a process in which many diverse factors are acting simultaneously. Mathematical treatment requires simultaneous treatment of all determinate factors, including both the systematic pressures (recurrent mutation, immigration and selection), which are wholly determinate in principle, and the cumulative effects of random fluctuations of gene frequencies, of which only the variance is determinate. Any one of the factors may play the dominating role for a time under specifiable conditions.

Conditions are held to be most favorable for a continuing process where there are certain states of dynamic equilibrium at many loci. This situation is found to the greatest degree in a population in which there is sufficient isolation of many local centers of population growth and emigration to provide the condition for continual trial and error. The "errors" are the relatively indeterminate elements in the situation: novel mutations at the gene level, and the effects of accidents of sampling, and of variations in the local conditions of selection and migration at the level of the local population. The "trials" are the orderly reactions of the species to changes of gene frequencies, due to more determinate factors, of which selection dominates in the long run. Where there are important secular changes in external relations, selection pressure dominates the situation almost completely until a new state of approximate adjustment is reached and trial and error processes again take over.

The reiteration of the above viewpoint has been stimulated by certain misinterpretations which have arisen. Several authors have attributed to the author the view that accidents of sampling constitute the most important evolutionary process and that conditions are more favorable for evolution the smaller the total population. This is a view that has been emphatically rejected from the first.

Especial attention is devoted to a somewhat different misinterpretation in a recent paper by R. A. Fisher and E. B. Ford. They hold that fluctuations of gene frequencies of evolutionary significance must be supposed to be due wholly either to variations in selection (which they accept) or to accidents of sampling. This antithesis is to be rejected. The fluctuations of some genes are undoubtedly governed largely by violently shifting conditions of selection

but for others in the same populations, accidents of sampling should be much more important and for still others both may play significant roles. It is a question of the relative values of certain coefficients.

An analysis of fluctuations in the frequency of a certain gene in a population of the moth *Panaxia dominula*, observed by Fisher and Ford and used by them as the basis for their generalizations, raises considerable doubt as to which category this particular gene belongs.

A comparison is made between the distribution of gene frequencies due to the cumulative effects of various types of random fluctuation in the presence of various pressures. Such comparisons support the view that random drift due to sampling in small local populations is an important member of this category and thus a factor of which account must be taken where there is a favorable type of population structure.

APPENDIX

The distribution of gene frequencies under diverse causes of fluctuation

The factors of evolution may best be brought under a common viewpoint by measuring each by the change which it tends to bring about in each generation in the gene (or chromosome) frequency (q) under consideration. They may be classified conveniently according to the degree of determinacy in their effects.

The term "pressure" has been used figuratively (Wright, 1929, 1931) for all evolutionary factors with recurrent directed effects capable at least in principle of precise mathematical formulation. The symbol Δq is used. The pressures of recurrent mutation and immigration have linear effects on gene frequency. They can introduce a gene into populations in which it has been absent. Selection pressure can be defined sufficiently broadly to include all processes (such as differential mortality, differential fecundity, differential emigration) which tend to change gene frequency systematically without either change of the hereditary material itself (mutation) or introduction from without (immigration). Selection pressure is necessarily zero either if $q = 0$ or $q = 1$ in contrast with mutation and immigration pressures.

Random fluctuations in gene frequency may be due to accidents of sampling or to fluctuations in the values of the coefficients involved in the evolutionary pressures. The symbol δq has been used for such a change. Direction is indeterminate but the variance $(\sigma^2_{\delta q})$ can be specified at least in principle.

In addition it seems necessary to recognize a category that is indeterminate both in direction and variance. This includes events that are unique or nearly so in the history of the species: nonrecurrent mutations, unique hybridizations, nonrecurrent selective events, unique extreme reduction in numbers, etc. The distinction between recurrent events and ones so rarely recurrent as to require treatment as indeterminate is, of course, an arbitrary one.

The systematic pressures (Δq) may lead to fixation or loss of a gene. If not, they tend to hold its frequency at a certain equilibrium point (or points): any value of q at which $\Delta q = 0$, provided that this is stable (Δq opposite in sign to $(q - \hat{q})$ where $\hat{q}$ is the equilibrium value). The random fluctuations (δq) tend to cause random drift from an equilibrium point. The resultant is a probability distribution $\varphi(q)$ which exhibits the frequencies with which the frequency of the gene in question takes all values between 0 and 1 in the long run. It is also the distribution of frequencies of this gene at any moment among a number of populations all subject to the same conditions. The formula for $\varphi(q)$ is a relatively simple function of Δq and $\sigma^2_{\delta q}$ (Wright, 1938).

$$\varphi(q) = (C/\sigma^2_{\delta q})e^{2\int (\Delta q/\sigma^2_{\delta q})dq},$$

where C is a constant such that

$$\int_0^1 \varphi(q)dq = 1.$$

Figures 1 to 7 are obtained by substituting various values of Δq and $\sigma^2_{\delta q}$ in this formula. Consider first, however, a somewhat more general case in which heterozygous mutants have a selective advantage s, homozygous mutants an advantage of $2s$ and immigration displaces the proportion m in each generation by immigrants with gene frequency q_I. We must distinguish the mean values of these coefficients ($\bar{s}$, $\bar{m}$, $\bar{q}_I$) and their standard deviation σ_s, σ_m and σ_{qI}, if they are subject to fluctuation. For small values of $\bar{s}$:

$$\Delta q = \bar{s}q(1 - q) - \bar{m}(q - \bar{q}_I).$$

Mutation pressure may be introduced by taking advantage of the equivalence of the theories of immigration pressure and mutation pressure. Letting $\bar{v}$ be the mean rate of mutation to the gene and $\bar{u}$ that from it per generation

$$\Delta q = \bar{s}q(1-q)+(\bar{v}+\bar{m}\bar{q}_I)(1-q)$$
$$-[\bar{u}+\bar{m}(1-\bar{q}_I)]q$$
$$= \bar{s}q(1-q)-(\bar{m}+\bar{u}+\bar{v})$$
$$\times[q-(\bar{v}+\bar{m}\bar{q}_I)/(\bar{m}+\bar{u}+\bar{v})].$$

For simplicity in most of what follows, $\bar{m}$ will be used in place of $(\bar{m} + \bar{u} + \bar{v})$ and $\bar{q}_I$ in place of $(\bar{v} + \bar{m}\bar{q}_I)/(\bar{m} + \bar{u} + \bar{v})$.

As indicated above random fluctuations in gene frequency may be due to fluctuations in selection (σ_s), in amount of immigration (σ_m), or in gene frequency of immigrants (σ_{qI}) as well as to accidents of sampling, and in general are due to some combination of all of these. We wish, however, to compare their separate effects.

(a) Fluctuations only in selection

$$\delta q = (s - \bar{s})q(1 - q)$$
$$\sigma^2_{\delta q} = \sigma_s^2 q^2(1-q)^2$$
$$\varphi(q) = C[q/(1-q)]^{2[\bar{s}-m(1-2q_I)]/\sigma_s^2}$$
$$\times q^{-2}(1-q)^{-2}e^{-2m[q_I(1-q)+(1-q_I)q]/\sigma_s^2 q(1-q)}$$

(b) Fluctuations only in amount of immigration

$$\delta q = -(m-\bar{m})(q-q_I)$$

$$\sigma^2{}_{\delta q} = \sigma_m{}^2(q-q_I)^2$$

$$\varphi(q) = C(q-q_I)^{2\,[s(1-2q_I)-\bar{m}-\sigma_m{}^2]/\sigma_m{}^2}$$
$$\times e^{-2s\,[(q-q_I)^2+q_I(1-q_I)]/\sigma_m{}^2(q-q_I)}$$

(c) Fluctuations only in gene frequency of immigrants

$$\delta q = m[q_I - \bar{q}_I]$$

$$\sigma^2{}_{\delta q} = m^2\sigma^2{}_{q_I}$$

$$\varphi(q) = Ce^{[6m\bar{q}_I q - 3q^2(m-s)-2sq^3]/3m^2\sigma^2{}_{q_I}}$$

(d) Fluctuations only from sampling (Wright, 1931)

$$\sigma^2{}_{\delta q} = q(1-q)/2N$$

$$\varphi(q) = Ce^{4Nsq} q^{4Nmq_I - 1}(1-q)^{4Nm(1-q_I)-1}$$

Figures (1) and (2) deal with the special case of genes for which the only pressure is that due to immigration ($m = .0001$) and gene frequency in the immigrants is .50.

Fig. 1

$$\Delta q = -m(q-.5)$$

$$\sigma^2{}_{\delta q} = \sigma_s{}^2 q^2(1-q)^2$$

$$\varphi(q) = Cq^{-2}(1-q)^{-2}e^{-m/\sigma_s{}^2 q(1-q)}$$

Fig. 2

$$\sigma^2{}_{\delta q} = q(1-q)/2N$$

$$\varphi(q) = C[q(1-q)]^{2Nm-1}$$

Figures 3, 4 and 5 relate to cases in which the pressure of favorable selection ($\bar{s} = .0002$) with no dominance is opposed by the pressure of immigration ($m = .0001, q_I = 0$). Mutational origin of the gene at a low rate is required to prevent its loss in extreme cases. In figure 5 this rate is taken as $v = 10^{-6}$.

Fig. 3

$$\Delta q = \bar{s}q(1-q) - mq$$

$$\sigma^2{}_{\delta q} = \sigma_s{}^2 q^2(1-q)^2$$

$$\varphi(q) = C[q/(1-q)]^{2(\bar{s}-m)/\sigma_s{}^2}$$
$$\times q^{-2}(1-q)^{-2}e^{-2m/\sigma_s{}^2(1-q)}$$

Fig. 4

$$\sigma^2{}_{\delta q} = \sigma_m{}^2 q^2$$

$$\varphi(q) = Cq^{2(s-\bar{m}-\sigma_m{}^2)/\sigma_m{}^2}e^{-2sq/\sigma_m{}^2}$$

Fig. 5

$$\Delta q = sq(1-q) - mq + v(1-q)$$

$$\sigma^2{}_{\delta q} = q(1-q)/2N$$

$$\varphi(q) = Ce^{4Nsq} q^{4Nv-1}(1-q)^{4Nm-1}$$

Figures 6 and 7 make comparisons between genes subject to different degrees of selection in a population of limited size ($N = 10{,}000$). In figure 6 it is assumed that selection favors heterozygotes equally over both homozygotes but varies in degree ($s = .01, .001, .0003$ or $.0001$).

Low rates of mutation, equal in both directions ($u = v = 10^{-6}$), are assumed to prevent permanent fixation.

Fig. 6

$$\Delta q = -[2v+2sq(1-q)][q-.5]$$

$$\sigma^2{}_{\delta q} = q(1-q)/2N$$

$$\varphi(q) = Ce^{4Nsq(1-q)} q^{4Nv-1}(1-q)^{4Nv-1}$$
$$= Ce^{40{,}000sq(1-q)}[q(1-q)]^{-.96}.$$

In figure 7, it is assumed that immigration at rate $m = .0001$ tends to maintain gene frequency at $q_I = .10$ but that this is disturbed to varying extents by favorable selection (no dominance). $s = 10^{-5}, 10^{-4}, 2 \times 10^{-4}$ and 10^{-3} respectively in a population of 10,000.

Fig. 7

$$\Delta q = sq(1-q) - m(q-q_I)$$

$$\sigma^2{}_{\delta q} = q(1-q)/2N$$

$$\varphi(q) = Ce^{4Nsq} q^{4Nmq_I - 1}(1-q)^{4Nm(1-q_I)-1}$$
$$= Ce^{40{,}000sq} q^{-.6}(1-q)^{2.6}$$

The frequencies in fixed classes in any of these cases are estimated where necessary from the subterminal classes by formulae (Wright, 1931)

$$f(0) = [f(1/2N)]/4N(mq_I+v),$$

$$f(1) = \{f[(2N-1)/2N]\}$$
$$/4N[m(1-q_I)+u],$$

where

$$f(q) = \varphi(q)/2N.$$

LITERATURE CITED

DOBZHANSKY, TH., A. M. HOLZ, AND B. SPASSKY. 1942. Genetics of natural populations. VIII. Concealed variability in the second and fourth chromosomes of *Drosophila pseudoobscura* and its bearing on the problem of heterosis. Genetics, 27: 463–490.

DOBZHANSKY, TH. AND B. SPASSKY. 1944. Genetics of natural populations. XI. Manifestation of genetic variants in *Drosophila pseudoobscura* in different environments. Genetics, 29: 270–290.

ELTON, C. S. 1924. Periodic fluctuations in the number of animals: their causes and effects. Brit. J. Exp. Biol. 3: 119–163.

FISHER, R. A. 1928. The possible modification of the response of the wild type to recurrent mutations. Amer. Nat., 62: 115–126.

——. 1930. The genetical theory of natural selection. Oxford, Clarendon Press. 272 pp.

——. 1935. Dominance in poultry. Phil. Trans. Roy. Soc. B, 225: 197–226.

FISHER, R. A., AND S. B. HOLT. 1944. The experimental modification of dominance in Danforth's short tailed mutant mice. Ann. Eug., 12: 102–120.

FISHER, R. A., AND E. B. FORD. 1947. The spread of a gene in natural conditions in a colony of the moth *Panaxia dominula* L. Heredity, 1: 143–174.

GOLDSCHMIDT, R. 1940. The material basis of evolution. Yale Univ. Press, New Haven. 436 pp.

HARLAND, S. C. 1936. The genetical conception of the species. Biol. Rev., 11: 83–112.

LACK, DAVID. 1947. Darwin's finches. Cambridge at the University Press. 208 p.

LUSH, J. L. 1943. Animal breeding plans. The Iowa State College Press, Ames, Iowa. 437 pp.

McPHEE, H. C., AND S. WRIGHT. 1925. Mendelian analysis of the pure breeds of live stock. III. The shorthorns. Jour. Hered., 16: 205–215.

STERN, CURT, AND ELIZABETH W. SCHAEFFER. 1943. On wild type iso-alleles in *Drosophila melanogaster*. Proc. Nat. Acad. Sci., 29: 361–367.

WRIEDT, C. 1930. Heredity in live stock. Macmillan & Co., London. 179 pp.

WRIGHT, S. 1929. Fisher's theory of dominance. Amer. Nat., 63: 274–279.

——. 1929. The evolution of dominance, Amer. Nat., 63: 556–561.

——. 1931. Evolution in Mendelian populations. Genetics, 16: 97–159.

——. 1932. The roles of mutation, inbreeding, crossbreeding and selection in evolution. Proc. 6th Internat. Congress of Genetics, 1: 356–366.

——. 1934. Physiological and evolutionary theories of dominance. Amer. Nat., 68: 25–53.

——. 1935. Evolution in populations in approximate equilibrium. Jour. Gen., 30: 257–266.

——. 1938. The distribution of gene frequencies under irreversible mutation. Proc. Nat. Acad. Sci., 24: 253–259.

——. 1940. The statistical consequences of Mendelian heredity in relation to speciation. In "The New Systematics," pp. 161–183 (edited by Julian Huxley). Clarendon Press, Oxford.

WRIGHT, S., TH. DOBZHANSKY, AND W. HOVANITZ. 1942. Genetics of natural populations. VII. The allelism of lethals in the third chromosome of *Drosophila pseudoobscura*. Genetics, 27: 363–394.

AN EXPERIMENTAL STUDY OF INTERACTION BETWEEN GENETIC DRIFT AND NATURAL SELECTION

Theodosius Dobzhansky and Olga Pavlovsky [1]

Department of Zoology, Columbia University, New York City

Received January 31, 1957

Introduction

The role of random genetic drift in the evolutionary process has, for about two decades, been one of the controversial issues in population genetics. Some authors have appealed to "drift" as a convenient explanation of the origin of differences among organisms for which no other explanations seemed to be available. But one's inability to discover the adaptive significance of a trait does not mean that it has none (cf. Dobzhansky, 1956). The hypothesis of random genetic drift should not be used as a loophole; to be accepted it requires a firmer basis than suspicion. Other authors seem to think that drift and natural selection are alternatives. As soon as a gene is shown to have any effect whatever on fitness, the conclusion is drawn that its distribution in populations must be determined solely by selection and cannot be influenced by random drift. But this is a logical non-sequitur. The important work of Aird *et al.* (1954) and of Clarke *et al.* (1956) disclosed that the incidence of certain types of gastrointestinal ulceration is significantly different in persons with different blood groups. This is, however, far from a convincing demonstration that the observed diversity in the frequencies of the blood group genes in human populations is governed wholly, or even partially, by selection for resistance to ulcers. To make such a conclusion tenable it would have to be demonstrated that the environments in which human racial differences have evolved actually favored greater resistance in certain parts of the

world and lesser resistance in certain other parts. Thus far no evidence has been adduced to substantiate any such claim.

As defined by Wright (1949) random genetic drift includes all variations in gene frequencies which are indeterminate in direction. Such variations are caused by accidents in gene sampling in populations of finite genetically effective size, as well as by fluctuations in the intensity or in the direction of selection, mutation and gene exchange between populations. Wright (1932, 1948, 1948, 1951) as well as the present writer (Dobzhansky, 1937–1941–1951) have stressed that random drift by itself is not likely to bring about important evolutionary progress. Indeed, variations in gene frequencies induced by random drift in small isolated populations are apt to be inadaptive, and hence likely to result in extinction of such populations. However, random drift may be important in conjunction with systematic pressures on the gene frequencies, particularly with natural selection. What is most necessary, then, is the type of experimental evidence that would permit analysis of the interactions between random drift and selection. Such evidence, although difficult to obtain, should be within the range of what is possible. Kerr and Wright (1954) and Wright and Kerr (1954) studied models of Drosophila populations in which the number of the progenitors in every generation was fixed arbitrarily, and in which classical laboratory mutants were used as traits subject to drift and to selection. In the experimental Drosophila populations described in the following pages naturally occurring genetic variants, inversions in the third

[1] The work reported in this article has been carried out under Contract No. AT-(30-1)-1151, U. S. Atomic Energy Commission.

Reprinted by permission of the authors from Evolution, **11**, 311–319 (1957).

chromosomes of *Drosophila pseudoobscura* were used. Severe limitation of the population sizes was introduced in some of the populations in only a single generation, at the beginning of the experiments. Experiments so conducted may to some extent reproduce genetic events which occur in natural populations.

PRELIMINARY EXPERIMENTS

It has been shown (see Dobzhansky, 1949 and 1954, for reviews) that heterozygotes of *Drosophila pseudoobscura* which carry two third chromosomes with different gene arrangements derived from the same locality are, as a rule, superior in Darwinian fitness to the corresponding homozygotes. The situation is more complex when flies of different geographic origins are hybridized. Chromosomal heterozygotes which carry two third chromosomes derived from different geographic regions may or may not exhibit heterosis. Experimental populations, bred in the laboratory in so-called population cages, behave differently depending upon whether the foundation stock of the population consists of flies of geographically uniform or of geographically mixed origin. In the former case, the chromosomes with different gene arrangements usually reach certain equilibrium frequencies. Replicate experiments, conducted with reasonable precautions to make the environments uniform, give results repeatable within the limits of sampling errors. With geographically mixed populations the results do not obey simple rules. The course of natural selection in such populations is often erratic; equilibrium may or may not be reached, or may be reached and then lost; replicate experiments do not give uniform results; heterosis may or may not be present at the start of the experiments, and may or may not develop in the course of selection in the experimental populations.

The indeterminacy observed in the populations of geographically mixed origin is however understandable (Dobzhansky and Pavlovsky, 1953; Dobzhansky, 1954).

Race hybridization releases a flood of genetic variability; the number of potentially possible gene combinations far exceeds the number of the flies in the experimental populations; natural selection perpetuates the genotypes which possess high adaptive values under experimental conditions, but it is a matter of chance which of the possible adaptive genotypes will be formed first in a given population. In some populations these genotypes will happen to be structural heterozygotes, and in others homozygotes.

We have tested about thirty experimental populations of mixed geographic origins, using different combinations of flies from diverse localities (Dobzhansky and Pavlovsky, 1953, and much unpublished data). Among them were two replicate populations, Nos. 119 and 120, which are relevant here. They were started on February 8, 1954, in wood-and-glass population cages used in our laboratory and described previously. The foundation stocks consisted of F_1 hybrids between 12 strains derived from flies collected near Austin, Texas in 1953 and 10 strains derived from Mather, California, in 1947. The Texas strains were homozygous for the Pikes Peak (PP) gene arrangement, and the California strains for the Arrowhead (AR) gene arrangement in their third chromosomes. In each of the two cages 2,395 flies of both sexes, taken from the same F_1 culture bottles of Texas by California crosses, were introduced. The populations were kept in an incubator at 25° C., samples of eggs deposited in the population cages were taken at desired intervals, larvae hatching from these eggs were grown under optimal conditions in regular culture bottles, and their salivary glands were dissected and stained in acetic orcein.

The course of the events in the populations Nos. 119 and 120 is shown in table 1 and figure 1. The percentage frequencies of PP chromosomes are given in this table, the frequencies of AR chromosomes are the balance to 100 per cent. Each sample is based on determination of the

TABLE 1. *Changes in the frequencies (in per cent) of PP chromosomes in two replicate experimental populations of* Drosophila pseudoobscura *of mixed geographic origin (Texas PP by California AR)*

Days from start	Population No. 119	Population No. 120	Chi-Square	P
0	50.0	50.0	—	—
35	49.3	48.7	0.02	0.90
70	39.0	40.7	0.08	0.75
105	42.3	36.7	1.01	0.35
250	30.0	43.7	6.01	0.01
300	29.0	40.7	4.50	0.03
365	26.3	42.0	15.60	0.001
425	25.0	41.7	9.37	0.002

gene arrangement in 300 third chromosomes (150 larvae, taken in 6 subsamples on 6 successive days). The first samples, 35 days from the start, showed little change from the original frequencies, 50 per cent, of the chromosomes. At 70 and 105 days the frequencies of PP diminished, about equally in both populations, as shown by the low chi-square (each chi-square has one degree of freedom). But at 250 days the frequency of PP diminished in the population No. 119, while it failed to change, or even increased, in No. 120. This situation persisted until April 9, 1955, about 425 days from the start, when the last samples were taken and the populations were discarded. The chi-squares shown in table 1 attest that the outcomes of natural selection in these two experimental populations were clearly unlike. It should be noted that the magnitude of the divergence between the replicate populations Nos. 119 and 120 is not exceptionally great for the type of experiments in which flies from geographically remote localities are involved.

MAIN EXPERIMENTS

Certain consequences should follow from the above interpretation of the indeterminacy observed in populations of geographically mixed parentage. The indeterminacy should be a function of the genetic variability in the foundation stock

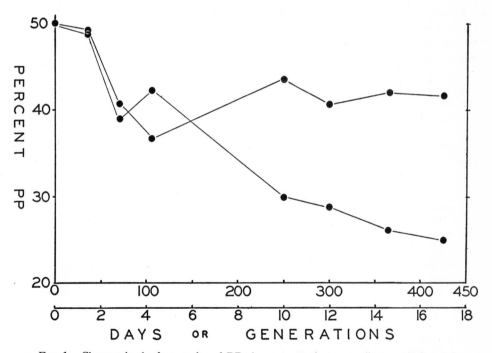

FIG. 1. Changes in the frequencies of PP chromosomes in two replicate experimental populations of mixed geographic origin (Texas by California).

of the populations. Chromosomes with PP and AR gene arrangements are recognizable under the microscope; their frequencies are made uniform in the foundation stock of all populations, and we observe changes in their frequencies as the experiment progresses. However, we infer that, apart from this overt variability in the frequency of the gene arrangements, there must exist also a large amount of genic variability released owing to gene recombination in the F_2 and later generations of interracial hybrids. Although there is no way of telling by how many genes the races differ, the number of the possible gene combinations must be several to many orders of magnitude greater than the number actually realized. The outcome of selection in the experimental populations should, then, be more variable in small than in large populations.

This working hypothesis is open to experimental test, but the experimental technique must be carefully thought through. One could make some experimental populations smaller than others by keeping them in cages of different sizes and with different amounts of food. The drawback of this would be that the environments of the populations of different sizes would be dissimilar. Therefore, we have chosen to vary the sizes of the foundation stocks of our populations, but to permit them to expand to equal size,

which, because of the high fecundity of the flies, they do within a little more than a single generation.

The same 12 Texas PP and 10 California AR strains were used in the main as in the preliminary experiments (see above). F_1 hybrids between them, which were necessarily heterozygous PP/AR, were raised in regular culture bottles, and so were the F_2 hybrids. In June 1955, 4,000 F_2 flies, about equal numbers being females and males and derived equally from the different crosses, were placed in a population cage. Between June 15 and 27, 15 cups with yeasted culture medium were inserted in the cage daily. The flies covered the medium with eggs overnight. The cups with the eggs were then withdrawn and placed in another population cage containing no adult flies. In this manner ten population cages, Nos. 145–154, were obtained on ten successive days. They were descended, then, from the same foundation stock of 4,000 F_2 interlocality hybrids. The frequencies of PP and AR chromosomes in the foundation stock are evidently 50–50. These are the "large" populations.

Ten groups of 20 F_2 flies each, 10 ♀♀ and 10 ♂♂, were taken from the same F_2 cultures which served as the source of the foundation stock for the "large" populations, care being taken to include in each group flies from all the F_2 cultures.

TABLE 2. *Frequencies (in per cent) of PP chromosomes in the experimental populations*

Large populations				Small populations		
No.	Oct. '55	Nov. '56		No.	Oct. '55	Nov. '56
145	39.3	31.7		155	37.7	18.0
146	42.3	29.0		156	30.7	32.0
147	29.3	34.7		157	31.0	46.0
148	38.0	34.0		158	32.3	46.7
149	33.3	22.7		159	34.3	32.7
150	36.0	20.3		160	41.7	47.3
151	40.3	32.0		161	37.3	16.3
152	41.0	22.3		162	25.3	34.3
153	37.0	25.7		163	37.7	32.0
154	42.0	22.0		164	25.3	22.0
Mean	37.85	27.44		Mean	33.33	32.73
Variance	15.30	26.96		Variance	26.73	118.91

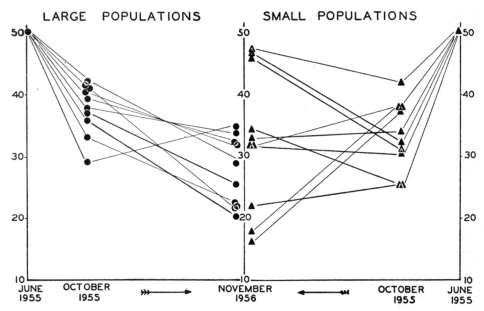

Fig. 2. The frequencies (in percent) of PP chromosomes in twenty replicate experimental populations of mixed geographic origin (Texas by California).

These groups of F_2 flies were placed in regular culture bottles and allowed to produce progenies. Each progeny was then transferred to population cages of the same type as those used for the "large" populations. Ten population cages, Nos. 155–164, were thus obtained. They are the "small" populations. It should be reiterated that the "large" and the "small" differed only in the foundation stocks, these being 4,000 and 20 flies respectively. All populations were kept at 25° C. and treated similarly in every way.

In October and November 1955, about 4 generations after the start, the populations were examined; egg samples were taken and the chromosomes in the salivary gland cells of the larvae that hatched from these eggs were studied. The gene arrangements in the chromosomes were determined and scored by Dr. Louis Levine. The results are summarized in table 2 and figure 2. As usual, each sample consisted of 300 chromosomes. The frequencies of PP varied from 29.3% to 42.3% in the "large" populations, and from 25.3% to 41.7% in the "small" ones.

The heterogeneity is significant in both; the chi-square for the "large" is 19.5 and for the "small" ones 35.9, which correspond to probabilities of about 0.02 and of much less than 0.001 respectively. The heterogeneity among the replicate experiments is, of course, not surprising in view of the outcome of the preliminary experiments (table 1), although in these latter a significant heterogeneity first appeared after somewhat more than 4 generations from the start. It may be noted (table 2) that the variance for the "small" populations (26.7) is ostensibly greater than for the "large" ones (15.3), but the F value is not significant. It may also be noted that the frequencies of PP chromosomes have declined from the 50% value in the foundation stock, the decline being somewhat greater in the "small" (33.3%) than in the "large" (37.8%) populations.

The next, and the final, test of the populations was made in November 1956, i.e., more than a year after the first test and about 19 generations after the populations were placed in the population cages. The preliminary experiments (table 1) show that the populations reach equilibria in the frequencies of PP and AR chromosomes within less than a year from the start. The samples, 300 chromosomes per cage, were taken in the usual manner and scored by one of us (Th. D). The results are reported in table 2 and figure 2.

It may be noted that the mean frequency of PP in the "large" populations is now 27.4% and in the "small" ones 32.7%. These means are not significantly different from each other, but the 1956 mean for the "large" populations is significantly lower than the 1955 mean. The outcomes of natural selection in the "large" and the "small" populations are, then, similar on the average. It is otherwise when the outcomes in the individual populations are considered. As shown in table 2 and figure 2, the frequencies of PP in the "large" populations range from 20.3% to 34.7%, and in the "small" ones from 16.3% to 47.3%. In both instances the heterogeneity is highly significant (the chi-square for the "large" population is 40.4 which, for 9 degrees of freedom, has a negligible probability of being due to chance. Both in the "large" and especially in the "small" populations the variance has increased during the year intervening between the two tests (1955–1956).

Most important of all is, however, that the "small" populations show a heterogeneity significantly greater than the "large" ones. The variances, 118.9 and 27.0, now give an F ratio of 4.4 which is significant at between the 0.025 and 0.010 levels. The greater heterogeneity is evidently due to the different magnitudes of the foundation stocks in these populations. This heterogeneity was indicated already by the tests in October 1955, but it has become significant as the selection continued during the year between the two tests. Finally, it may be pointed out that there appears to be no significant correlation between the status of a given population in 1955 and 1956. For example, No. 160 had the highest frequency of PP in both tests (Table 2), but No. 161 which had the lowest frequency in 1956 had an above average frequency in 1955.

DISCUSSION

The results of the present investigation can be stated very simply: Although the trait studied (the gene arrangement in the third chromosome) is subject to powerful selection pressure, the outcome of the selection in the experimental populations is conditioned by random genetic drift. The either-selection-or-drift point of view is a fallacy.

In our experiments, the heterozygotes which carry two third chromosomes with different gene arrangements are heterotic; natural selection in the experimental populations establishes equilibrium states at which both gene arrangements occur with certain frequencies; these frequencies are determined by the relative fitness of the homozygotes and heterozygotes. Now, the environments being reasonably uniform in all experimental populations, the outcome of the selection processes in the replicate experiments should also be uniform. And so it is, in experimental populations of geographically uniform origin. But it is not so in geographically mixed populations. In the latter, the selective fates of the chromosomal gene arrangements become dependent upon the polygenic genetic background, which is highly complex and variable because of the gene recombination that is bound to occur in populations descended from race hybrids. Here random drift becomes operative and important. It becomes important despite the populations being small only at the beginning of the experiments, because the foundation stocks in some populations consisted of small numbers of individuals. Thereafter, all the populations expand to equal sizes, fluctuating roughly between 1,000 and 4,000 adult individuals. Such populations can be regarded as small only in relation to the number of gene recombinations which are possible in populations of hybrid origin.

For reasons that are not far to seek, geneticists visualize the evolutionary process usually in terms of the destinies of single genes. With the notable exception of the contributions of Wright (1932 and subsequent work), this is the frame of reference of most of the mathematical theory of population genetics. This makes manageable an otherwise impossibly complex topic, and yet the oversimplified models usually suffice for understanding of microevolutionary processes. But as we move into the realm of mesoevolution (Dobzhansky, 1954), not to speak of macroevolution, it becomes indispensable to consider not only the destinies of single genes but also of integrated genotypes, and finally of the gene pool of Mendelian populations. In our experiments, the foundation stock of the populations consisted of F_2 hybrids between rather remote geographic races; a highly variable gene pool arose owing to the hybridization; random drift caused different segments of this gene pool to be included in the foundation stocks of each population, especially in the small ones; natural selection then produced divergent results in different populations, especially again amongst the small ones.

It is now logical to inquire whether the events observed in our experimental populations resemble situations which occur in nature. The excellent work of Dowdeswell and Ford (1952, 1953) and Ford (1954) has disclosed a most suggestive case. Populations of the butterfly *Maniola jurtina* are rather uniform throughout southern England, despite some obvious environmental diversity in different parts of this territory. In contrast to this, the populations of the same species show quite appreciable divergence on the islands of the Scilly archipelago, although these islands are within only a few miles of each other and their environments appear rather uniform. Especially remarkable is the divergence observed between the populations of certain small islands, while larger islands have more nearly similar populations. The small islands happen, however, to be situated between the larger ones. The investigators have estimated

that the populations of the small islands consist of numbers of individuals of the order of 15,000 and that the populations of the large islands must be considerably greater. The authors conclude that the genetic divergence between these populations must be produced entirely by selection, random drift being inconsequential. The evidence is, however, weighed in favor of the view that the genetic divergence was initiated by the island populations being derived from small numbers of immigrants from the mainland or from other islands. These immigrants introduced somewhat different sets of genes on each island, whereupon natural selection built different genetic systems in the different populations.

The divergence between island and mainland populations has been studied also by Kramer and Mertens (1938) and by Eisentraut (1950) in lizards, and by Lowe (1955) in mammals and reptiles. Most data agree in showing that the divergence is greater on smaller than on larger islands, and greater on islands more remote from the mainland than on those which are apt to receive immigrants most frequently. Many authors, including this writer (Dobzhansky, 1937, 1941), interpreted these situations as arising through random drift in populations of continuously small size, or frequently passing through narrow "bottlenecks." This interpretation need no longer be sustained. It is more probable, especially in the light of the experiments described in the present article, that in the island populations we are observing the emergence of novel genetic systems moulded by interaction of random drift with natural selection.

Mayr (1954) has pointed out that conspicuous divergence of peripherally isolated populations of a species is a fairly general phenomenon, well known to systematists. He rightly concludes that this divergence cannot be due entirely to random drift "in the ordinary sense," i.e., to fluctuations of the gene frequencies in populations of persistently small size. Indeed, some of the peripheral populations consist of thousands or even millions of individuals. Mayr's interpretation can be stated best in his own words: "Isolating a few individuals (the 'founders') from a variable population which is situated in the midst of a stream of genes which flows ceaselessly through every widespread species will produce a sudden change of the genetic environment of most loci. This change, in fact, is the most drastic genetic change (except for polyploidy and hybridization) which may occur in a population, since it may effect all loci at once. Indeed, it may have the character of a veritable 'genetic revolution.' Furthermore, this 'genetic revolution,' released by the isolation of the founder population, may well have the character of a chain reaction. Changes in any locus will in turn affect the selective values at many other loci, until finally the system has reached a new state of equilibrium." The outcome of our experiments described above may, in a sense, be regarded as experimental verification of Mayr's hypothesis.

SUMMARY

Twenty replicate experimental populations of *Drosophila pseudoobscura* were kept in a uniform environment for approximately 18 months. The foundation stocks of all the populations consisted of F_2 hybrids between flies of Texas origin which had the PP gene arrangement in their third chromosomes, and flies of California origin with the AR gene arrangement in the same chromosome. In ten of the populations the founders numbered 4,000 individuals; the other ten populations descended from only 20 founders each.

The frequencies of PP and AR chromosomes in all the populations were originally 50 per cent. Eighteen months later, the frequencies of PP varied from about 20 to 35 per cent in the populations descended from the large numbers of founders, and from 16 to 47 per cent in those descended from small numbers of the founders. The heterogeneity of these frequencies of PP chromosomes observed in the replicate populations is statistically highly significant. More important still, the heterogeneity is significantly greater in the populations descended from small numbers of founders than in those descended from large numbers of founders.

Heterozygotes which carry a PP and an AR third chromosome are superior in adaptive value to the PP and AR homozygotes. Therefore, the frequencies of PP and AR chromosomes in the experimental populations are controlled by natural selection. However, the heterogeneity of the results in the replicate populations is conditioned by random genetic drift.

Only some of the possible combinations of the genes of the Texas and California genomes are actually realized in the populations. The segments of the gene pool which arise from race hybridization are smaller, and therefore less uniform, in the populations descended from small than in those descended from large numbers of founders. It may reasonably be inferred that evolutionary changes involving interactions of natural selection and random drift of the kind observed in our experiments are not infrequent in nature.

ACKNOWLEDGMENTS

We take pleasure in acknowledging our obligations to our colleague Professor Howard Levene, and to Dr. Bruce Wallace of the Long Island Biological Laboratories, for their counsels regarding the statistical and experimental procedures; to Professor Louis Levine for the examination of the chromosomal constitution of the experimental populations in October of 1955; to Mr. and Mrs. B. Spassky for the maintenance of the experimental populations during the two months when both authors were absent from New York; and to many colleagues and friends for many discussions of the problems and issues dwelt upon in the present article.

LITERATURE CITED

AIRD, I., H. H. BENTALL, J. H. MEHIGAN, AND J. A. FRASER ROBERTS. 1954. The blood groups in relation to peptic ulceration and carcinoma of the colon, rectum, breast, and bronchus. Brit. Med. Journ., 2: 315–321.

CLARKE, C. H., J. W. EDWARDS, D. R. W. HADDOCK, A. W. HOWELL EVANS, R. B. McCONNELL, AND P. M. SHEPPARD. 1956. ABO blood groups and secretor character in duodenal ulcer. Brit. Med. Journ., 2: 725–730.

DOBZHANSKY, TH. 1937–1941–1951. Genetics and the Origin of Species. Columbia University Press, New York (1st, 2nd and 3rd editions).

——. 1949. Observations and experiments on natural selection in Drosophila. Proc. 8th Internat. Cong. Genetics: 210–224.

——. 1954. Evolution as a creative process. Proc. 9th Internat. Cong. Genetics, 1: 435–449.

——. 1956. What is an adaptive trait? Amer. Naturalist, 20: 337–347.

——. 1957. Genetics of natural populations. XXVI. EVOLUTION (in press).

——, and O. PAVLOVSKY. 1953. Indeterminate outcome of certain experiments on Drosophila populations. EVOLUTION, 7: 198–210.

DOWDESWELL, W. H., AND E. B. FORD. 1952. Geographical variation in the butterfly Maniola jurtina. Heredity, 6: 99–109.

——, AND E. B. FORD. 1953. The influence of isolation on variability in the butterfly Maniola jurtina. Symp. Soc. Exp. Biol., 7: 254–273.

EISENTRAUT, M. 1950. Die Eidechsen der spanischen Mittelmeerinseln und ihre Rassenaufspaltung in Lichte der Evolution. Berlin.

FORD, E. B. 1954. Problems in the evolution of geographical races. In: Evolution as a Process: 99–108.

KERR, W., AND S. WRIGHT, 1954. Experimental studies of the distribution of gene frequencies in very small populations of Drosophila melanogaster. EVOLUTION 8: 225–240.

KRAMER, G., AND R. MERTENS. 1938. Rassenbildung bei west-istrianischen Inseleidechsen in Abhangigkeit von Isolierungsalter und Arealgrosse. Arch. Naturgesch., 7: 189–234.

LOWE, CH. H. 1955. An evolutionary study of island faunas in the Gulf of California, Mexico, with a method of comparative analysis. EVOLUTION, 9: 339–344.

MAYR, E. 1954. Change of genetic environment and evolution. In: Evolution as a Process: 157–180.

WRIGHT, S. 1932. The roles of mutation, inbreeding, crossbreeding and selection in evolution. Proc. 6th Internat. Congress Genetics, 1: 356–366.

——. 1948. On the roles of directed and random changes in gene frequency in the genetics of populations. EVOLUTION, 2: 279–294.

——. 1949. Population structure in evolution. Proc. Amer. Philos. Soc., 93: 471–478.

——. 1951. Fisher and Ford on "The Sewall Wright Effect." Amer. Scientist, 39: 452–479.

——, AND W. KERR. 1954. Experimental studies of the distribution of gene frequencies in very small populations of Drosophila melanogaster. EVOLUTION, 8: 225–240.

MEIOTIC DRIVE IN NATURAL POPULATIONS OF *DROSOPHILA MELANOGASTER*. III. POPULATIONAL IMPLICATIONS OF THE SEGREGATION–DISTORTER LOCUS[1,2]

Yuichiro Hiraizumi, L. Sandler and James F. Crow

Department of Genetics, University of Wisconsin, Madison, Wisconsin

Received February 29, 1960

If, among the successful gametes from heterozygotes, one allele is regularly included in more than half, it may increase in frequency even if it has a harmful effect. Unequal gamete production, when attributable to the mechanics of meiosis, has been called meiotic drive (Sandler and Novitski, 1957). An example is segregation-distortion in *Drosophila melanogaster*, the cytogenetic behavior of which has been reported by Sandler, Hiraizumi and Sandler (1959) and Sandler and Hiraizumi (1959).

The observations that are relevant to this discussion are: 1. Segregation-distortion depends on a locus named *Segregation-distorter* (*SD*), which is located in the centromeric heterochromatin of chromosome II. 2. Males heterozygous for *SD* and a normal chromosome transmit the *SD*-carrying chromosome in great excess; this excess is not due to post-zygotic mortality, nor is there any reduction in the fertility of *SD*/+ males. 3. Segregation in *SD*/+ females is normal. 4. It appears necessary, in order for segregation-distortion to occur, for the *SD* locus to synapse with the *SD*+ allele on the homologous chromosome; for, if the *SD*+-bearing chromosome is structurally abnormal in the *SD* region, the distortion is reduced and usually eliminated altogether. 5. Males homozygous for *SD* have normal segregation ratios.

The purpose of this paper is (1) to show that segregation-distortion does in fact occur in nature and that the population consequences are qualitatively in agreement with expectations from the theory of meiotic drive; (2) to show that the results from experimental populations bear out the quantitative predictions insofar as these have been tested; (3) to present a mathematical treatment of the population consequences of some special cases of meiotic drive with special emphasis on those phenomena which bear on the behavior of *SD*; and (4) to consider the particular way in which one population of Drosophila has minimized the detrimental effects of the spread of *SD*.

SD IN NATURAL POPULATIONS

In a collection of Drosophila, made in 1956 from a natural population in Madison, Wisconsin, six chromosomes bearing the *SD* locus were recovered in a total of 183 second chromosomes tested. Among these six *SD*-bearing chromosomes, five also carried a recessive lethal. Allelism tests revealed that the lethal carried by these five chromosomes was the same. Moreover, salivary gland examination showed that the five lethal-bearing chromosomes carried two inversions in the right arm of chromosome II, a small proximal and a large distal inversion, which together cause almost complete linkage of the *SD* gene, the lethal, and the two inversions. It has so far been impossible to separate the proximal inversion from the lethal. The remaining lethal-free *SD* line contains only the more distal of the two inversions and also exhibits a reduced frequency of crossing over (although higher than in the other lines). We designate the doubly inverted lines as *SD-5* type, the

[1] Paper No. 812 of the Genetics Division.

[2] Supported by Grant No. G6188 from the National Science Foundation.

Reprinted by permission of the authors from EVOLUTION, **14**, 433–444 (1960).

lethal-free singly inverted line as *SD-72* type.

The high frequency of *SD* in this population, since it is in most instances inseparable from a lethal, is a direct demonstration that segregation-distortion is effective in maintaining gene frequencies against opposing selection. Indeed, the homozygous *SD* locus itself causes a reduced viability as is shown by the fact that the lethal-free *SD-72* line has a larval viability of only 68 per cent that of Canton-S, a standard laboratory inbred stock.

In 1958, another wild collection was made in Madison approximately three miles from the site of the original collection. Again, *SD*-bearing chromosomes were recovered. Unfortunately, collections could not be made at the original site because building construction had spoiled the location for Drosophila collecting. In the 1958 collection, *SD*-bearing chromosomes of at least two types were recovered. One of these appears to be indistinguishable from the *SD-5* type. Among the others several have given a crossover pattern different from either the *SD-5* or *SD-72* types. The distal inversion of *SD-72* permits crossing over only proximal to it, while the two inversions of *SD-5* permit crossovers only distal to both. The new type has both proximal and distal crossovers. The reason for supposing that this is not the same as the proximal inversion of *SD-5* is that it contains no lethal.

Since the new collection was made near the home of one of us (JFC), it is possible that the *SD-5* type is descended from laboratory escapees. The fact that a new inversion type appears to be present makes it very unlikely that all the *SD*'s are from this source. It is, however, completely clear that the *SD* locus on these new chromosomes is identical with the *SD* loci previously recovered by all criteria applied. These are: 1. The locus is able to exhibit the phenomenon of segregation-distortion. 2. *SD* from the original collection does not lead to distorted ratios when heterozygous with the newly recovered *SD*-bearing chromosomes. 3. The new *SD* alleles are also located near the centromere. We designate these new *SD*-bearing chromosomes as *SD-100* type, although several types may actually be included.

From the foregoing we see that all of the *SD* loci recovered in nature have been associated with inversions which are extremely efficient crossover suppressors for the right arm of chromosome II. Crossover data from all of the tested *SD* lines are given in table 1.

The invariable association of *SD* with inversions is a surprising observation, since it is well known that inversions are relatively rare in wild populations of *D. melanogaster* (Dubinin, *et al.*, 1937; Ives, 1947). It thus appears most probable that the inversions are somehow maintained because of the presence of *SD*. It is, in fact, clear from previously reported experimental results (Sandler and Hiraizumi, 1959) that this is true. For the rare recombinant chromosomes containing *SD* all give less distorted ratios than the original chromosomes from which they were derived.

As stated earlier, the relative viability of the lethal-free homozygous *SD-72* line is about two-thirds of normal. This, of course, is the viability under nearly ideal laboratory conditions, and it seems

TABLE 1. *Frequencies of various recombinant types from the cross* SD(*In*)/cn bw ♀ ♀ ✕cn bw ♂ ♂

SD type	Non-crossover	Constitution of crossovers				Total
		SD bw	cn In	SD In bw	cn	
SD-72	7,535	9	5	0	0	7,549
SD-5	9,305	0	0	1	0	9,306
SD-5*	1,246	0	0	4	5**	1,255

* This high rate of crossing over was observed in this experiment only and not in tests of the inversion-bearing recombinants from this line. This result is not understood at present.

** One of these *cn* recombinants was lost before tests could be made. It is included in this class because of the identity of the other four *cn* recombinants.

reasonable that in nature *SD-72* might be effectively lethal or semi-lethal. On the other hand, it appears that the *SD-5* type lines, although completely lethal when homozygous, have, on the average, a higher and more stable distribution of *k* values (*k* = proportion of functional *SD* gametes from a heterozygote). Therefore, it might be that the *SD-5* type lines accumulate more rapidly than *SD-72* in a population. It could be, alternatively, that *SD-72* is an *SD-5* type that had recently lost the lethal and the associated proximal inversion and was, at the time of the collection, in the process of replacing the *SD-5* chromosomes. This matter will be considered again in succeeding sections.

One of the most interesting and important observations from the original 1956 collection was the following. Among the normal, SD^+, chromosomes in the population, most of those tested have been partially "insensitive" to the distorting action of *SD*. When heterozygous *SD-5* males are tested with the "standard" *cn bw* tester stock, the average *k* value is almost invariably higher than 0.95. When, however, a sample of three wild chromosomes collected, in 1956, from the Madison population from which *SD* was recovered were tested, the average *k* values were 0.87, 0.85, and 0.78 (Sandler, Hiraizumi and Sandler, 1959). Although the number of chromosomes so examined is small, it is still clear that a high proportion of second chromosomes in this population are relatively insensitive to the distorting action of *SD*. It is, to be sure, true that most laboratory stocks carry second chromosomes which are also relatively insensitive to *SD*. But on the other hand, five populations collected in nature from various parts of Japan were tested for the presence of *SD* loci and also for their sensitivity to *SD-5*. Here it was found that none of these five populations contained *SD* nor did any contain insensitive alleles. In fact, the sensitivity of the Japanese wild type strains was at least that of the

TABLE 2. *Tests of the sensitivity of second chromosomes in five Japanese populations and the Madison population. The cross is*

SD-5/Cy ♀ ♀ ✕ SD-5/+ ♂ ♂

Source of + chromosome	Phenotype of progeny		
	Cy	+	k*
Hayahoshi	453	4	0.99
Ishima	589	10	0.98
Otaru	685	3	0.99
Tokyo	461	0	1.00
Uwajima	683	4	0.99
Madison	1,002	166	0.83

* $k = 1 - 2r/1 - r$ where *r* is the ratio of wild progeny to total progeny.

standard tester stock. The results of such tests and the *k* values for these Japanese wild type lines are given in table 2.

Although it is clear that the need for a further study of the geographical distribution of *SD* loci and insensitive SD^+ alleles remains, there is, from these data, at least the indication that there may be an association between the presence of the *SD* alleles and insensitive SD^+ alleles. This association could come about, perhaps, because insensitive SD^+ alleles arise spontaneously and accumulate in populations because of the presence of *SD*, or it might be that insensitive alleles arise only by some process that depends on the presence of the *SD* allele (Sandler and Hiraizumi, 1959). This point will be developed below.

MATHEMATICAL RESULTS

SD can exist in a variety of states, each of which is recognizable by a characteristic distribution of *k* values. Furthermore, these states can be induced by appropriate mating schemes. For example, there are *SD* alleles which produce, from individual test males, a distribution of *k* values which is essentially flat and ranges from no distortion to *k* values approaching unity.

Even alleles which are stable produce *k* values differing from those observed when heterozygous with the "standard tester" chromosome depending on the sex of the parent contributing the SD allele to the tested male ("conditional distortion") and depending on the SD^+ allele in the *parent* of the tested male.

Additional complications arise because it is found that SD^+ alleles exist in a variety of states each of which has a characteristic k distribution when tested with some standard tester SD chromosome. These states of SD^+, furthermore, are also modifiable by genetic manipulation.

For these reasons, a completely general theory of meiotic drive would appear to be difficult in the extreme, if not impossible. Consequently, we content ourselves here with mathematical treatments of special and necessarily simplified cases.

An important characteristic of meiotic drive in cases so far reported is that its effect is restricted to one sex. This causes complications in the mathematical treatment. Therefore we shall start with a simple model in which meiotic drive operates in both sexes in the same way, and then consider the case where the effect is different in the two sexes.

Meiotic Drive in Both Sexes

Sandler and Novitski (1957) showed that a driven element, which arises in a population, will increase in frequency if $2W_{01}k > 1$, where W_{01} is the fitness of the heterozygote and k is the segregation ratio as before. This can be shown as follows:

Let A_0 and A be a driven element and its normal alternative respectively, and W_{00}, W_{01} and 1 be the fitness of A_0A_0, A_0A and AA. Then

$$\Delta q = \frac{q(1 - q)[q(W_{00} - 2W_{01} + 1) + (2W_{01}k - 1)]}{\bar{W}}$$

or, equivalently,

$$\Delta q = \frac{-(2W_{01} - W_{00} - 1)q(1 - q)(q - \hat{q})}{\bar{W}},$$

where

$$\hat{q} = \frac{2W_{01}k - 1}{2W_{01} - W_{00} - 1}, \qquad \bar{W} = W_{00}q^2 + 2q(1 - q)W_{01} + (1 - q)^2$$

and q is the frequency of A_0. At the time A_0 appears in the population we may take $q \to 0$ and for $\Delta q > 0$ we must have $2W_{01}k - 1 > 0$. At equilibrium, $\Delta q = 0$ which leads to $\hat{q} = \dfrac{2W_{01}k - 1}{2W_{01} - W_{00} - 1}$, where $\hat{q}$, the equilibrium frequency, is necessarily between 0 and 1.

(1) If $(2W_{01} - W_{00} - 1) > 0$ the equilibrium is stable because Δq is positive when $q < \hat{q}$ and negative when $q > \hat{q}$. Therefore the condition for a stable equilibrium is, $2W_{01} - W_{00} - 1 > 2kW_{01} - 1 > 0$ or $1 - \dfrac{W_{00}}{2W_{01}} > k > \dfrac{1}{2W_{01}}$. When $k \geqslant 1 - \dfrac{W_{00}}{2W_{01}} > \dfrac{1}{2W_{01}}$ (the right hand side of the inequality comes from $2W_{01} - W_{00} - 1 > 0$), Δq is positive for all values of $q < 1$ and this is the condition for fixation of the driven element.

(2) If $(2W_{01} - W_{00} - 1) < 0$, the equilibrium is unstable and the condition for this is, $2W_{01} - W_{00} - 1 < 2kW_{01} - 1 < 0$ or $1 - \dfrac{W_{00}}{2W_{01}} < k < \dfrac{1}{2W_{01}}$. A_0 is fixed

if $q_0 > \hat{q}$ and is lost if $q_0 < \hat{q}$ where q_0 is the initial frequency of A_0. When $\hat{q} \leqslant 0$, the driven element will be fixed regardless of its initial frequency (supposing $q_0 \neq 0$), and the condition for this is $k \geqslant \dfrac{1}{2W_{01}} > 1 - \dfrac{W_{00}}{2W_{01}}$. This is another condition for fixation of A_0.

(3) If $(2W_{01} - W_{00} - 1) = 0$, A_0 is fixed when $k > \dfrac{1}{2W_{01}} \left(= 1 - \dfrac{W_{00}}{2W_{01}} \right)$ and is lost when $k < \dfrac{1}{2W_{01}} \left(= 1 - \dfrac{W_{00}}{2W_{01}} \right)$. There is no frequency change when $k = \dfrac{1}{2W_{01}} = 1 - \dfrac{W_{00}}{2W_{01}}$.

Under random mating the effect of a driven element is always to reduce the average population fitness, unless, of course, the element itself has some other effect that is beneficial. This can be shown as follows:

The average fitness of the population is

$$\bar{W} = q^2 W_{00} + 2q(1 - q)W_{01} + (1 - q)^2.$$

When $\dfrac{d\bar{W}}{dq} = 0$, $q_{max} = \dfrac{W_{01} - 1}{2W_{01} - W_{00} - 1}$, which is equal to $\hat{q}$ only when $k = \tfrac{1}{2}$.

With inbreeding the situation may be different. For example, if the SD locus is heterotic, there are some values of $k > \tfrac{1}{2}$ that give a fitness greater than for $k = \tfrac{1}{2}$.

Another interesting question arises if a new normal element appears in the population which is partially or completely insensitive to the driven effect. If the new element is otherwise neutral, it will have an advantage relative to the remaining normal elements and may replace all of them.

To consider this, let A_0 and A_i $(i \neq 0)$ be a driven element and its alternatives having gametic frequencies q_0 and q_i. Let the fitness of $A_0 A_i$ and $A_i A_j$ $(j, i \neq 0)$ be W_{0i} and 1 and the segregation ratio of $A_0 A_i$ be k_i respectively. Then

$$\Delta q_i = \frac{q_i}{\bar{W}} \left[2q_0 W_{0i}(1 - k_i) + (1 - q_0) \right] - q_i.$$

Let

$$q_i = \phi_{ij} q_j (i, j \neq 0)$$

then

$$\frac{dq_i}{dt} = \phi_{ij} \frac{dq_j}{dt} + q_i \frac{d\phi_{ij}}{dt}$$

and we get

$$\frac{d\phi_{ij}}{dt} = \frac{2q_i q_0}{q_j \bar{W}} \left[W_{0i}(1 - k_i) - W_{0j}(1 - k_j) \right].$$

Here the sign of $\dfrac{d\phi}{dt}$ is determined by the sign of $[W_{0i}(1 - k_i) - W_{0j}(1 - k_j)]$. Therefore the A_i $(i \neq 0)$ which has the largest value of $W_{0i}(1 - k_i)$ will replace the remaining A_j's $(j \neq 0, j \neq i)$. Consider the A_i which has the maximum value of $W_{0i}(1 - k_i)$. As t goes to infinity, its frequency approaches $1 - q_0$ and it is seen that $\dfrac{dq_i}{dt} \rightarrow \dfrac{q_0(1 - q_0)}{\bar{W}} \left[q_0(2W_{0i} - 1 - W_{00}) - (2W_{0i}k_i - 1) \right]$, where W_{00} is the fitness of $A_0 A_0$, as in the two allele case discussed earlier.

It would appear at first sight as if the introduction and accumulation of an insensitive element would increase the population fitness. Although this would usually be the case, it is not invariably so. For example, if the insensitive element results in an increase in fitness when heterozygous with the driven element, it may replace the existing sensitive element and yet cause a reduction in population fitness at the new equilibrium. The following is a numerical example.

(1) A_0 and A_1 $W_{00} = 0$ $k_1 = 0.9$ $W_{01} = 0.6$
(2) A_0 and A_2 $W_{00} = 0$ $k_2 = 0.8$ $W_{02} = 1.0$

The value of $W_{01}(1 - k_1)$ is 0.06; $W_{02}(1 - k_2)$ is 0.20. Therefore A_2 replaces A_1. In case (1) $\hat{q}_0 = 0.4$ while in case (2) it is 0.6. The equilibrium average fitnesses, $\bar{W}$, are 0.648 and 0.640, respectively.

MEIOTIC DRIVE DIFFERENT IN THE TWO SEXES

We now consider the case in which the k value is different in the two sexes. A special case has already been worked out by Bruck (1957), but here we are more general.

Let D and d be a driven element and its normal alternative having a segregation ratio k_1 in males and k_2 in females. Let p and P be the gametic frequency of D in males and females respectively. Let W_{00}, W_{01} and 1 be the fitness of three genotypes DD, Dd and dd in either sex, and let

$$p = \phi P$$

In the next generation,

$$\phi' = \frac{W_{00}pP + k_1 W_{01}[p(1 - P) + P(1 - p)]}{W_{00}pP + k_2 W_{01}[p(1 - P) + P(1 - p)]},$$

where ϕ' is the ϕ in the next generation.

We shall consider here the important special case in which $W_{00} = 0$ (i.e., homozygous D is lethal). Substituting in the above equation,

$$\phi = \frac{p}{P} = \frac{k_1}{k_2}.$$

This relation is true not only at equilibrium, but also in any generation except, of course, the first. Therefore, we take

$$\phi_{(t)} = \frac{k_1}{k_2}.$$

Let

$$\psi = \frac{1 - p}{p} \quad \text{and} \quad \eta = \frac{1 - P}{p} \quad (\psi \text{ and } \eta \text{ are dependent}).$$

Then we have

$$\psi' = \frac{\psi\eta + W_{01}(1 - k_1)\left(\eta + \dfrac{k_2}{k_1}\psi\right)}{W_{01}k_1\left(\eta + \dfrac{k_2}{k_1}\psi\right)},$$

where ψ' is the ψ in the next generation.

Putting $\eta = \psi + \left(1 - \dfrac{k_2}{k_1}\right)$, we have

$$\Delta\psi = \frac{\psi^2[1 - W_{01}(k_1 + k_2)] + \psi\left[W_{01}\left\{(1 - k_1)\left(1 + \dfrac{k_2}{k_1}\right) - (k_1 - k_2)\right\} + \left(1 - \dfrac{k_2}{k_1}\right)\right] + W_{01}(1 - k_1)\left(1 - \dfrac{k^2}{k_1}\right)}{W_{01}k_1\left(\eta + \dfrac{k_2}{k_1}\psi\right)}$$

Without losing generality, we may assume $k_1 > k_2$. It can then be shown that:

(1) If $1 - W_{01}(k_1 + k_2) > 0$ or $W_{01} < \dfrac{1}{k_1 + k_2}$, $\Delta\psi$ is always larger than zero for any values of p and P. This implies $\psi_{(t)}$ goes to infinity as t goes to infinity, or since $\psi = \dfrac{1 - p}{p}$, p must go to zero and D is eliminated.

(2) If $W_{01} > \dfrac{1}{k_1 + k_2}$, $\Delta\psi$ is positive if

$$\psi^2[W_{01}(k_1 + k_2) - 1] - \psi\left[W_{01}\left\{(1 - k_1)\left(1 + \dfrac{k_2}{k_1}\right) - (k_1 - k_2)\right\} + \left(1 - \dfrac{k_2}{k_1}\right)\right] - W_{01}(1 - k_1)\left(1 - \dfrac{k_2}{k_1}\right) < 0.$$

Hence ψ increases when

$$\frac{b - \sqrt{b^2 + 4ac}}{2a} < \psi < \frac{b + \sqrt{b^2 + 4ac}}{2a},$$

where

$$a = W_{01}(k_1 + k_2) - 1 > 0;$$

$$b = W_{01}\left\{(1 - k_1)\left(1 + \dfrac{k_2}{k_1}\right) - (k_1 - k_2)\right\} + \left(1 - \dfrac{k_2}{k_1}\right);$$

$$c = W_{01}(1 - k_1)\left(1 - \dfrac{k_2}{k_1}\right) > 0.$$

Since $\dfrac{b - \sqrt{b^2 + 4ac}}{2a} < 0$ and $\dfrac{b + \sqrt{b^2 + 4ac}}{2a} > 0$ for any value of b, this must imply that ψ increases when ψ is smaller than a certain positive constant, $\hat{\psi}$, determined by W_{01}, k_1 and k_2, and decreases when ψ is larger than this constant. Therefore there is a stable equilibrium with the frequency $\hat{\psi} = \dfrac{b + \sqrt{b^2 + 4ac}}{2a}$.

Since $\hat{\psi} = \dfrac{1 - \hat{p}}{\hat{p}}$, we get the equilibrium frequencies of p and P, i.e.,

$$\hat{p} = \frac{1}{1 + \hat{\psi}}, \qquad \hat{P} = \frac{k_2}{k_1(1 + \hat{\psi})}.$$

SD in Experimental Populations

It has now been shown that meiotic drive, considering the special case of segregation-distortion, can operate in nature, and some of the theoretical consequences in populations have been developed. We now consider the behavior of *SD* in experimental populations.

Five large population cages containing *SD* were started with the following initial constitutions: (A) 100% *SD-5/* Canton-S heterozygotes; (B) 6% *SD-5/* Canton-S heterozygotes and 94% Canton-S homozygotes; (C) 100% *SD-72/* Canton-S heterozygotes and (D) 28% *SD-72/*Canton-S heterozygotes and 72% Canton-S homozygotes; and, finally (E) 4% *SD-72/cn bw* heterozygotes and 96% *cn bw* homozygotes.

The wild-type chromosome in these population cages was Canton-S for the reason that this is a well-known, highly inbred, laboratory strain, and also because it shows a degree of sensitivity similar to those chromosomes collected from the same Madison population as were the *SD* alleles themselves. Samples

were taken from these cages at intervals over the test period and the frequency of *SD* and the average k value were determined at each sampling. These results are given in table 3.

The method of sampling was as follows. Dishes containing medium were placed in the cages for two days and the adults which developed from the deposited eggs were collected. For cages A and B, males so collected were individually crossed to *SD-5/Cy* females and, from the ratio of *Cy* to non-*Cy* F_1, they could be classified as being *SD/+* or *+/+*. The k values for each *SD/+* males was then computed (see footnote to table 2). For cages C and D, collected females were individually crossed to males of the standard tester *cn bw* stock, and a single F_1 male from each such cross was tested for distortion. This gives an estimate of the frequency of *SD* only; the k values are of less interest since they reflect the sensitivity of the *cn bw*, not the Canton-S, *SD+*-bearing chromosomes. For cage E, the *SD* locus is marked by cn^+ (see Sandler

TABLE 3.   *The results from population cages containing* SD-*bearing chromosomes*

Initial constitution (the + chromosomes are Canton-S)			
Cage A:	*SD-5/+* 100 pairs;	*+/+*	0 pairs;
Cage B:	*SD-5/+* 48 pairs;	*+/+*	752 pairs;
Cage C:	*SD-72/+* 100 pairs;	*+/+*	0 pairs;
Cage D:	*SD-72/+* 64 pairs;	*+/+*	164 pairs;
Cage E:	*SD-72/cn bw* 32 pairs;	*cn bw/cn bw*	772 pairs;

Days after construction	Gene frequency of *SD* in zygotes in cage					Average k value in cage	
	A	B	C	D	E	A	B
0	0.50	0.03	0.50	0.14	0.02	(0.80)	
22	0.22	0.07	—	—	—	0.76	0.78
56	0.18	0.06	—	—	—	0.71	0.80
97	0.12	—	—	—	—	0.77	—
175	—	—	0.36	—	—	—	—
196	—	—	—	0.33	—	—	—
212	0.11	0.10	—	—	—	0.74	0.68
303	—	—	—	—	0.76	—	—

	Cages A and B	Cages C and D	Overall average
Average for last sample	0.11	0.35	$k = 0.75$

and Hiraizumi, 1959) so that estimates of the gene frequencies are direct. However, the reduction in viability of homozygous *cn bw* individuals, owing to homozygosity for these mutant alleles, makes this frequency less meaningful.

We may note that in the last samples, the final frequency of *SD* is nearly the same, whether the initial frequency was high or low suggesting that the cages had been kept long enough to have attained approximate equilibrium. This observed equilibrium is 0.10 and 0.11 in the two *SD-5* cages. A hypothetical population with $k = 0.75$ for males and 0.50 for females, and a 12 percent reduction in fitness of the *SD-5* heterozygote would reach an equilibrium frequency of 0.12. (See preceding section for methods.) These are, in fact, the measured k values, and the assumption of a six percent reduction in viability due each to the *SD-5* allele and to the associated lethal is reasonable in view of the results of Hiraizumi and Crow (1960). Thus the behavior of experimental populations is, roughly at least, predictable from the theory.

For those cages containing *SD-72* as a source of *SD*, we have considerably less independent information. We do not know the average k value of *SD-72* against Canton-S, nor the viability of homozygotes and heterozygotes under cage conditions. We see, however, that *SD-72* does maintain a high equilibrium frequency of *SD*; higher, indeed, than the *SD-5* type lines. This makes it rather surprising that, in nature, *SD-72* had a much lower frequency than *SD-5* (if the small 1956 Madison population is representative). This suggests that, among the various explanations of the relative frequencies of *SD-5* and *SD-72*, the most likely is that the *SD-72* type had just arisen, as a derivative of the *SD-5* type, and had not, at the time of collection, yet replaced *SD-5*.

It was mentioned previously that an important observation in the natural populations was that a high proportion

of the non-*SD*-bearing, structurally normal, second chromosomes were relatively insensitive to the distorting action of *SD*. There are two possibilities to explain this: (1) insensitive alleles arise spontaneously and, in populations containing *SD*, have a positive selective value (according to the theory presented in the previous section), or (2) the *SD* locus itself (or an insensitive SD^+ allele) produces insensitivity in normal alleles. Although it certainly is true that induction of one allele by another is an unlikely proposition, for the specific case of *SD* this may not be a real objection because such inductions are common in the *SD* system and have been found in a wide variety of genetic circumstances. Such changes are called "translocal modifications" (Sandler and Hiraizumi, 1959). The cage of interest in this connection is that containing *SD-72* and the standard tester *cn bw* chromosome. The reason that this is of particular interest is that the *cn bw* chromosome introduced there has been subjected to tests for sensitivity many times in the course of experiments on *SD*, and has been found to be completely sensitive. For this reason, a sample of *cn bw* chromosomes was collected from the *SD-72/cn bw* cage and tested for sensitivity 303 days after the cage was started. The frequency of the three genotypes, SD/SD, SD/SD^+ and SD^+/SD^+ was 0.55, 0.42, and 0.03 respectively, giving a gene frequency for *SD* of 0.76. Fifteen *cn bw* chromosomes from this cage were tested for sensitivity, and of these, three showed very reduced k values in heterozygotes with *SD-5*; that is, k values less than 0.80. Thus insensitive alleles are recovered from populations originally consisting of only *SD* and sensitive SD^+ alleles. Since the total number of generations in this population cage was about 20 (supposing roughly 15 days for each generation), the observed frequency of insensitive SD^+ alleles is surprisingly high. Indeed, it seems too high to be accounted for by selection alone. Thus, although there is certainly selection operating here, there are also probably other mechanisms causing the accumulation of insensitive alleles. In any event, it is true that insensitivity appears to be a concomitant of having SD in populations.

This raises a rather interesting point. Is it possible that a more sensitive test for SD in natural populations than a search for SD itself might be a survey for insensitive SD⁺ alleles? This would be better for the reason that when enough insensitive alleles have accumulated in the population it could result in the elimination of SD altogether. Presumably, however, the insensitive alleles, being selectively indifferent once SD is eliminated from the population, would persist, and so such a survey could reveal, not only populations containing SD, but those populations which had possessed SD in the past.

DISCUSSION

In a general way, it is clear that a locus, a chromosomal segment, or a whole chromosome, which exhibits meiotic drive, has an advantage for the reason it is present disproportionately often in the gametes contributing to each generation and, therefore, will tend to increase in frequency in a population.

The frequency of SD in natural populations has not been as high as would be expected from the k values observed in the laboratory (Sandler, Hiraizumi, and Sandler, 1959). In the 1956 collection 6 SD-bearing second chromosomes were found among 183 tested chromosomes. In the 1958 collection there were 7 SD's among a total of 301 chromosomes. These correspond to calculated allele frequencies of 3.3% and 2.3%. However, this is somewhat of an overestimate because the probability of detecting an SD allele from a heterozygous wild male is greater than 1/2. If the k value were 1, the values would be half as large, and this is a minimum esti-

mate. The equilibrium value in the cage experiments was about 10%. Therefore there must be mechanisms suppressing the frequency of SD alleles in nature.

If the driven element has a selective fitness as high or higher than the alleles which are not driven, then it ought to become fixed in the population. Under these circumstances, the main effect of the phenomenon of meiotic drive would be to accelerate the rate of increase of this element in a manner analogous to periodic selection or orthoselection in bacteria (Atwood, et al., 1951). If the driven element has a higher selective fitness than the other elements, this means an increase in the total fitness of the population. In this case, however, the maximum fitness toward which the population proceeds is the same irrespective of whether the most fit element is driven or not, but at any time prior to the attainment of maximum fitness, drive will cause a higher fitness.

Although this process may occasionally have happened in the course of evolution, it is likely to have been rare, for the obvious reason that most new mutants (or new genetic entities of any sort) wil have a lower fitness than the already existing ones and, therefore, the new instances of drive are usually selectively disadvantageous. Certainly it is true that all of the known cases of meiotic drive are associated with a reduction in fitness. Thus, the accumulation of the driven element will generally tend to lower the overall fitness of the population. This lowering of fitness may be quite extreme, but yet not sufficient to stop the accumulation of the driven element and thus may lead to extinction.

In nature, it is perhaps worth noting, the fitness of an equilibrium population must be determined in a very complicated way, and there may be conditions under which a driven element, which is itself detrimental, might cause an increase in the overall fitness of an equilibrium population. The driven element, for example, might be linked with a beneficial gene and for a time at least, may cause an increase in the rate of accumulation of this beneficial linked gene, and hence initially increase the fitness of the population. Of course, eventually the linked gene and the driven element will become randomized with respect to each other and then, provided the driven element is still present, the population fitness will decline. However, if, in this process, some mechanism for overcoming the driven effect has been evolved, then the beneficial gene would have been incorporated into the population more rapidly than it could have otherwise.

An additional situation where a meiotic drive mechanism would be of advantage is where a balanced lethal situation already exists. In this case a mechanism that favors an excess of one chromosome in the gametes of one sex and the homologous chromosome in the other sex would decrease the proportion of lethal homozygotes. If a drive mechanism were to exist in one sex there would be strong selective pressure for such a mechanism acting on the homologous chromosome in the opposite sex.

From these considerations, we can conclude that by and large the population will suffer from having a meiotic drive mechanism, and unless there is some way in which the population can increase its own fitness even in the presence of a driven element, the population must either suffer a reduced fitness or find some mechanism to suppress or eliminate the effects of the driven element. Certain ways in which this might happen have been considered by Sandler and Novitski (1957).

In this connection, the segregation-distortion system is particularly interesting, because here we know at least one way by which the deleterious effect of *SD* was reduced. Namely, this population has accumulated insensitive *SD*+ alleles which reduce the efficacy of the drive mechanism, and thus the equi-

librium frequency of *SD*. Indeed, it may be that eventually insensitive alleles would become sufficiently widespread so as to cause elimination of *SD* entirely. We may recall that in Japanese populations in which no *SD* loci have been detected, no insensitive alleles were found.

We have seen that an insensitive allele will tend to replace a sensitive allele because of its greater frequency of transmission through *SD* heterozygotes. However, a non-allelic modifier of the k value would not have such an advantage. Thus, successful modifiers will tend to be allelic with the driven locus or very closely linked (if the cytogenetic mechanism permits).

It might be mentioned that if a mechanism of meiotic drive were to become homozygous in a population, the consequence would be that when this population is examined no apparent drive mechanism exists. It has occurred to us (and independently to others with whom we have discussed the problem) that an interesting screen for the detection of drive mechanisms would be to examine segregation ratios of hybrids carrying chromosomes from widely separated populations such as those from different continents.

Finally, meiotic drive has many kinetic properties in common with gametic, cytoplasmic, and asexual selection. Formally, meiotic drive is equivalent to gamete selection when the competition is only between gametes from the same individual. It is interesting to note that the rate of gene frequency change is exactly half as fast for meiotic drive as for selection between pooled gametes, as first shown by Haldane (1924).

SUMMARY

An attempt has been made to demonstrate empirically three points: (1) That meiotic drive can be an operative evolutionary force. The demonstration of this is simply that we find, in natural populations of Drosophila, high frequencies of *SD* loci which are themselves associated with a reduced fitness. (2) That the quantitative predictions from considerations of what ought to happen when meiotic drive appears in a population are, roughly at least, true. The demonstration here is that the equilibrium frequencies and the rate of change in these frequencies in experimental cages of Drosophila containing *SD* are in rough agreement with quantitative prediction. And, finally, (3) to show at least one way in which a population, whose fitness is being reduced by the spread of detrimental driven loci may counteract this detrimental effect. In this instance, the result is accomplished by the accumulation of *SD*+ alleles insensitive to the distorting action of *SD*. This accumulation is either by selection alone or possibly by selection and induction of insensitive alleles by a process analogous to (or identical with) the previously reported phenomenon of translocal modification. A mathematical analysis of a number of special cases of meiotic drive is included.

ACKNOWLEDGMENT

We should like to thank Drs. Sewall Wright and Motoo Kimura for reading the manuscript and checking the mathematical formulae. We are also indebted to Mrs. Elaine Mange for permission to quote some of her unpublished data.

LITERATURE CITED

ATWOOD, K. C., L. K. SCHNEIDER, AND F. J. RYAN. 1951. Selective mechanisms in bacteria. Cold Spring Harbor Symp. Quant. Biol., 16: 345–354.

BRUCK, D. 1957. Male segregation ratio advantage as a factor in maintaining lethal alleles in wild populations of house mice. Proc. Nat. Acad. Sci., 43: 152–158.

DUBININ, N. P., M. N. SOKOLOV, AND G. G. TINIAKOV. 1937. Intraspecific chromosome variability. J. Biology (Moscow), 6: 1007–1054.

DUNN, L. C. 1953. Variations in the segregation ratio as causes of variations of gene frequency. Acta. Genet. et Statist. Med., 4: 139–147.

HALDANE, J. B. S. 1924. A mathematical theory of natural and artificial selection. Trans. Cambridge Phil. Soc., 23: 19–41.

HIRAIZUMI, Y., AND J. F. CROW. 1960. Heterozygous effects on viability, fertility, rate of development and longevity of Drosophila chromosomes that are lethal when homozygous. Genetics, 45: 1071–1084.

IVES, P. T. 1947. Second chromosome inversions in wild populations of *Drosophila melanogaster*. EVOLUTION, 1: 42–47.

SANDLER, L., AND E. NOVITSKI. 1957. Meiotic drive as an evolutionary force. Am. Naturalist, 41: 105–110.

——, AND Y. HIRAIZUMI. 1959. Meiotic drive in natural populations of *Drosophila melanogaster*. II. Genetic variation at the segregation-distorter locus. Proc. Nat. Acad. Sci., 45: 1412–1422.

——, AND IRIS SANDLER. 1959. Meiotic drive in natural populations of *Drosophila melanogaster*. I. The cytogenetic basis of segregation-distortion. Genetics, 44: 233–250.

THE EVOLUTIONARY DYNAMICS OF A POLYMORPHISM
IN THE HOUSE MOUSE[1]

R. C. LEWONTIN AND L. C. DUNN

Department of Biology, University of Rochester, Rochester, New York and
Department of Zoology, Columbia University, New York, New York

Received November 30, 1959

OVER the past several years DUNN and his collaborators have shown that most wild populations of *Mus musculus* in the United States are polymorphic for variant alleles at the T (Brachy, short tail) locus (DUNN and SUCKLING 1956; DUNN 1957). A mutant t allele at this locus has been identified in each of 16 different populations, and only one population thus far tested has been shown with any degree of certainty to be free of such alleles.

This widespread polymorphism has several remarkable features which make it unlike other polymorphic systems so far studied. First, of 16 alleles from wild populations, 13 are unconditional prenatal lethals when homozygous ($t^{w1, 3, 4, 5, 6,}$ $^{10, 11, 12, 13, 14, 15, 16, 17}$). The remaining three ($t^{w2, 7, 8}$) although viable when homozygous, are completely male sterile. Thus, even if it is supposed that the viability of homozygotes for these latter alleles is as high as for normal homozygotes, and that the fertility of homozygous females is normal, the t^w alleles are at least semilethal in a genetic sense. In the ordinary course of events such alleles should be reduced to an extremely low frequency in a population unless some other mechanism countervened to maintain them.

The second unusual aspect of this polymorphism is the abnormal ratio of $+$ and t gametes in the effective sperm pool of heterozygous males ($+/t^w$). About 95 percent of the offspring of $+/t^w$ males carry the t^w allele while only five percent carry the $+$ allele from the father. Determinations of this ratio can be made by utilizing the dominant allele T. Heterozygotes $T/+$ have short ("Brachy") tails, heterozygotes T/t^w are completely tailless, and heterozygotes $t^w/+$ have normal tails (CHESLEY and DUNN 1936). Test matings of two sorts can be made.

A.	♂ T/t^w	×	♀ $+/+$	
	tailless		normal	
B.	♂ $+/t^w$	×	♀ $T/+$	
	normal		Brachy	

Normal Mendelian segregation would result in equal numbers of Brachy ($T/+$) and normal ($t^w/+$) offspring from type A matings. From type B matings normal segregation would produce equal numbers of $+/+$ (normal), $+/t^w$ (normal), $T/+$ (Brachy) and T/t^w (tailless) offspring. The ratio of Brachy to tailless offspring reveals the ratio of $+$ to t in the effective sperm pool. Such matings

[1] This investigation, including the cost of extra pages, was supported by a research grant, RG-6223, from the Division of Research Grants, Public Health Service and by Atomic Energy Commission Contract AT(30-1) 1804.

of males heterozygous for a t allele from a wild population always produce a large excess of offspring carrying t^w. As the results of both type A and type B matings have been in complete accord with each other when tested, most of the characterization of segregation ratios has been carried out with the more efficient type A mating system (DUNN 1957). Table 1 shows the pooled results of all type A tests so far run on alleles of wild origin. The great excess of t^w gametes in the effective pool of sperm from heterozygous males is striking. These results cannot be ascribed to intrauterine selection against Brachy embryos for two reasons. First the results of type B matings are the same, and second, the cross of T/t^w females by normal males produces Brachy and normal offspring in equal numbers (Table 1), DUNN 1957.

Thus, the mutant alleles, although lethal or semilethal in homozygotes, are present in great excess in the effective sperm of heterozygous males and in normal proportions in the ova of heterozygous females.

Finally, there is some evidence of a greater fitness of heterozygous males relative to homozygous normal males (DUNN, BEASLEY and TINKER 1958). This is as yet preliminary, involving only a single allele, t^{w11}, and based upon a small number of animals. Taken at face value, the data show the heterozygous males $+/t^{w11}$ to have a fitness of 1.76 times that of homozygous normal males. This estimate is based upon only 53 individuals, however, and should not be given too much weight. In the same experiment only 19 females could be successfully tested and these showed no evidence of differential fitness. Nevertheless, the suspicion of

TABLE 1

Pooled segregation ratios of tailless males, heterozygous for t *alleles, each derived from a different wild population*

1 Males tested*	Offspring classified at birth			
	2 Normal ($+/t^w$)	3 Brachy $+/T$	4 Total	5 Ratio of t^w
T/t^{w1}	325	38	363	.895
T/t^{w2}	325	17	342	.950
T/t^{w3}	355	3	358	.992
T/t^{w4}	187	5	192	.974
T/t^{w5}	479	30	509	.941
T/t^{w6}	230	4	234	.983
T/t^{w7}	214	16	230	.930
T/t^{w8}	178	25	203	.876
T/t^{w10}	240	7	247	.972
T/t^{w11}	518	19	537	.965
T/t^{w12}	412	19	431	.956
T/t^{w13}	502	11	513	.979
T/t^{w14}	392	21	413	.949
T/t^{w15}	415	41	456	.922
T/t^{w16}	107	6	113	.947
T/t^{w17}	336	1	337	.998
All males	5,215	263	5,478	.952
All females T/t^w	199	188	387	.517

* Fives males of each allelic type were tested by mating with wild type $+/+$ females.

heterosis from the male data suggests that an intensive study of this aspect of the problem would be worthwhile.

Maintenance of the polymorphism

In the light of our present knowledge of the action of the t^w alleles it would seem that the polymorphism in nature is maintained by a balance between selective elimination of the mutant alleles in homozygous condition and the replenishment of these alleles by the extremely aberrant segregation ratio in heterozygous males. In addition, there is the possibility of heterosis as a balancing force.

There are two models that may be constructed for the evolution of the polymorphism, one deterministic and the other stochastic, i.e., involving chance processes. The deterministic model assumes that natural populations have very large breeding size, effectively infinite, and that the opposing forces of selection and abnormal segregation are entirely responsible for the state of the polymorphism in any population. The stochastic model, on the other hand, rejects the assumption of infinite population size and allows for the effect of random genetic drift and the probablistic nature of selection. It is this latter model which is certainly closer to the real situation and, as we will presently show, more nearly explains what is observed in nature.

The general stochastic theory of population genetics is, as is well known, due to SEWALL WRIGHT. He has shown, in a series of papers too numerous to cite, that finite population size leads to fixation of alleles at rates which depend on population size, migration, mutation, selection, etc. The most general summary of this theory is to be found in WRIGHT (1949), and the results of the present paper are in accord with his general predictions.

The deterministic model

The first algebraic solution to the problem of the balance between selection and abnormal segregation ratio was given by PROUT (1943). This solution placed no restriction on the relative fitnesses of the genotypes but turns out to be incorrect when the segregation ratio is not equal in the two sexes. Because of this latter restriction, PROUT's solution is not applicable to the problem at hand.

BRUCK (1957) has given a series of expressions for the equilibrium gene frequency and frequency of heterozygotes for the case of a recessive lethal with abnormal segregation in one sex only. This solution is considerably closer to the situation in Mus and would be completely applicable except for the few nonlethal alleles and the fact that fitness values may be different in the two sexes. As a first approximation to the natural situation, however, BRUCK's model is quite satisfactory. Letting

m = proportion of t^w gametes in the effective sperm pool
$\hat{p}$ = equilibrium frequency of + alleles among adults
and
$\hat{h}$ = equilibrium frequency of heterozygotes among adults
then

(1) $\hat{p} = 1/2 + \dfrac{\sqrt{m(1-m)}}{2m}$

and

$$(2) \quad \hat{h} = 2(1 - p) = 1 - \sqrt{\frac{1 - m}{m}}$$

Referring to Table 1, the lowest value of m is that for t^{w8} ($m = .876$), and the highest is for t^{w17} ($m = .998$). The average of all ratios is .952. Substituting these three values in equations (1) and (2) above we find

$$t^{w8}: \quad \hat{p} = .688 \quad \hat{h} = .624$$
$$t^{w17}: \quad \hat{p} = .522 \quad \hat{h} = .956$$
$$\text{average:} \quad \hat{p} = .614 \quad \hat{h} = .772$$

Thus, between 60 and 95 percent of the adults in natural populations should be heterozygous for a mutant t allele. As we will discuss in a later section, this is much too high a frequency to correspond to what is actually found in nature. If, in addition, there is heterosis, the difficulty is exacerbated so that, in a sense, the deterministic solution proves too much.

The stochastic model

The deterministic model does not take into account the inbreeding which results from the restricted breeding size of Mus populations.

Although there are no direct observations from which the effective size of a breeding unit in this species can be estimated, the indications are that it is limited. The home ranges in a few populations studied appear to be small (review in BLAIR 1953); there are differences among local groups in the frequencies of different phenotypic characters (DUNN, BEASLEY and TINKER 1960; DEOL 1958); gene frequency observations show that different local groups are polymorphic for different alleles at one locus (t alleles) (DUNN 1957). The species population appears to consist of many partially separated breeding groups, each small in relation to the whole population. Although some local groups reach high densities and numbers (SOUTHWICK 1958), they probably pass through small population minima, and it is these which exercise a controlling effect on the evolution of gene frequencies. For these reasons, a useful approach in the construction of models is to test the effects on gene frequencies of small effective size of the breeding unit.

One method of dealing with the interaction of selection, segregation abnormality, and restricted population size is the construction of a stochastic model of population dynamics. Such a stochastic model may be analysed either by the algebraic theory of stochastic matrices (FELLER 1950) or by a *Monte Carlo* procedure. We have chosen the latter method as being the more efficient for our essentially exploratory study. In a Monte Carlo procedure, a mechanical or numerical analogue of a real population is formed and the rules by which the analogue population reproduces itself are made to conform with genetic rules of meiosis, fertilization, and selection. In addition chance plays a role in determining whether a given individual will survive and leave offspring. The mechanisms for Monte Carlo sampling may be beads mixed in an urn, numbers chosen from a table of random numbers, cards chosen from a shuffled pack, etc. The first suggestion that such procedures might be useful for the t allele problem was made to one of us by PROF. GERT BONNIER in 1956. PROF. BONNIER saw clearly that finite population size must lead to eventual fixation of the normal alleles in contrast to the prediction of the deterministic model. He further suggested that "migrations of single but vigorous $+/t$ males" might be responsible for maintenance of the polymorphism. As will be shown later, we reach essentially the same conclusions.

As an analogue to a natural population we have used the IBM 650 digital computer. The scheme of the Monte Carlo program is shown in Figure 1. A two-digit number represents each individual. Because of the nature of the computer, it was convenient to let 88 stand for $+/+$, 89 for $+/t$, and 99 for t/t genotypes. $N\delta$ males and $N♀$ females are initially loaded into the machine in any desired genotypic combination. A separate sperm and ovum pool are calculated and stored. As the number of gametes is very large compared with the number of adults, the gametic pools are computed deterministically, using predetermined values of $m\delta$ and $m♀$, the segregation ratios for males and females. What is actually stored are the proportions $p\delta$ and $p♀$ of two gametes in each pool. Next, a random number is generated by the method of BOFINGER and BOFINGER (1958). This number which lies between zero and one determines whether an eight or a nine gamete is chosen from the sperm pool. If the number is less than or equal

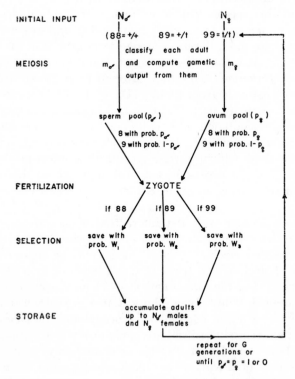

FIGURE 1.—Schematic representation of the Monte Carlo program for the 650 computer. Each stage is more fully explained in the text.

to $p\delta$ an eight is chosen, while if it is greater than $p\delta$ a nine is chosen. The same procedure is repeated for the pool of ova with the result that a zygote is formed which may be an 88, 89, or 99. The zygote so formed is classified as to its genotype in preparation for the selection phase. A new number is generated and if this number is less than or equal to W, the fitness of the particular genotype of the zygote just formed, the individual is saved and stored as an adult of the next generation. Otherwise, it is discarded. The processes of gamete choice, fertilization, and selection are repeated until $N\delta$ males have been saved and stored. Obviously this means that some larger number of males must be generated since selection discards a certain proportion of generated individuals. If necessary, the male fitness values are now replaced by female fitnesses and the entire process is repeated until $N\mathcal{Q}$ females have been saved, whereupon the saved males and females become the adults of the next generation, replacing the input males and females. The entire cycle from adults to adults is repeated until a predetermined number of generations has passed, or until the population is completely homozygous, whichever occurs first. During the computation the following information is printed each generation:

G: the generation number
$D\delta$: number of $+/+$ adult male parents
$H\delta$: number of $+/t$ adult male parents
$R\delta$: number of t/t adult male parents
$D\mathcal{Q}$: number of $+/+$ adult female parents
$H\mathcal{Q}$: number of $+/t$ adult female parents
$R\mathcal{Q}$: number of t/t adult female parents
p: frequency of $+$ allele among parental adults
$p\delta$: frequency of $+$allele in sperm produced by parents
$p\mathcal{Q}$: frequency of $+$allele in ova produced by parents.

The parameters that are assigned before the program is run are:

$N\delta$: number of adult males maintained
$N\mathcal{Q}$: number of adult females maintained
$W1\delta$: fitness of $+/+$ males
$W2\delta$: fitness of $+/t$ males
$W3\delta$: fitness of t/t males
$W1\mathcal{Q}$: fitness of $+/+$ females
$W2\mathcal{Q}$: fitness of $+/t$ females
$W3\mathcal{Q}$: fitness of t/t females
$m\delta$: proportion of t gametes from a heterozygous male
$m\mathcal{Q}$: proportion of t gametes from a heterozygous female
Gmax: maximum number of generations for run.

In addition, the exact genotypic composition of the initial generation must be specified. About 1.5 seconds are required to compute each generation for the parameter sets used in this study.

The general approach was to make a large number of runs with identical parameter sets and input populations in order to get an idea of the distribution of results. No two runs are identical because of the random effects introduced. Thus, making 100 runs with the same set of parameters is equivalent to setting up 100 experimental populations all with the same forces of selection, random drift and segregation. It is then possible to deal with means and variances just as in experiments with real populations.

Results of the Monte Carlo trials

Table 2 shows the various sets of parameters used and the number of runs for each parameter set. Because of the lack of any decisive information to the contrary, the fitnesses of males and females were assumed to be the same; the homozygous normal and heterozygotes were assumed to have the same fitness, and the female segregation ratio was assumed to be normal. The data so far available validate the last assumption.

A. *The large populations:* Sets 1 and 2 were not run more than a few times because it became evident that they were behaving in a virtually deterministic manner. The effective population sizes of 50 and 20, respectively, for these two sets were too high for any appreciable random effect to be felt. Examination of the output from each generation showed that it was extremely unlikely that populations with these parameters would reach fixation before many hundreds of generations. The pertinent statistics for parameter sets 1 and 2 are given in Table 3. These are based upon all generations except the first two in each run. The first two generations are eliminated in each case to avoid the effect of the initially imposed frequencies. As the table shows, the observed means are very close to the theoretical value of $p = .615$ from BRUCK's equation. It should be noted, however, that the confidence intervals for p do not quite overlap the theoretical value. Both observed values are smaller than theoretical, the small population deviating more than the large. As will be discussed below, this effect is even stronger in the still smaller populations. As expected, the variance and range of values for set 1 is less than for set 2, but even in set 2 the closest approach to homozygosis was six $+/+$ males, four $+/t$ males, and ten $+/+$ females. Because

TABLE 2

Parameter sets for Monte Carlo trials

					Initial composition						Number of runs
						Male*			Female†		
Set	$N\male$	$N\female$	$m\male$	G max.	$+/+$	$+/t$	t/t	$+/+$	$+/t$	t/t	
1	25	25	.95	50	6	13	6	6	13	6	3
2	10	10	.95	200	2	6	2	2	6	2	3
3	4	4	.95	200	1	2	1	1	2	1	50
4	4	4	.90	200	1	2	1	1	2	1	50
5	2	6	.95	200	0	2	0	2	4	0	101
6	2	6	.95	100	1	1	0	6	0	0	119
7	2	6	.95	100	2	0	0	5	1	0	30
8	2	6	.98	200	0	2	0	2	4	0	56
9	2	6	.98	100	1	1	0	6	0	0	58
10	2	6	.90	200	0	2	0	2	4	0	56

* In all cases the fitness values for males and females are $W_1 = W_2 = 1$, $W_3 = 0$.
† Female segregation is normal ($m\female = .50$).

TABLE 3

Statistics calculated from parameter sets 1 and 2 of the Monte Carlo trials

Set	Total generations	$\bar{p}$	$\bar{q}$	σ_p^2	σ_p	$\sigma_{\bar{p}}$	95 percent conf. int. for p
1	144	.6042	.3958	.00296	.0544	.00453	.5953–.6131
2	594	.5941	.4069	.00591	.0769	.00316	.5879–.6003

	Extremes							
	Female		Male				
Set	+/+	+/t	+/+	+/t	p	q	h
1	14	11	17	8	.81	.19	.38
	1	24	0	25	.51	.49	.98
2	6	4	10	0	.90	.10	.20
	0	10	0	10	.50	.50	1.00

of the segregation ratio in males, this high frequency of the + allele was immediately reduced in the next generation. It is this sort of result which led us to abandon these parameter sets and consider smaller population sizes.

B. *Small populations:* Because of the very large number of generations and runs, only a sample of the data has been analyzed for parameter sets 3–10. In all that follows, statistics are based on every tenth generation in each run.

For any given parameter set all populations (runs) were started with the same composition. After one generation, however, because of the random events in the model, all populations no longer have the same gene frequency but form a frequency distribution. A typical result is shown in Figure 2 for parameter set 5. The abscissa of each histogram is marked off in gene frequency, p, of the + allele. Since the total number of individuals is eight, there are only 16 genes in the population at the t locus so that p is always a multiple of $1/16$. The ordinate of each histogram shows the proportion of all populations (runs) having the given value of p. Results are plotted for generations 10, 20, 30, . . . 200. The trend in the observed frequencies (black bars) is obvious. As the number of generations increases, the proportion of populations reaching fixation of the + allele ($p = 1.0$) increases so that by generation 200, 84 percent of all populations are fixed. In the unfixed populations the most frequent class is $p = .50$ and the distribution is J-shaped. This J-shaped distribution is fairly stable in form over the entire set of 200 generations, the only change being a gradual decrease in the total frequency of unfixed populations. This stability is shown by the clear bars which represent the distribution of unfixed classes readjusted to give a total frequency of unity. That is, the clear bars show the proportion of *as yet unfixed* populations which fall in each class. The existence of such a stable distribution of unfixed classes is in accordance with the prediction of WRIGHT (1937).

Rates of fixation

The proportion of populations fixed for the normal allele in successive generations is given in Tables 4 and 5. Table 4 shows the proportion of previously unfixed populations which become newly fixed in each ten-generation period.

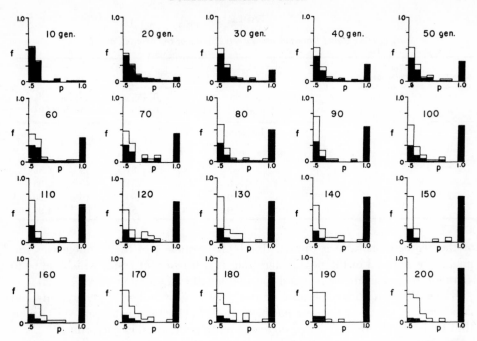

FIGURE 2.—Frequency distributions of gene frequencies in successive generations. The ordinate shows the proportion of all populations (runs) having a given gene frequency. The abscissa shows the values of p, the frequency of the normal allele. Black bars are the distributions of all runs. Clear bars are the conditional distributions for unfixed classes. Based on the data from parameter set 5.

They are then the *fixation rates* per ten generations. In Table 5 the cumulative proportions of fixed populations are given, and this latter information is plotted in Figure 3.

A number of interesting comparisons can be made by holding all parameters constant except one. The effect of a change in population size can be seen by comparing set 3 with set 5, and set 4 with set 10. Sets 3 and 5 both have a segregation ratio of .95 but set 3 with four males and four females has a higher effective population size ($N = 8$) than does set 5 ($N = 6$). The effective population size is calculated from the relation

$$N = \frac{4 N\delta\, N\female}{N\delta + N\female}$$

Similarly, sets 4 and 10 both have $m = .90$ but again have population sizes 8 and 6 respectively. As shown by the means at the bottom of Table 4, the fixation rates of the smaller populations are between one and a half and two times as large as for the larger populations. These mean fixation rates are roughly the equilibrium rates since generations 10 and 20 are not included in their calculation. The result of the difference in fixation rates between large and small populations is shown in Table 5 and Figure 3 as a difference in the proportion of populations fixed after n generations. In the case of set 10, for example, all populations are fixed by

TABLE 4

Fixation rates per ten generations

Generation	Set						
	3	4	5	6	8	9	10
10	.000	.040	.020	.218	.018	.207	.054
20	.000	.083	.051	.140	.036	.065	.189
30	.060	.113	.117	.125	.075	.070	.209
40	.064	.128	.108	.086	.020	.000	.294
50	.023	.059	.054	.125	.042	.075	.291
60	.070	.031	.101	.107	.022	.027	.059
70	.000	.129	.097	.060	.022	.083	.313
80	.075	.074	.107	.064	.045	.000	.181
90	.000	.120	.100	.068	.000	.000	.333
100	.054	.136	.022	.073	.071	.061	.000
110	.029	.000	.067	. . .	.026	. . .	.000
120	.059	.034	.095	. . .	.000	. . .	.333
130	.031	.111	.000	. . .	.000	. . .	.500
140	.064	.250	.184	. . .	.000	. . .	.000
150	.069	.000	.065	. . .	.026	. . .	.000
160	.037	.167	.103	. . .	.054	. . .	.500
170	.077	.000	.038	. . .	.029	. . .	.000
180	.083	.000	.080	. . .	.000	. . .	1.000
190	.091	.100	.130	. . .	.058	. . .	. . .
200	.250	.222	.150	. . .	.031	. . .	. . .
Weighted mean	.055	.103	.090	.093	.030	.041	.234

TABLE 5

Cumulative fixation rates. Proportion of all runs of each set which are fixed by a given generation

Generation	Set						
	3	4	5	6	8	9	10
10	.00	.04	.02	.22	.02	.21	.05
20	.00	.12	.07	.33	.05	.26	.23
30	.06	.22	.18	.41	.12	.31	.39
40	.12	.32	.27	.45	.14	.31	.57
50	.14	.36	.31	.53	.18	.36	.70
60	.20	.38	.38	.58	.20	.38	.71
70	.20	.46	.44	.61	.21	.43	.80
80	.26	.50	.50	.63	.25	.43	:84
90	.26	.56	.54	.66	.25	.43	.89
100	.30	.62	.55	.68	.30	.47	.89
110	.32	.62	.58	. .	.32	. .	.89
120	.36	.64	.62	. .	.32	. .	.93
130	.38	.68	.62	. .	.32	. .	.96
140	.42	.76	.69	. .	.32	. .	.96
150	.46	.76	.71	. .	.34	. .	.96
160	.48	.80	.74	. .	.37	. .	.98
170	.52	.80	.75	. .	.39	. .	.98
180	.56	.80	.77	. .	.39	. .	1.00
190	.60	.82	.80	. .	.43	. .	1.00
200	.68	.86	.83	. .	.45	. .	1.00

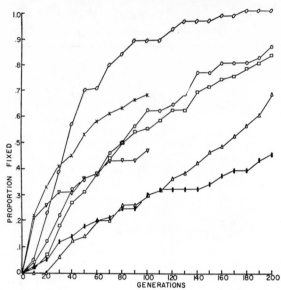

FIGURE 3.—Proportions of populations fixed for the normal allele in successive generations. Triangles: set 3; circles: set 4; squares: set 5; crosses: set 6; vertical bars: set 8; inverted triangles: set 9; oblique circles: set 10.

generation 180, while only 80 percent of the populations in set 4 are fixed at that time.

The effect of changes in segregation ratio can be estimated by comparing set 3 with set 4, and set 5 with set 8 and with set 10. In each case the lower the segregation ratio the greater the fixation rate. Sets 10, 5 and 8 have segregation ratios respectively of .90, .95 and .98. Their mean fixation rates are .234, .090 and .030. One way of comparing fixation rates is from the "half-life" of each set, that is, the number of generations required for 50 percent of the populations to be fixed. For sets 10, 5 and 8, these half-lives are approximately 36, 80 and 220 generations, the last figure coming from an extrapolation.

Finally, the role of different initial compositions can be studied. Sets 5 and 6 are identical except that each population in set 6 began with all wild type individuals with the exception of a single heterozygous male. Table 4 shows that the *mean equilibrium* fixation rates are virtually identical for these two sets (.090 and .093 respectively). The very large difference in total fixation between the sets as given in Table 5 and Figure 4 is entirely due to the high fixation rate in the first few generations. If the single mutant allele from the heterozygous male succeeds in "infecting" the population, there will no longer be any effect of its originally low frequency. The same phenomenon can be seen in the comparison between sets 8 and 9. The probability of a successful infection of a pure normal population with a t allele is fairly high in both cases. For set 6 ($m = .95$) the introduced t allele lasts more than 20 generations in 67 percent of the trials. The comparable figure for set 9 ($m = .98$) is 74 percent. As is to be expected, the higher the segregation ratio the greater the probability of successful infection.

In one set, 7, ($m = .95$) which is not shown in any detail, a single heterozygous

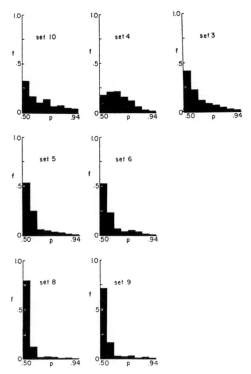

FIGURE 4.—Stable distributions of unfixed populations for various parameter sets.

female was introduced into an otherwise normal population. In 30 runs, only two populations remained unfixed for more than 20 generations (31 and 98 generations to fixation), two were fixed between the tenth and twentieth generations, and the remaining 26 populations were fixed before the seventh generation. Thus, the lack of an abnormal segregation ratio in the female makes it extremely unlikely that a *t* allele brought in by a female will survive. The difference between the case of migrant females and migrant males lies essentially in the difference between the initial frequencies of the *t* allele in the gametic pool. Clearly, it is not the initial adult composition that matters but the proportions of *T* and *t* gametes which they produce.

The probability of successful introduction of a mutant allele into an otherwise normal population is an important consideration in the maintenance of the polymorphism, and we shall return to this point in discussing the role of breeding structure and migration.

The stable distribution of gene frequencies

In addition to comparing fixation rates from one parameter set to another, we may also examine the effects of parameter changes on the distribution of unfixed populations. Figure 4 shows the stable distributions of sets 3, 4, 5, 6, 8, 9 and 10. These are constructed by pooling the distributions of generations 30–200 (30–100 for sets 6 and 8) to give an average distribution of unfixed classes. The first two periods are not used so that the initial population composition will not affect the results.

The effect of population size is shown by comparison of the distributions for set 3 with set 5, and set 4 with set 10. In both cases the smaller populations show a higher frequency in the extreme left-hand class, $p = .50$, and consequently lower frequencies in the other classes. Table 6 contains the probabilities associated with x^2 tests for the differences between the distributions of different parameter sets. As these probabilities show, the effects of changing the population size are highly significant. The piling up of populations in the left-hand class is a result of the asymmetry of natural selection. A smaller population size causes greater genetic drift both toward lower and higher frequencies of the $+$ allele with a consequent depletion of intermediate classes. Since t/t homozygotes are lethal, however, the frequency of the $+$ allele can never fall below 0.50. The populations that would ordinarily go to fixation at $p = 0$ are then piled up at the barrier imposed by selection at $p = .50$.

Another view of the same effect can be obtained from the means and variances of the distributions as listed in Table 7. The results of t tests for differences between these means are given in Table 6. In discussing the large populations it was noted that the mean values of p were significantly lower than the theoretical

TABLE 6

Probabilities resulting from tests for the difference between parameter sets that differ in one parameter

Set	3	4	5	6	8	9	10
3		$<.001$	$<.001$	. . .	. . .	. . .	. . .
4	$<.001$		. . .	. . .	. . .	. . .	.001
5	$<.001$	. . .		.84	$<.001$	. . .	$<.001$
6	. . .	. . .	.60		. . .	. . .	. . .
8	. . .	. . .	$<.001$	. . .		.27	$<.001$
9	. . .	. . .	. . .	. . .	.12		. . .
10	. . .	.80	$<.001$	. . .	$<.001$	. . .	

Above the diagonal: χ^2 tests for the difference between the stable distributions of Figure 4.
Below the diagonal: t tests for the difference between means of Table 7.

TABLE 7

Means and variances of the stable distributions of unfixed classes of Figure 4

Set	$\bar{p}$	$\bar{q}$	σ_p	σ_p	$\sigma_{\bar{p}}$	95 percent conf. int. for p	$P_{theor.}$
3	.5935	.4065	.0130	.1139	.0047	.5843–.6027	.6147
4	63.88	.3612	.0117	.1079	.0058	.6275–.6501	.6667
5	.5656	.4344	.0101	.1003	.0036	.5586–.5726	.6147
6	.5692	.4308	.0109	.1043	.0052	.5591–.5793	.6147
8	.5290	.4710	.0056	.0746	.0028	.5235–.5345	.5714
9	.5380	.4620	.0067	.0818	.0049	.5285–.5475	.5714
10	.6356	.3644	.0186	.1363	.0115	.6131–.6581	.6667

values derived from BRUCK's equation. This is even more true of the small populations, and those with effective size 6 deviate more from the theoretical values
than those with effective size 8, although the difference between sets 4 and 10 is
clearly not significant. This lowering of the mean of unfixed classes is a result of
the greater genetic drift with a piling up of populations at the lower limit of
$p = .50$.

The consequence of a change in segregation ratio is reflected in the difference
among sets 10, 5 and 8. As Figure 4 shows, an increase in m from .90 to .95 to .98
causes a piling up of the distribution at the left end. These differences are significant (Table 6) and are perfectly paralleled by a drop in the mean value of p
from .6356 to .5656 to .5290 respectively. The concentration of the unfixed classes
around $p = .50$ for high segregation ratios is also in accord with the slower rate
of fixation observed for these parameter sets.

Finally, the lack of any detectable effect of initial composition on the equilibrium rate of fixation is paralleled by a lack of difference in the stable distributions of unfixed populations. The distribution for set 5 is virtually identical with
that for set 6, and an almost equal degree of similarity exists between the distributions for sets 8 and 9. The x^2 tests for differences between 5 and 6 and
between 8 and 9 are nonsignificant as contrasted with the other comparisons
in Table 6. The similarity between the distributions for sets 5 and 6 and for sets
8 and 9 is also shown by their means in Table 7.

Comparisons with populations in nature

The observations on the geographic distribution of t alleles were obtained
before the models were derived and were primarily designed to detect and accumulate for genetic study a variety of t alleles from different sources. Gene
frequencies were thus obtained only as by-products of this general sampling
process, and in nearly all cases are based on very small samples. While they are
adequate to give some clues to the state of this locus in wild populations, they
cannot serve as strict tests of the applicability of the models to conditions in
nature.

Mice were obtained from traps set in 31 localities distributed over the United
States with one site sampled in Nova Scotia; and in addition samples were
obtained from three enclosed populations descended from wild mice captured in
three additional localities. The methods of trapping varied. Usually one or a few
traps were set to test whether Mus was present. At first this was done in buildings;
later eight feral populations were sampled. Since the object was mainly to capture
mice from the locality, it is quite possible that mice caught at different times in
the locality came from different breeding units or families, and there is some
suggestion in the testing records that this occurred. It is evident therefore that
mice from different trapping stations in the same locality may or may not represent samples from the same breeding unit. Although the mice in the localities of
capture have been referred to as "populations," this has only a general geographic, not a strict biological meaning.

All animals were tested individually by matings to Brachys $(T/+)$ at Nevis

Biological Station. At least one heterozygote ($+/t^w$) was found in the sample from each of 14 localities and from each of three enclosed populations. Of 66 mice tested from 14 localities, 23 were $+/t^w$. Sample sizes per locality ranged from one to ten. It is obvious that because of small and variable sample sizes and the method of trapping, no reliable gene frequency can be based on the above. It does show, however, that heterozygotes for these alleles are rather common (minimum frequency about 35 percent) in the populations in which they occur.

Better estimates can be obtained from extensive tests of enclosed populations bred in captivity. One of these has been maintained for 13 years at the Rockefeller Institute for Medical Research in New York, having originated from a few wild mice captures in New York City and Philadelphia in 1946. The breeding colony is kept at 125–250 individuals in the winter, reduced to about a dozen pairs each summer, so considerable inbreeding has occurred. Four samples from this population kindly supplied by DR. HOWARD SCHNEIDER, have been tested (Jan. '52, June '52, June '55, June '59). Heterozygote frequencies have remained at 50–60 percent. Up to now, of 197 animals tested 110 (or 56 percent) have been $+/t^w$.

One population in Rumford, Virginia, which was sampled by A. B. BEASLEY yielded in 1955 one $+/t^w$ out of eight tested. In the spring of 1959 an attempt was made by JOHN BEASLEY to trap all the animals in this barn. Of 41 animals captured 14 have completed tests. Eight of these (57 percent) are $+/t^w$. A similar attempt was made to capture all mice in a feed room of an isolated barn near Storrs, Connecticut. Of seven which bred in captivity, five were $+/t^w$. These experiences suggest that where t alleles occur, heterozygotes reach frequencies of 50–60 percent; the scattered small samples yield estimates below this value.

Testing of successive samples from Clinton, Montana, supplied by MISS VIRGINIA VINCENT suggest a possible reason for such discrepancies. A sample of 11 taken from this station (in a small barn) in September 1957 all proved to be $+/+$; a sample of three taken in October 1958 all proved to be $+/t^w$. Some of the latter may have come from the nearby house. The combined estimate is 3/14, but this may include family groups with high and with low frequencies.

Samples from 17 localities failed to yield a $+/t^w$ animal. The sample sizes tested were in general small, in 13 cases five or less. From only one locality (Great Gull Island in Long Island Sound) were sufficient mice tested (40) to give a high probability that t alleles were not present.

The general picture that emerges from this survey is that local groups of Mus free from t alleles are probably rare in the continental area. The only one established as t free is on a well isolated coastal island. Where t alleles occur they seldom or never reach the frequencies predicted by the deterministic model based on the average male segregation ratios actually found.

An effect of applying the stochastic model to small breeding groups is to suggest a reason for the failure of the deterministic model to fit the actual results. The equilibrium predicted by the latter model is not attained because of the chance loss of such alleles in small breeding groups. The general trend in the small groups is clearly toward fixation of wild type alleles. This process is, to be sure, retarded by very high values of the segregation ratio, but the direction is clear; an appreciable portion become fixed with the passage of time.

This process would produce a dichotomy amongst family groups in the same locality, some fixed, others unfixed, and the average gene frequencies for the locality would be determined largely by the proportions between such groups in the locality.

The sampling methods used heretofore are inadequate to test whether something like the above situation obtains in nature, but at least we know now what kind of observations must be made. Family and household structure must be known, and methods designed for the capture of households or extended families.

In the few cases in which collections of families have been studied (Rockefeller and Virginia samples) the average gene frequencies are not far from those predicted on the stochastic model and far below those predicted on the deterministic model. This cannot be taken as validation of the model until other variations in parameters have been shown to correspond to those assumed in the model.

A new and useful view of the methods by which t alleles may spread to new populations is also given by the analog calculations. It appears that alleles must travel in males in order to have a good chance of persisting in the newly "infected" population. This gives new impetus to studies of relative mobilities of the two sexes as factors in gene dispersal. This may have special importance in this case, since an implication of the stochastic model is that t lethals are at best "genes of passage" in small breeding groups because of the probability of chance loss. Those which are found, therefore, may have been acquired rather recently from migrants. This is more probable than acquisition by mutation since, as yet, we know of no instance of mutation of the wild type allele to t.

A final point which emerges from the stochastic model concerns selection among the various t alleles. Table 1 shows that all the t alleles found in natural populations exhibit very high segregation ratio abnormalities. This is not true, however, of all "mutant" alleles at this locus. In addition to the alleles of wild origin there are 19 alleles at this locus which have arisen in the laboratory. These arose from balanced lethal lines of the type T/t^n, in the form of single normal-tailed individuals which later proved to be t^n/t^x. When the segregation ratios of the newly arisen laboratory "mutants" are compared with alleles from wild populations, a radical difference, shown in Table 8, is found. Newly arisen alleles have segregation ratios ranging from very high to very low with a distinct mode at .50. Clearly the wild alleles are a selected sample of all the possible "mutations"

TABLE 8

Distribution of male segregation ratios for t alleles extracted from wild populations and for t alleles arisen in the laboratory by mutation from other t alleles

	.99 .90	.89 .80	.79 .70	.69 .60	.59 .55	* .50	.49 .45	.44 .40	.39 .30	.29 .20	n
Wild alleles	15	1	0	0	0	0	0	0	0	0	16
Newly arisen alleles	3	1	0	0	2	8	2	1	2	0	19

* Ratios within $\pm 2 \sigma$ of .5, i.e., normal ratios.

at this locus, selected for high segregation ratio in favor of the mutant. The deterministic model would not predict such selection since any mutant allele with a segregation ratio above .50 would be maintained in a stable equilibrium. The stochastic model, however, does predict the selection of mutants with higher segregation ratios. The Monte Carlo results showed the rate of loss of t alleles due to random drift to be very sensitive to the value of m. Alleles with relatively small segregation advantages would be lost quite rapidly with the result that the only alleles still seen in natural populations are those with high values of m. As time goes on this concentration of alleles at the high end of the range should become even sharper. These considerations once more emphasize that the polymorphism for t alleles is a transient one and very probably subject to violent oscillations. New alleles arise occasionally from old ones by a process which is not understood but which may involve recombination. Such new alleles as have high segregation ratios have a high probability of spreading in the population and of "infecting" other populations by the migration of heterozygous males. The alleles then spread in the species but are constantly being lost by drift and revived by migration. Eventually they must be lost entirely only to be replaced by yet another rare mutant of high segregation advantage.

SUMMARY

Wild populations of *Mus musculus* are polymorphic for mutant alleles at the t locus. When homozygous, these alleles are usually unconditional prenatal lethals, but a few are viable and male-sterile. Heterozygous males have an average of 95 percent t-bearing sperm in their effective sperm pool. This abnormal segregation ratio opposes the loss of the t alleles due to their lethal effect. Deterministic models for the evaluation of this polymorphic system predict (1) that any allele with a segregation ratio above .50 should be maintained in a stable equilibrium, and (2) that alleles with segregation ratios of the order of 95 percent should be in such high frequency as to make between 60 and 95 percent of the population heterozygous. Neither of these predictions is in accord with the observations from nature since: (1) only alleles with very high segregation ratio are found in contrast to the range known in laboratory mutants and (2) populations contain about 35 percent to 50 percent heterozygotes.

A stochastic model has been constructed, and results of this model were obtained by Monte Carlo procedures on a digital computer. These results show that for populations composed of small family groups there will be a loss of the t allele due to random genetic drift. The rate of loss is sensitive to differences in segregation ratio so that only alleles with a high ratio will remain in the population for appreciable periods. A geographical population will be composed mainly of family groups fixed for the wild type allele and of family groups with a high frequency of the mutant t allele. A normal population is easily "infected" with a mutant allele if this allele is carried into the population by a heterozygous male. These results are all in good accord with observations from nature insofar as the sampling methods thus far used permit a comparison.

LITERATURE CITED

BLAIR, W. F., 1953   Population dynamics of rodents and other small animals. Advances in Genet. **5**: 1–41.

BOFINGER, E., and V. J. BOFINGER, 1958   On a periodic property of pseudorandom sequences. J. Assoc. for Computing Machinery **5**: 261–265.

BRUCK, D., 1957   Male segregation ratio advantage as a factor in maintaining lethal alleles in wild populations of house mice. Proc. Natl. Acad. Sci. U.S. **43**: 152–158.

CHESLEY, P., and L. C. DUNN, 1936   The inheritance of taillessness (anury) in the house mouse. Genetics **21**: 525–536.

DEOL, M. S., 1958   Genetical studies on the skeleton of the mouse. XXIV. Further data on skeletal variation in wild populations. J. Embryol. and Exp. Morphol. **6**: 569–574.

DUNN, L. C., A. B. BEASLEY, and H. TINKER, 1958   Relative fitness of wild house mice heterozygous for a lethal allele. Am. Naturalist **92**: 215–220.

   1960   Polymorphism in wild populations of *Mus musculus*. J. Mammal. (in press).

DUNN, L. C., 1957   Studies of genetic variability in populations of wild house mice. II. Analysis of eight additional alleles at locus *T*. Genetics **42**: 299–311.

DUNN, L. C., and J. SUCKLING, 1956   Studies of genetic variability in populations of wild house mice. I. Analysis of seven alleles at locus *T*. Genetics **41**: 344–352.

FELLER, W., 1950   *An Introduction to Probability Theory and Its Applications*. John Wiley and Sons. New York.

PROUT, T., 1953   Some effects of the variations in segregation ratio and of selection on the frequency of alleles under random mating. Acta Genet. et Statist. Med. **4**: 148–151.

SOUTHWICK, C. H., 1958   Population characteristics of house mice living in English corn ricks: density relationships. Proc. Zool. Soc. London **131** (Pt. 2): 163–175.

WRIGHT, S., 1937   The distribution of gene frequencies in populations. Proc. Natl. Acad. Sci. U.S. **23**: 307–320.

   1949   Adaptation and selection. *Genetics, Paleontology and Evolution.* Edited by G. L. JEPSON, G. G. SIMPSON, and E. MAYR. Princeton University Press. Princeton, N.J.

GENETICS OF NATURAL POPULATIONS. XXVII.

THE GENETIC CHANGES IN POPULATIONS OF *DROSOPHILA PSEUDOOBSCURA* IN THE AMERICAN SOUTHWEST

Theodosius Dobzhansky [1]

Department of Zoology, Columbia University, New York

Received February 4, 1958

Introduction

Evolutionary changes in time are studied mainly by paleontologists. However, in some exceptional cases evolutionary changes are rapid enough to be perceived within the human lifetime. This is true of some species of Drosophila. Drosophila populations which are polymoryphic for the gene arrangement in their chromosomes can be described in terms of the relative frequencies of the karyotypes which they contain. However, the genetic composition of a population may change perceptibly with time. Changes from year to year, as well as cyclic seasonal changes, have been reported in the populations of *Drosophila pseudoobscura* on Mount San Jacinto, in California (Dobzhansky, 1947; Epling and Lower, 1957). In the Yosemite Park region of the Sierra Nevada, in California, such changes have been described both in *D. pseudoobscura* and in *D. persimilis* (Dobzhansky, 1952, 1956).

The causation of the year-to-year changes in the genetic composition of populations is obscure. In the Yosemite Park region, third chromosomes with the ST gene arrangement tended to decrease, and chromosomes with the AR gene arrangement tended to increase in frequencies, between 1945 and 1950. The direction of the changes became reversed between 1951 and 1957, and, as will be shown below, the frequencies observed in 1957 matched those in 1945 rather well.

[1] The work reported here has been carried out under Contract no. AT-(30-1)-1151, U. S. Atomic Energy Commission.

Dobzhansky (1952, 1956) put forward the working hypothesis that these changes may have been caused by successions of years of drought and of years with more abundant precipitation. For the Yosemite Park region the facts have thus far favored this hypothesis. However, the changes on Mount San Jacinto (which involved a different pair of chromosomes, those with ST and CH gene arrangements) did not correlate too well with the variations in the annual precipitation (Epling *et al.*, 1953).

A different sort of change, involving third chromosomes with the PP gene arrangement, was observed in populations of the Yosemite Park region of California since 1946. In 1939–1941, PP chromosomes were common, or even predominant, in the populations of Texas and of the eastern slope of the Rocky Mountains in Colorado. To the west of the Rockies, in Colorado, New Mexico, and Arizona, PP chromosomes showed steep descending gradients westward (Dobzhansky, 1944, tables 13–19). In California, only four PP chromosomes were found before 1946, among the almost 20,000 (more precisely 19,879) chromosomes examined from this state and the adjacent part of Nevada. These four chromosomes came from populations of three different localities, two localities in the Coast Ranges north of the San Francisco Bay, and one in southern Sierra Nevada. The incidence of PP in California was therefore about 0.02 per cent.

In 1946, a PP chromosome was however found among 336 chromosomes studied from the population of Mather,

Reprinted by permission of the author from Evolution, 12, 385–401
(1958).

in the Yosemite Park region of the Sierra Nevada. None were found among 308 chromosomes taken at Mather in 1945. Since 1946 the incidence of PP at Mather increased steadily, reaching about 11 per cent in 1954 (Dobzhansky, 1956, p. 86). This rise of PP showed no correlation of any sort with the oscillations in the frequencies of ST and AR mentioned above. Nor was the rise of PP confined to the population of Mather and neighboring localities in the Yosemite Park region. In July of 1951, PP chromosomes were found at Piñon Flats on Mount San Jacinto, in southern California, a locality about 335 air miles distant from Mather (Epling and Lower, 1957). In 1956 the frequency of PP at Piñon Flats stood at 7.7 per cent. Since about 22,000 third chromosomes were examined from Piñon Flats between 1939 and 1952 by the present writer and by Epling and his collaborators, it is certain that PP was very rare or absent in that locality before 1952. Its appearance and rise there had a quality of dramatic suddenness. In 1955, 6.3 per cent of PP was recorded also in the population of Charleston Peak, Nevada (Epling and Lower, 1957), where none was found in 1937 by the present writer. Charleston Peak is roughly 189 miles distant from Piñon Flats and 246 miles from Mather.

The discovery of the rise of PP in regions as remote as Yosemite, San Jacinto, and Charleston Peak suggested that a quite unexpected evolutionary change may be taking place in the populations of *Drosophile pseudoobscura* of a large territory. In the summer of 1957 population samples were accordingly taken in 20 localities in California, Utah, Arizona, and Colorado, in or near which the populations had been sampled earlier, mostly around 1940. A comparison of the genetic composition of the 1957 samples with the earlier ones permits an approximate definition of the nature and of the area in which the genetic changes have occurred (see figs. 1 and 2), although

the causation of these changes still remains an enigma.

MATERIAL

Drosophila flies are collected by attracting them to fermenting banana bait exposed in their natural habitats. In 1957 the bait was exposed in metallic trap cans, while the early collecting was made with bait in half-pint milk bottles or in paper drinking cups. Whenever convenient, the collecting in 1957 was made in exactly the same territory in which the old samples were collected; in some instances the baits were placed literally under the same trees. In some localities this was for various reasons not feasible, and the 1957 samples were then taken in localities up to 20 miles distant from the old ones. In the descriptions below such non-identical localities are marked with asterisks *.

Most of the chromosome structures were diagnosed in the immediate progenies of wild females, a single larva (two third chromosomes) being taken from each progeny for the cytological examination in acetic orceine smear preparations. A part of the early data (probably not more than one-fifth of the total) came however from progenies of wild males crossed to laboratory females with known gene arrangements in their third chromosomes. In rare instances (when the samples collected were small) eight larvae from the progeny of a single wild female were examined, and the gene arrangements in four third chromosomes were deduced.

YOSEMITE PARK REGION OF CALIFORNIA

A summary of the data for the Mather locality is presented in table 1. In this table and elsewhere, the names of the chromosomal types are abbreviated as follows: AR = Arrowhead, CH = Chiricahua, OL = Olympic, PP = Pikes Peak, SC = Santa Cruz, ST = Standard, and TL = Tree Line. These chromosomal types are described and pictured in Dobzhansky 1944. Except for the 1957

TABLE 1. *Gene arrangements in the population of Mather, Yosemite Park region, California*

Year	ST	AR	CH	PP	TL	SC	CL	n
1945	35.7	35.7	17.2	—	10.4	0.6	0.3	308
1946	30.9	36.6	17.1	0.3	10.6	2.5	2.1	336
1947	31.0	38.3	20.1	0.6	6.9	1.9	1.1	806
1950	20.3	49.8	17.4	2.8	8.7	0.7	0.2	812
1951	29.2	43.2	11.2	4.6	9.6	1.2	1.1	856
1954	27.0	37.0	12.1	11.1	11.1	0.7	0.7	2306
1957	45.3	33.2	3.8	9.8	6.3	1.6	0	316

sample, the data in table 1 have been published in Dobzhansky, 1948, 1952, and 1956.

The most striking fact which emerges from a study of table 1 is that PP chromosomes have steadily risen in frequencies from an ostensible zero in 1945 to roughly 10 per cent in 1954 and 1957. Almost equally dramatic has been the decline in the frequencies of CH chromosomes, from about 17 per cent in 1945 to only 4 per cent in 1957. As will be shown below, PP chromosomes waxed and CH chromosomes waned throughout most of California, and it is tempting to suppose that the changes in these two chromosomal types had a common cause.

The two other chromosomes which changed in frequencies were ST and AR. Here the situation is complicated by the fact that these chromosomes undergo, at Mather, also seasonal frequency changes (Dobzhansky, 1948, 1952, 1956). Since the samples in different years were not taken uniformly throughout the season, the yearly totals are not strictly comparable (no seasonal changes occur at Mather in PP or CH chromosomes). As mentioned in the Introduction, the frequency changes in ST and AR were opposed in sign, and there was a discernible trend between 1945 and 1950, which became reversed between 1951 and 1957. The status of the Mather population in 1957 about matched that in 1945 as far as ST and AR were concerned. No appreciable changes occurred in the rarer gene arrangements TL, SC, and OL. For more detail see the papers quoted above.

PP chromosomes were found, since 1946, not only at Mather but also in other localities in the Yosemite Park region, namely at Jacksonville and at Lost Claim, both at elevations below that of Mather, and at Aspen Valley and Porcupine Flat, above Mather (Dobzhansky, 1948). The increases have apparently been progressive, PP reaching the frequency of 6.6 per cent in 1951 at Aspen Valley and 7.1 per cent (in a small sample) at Porcupine (Dobzhansky, 1952). There have also been ostensible declines in the frequencies of CH in both places, but the samples were not extensive enough to make this statistically significant.

SIERRA NEVADA OUTSIDE YOSEMITE

Comparable population samples are available for four localities in the Sierra Nevada, two of them to the North and two to the South of the Yosemite Park region. A sample was taken at Deer Creek, in the Lassen National Forest in July of 1940, and another (by Prof. H. Phaff) in September 1957. Concerning the data for the 1940 samples, see Dobzhansky, 1944. The composition of these samples was as follows (EP stands for Estes Park gene arrangement):

	ST	AR	CH	PP	TL	SC	OL	EP	n
Lassen N.F., 1940	28.6	60.7	3.6	—	3.6	0.9	2.7	—	112
Lassen,* 1957	45.2	30.6	—	6.5	11.3	4.8	—	1.6	62

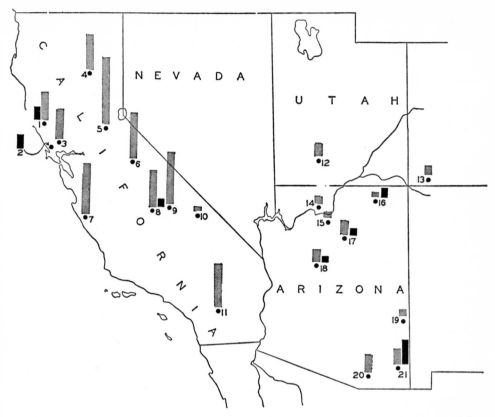

FIG. 1. Frequencies of third chromosomes with the PP gene arrangement, in population samples of *Drosophila pseudoobscura* taken in 1940 (black columns) and in 1957 (dotted columns). 1—Mendocino County; 2—Sonoma County; 3—Mount St. Helena; 4—Lassen Nat. Forest; 5—Placerville; 6—Yosemite Park; 7—Santa Lucia Mts.; 8—Sequoia Park; 9—Lone Pine Canyon; 10—Panamint Mts.; 11—Mount San Jacinto; 12—Bryce Park; 13—Mesa Verde Park; 14—Kaibab Nat. Forest; 15—Grand Canyon Park; 16—Black Mesa—Betatakin; 17—Flagstaff; 18—Prescott; 19—Morenci; 20—Sonoita; 21 Chiricahua Mts.

It is evident that the composition of the Lassen population underwent a considerable change between 1940 and 1957. Like in the Yosemite region, there appeared PP chromosomes, while CH ostensibly disappeared. Moreover, the frequency of ST rose, while that of AR was almost halved. There may have been also changes in other chromosomal types, but this is not certain. Samples were taken between Placerville and Camino in July 1940 and July 1957. Their composition was as follows:

Like at Yosemite and at Lassen, there has been a striking rise of PP chromosomes and a drop in CH. Again like at Lassen, there has been a strong rise of ST and a drop in AR (no samples are available from Mather before 1945, and, as stated above, there have been complex changes since then in the frequencies of ST and AR). At Placerville, there has also been a drop in TL, SC, and OL, which apparently was not parallelled at Lassen.

	ST	AR	CH	PP	TL	SC	OL	n
Placerville, 1940	26.9	26.9	6.5	—	13.9	18.5	7.4	108
Placerville, 1957	57.0	15.0	1.3	12.0	4.3	9.0	1.3	300

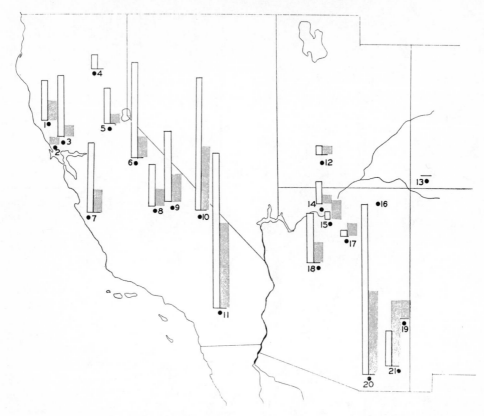

FIG. 2. Frequencies of third chromosomes with the CH gene arrangement, in population samples of *Drosophila pseudoobscura* taken around 1940 (white columns) and in 1957 (lined columns). The localities are numbered as in figure 1.

The samples taken at Atwell Mill, Sequoia National Park, in August 1940 and July 1957 are both much smaller than would be desirable. In this locality, *Drosophila pseudoobscura* is actually a rather rare species, most of the Drosophila flies being *D. azteca, D. persimilis,* and *D. miranda.* These samples are nevertheless interesting because the only PP chromosome found in the Sierra Nevada populations before 1946 came from the Atwell Mill sample, as shown below:

	ST	AR	CH	PP	TL	SC	OL	n
Sequoia Park, 1940	45.6	41.2	4.4	1.5	4.4	1.5 .	1.5	68
Sequoia Park, 1957	56.3	28.1	3.1	6.2	3.1	3.1	—	32

TABLE 2.   *Gene arrangements in the population of the Lone Pine Canyon, in the Sierra Nevada of California*

Year	ST	AR	CH	PP	TL	SC	OL	n
1937	21.7	69.5	8.5	—	—	—	—	46
1938	21.3	56.4	18.0	—	3.2	—	1.1	94
1940	18.2	58.2	12.7	—	9.1	—	1.8	55
1957	25.6	51.3	5.1	9.0	7.7	1.3	—	78

Despite the unsatisfactory smallness of the samples they indicate the occurrence of the same changes as elsewhere in the Sierra Nevada—increase in PP and a drop in CH, increase in ST and a drop in AR. It may be actually more fair to compare the 1957 sample with combined samples taken in 1940 not only at Atwell Mill but also in four other localities in the Sequoia Park. The chromosomal types had the following incidence in the combined samples:

	ST	AR	CH	PP	TL	SC	OL	n
Sequoia Park, 1950	39.6	40.1	7.7	0.7	6.3	1.4	4.2	142

The change between 1940 and 1957 comes out even more distinctly. Lone Pine Canyon, on the eastern slope of the Sierra Nevada at the foot of Mount Whitney, is a locality in which samples were taken in 1937, 1938, 1940 (see Dobzhansky, 1944), and 1957. Like at Atwell Mill, *D. pseudoobscura* is a minority of the flies which inhabit the Lone Pine Canyon, and the samples are small. Nevertheless, they show a very clear picture (table 2). No PP chromosomes were found in 1940 or earlier, but their frequency stood at 9 per cent in 1957. The frequencies of CH and AR stood lower, and of ST ostensibly higher in 1957 than in the earlier samples. Similar changes have, thus, taken place in every locality in the Sierra Nevada for which data are available, both on the western and on the eastern slope.

COAST RANGES OF CALIFORNIA

In October 1937 and in April 1938, Prof. A. H. Sturtevant collected small samples of *D. pseudoobscura* near Hopland and near Sebastopol, California. These samples were remarkable because they contained three of the four PP chromosomes which were found in California prior to 1946 (Dobzhansky, 1944). However, since only 16 chromosomes were examined from Hopland and 30 from Sebastopol, the frequencies of the karyotypes in these samples may be misleading. The Hopland sample is, therefore, combined with two other samples from Mendocino County, taken at Ukiah and at Mendocino in 1940 (Dobzhansky, 1944). This combined sample (1937–1940) may be compared to that taken in June 1957 at the University of California Experiment Station, northeast of Hopland:

	ST	AR	CH	PP	TL	SC	OL	n
Mendocino Co., 1938–40	51.0	37.5	7.3	1.0	—	3.1	—	96
Hopland,* 1957	55.5	25.0	3.5	5.0	1.5	8.0	1.5	200

Although the differences are small, they go in the same directions as those observed in the populations of the Sierra Nevada discussed above. There has been an increase in PP and a corresponding decline in CH, an ostensible increase in ST and a drop in AR. The frequency of PP at Hopland was, in 1957, not higher, and perhaps it was lower, than in the Sierra Nevada at the same time (see above). This should be noted because the early date of the discovery of PP at Hopland may have indicated that this locality was near the center from which PP chromosomes spread to other parts of California.

The 30 chromosomes from the Sebastopol samples taken in 1957 and 1938 may be combined with other samples taken at the same times in other localities in Sonoma County, namely at Guerneville, Forestville, and Cotati. The comparison with the sample taken near Guerneville in June of 1957 is as follows:

	ST	AR	CH	PP	TL	SC	OL	n
Sonoma Co., 1937–38	43.7	12.5	—	2.1	—	36.5	—	96
Guerneville,* 1957	61.0	14.5	1.0	7.0	5.0	11.0	0.5	200

The population of Sonoma County, like those of the Sierra Navada and of Mendocino County, had PP and ST chromosomes increasing, and AR chromosomes decreasing in frequencies between 1938 and 1957. However, CH chromosomes were not recorded at all in the Sonoma County samples in 1937–1938, while in 1957 they occurred there as a rather rare karyotype. This makes the Sonoma population an exception, since in 1940 and earlier the CH chromosomes were fairly common throughout California (Dobzhansky, 1944). The 1937–1938 Sonoma samples showed also an extraordinarily high frequency of SC chromosomes; by 1957 the frequency of SC fell to a value not much, if at all, higher than in other samples from the Coast Ranges.

Another locality in the Coast Ranges in which samples were taken both in July 1940 and in June 1957 is Mount St. Helena, near the boundary of Napa and Lake Counties. The results are as follows:

	ST	AR	CH	PP	TL	SC	OL	n
St Helena, 1940	35.2	20.4	11.1	—	17.6	12.0	1.8	108
St. Helena, 1957	51.0	19.5	2.0	5.0	13.5	7.5	1.5	200

No PP chromosomes were found on St. Helena in 1940, while in 1957 they have reached a frequency of 5 per cent. The frequency of CH has strikingly declined, while that of ST has increased. There was no change in AR, and SC has ostensibly waned. On the whole, the three populations in the Coast Ranges north of San Francisco Bay have shown similar changes—increases in PP and in ST. It may however be noted that while in 1937–1940 these populations differed among themselves rather strikingly in composition, they converged and became rather alike by 1957. It is worthwhile to reiterate that the frequency of PP in 1957 stood in these populations at a level which was apparently lower than in the Sierra Nevada populations, despite the fact that it was in the Coast Ranges that three out of the four PP chromosomes recorded in California before 1946 were found.

Comparable population samples were taken in May 1940 and in July 1957 near Tassajara Hot Springs, in Santa Lucia Mountains, in the Coast Ranges south of the San Francisco Bay. The composition of these samples was as follows:

	ST	AR	CH	PP	TL	SC	OL	n
Santa Lucia Mts., 1940	51.0	20.3	12.5	—	1.9	13.5	1.0	104
Santa Lucia Mts., 1957	54.0	23.0	4.0	9.0	2.0	7.5	0.5	200

No PP chromosomes were found in 1940, while in 1957 their frequency stood at 9 per cent; CH and SC chromosomes became less common. The changes in the Santa Lucia Mountains have, thus, been parallel to those in the Coast Ranges north of the San Francisco Bay, except that the frequencies of ST and AR remained unchanged; this may be due to the fact that the sample in 1940 has been taken much earlier in the season than in 1957.

MOUNT SAN JACINTO, CALIFORNIA

Between 1939 and 1946, population samples were taken at irregular intervals in three localities on Mount San Jacinto,

TABLE 3. *Gene arrangements in the population of Wildrose Canyon, Panamint Mts., California*

Year	ST	AR	CH	PP	TL	SC	MM*	n
1937	13.8	67.4	18.4	—	—	—	—	224
1938	34.0	37.8	25.0	—	0.6	1.9	0.6	156
1939	35.0	45.8	15.3	—	3.2	0.5	—	190
1940	24.5	43.4	26.4	—	5.7	—	—	106
1957	25.5	58.9	11.2	0.9	2.7	0.4	0.4	224

* MM = Mammoth gene arrangement.

in southern California, and studied by Dobzhansky (summary in Dobzhansky, 1947), and thereafter by Epling and his collaborators (summary in Epling and Lower, 1957). As stated in the Introduction, PP chromosomes were found on San Jacinto first in 1951, and in 1952–1956 they reached frequencies of 8.7, 8.8, and 6.6 per cent in the three localities sampled by Epling and Lower (l. c., p. 248). Prof. Carl Epling kindly permits me to quote his unpublished observations of the corresponding frequencies of PP chromosomes in 1957—7.7, 7.6, and 5.9 per cent.

Like in the Sierra Nevada and in the Coast Ranges, the frequencies of CH have decreased also on San Jacinto—from 28.0 to 15.4 per cent, and from 39.4 to 28.2 per cent in the two localities for which comparable data exist for 1939–1942 and for 1952–1956. There has also been a relatively small net increase of ST and some loss of AR chromosomes. Furthermore, Epling and Lower record the appearance in 1953 of OL chromosomes which were not recorded earlier in San Jacinto populations.

DEATH VALLEY REGION, NEVADA, UTAH, AND COLORADO

From 1937 to 1940, population samples were taken annually in the upper part of Wildrose Canyon, in the Panamint Mountains of California. A sample was taken in the same locality in July 1957. Panamint is a high mountain range standing between the arid Death Valley to the east and Panamint Valley to the west; the Drosophila population of Panamint Range exchanges migrants with populations of

regions more congenial for Drosophila, in the Sierra Nevada and elsewhere, presumably only rarely. The behavior of this relatively isolated population is interesting. The data are summarized in table 3.

A significant rise in ST, and a drop in AR chromosomes, have taken place in the Panamint population between 1937 and 1938, but no further significant changes occurred from 1938 to 1940 (see Dobzhansky, 1944, p. 112). The frequencies of ST and AR in the 1957 sample lie almost exactly half way between those in 1937 and 1938. However, two PP chromosomes were found in the 1957 sample, while they were absent in the earlier ones. The incidence of CH was in 1957 the lowest recorded. Statistically considered, the emergence of PP and the waning of CH in 1957 do not represent significant changes; however, since exactly these changes have been observed throughout California between 1940 and 1957, they are probably real also in the Panamint population. It is worthy of note in this connection that the sample of Drosophila taken in 1957 in Wildrose Canyon contained 3 individuals of *D. persimilis*, a species never before recorded in this locality, although in 1938 it was encountered in another canyon of the Panamint Range by Dr. P. C. Koller.

The Charleston Range in southern Nevada is isolated by deserts from other territories favorable for Drosophila only slightly less securely than is the Panamint Range. No PP was found among 256 chromosomes taken on Charleston in

1937 (Dobzhansky and Queal, 1938), but the frequency of PP stood at 6.3 per cent in 1955, while CH changed from 19.1 to 9.4 per cent (Epling and Lower, 1957). Nor were PP chromosomes found in 1937 on other mountain ranges in southern Nevada and in the adjacent Death Valley of California (Dobzhansky and Queal, 1938). The only other collection from Nevada was made in June of 1950 at the Lehman Caves National Monument, about 200 miles northeast of Charleston Range. The composition of this sample was as follows:

	ST	AR	CH	PP	EP	n
Lehman Caves, 1950	7.0	84.0	6.0	1.0	2.0	100

The presence of PP and EP (= Estes Park) chromosomes should be noted; as shown above, EP suddenly appeared on Mount San Jacinto in southern California, and at Lassen, in the northern part of that state. The population samples taken at Bryce Canyon National Park in southern Utah, had the following composition:

	ST	AR	CH	PP	n
Bryce Canyon, 1940	2.0	96.0	2.0	—	100
Bryce Canyon, 1950	4.8	92.9	2.4	—	84
Bryce Canyon, 1957	2.6	93.2	1.6	2.6	190

No significant changes have occurred in this population since 1940; although PP chromosomes were not met with in the two earlier samples, their frequency in 1957 was still so low that they may have been similarly frequent but overlooked in 1940 and 1950. No adequate early samples from elsewhere in the state of Utah have been studied, but the following two samples, taken at Heber, some 190 miles to the north of Bryce in April 1950, and in a canyon west of Ferron, some 108 northeast of Bryce in September 1950, by Prof. H. Spieth and by the writer respectively, are of some interest:

	ST	AR	CH	PP	n
Heber, 1950	—	92.0	2.0	6.0	50
Ferron, 1950	6.4	87.3	4.5	1.8	110

Dobzhansky (1944) has recorded the presence of PP chromosomes in a small sample from Uinta Mountains, in the northern part of the state, taken in 1941. In contrast to California populations, there is no reliable evidence of changes having taken place in recent years in Utah populations.

In southwestern Colorado, samples were taken in July 1940 (by Prof. W. P. Spencer) and in July 1957 (by the writer) at Mesa Verde National Park. The composition of these samples was as follows:

	AR	PP	EP	CC	n
Mesa Verde, N.P., 1940	100.00	—	—	—	100
Mesa Verde, N.P., 1957	96.5	1.5	0.5	1.5	200

Only AR chromosomes were encountered in 1940, while in 1957 PP, EP (= Estes Park), and CC (= Cochise) gene arrangements have also been re-

corded. The last named karyotype was
found originally in a single third chromosome from a sample collected in Chiricahua Mts. in southeastern Arizona in
1935. It was not seen again until the
1957 sample from Mesa Verde was examined. Nevertheless, on purely statistical grounds, the occurrence of changes
in the Mesa Verde population between
1940 and 1957 is not securely established.
It should be noted that PP chromosomes
were common, or even predominant, in

the samples taken in the Front Range of
the Rocky Mountains of Colorado in 1941,
and EP chromosomes were no great rarity
(Dobzhansky, 1944). They occurred also
in the samples taken in September 1950
at the Gunnison National Monument
(about 100 miles north of Mesa Verde),
and near Salida in the Sangre de Cristo
Range (about 100 miles northeast of
Mesa Verde). The composition of these
samples were as follows:

	ST	AR	PP	TL	EP	OL	n
Gunnison, N. M., 1950	3.3	81.6	8.6	1.3	5.3	—	152
Sangre de Cristo, 1950	—	41.7	20.8	29.2	4.2	4.2	24

ARIZONA

Comparable population samples, taken
in 1940 or 1941 and again in 1957, are
available from eight localities, or pairs of
adjacent localities.[2] The data are summarized in table 4. It can be seen that
in only one of the eight localities, at
Prescott, has the population changed not
only significantly in a statistical sense,
but also in the same direction in which the
California populations have also changed
during the same time period—gains of
ST and PP, and losses of CH and AR
chromosomes. The populations of the
other seven localities listed in table 4
seem to have remained more or less static.

---

[2] The 1940 sample at Flagstaff was taken in
a wood some two miles north of the junction
of the U. S. highways 89 and 66, and in 1957 at
the foot of the San Francisco Peak to the north
of the Museum of Northern Arizona. In 1940,
a sample was taken on Black Mesa, southwest
of Marsh Pass, and in 1957 near the Betatakin
Ruin. In 1940, three small samples were taken
in Grant County, New Mexico (cf. Dobzhansky,
1944), and in 1957 in the public picnic grounds
north of Morenci. The Sonoita Samples of
1941 and 1957 were taken some miles apart,
respectively to the south and to the north of
the village of that name. The 1940 sample from
the South Rim of Grand Canyon was, owing to
an omission, not listed on p. 85 in Dobzhansky,
1944; its composition was exactly like that from
Cape Royal recorded in the publication just
quoted.

Thus, CH chromosomes have ostensibly
declined in frequencies at Kaibab and at
Sonoita, but have risen at Grand Canyon,
Flagstaff, and Chiricahua. ST chromosomes seem to have waxed at Kaibab,
Grand Canyon, and Flagstaff, and waned
at Betatakin and Sonoita. PP seems to
have risen at Kaibab, Grand Canyon,
Flagstaff, and Sonoita, but fallen at Chiricahua. It is interesting to note the re-
discovery of the Cochise gene arrangement in Chiricahua Mountains, where it
was found first in 1935 (see above).

TEXAS

In 1939–1940, PP chromosomes were
the predominant karyotype in Texas,
much less frequent in Arizona and Utah,
and vary rare in California. In 1957, the
frequencies of PP remained unchanged
in Arizona and Utah (except perhaps at
Prescott), but increased very sharply in
California (except possibly in the Panamint Range). It is interesting to inquire
whether any changes have taken place in
the frequencies of PP in their "distribution center" in Texas. In 1939 and 1940,
Prof. J. T. Patterson kindly sent to the
writer samples of the population of *Drosophila pseudoobscura* collected at different
seasons in the neighborhood of Austin,
Texas. In these samples, the frequencies

TABLE 4. *Gene arrangements in populations of Arizona*

Population	Year	ST	AR	CH	PP	TL	CC	n
Kaibab N. F.	1940	—	96.0	4.0	—	—	—	100
Kaibab N. F.	1957	9.0	88.5	1.0	1.5	—	—	200
Grand Canyon, S. Rim	1940	1.0	98.0	1.0	—	—	—	100
Grand Canyon, S. Rim	1957	5.5	91.0	2.5	1.0	—	—	200
Flagstaff	1940	1.0	97.0	1.0	1.0	—	—	100
Flagstaff*	1957	6.5	89.0	2.0	2.5	—	—	200
Black Mesa	1940	4.4	94.1	—	1.6	—	—	68
Betatakin*	1957	3.0	96.5	—	0.5	—	—	200
Prescott	1940	11.0	79.0	9.0	1.0	—	—	100
Prescott	1957	23.0	71.5	3.5	2.0	—	—	200
Grant Co., N. M.	1940–1941	3.2	96.0	—	—	0.8	—	124
Morenci*	1957	1.0	94.5	3.0	1.5	—	—	200
Sonoita	1941	7.1	59.5	33.3	—	—	—	42
Sonoita*	1957	2.0	80.0	15.0	3.0	—	—	200
Chiricahua Mts.	1940	0.5	88.5	6.3	4.2	0.5	—	192
Chiricahua Mts.	1957	0.2	85.0	11.5	2.5	0.2	0.5	400

of PP were lower, and the frequencies of AR were higher, in early spring (March and April) than in late spring (May) or in autumn (see Table 11, p. 113, Dobzhansky, 1944). The writer took samples in the vicinity of Austin in March and April of 1953, although not in exactly the same neighborhoods as Prof. Patterson did earlier. A summary of the findings in these samples is as follows:

	ST	AR	PP	TL	EP	TX	OL	n
Austin, Texas, 1939–41	—	22.1	69.5	6.2	0.7	—	1.5	1100
Austin, 1953	2.0	38.5	54.5	4.0	0.5	0.5	—	200

In 1953, PP was still the predominant gene arrangement at Austin, Texas, although its frequency has dwindled appreciably since 1939–1940. The frequency of AR has, on the contrary, increased. How permanent these changes may turn out to be cannot be decided from the data now available.

THE SEX-RATIO

All the variant gene arrangements discussed above are in the third chromosome. Some of the populations of *Drosophila pseudoobscura* are polymorphic also with respect to the structure of the X-chromosome, in which a Standard and a so-called "sex-ratio" (SR) gene arrangement can be distinguished. The incidence of SR in different populations, as observed in 1940–1941, is summarized in Dobzhansky, 1944. Table 5 compares the states of the populations in 1940–1941 and in 1957, for the localities in which observations are available both at the beginning and at the end of this time interval. The only instance of apparently significant change is the apparent increase of the frequency of SR in the 1957 sample from Morenci, Arizona, compared to the 1940–1941 data from the neighboring Grant County, New Mexico. With this exception, no systematic trends in the frequencies of SR are indicated by the data.

DISCUSSION

To understand the nature of the genetic changes observed in the populations of *Drosophila pseudoobscura* one must take cognizance of two salient facts. First, the changes have affected populations of a very large territory. Secondly, the changes involved not only the spread of

TABLE 5. *Percentages of X-chromosomes containing the "Sex-Ratio" condition*

Locality	Year	SR	n	Locality	Year	SR	n
Lassen N. F.	1940	11.8	85	Grand Canyon	1940	10.0	80
Lassen*	1957	16.1	31	Grand Canyon	1957	14.9	148
Placerville	1940	8.0	88	Flagstaff	1940	23.2	82
Placerville	1957	5.6	195	Flagstaff*	1957	24.3	144
Mendocino Co.	1938–40	7.2	69	Prescott	1940	21.1	71
Hopland*	1957	5.0	139	Prescott	1957	21.6	148
St. Helena	1940	10.7	84	Grant Co., N. M.	1940–41	12.5	88
St. Helena	1957	3.0	133	Morenci*	1957	25.7	144
Santa Lucia Mts.	1940	4.9	81	Sonoita	1941	33.3	30
Santa Lucia Mts.	1957	3.8	132	Sonoita*	1957	21.1	152
Bryce Canyon	1940	8.0	87	Chiricahua Mts.	1940	18.5	135
Bryce Canyon	1957	10.4	115	Chiricahua Mts.	1957	17.6	324
Mesa Verde N. P.	1940	10.3	78	Austin	1939–41	11.3	974
Mesa Verde N. P.	1957	10.3	136	Austin*	1953	14.8	122
Kaibab N. F.	1940	10.5	86				
Kaibab N. F.	1957	11.9	151				

a hitherto rare genetic variant, but also a reconstruction of the gene pool of the population, in which at least two components underwent apparently correlated changes.

The appearance and spread of PP chromosomes was first recorded in the population of Mather and of other localities in the Yosemite Park region of the Sierra Nevada of California (Dobzhansky, 1952, 1956). At present it is clear that PP chromosomes have greatly increased in frequencies in most of California (with the possible exception of the isolated Panamint Range in the Death Valley region) and perhaps also in parts of adjacent states (Charleston Mountains in Southern Nevada and Prescott in Arizona). But the rise of PP chromosomes was not species-wide; no increase in PP has apparently occurred over most of Arizona or at Bryce Park, Utah. In Texas, which is the region where PP was and is most frequent, there may have been even a decline in its predominance.

Until 1951, the situation at Mather looked as if PP chromosomes were rising in frequency while CH chromosomes remained static (c.f. table 1). But since 1951 it became clear that CH suffered a recession, as if the increase of PP was taking place at the expense specifically of the CH component of the gene pool. The data reported in the present article show that this is indeed what has happened all over California, and also at Prescott and at Sonoita, Arizona. However, the eclipse of CH was again not species-wide; in 1940 CH had occurred as a fairly rare karyotypic variant in much of Arizona, and it has not disappeared by 1957; it may have even gained in frequency in the population of Chiricahua Mountains. Comparing the composition of the populations in 1940 and in 1957, we find that there has been also a gain of ST and a loss of AR chromosomes in most localities in California. The data for the intervening years, available only for the population of Mount San Jacinto and of the Yosemite Park region, do not show however consistent and continuous trends. At Yosemite there was a downward trend in ST and an upward one in AR between 1946 and 1951, which became reversed since 1951. These trends and their reversal show an ostensible correlation with the successions of dry and wet years (Dobzhansky, 1952, 1956). On San Jacinto, the trends were less clearly pronounced or even absent (Dobzhansky, 1947, Epling and Lower, 1957).

There is no doubt that the genetic changes observed were real and not due to mistakes, such as mis-diagnosis of the gene arrangements in the salivary gland preparations in the early work. The configurations formed by the different combinations of the gene arrangements in the third chromosomes of *Drosophila pseudoobscura* are characteristic and recognizable in moderately good preparations (Dobzhansky, 1944). Errors may creep into any human effort, but it happens that the PP gene arrangement is identifiable most easily, since it involves a break in the chromosome in a far more proximal position than in any other gene arrangements which occur in populations living north of the Mexican border. It would be quite impossible to overlook or to misclassify PP chromosomes if they were found at all frequently in California populations prior to 1946. The CH chromosomes can be misclassified more easily in certain combinations, but the gene arrangements with which CH could conceivably be confused (SC, TL, EP, OL) are rare in most populations, and they have shown no apparent increases in frequencies in the samples in which CH declined.

After the publication of Dobzhansky 1956 article, at least two colleagues have independently urged, in private communications, that the increase of PP in California might be explained by a mass migration of the populations of Texas and the Rocky Mountains westward to California, and predicted that Arizona and Utah will now show much higher frequencies of PP than they showed in 1940, and probably higher than observed in California populations. This hypothesis, in at least its original form, is now excluded. The 1957 collections have demonstrated not only that PP chromosomes failed to increase appreciably in Arizona and in Utah, but also disclosed a drop in CH throughout California, apparently compensating for the increase in PP. A mass migration of flies from Texas to California would not only increase the frequencies of PP in Arizona and California but would also reduce the incidence of ST chromosomes, which are very rare in Texan populations. In reality, ST chromosomes became more frequent than they were in California, and possibly also in some Arizona populations.

The genetic reconstruction of California populations must have been brought about by indigenous causes. Two kinds of causes may be considered. First, the environment in which the flies live may have become more favorable for carriers of PP chromosomes, and less favorable for CH. Secondly, PP chromosomes may have acquired, by mutation or by recombination, a new and adaptively superior gene complement. The rule of parsimony of assumptions makes it inadvisable to assume both environmental changes and changes in the genetic contents of PP chromosomes.

To prove that no environmental changes affecting the welfare of the flies have occurred is impossible, especially given the rudimentary state of our knowledge of the fly ecology. All that can be said is that no obvious and directional changes in any environmental components are known to have been taking place in California between 1940 and 1957, except for changes brought about by human activities. As stated above, the changes in the frequencies of ST and AR chromosomes in the Yosemite Park region may have been correlated with drought and wet years (Dobzhansky, 1952, 1956), but the changes in PP and CH evince no parallelism with these climatic fluctuations. It should be noted that different parts of California are extremely diverse in climatic and edaphic conditions, and in flora and fauna. Since PP has waxed and CH waned throughout California, an environmental agent which could be held responsible would have to be of a very general nature, such as a general climatic change. No such change is known to have occurred.

Human agencies must be considered, especially since the genetic changes in *Drosophila pseudoobscura* remind one of the industrial mechanism which has, within about a century, altered the characteristics of some species of Lepidoptera (Kettlewell, 1955, 1956, and other work). A notable growth of human populations, expansion of industries, and increasing use of insecticides have been taking place in California, especially since the War. It would obviously be desirable to test the different karyotypes of *D. pseudo-obscura* for possible differential resistance to widely used insecticides and industrial fumes. The character of the expansion of PP and of contraction of CH karyotypes in California does not however suggest that human agencies are responsible. Indeed, if these changes were man-induced, one would expect them to be most pronounced in the vicinity of the great population centers—Los Angeles and the San Francisco Bay area. This does not appear to be the case. In fact, the increase of PP and the decrease of CH in the populations of Lone Pine Canyon and of Charleston Peak (see above) militate against hypotheses that human agencies are responsible. The former locality lies on the esatern slope of the Sierra Nevada, at the foot of Mount Whitney, the highest peak in the continental United States. Charleston Peak is surrounded by deserts. Both localities are remote from large population centers and well protected from industrial fumes and similar influences. Several colleagues suggested, in conversations, that the changes in *D. pseudoobscura* may have been caused by the fallout from atomic weapon tests. Charleston Peak almost overlooks the Proving Grounds; however, the products of the explosions are carried by atmospheric currents chiefly in a northeasterly direction, i.e., away from California where the genetic changes have taken place.

The possibility that PP chromosomes may have acquired a new property which made them more favorable to their possessors in California environments than they were before 1940 is quite credible. There is no doubt that PP chromosomes were, though rarely, found among the inhabitants of at least some localities in California in and before 1940. The chromo-

somal polymorphism is maintained in natural populations of Drosophila chiefly, though not exclusively, by superior fitness of the heterozygotes for various combinations of the gene arrangements present in a given population.[3] A mutation and/or a lucky crossover might, then, produce a chromosome favorable in combination with other types of chromosomes prevalent in California population, and particularly with PP, although relatively unfavorable in heterozygotes with CH. Natural selection would, then, not only favor the spread in populations of the "new" chromosomes, but also promote such a reconstruction of the gene pool that the frequency of PP would grow and that of CH would decline. The supposition that the new and favorable gene combination arose in a PP chromosome would also explain the rise of PP, but it would hardly account for the apparently correlated drop in CH, since PP/CH heterozygotes are rather rare in most populations. It may, of course, be that the rise of PP and the drop of CH are not interrelated.

In contrast to the environmental hypothesis, the difficulty of the hypothesis of genetic change is to explain the great

[3] Epling *et al.* (1953, 1955, 1957) deny this. These authors labor under a misapprehension that heterosis in chromosomal heterozygotes must necessarily manifest itself in disturbances of the Hardy-Weinberg equilibria in populations. Such disturbances are not observed in some populations, and the authors see themselves forced to find another explanation for the recorded seasonal and other changes in the frequencies of some karyotypes. They conjecture that the seasonal changes in the frequencies of certain gene arrangements in the third chromosome are due to advantage of increased recombination in chromosomes other than the third at some seasons and to disadvantage at other seasons. This conjecture is gratuitous. But even if it were true, the hypothesis would not fit the evidence. The second-order selection which would favor certain third chromosomes because of their effects on recombination in other chromosomes would be altogether too weak to account for the rapidity of the changes actually observed. For other data which contradict the conjecture of Epling *et al.* see Levene and Dobzhansky (1958).

magnitude of the territory in which the populations have become altered in composition. It is most unlikely that mutations or crossovers which made PP chromosomes adaptively advantageous and CH disadvantageous could have arisen by accident in many places in different parts of California at about the same time. If, however, the genetic change appeared in only one place, how could it spread over tens of thousands of square miles? *Drosophila pseudoobscura* is one of the few organisms for which something is known concerning the average distance between the places where an individual is born and where it reproduces. This distance depends greatly on the temperature of the environment; however, Dobzhansky and Wright (1947) found that about 95 per cent of the progeny of released flies with a certain genetic marker was found ten months after the release within a circle with a radius of about 1.76 Km centered on the point of release. The standard deviation of the distribution of the genetic marker in question was estimated to lie between 0.43 and 0.72 Km. With dispersal rates of this magnitude a genetic change which arose at the geographic center of California would, if not aided by strongly favorable selection pressure, need time on quasi-geological scale to spread throughout that state.

In considering the spread of adaptively favorable traits, two kinds of movements should however be distinguished (Dobzhansky, 1956). First, genes diffuse from population to population because an individuals (or a spore or a pollen grain) migrate, actively or passively, over a certain average distance from the place where they were born or liberated. This kind of migration is, in Drosophila, too slow to account for the observed changes in the genetic constitution of populations. Secondly, organisms may occasionally be transported over long distances by atmospheric currents and other forces beyond their active control. Accidental transport of insects by man, in freight or by campers, belongs to this category. Of necessity, such long-distance transport will be spasmodic, irregular and hard to experiment with; and yet, agencies of this sort must be invoked to explain the genetic changes observed.

Prof. Ch. L. Remington has kindly called my attention to the work of Henson (1951) and Greenbank (1957) on the spruce budworm moth, *Choristoneura fumiferana*. Large numbers of these moths are sometimes drawn into the updrafts of air which occur during the passage of cold frontal air masses, and then deposited by the downdrafts at considerable distances from their places of origin. The importance of this kind of transport would seem to be reduced in Drosophila by the habit of these insects to remain quiescent on windy days. Some exchange of individuals between populations of fairly remote localities may nevertheless occur by some such means. This migration will probably be of no importance for genetic variants which are adaptively neutral or negative, but it may be quite important when the migrants carry favorable genetic traits which are absent in the population into which they are introduced. Natural selection will then enhance their prevalence in their new habitats and open the possibility of further spread.

As pointed out above, the genetic changes observed in the California populations of *Drosophila pseudoobscura* rival in magnitude the changes involved in the spread of the industrial melanism in several European species of moths. Although this possibility cannot be completely excluded, it seems that the changes in Drosophila, in contrast to the industrial melanism, have not been brought about by human interference with the habitats of these insects. If so, these changes would have to be recognized as the most clear-cut evolutionary alterations, not provoked by man, ever witnessed in nature in a free-living species. These changes seem to be more extensive than those in the other comparable cases —the alteration of the frequencies of the color phases in the red fox in Canada (Butler, 1947, 1951), and in the beetle *Harmonia axyridis* in Japan (Komai, Chino, and Hosino, 1950; Komai, 1954, 1956). The participation or non-participation of man in these later changes is uncertain.

SUMMARY

Data are presented showing that populations of *Drosophila pseudoobscura* of ten localities in different parts of California have changed between 1940 and 1957 in the same direction—appearance and increase of the frequencies of chromosomes with PP gene arrangement and decrease of chromosomes with CH gene arrangement. Since PP chromosomes are most prevalent in the populations of Texas and of the eastern slope of the Rocky Mountains, it is important to note that no appreciable increases in the frequencies of PP have taken place in nine of the ten localities in Arizona and Utah for which samples taken in 1940 (or 1941) and in 1957 are available.

The causes which have brought about the genetic changes in the California populations are unknown. The changes seem not to be provoked by human interference with the habitats of the flies; at any rate, the changes are no greater in localities close to the regions of greatest concentration of human populations than in localities far from such regions.

ACKNOWLEDGMENTS

The collecting of the samples of Drosophila populations in the summer of 1957 was carried out in cooperation with Mr. Howard Bausum and Mrs. N. Dobzhansky. Mrs. O. Pavlovsky, Mrs. N. Spassky, and Mr. H. Bausum have made many of the preparations of the larval salivary glands for chromosome studies, although the chromosomes were diagnosed and scored exclusively by the author. Drs. Jens Clausen and W. M. Hiesey most kindly placed at the disposal of the collectors the field station of the Carnegie Institution at Mather, California. Drs. H. S. Colton and E. B. Danson, Directors of the Museum of Northern Arizona at Flagstaff, and Dr. Mont Cazier, Director of the Southwestern Research Station of the American Museum of Natural History in the Chiricahua Mountains, Arizona, have extended the hospitality of the respective institutions and their laboratories. Thanks are also due to Drs. J. A. Beardmore, C. L. Remington, G. L. Stebbins, and Bruce Wallace for their suggestions and useful discussions.

Note added in proof.—Professor Carl Epling has very kindly communicated to the writer the composition of the samples of *Drosophila pseudoobscura* taken, in April–June of 1958, in several localities on the margins of San Gabriel Valley of southern California. This Valley is densely settled by man and contains important centers of industrial and agricultural activities. If the increases of the frequencies of PP chromosomes observed throughout California between 1946 and 1957 were due to man-made changes in the fly environments (contamination by insecticides, "smog," or almost any other man-induced alterations), one would expect the PP chromosomes to be especially frequent in the localities sampled by Professor Epling. This expectation is not borne out by the data. The percentages of PP chromosomes, and the numbers of the chromosomes examined (in parentheses), are as follows. Tuna Canyon, Santa Monica Mts—3.9% (228); Camp Rincon—16.1% (56); Santa Ana Mts—1.7% (116); Keen Camp, Mount San Jacinto—4.0% (78); Pinon Flats—3.1% (224) and 8.3% (168). This makes it very improbable that the changes in the genetic composition of the *Drosophila pseudoobscura* populations have been caused by man's interference with the habitats of the fly. It begins to look more and more as if the changes are due to emergence of novel coadapted gene complex within the gene pool of the California populations. Such gene complexes could yield superior fitness in heterozygotes with other gene complexes present in the same populations, and spread more and more widely in space.

LITERATURE CITED

BUTLER, L. 1947. The genetics of the color phases of the red fox in the Mackenzie river locality. Can. J. Research, D, **25**: 190–215.
——. 1951. Population cycles and color phase genetics of the colored fox in Quebec. Can. J. Zool., **29**: 24–41.

DOBZHANSKY, TH. 1944. Chromosomal races in *Drosophila pseudoobscura* and *Drosophila persimilis*. Carnegie Inst. Washington, Publ. 554: 47–144.

——. 1947. A directional change in the genetic constitution of a natural population of *Drosophila pseudoobscura*. Heredity, 1: 53–64.

——. 1948. Genetics of natural populations. XVI. Genetics, 33: 158–176.

——. 1952. Genetics of natural populations. XX. EVOLUTION, 6: 234–243.

——. 1956. Genetics of natural populations. XXV. EVOLUTION, 10: 82–92.

—— AND M. L. QUEAL. 1938. Genetics of natural populations. I. Genetics, 23: 239–251.

—— AND S. WRIGHT. 1947. Genetics of natural populations. XV. Genetics, 32: 303–324.

EPLING, C., AND W. R. LOWER. 1957. Changes in an inversion system during a hundred generations. EVOLUTION, 11: 248–258.

——, D. F. MITCHELL, AND R. H. T. MATTONI. 1953. On the role of inversions in wild populations of *Drosophila pseudoobscura*. EVOLUTION, 7: 342–365.

——. 1955. Frequencies of inversion combinations in the third chromosome of wild males of *Drosophila pseudoobscura*. Proc. Nat. Acad. Sci., 41: 915–921.

——. 1957. The relation of an inversion system to recombination in wild populations. EVOLUTION, 11: 225–247.

GREENBANK, D. O. 1957. The role of climate and dispersal in the initiation of outbreaks of the spruce budworm in New Brunswick. Can. J. Zool., 35: 385–403.

HENSON, W. R. 1951. Mass flights of the spruce budworm. Can. Entomologist, 83: 240.

KETTLEWELL, H. B. D. 1955. Selection experiments on industrial melanism in the Lepidoptera. Heredity, 9: 323–342.

——. 1956. Further selection experiments on industrial melanism in the Lepidoptera. Heredity, 10: 287–301.

KOMAI, T. 1954. An actual instance of micro-evolution observed in an insect population. Proc. Japan Acad., 30: 970–975.

——. 1956. Genetics of ladybeetles. Advances in Genetics, 8: 155–188.

——, M. CHINO, AND Y. HOSINO. 1950. Contributions to the evolutionary genetics of the lady-beetle, Harmonia. Genetics, 35: 589–601.

LEVENE, H., AND TH. DOBZHANSKY. 1958. New evidence of heterosis in naturally occurring inversion heterozygotes in *Drosophila pseudoobscura*. Heredity, 12: (in press).

FURTHER SELECTION EXPERIMENTS ON INDUSTRIAL MELANISM IN THE *LEPIDOPTERA*

Dr H. B. D. KETTLEWELL

Genetic Laboratories, Department of Zoology, University of Oxford

Received 22.iii.56.

1. PREVIOUS EXPERIMENTS

In a previous paper (Kettlewell, 1955), I recorded the results of extensive mark-release-recapture experiments undertaken in 1953 on the Peppered Moth, *Biston betularia* Linn. and its two melanic forms, *carbonaria* Jordan and *insularia* Th-Mieg (plate II, fig. 6). These experiments were carried out in a circumscribed area of woodland, the Christopher Cadbury Bird Reserve, situated about six miles from the industrial and heavily polluted area of Birmingham. The results then obtained may be summarised as follows :

(*a*) When released on to available trunks and boughs, their normal resting places, over 97 per cent. of *carbonaria* (the black form) appeared to the human eye to be inconspicuous. Conversely, nearly 89 per cent. of the light form of the Peppered Moth were adjudged conspicuous (plate I, fig. 2).

(*b*) Direct observation on the released insects showed that by late afternoon 54 per cent. of the light form had disappeared but only 37 per cent. of the *carbonaria*. Furthermore, we witnessed both Robins (*Erithacus rubecula* L.) and Hedge Sparrows (*Prunella modularis* L.) take the moths from off the trees, and they did this selectively and, on the majority of occasions, in an order of conspicuousness as previously scored by us.

(*c*) Recapture figures, reflecting a differential mortality rate, showed that more than twice as many *carbonaria* survived as *typical* (27·5 to 13 per cent.) (fig. 1*a*).

These experiments showed that birds act as selective agents and that the melanic forms of *betularia* are at a cryptic advantage in an industrial area such as Birmingham. It was essential to repeat these observations during a subsequent season and to extend them by carrying out comparable mark-release-recapture experiments in un-polluted countryside. This paper provides details of such work, which was undertaken in 1955.

2. A REPEAT OF THE SELECTION EXPERIMENTS IN THE BIRMINGHAM DISTRICT

Immediately following successful mark-release-recapture experiments in the summer of 1955 in an unpolluted wood in Dorset (recorded later in this paper) we moved camp to the Christopher Cadbury Bird

Reprinted by permission of Oliver & Boyd, Ltd. from HEREDITY,
10, 287–301 (1956).

TABLE 1

Release experiments for B. betularia *(males only)*
Rubery, near Birmingham, 1955

Date	Releases			Total	Catches			Total	Recaptures			Total
	C	T	I		C	T	I		C	T	I	
8.7	54	23	(5)	82	62	7	5	74	...	...	...	...
9.7	...	...	...	...	73	11	1	85	33	11	0	44
10.7	100	41	(4)	145	51	5	2	58	3	2	0	5
11.7	...	...	...	...	50	7	2	59	46	2	(2)	50
12.7	...	...	...	...	89	7	5	101	0	1	0	1
13.7	...	...	...	...	25	4	0	29	...	...	...	...
14.7	...	...	...	...	53	2	1	56	...	...	...	...
15.7	...	...	...	...	20	2	2	24	...	...	...	...
16.7	...	...	...	...	13	2	0	15	...	...	...	...
17.7	...	...	...	...	20	2	0	22	...	...	...	...
18.7	...	...	...	...	15	2	2	19	...	...	...	...
19.7	...	...	...	...	5	1	0	6	...	...	...	...
20.7	...	...	...	...	10	1	0	11	...	...	...	...
Totals	154	64	(9)	227	486	53	20	559	82	16	2	100

	1955			Total	1953			Total
	C	T	I		C	T	I	
Wild Birmingham population per cent. phenotype (fig. 11)	*86·94*	*9·48*	*3·58*	559	*85·03*	*10·14*	*4·83*	621
Per cent. return of releases = recaptures	*53·25*	*25*	*(22·2)*	100	*27·5*	*13·0*	*17·4*	149

The letters C, T, and I stand for *carbonaria, typical* and *insularia*
respectively throughout this paper

TABLE 1A

Birmingham recaptures, 1953 (See Appendix)

Date	Observed			Total	Expected		
	C	T	I		C	T	I
25.6	5	1	2	8	2·50	3·00	2·50
26.6	0	0	0	0	0	0	0
27.6	0	1	2	3	1·68	0·56	0·76
28·6	9	4	2	15	8·81	5·00	1·19
29·6	0	0	0	0	0	0	0
30.6	17	2	1	20	13·89	5·10	1·57
1.7	41	6	0	47	37.11	8·66	1·24
2.7	30	2	1	33	24·92	7·07	1·01
3.7	26	2	0	28	22·94	5·06	0
4.7	12	0	0	12	10·18	1·52	0·30
Totals	140	18	8	166	121·46	35·97	8·57

Reserve near Birmingham, which I had chosen in 1953 as being likely
to offer the optimum conditions for my requirements.   I had three
objects in view in this undertaking.   Firstly to repeat a small mark-
release experiment similar to that of 1953.   Secondly, to give Dr
Tinbergen an opportunity of filming the experiments so as to make

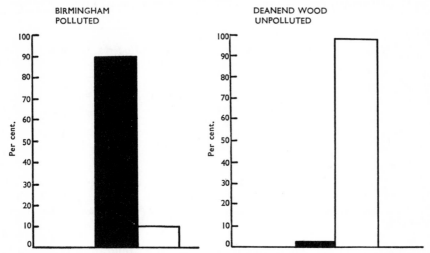

FIG. 1.—Local Population Frequencies.

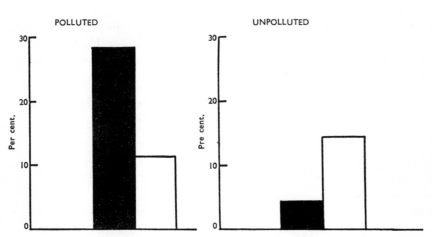

FIG. 1a.—Recapture Frequencies.

a visual record of them in the same way that he had done previously
in Dorset, and thirdly to check the local phenotype frequencies, after
having released 137 male and 34 female *typical betularia* in 1953.

(a) *Mark-release-recapture results.*   Altogether a total of 227 *betularia*
were released over two periods, 154 *carbonaria*, 64 *typical* (and 9 *insularia*),
see table 1.   Of these, I recaptured a total of 100, 82 being *carbonaria*,
16 *typical* (and 2 *insularia*), see tables 1 and 1A.   This represents a

return of 52·25 per cent. of the *carbonaria* release and 25 per cent. of the *typical* (*insularia* 22·2). Once again we recaptured twice as many of the black form as of the light, but this differed from the 1953 releases which were spread over 11 days, when we recaught 27·5 per cent. of *carbonaria* and 13 per cent. of *typical*. Whether the present increased return rate was due to the greater efficiency of our recapture

TABLE 2

Observation on predation of B. betularia, *by Redstarts for 2 days only (by Dr N. Tinbergen from his hide), Birmingham, 1955*

	Typical	*Carbonaria*	Total
19.7 a.m.	12	3	15
20.7 a.m.	14	3	17
p.m.	17	9	26
Total .	43	15	58

N.B.—Replenished to equality as soon as all three of either phenotype had been taken.

methods, or to decreased predation, diminished migration or a small natural population, I am unable to say. But it is important to note that the *relative* return figures were of the same order as in my previous series of experiments.

(b) Dr Tinbergen succeeded in filming Redstarts (*Phœnicurus phœnicurus* L.) taking and eating our releases (plate II, fig. 5), and I am able to give in table 2 his records of the predation which took

TABLE 3

Comparative methods of collecting at M.V. light and assembling traps for 6 nights only. Birmingham, 1955

	8th July			9th July			10th July			11th July			12th July			13th July			Totals		
Phenotypes	C	T	I	C	T	I	C	T	I	C	T	I	C	T	I	C	T	I	C	T	I
M.V. light traps	32	6	2	9	5	0	23	4	2	19	1	0	72	7	4	12	2	0	167	25	8
Assembling traps	30	1	3	97	17	1	31	3	0	77	8	4	17	1	1	3	0	2	255	30	10

place on two days whilst he kept observation from a hide. In each case the two forms were released in equality and subsequently replenished at intervals *after all of one form had been taken*. In this way, he recorded that 43 of the pale *typical* form were eaten to 15 of the black form *carbonaria* and, on the majority of occasions, two or more *typicals* were eaten before a *carbonaria* was discovered. Once again we were able to show that the presence of a conspicuous light coloured *typical* immediately put the better hidden *carbonaria* at a disadvantage which they would not otherwise have incurred if they had been released on their own.

(c) A total of 559 wild *betularia* were caught over a period of 13 nights, *carbonaria* 486, *typical* 53 and *insularia* 20, giving the percentages respectively of 86·94, 9·48 and 3·58 (see table 1). This compares with 621 *betularia* taken over 11 nights in 1953 with *carbonaria* 85·03 per cent., *typical* 10·14 per cent. and *insularia* 4·83 per cent. Furthermore, table 3 demonstrates that for the 6 nights on which light and assembling traps were both in operation the total catch (= wild population+releases) showed a similar proportion of each phenotype as coming to both methods of collecting. It again compares with the high degree of consistency with my 1953 figures, see table 3A.

TABLE 3A

Comparison of the proportion (per cent.) of phenotypes which came to M.V. light and to assembling

Year	Birmingham 1953 (for 10 nights)				Birmingham 1955 (for 6 nights)			
Phenotypes	C	T	I	Total	C	T	I	Total
M.V. light— Totals . .	263	47	24	**433**	167	25	8	**200**
Percentage .	*83·60*	*10·85*	*5·55*	*100*	*86·44*	*10·17*	*3·39*	*100*
Assembling— Totals . .	281	34	13	**328**	255	30	10	**295**
Percentage .	*85·68*	*10·36*	*3·96*	*100*	*83·5*	*12·5*	*4*	*100*

This small repeat experiment fully corroborated the findings of the previous one, namely that the pale *typical* form, as found in unpolluted countryside, is at a cryptic disadvantage in an industrial area. The fact that birds eliminate these selectively, thereby affecting the evolution of the Peppered Moth, was again recorded.

3. SELECTION EXPERIMENTS IN UNPOLLUTED COUNTRYSIDE

It can be presumed that melanic mutations take place at intervals throughout the range of *Biston betularia*. To test their selective advantages or disadvantages by mark-release-recapture experiments, it would be advantageous, therefore, to choose a location where the melanic *carbonaria* was only maintained by recurrent mutation. A wood having such specifications and, at the same time, suitable in other requirements such as offering isolation and free access by rides was not easy to find. Moreover, amenities for housing the very large number of pupæ necessary to ensure specimens for release had to be available on the site. A large number of woods in Devon and Cornwall, where only the *typical* light coloured form of *Biston betularia* occurs, were investigated, but were found to be unsuitable for one reason or another. Eventually a peninsula of extremely heavily lichened woodland was found in Deanend Wood, Dorset (fig. 2), and in 1954 I was able to visit it for a single night with a view to collecting a random sample of *betularia* Twenty specimens were taken assembling to virgin females, of which 19 were *typical* and 1 *insularia*. There were

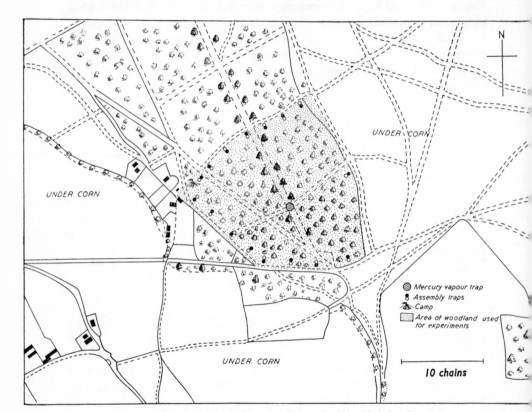

Fig. 2.—Deanend Wood, Dorset. Drawn by Miss Christine Court.

no *carbonaria*. Furthermore, leaf washings from locally collected samples showed a small degree of pollution only. Accordingly, in 1955, in mid-June, I set up camp in these woods. Suitable sheds were found to house the three thousand *betularia* pupæ. An electric generator with mercury vapour traps was installed in the centre ride and the periphery of the wood was lined with cages destined to contain virgin females, so that at night the whole release area would be subject to a concentration of female assembling scent and this, no doubt, succeeded in holding a proportion of our male releases within the area of woodland.

The experiments were designed so that each aspect of the work could be compared with the previous Birmingham results, and the methods employed came under the following headings :

(1) Scoring values as gauged by human standards.
(2) Direct observation as to what happened to the individuals so scored.
(3) Recapture figures which provided data over longer periods.

On every occasion, recapture results were assessed on male Peppered Moths only, because of the impossibility of recapturing females. However, these were used as releases for continuous observation from hides where, at the same time as a film record which was made, the order of predation of each insect was noted.

(i) *Scoring values for crypsis*

The technique of scoring previously used was to assess, in the first place at a distance of two yards, whether a released moth was (*a*) conspicuous, or (*b*) inconspicuous. Subsequently, three categories were allowed for each, so that the score for (*a*) would be either −1, −2, or −3, and for (*b*) +1, +2, or +3, depending on the distance at which the insect faded into its background. As pointed out in the previous paper, this method of scoring worked satisfactorily in the Birmingham experiments. It came as a surprise then to find that, of 120 *typicals* released in Deanend Wood during the first few days, all were classed as inconspicuous, with 85 per cent. scoring +3. Conversely, all 75 *carbonaria* scored by us appeared conspicuous and 80 per cent. of these scored −3. In view of the random sample of the release points selected, it appeared unnecessary to continue the arduous procedure of scoring the cryptic value of each individual release, and it was accepted that in these woods, to the human eye, the majority of the light *typical* form were extremely well hidden, and the *carbonaria* were nearly always conspicuous (plate I, fig. 1).

(ii) *Direct observation*

(*a*) *A record of the number of individuals present or absent by late afternoon.* Early on in the experiments an apparent deficiency of the light *typical* form was recorded when the afternoon check on releases took place. There were also many *carbonaria* missing. In the present work, in regard to the other melanic *insularia*, the numbers used, though quoted, were so small that they have no significance. It became increasingly obvious that one was passing over the *typical* form on the lichened tree trunks, and they are practically impossible to see. To test this, I did a check immediately following the morning's release, in an area where my continual presence prevented predation. All the *carbonaria* were present, but over 30 per cent. of the *typicals* were unaccounted for. The cryptic efficiency of the *typical* on a lichened background is, in fact, greater than that of *carbonaria* on the blackened Birmingham tree trunks. For this reason, this type of recording was discontinued.

(b) *Observation from hides.* In the course of filming, Dr Niko Tinbergen, who had to spend the greater part of each day in a hide, recorded the order in which predation occurred. These figures are added to my own observations. It must be emphasised that these records were of concentrations of female *betularia* necessary for photography, but that they played no part in my release-recapture figures. On each occasion, an equal number of black and white forms were used at the commencement, but it was found impracticable to replace each phenotype after it had been taken. Their numbers were

TABLE 4

Direct observation on predation by five species of birds.
Deanend Wood, Dorset, 1955

	Observer	Carbonaria	Typical	
Spotted Flycatcher . . .	N. T.	46	8	
(*Muscicapa striata* L.)	H. B. D. K.	35	1	
Nuthatch	N. T.	22	8	
(*Sitta Europaea* L.)	H. B. D. K.	9	0 (first day)	
	H. B. D. K.	9	3 (second day)	
Yellow Hammer . . .	N. T.	8	0	
(*Emberiza citrinella* L.)	H. B. D. K.	12	0	
Robin	N. T.	12	2	
(*Erithacus rubecula* L.)				
Thrush	N. T.	11	4	
(*Turdus ericetocum* L.)				
Total predation observed (for days when records were kept)	...	164	26	Total **190**

Note.—On all occasions these observations commenced with equal numbers of both phenotypes. We replaced them when all of one phenotype had been taken.

replenished after the last of one phenotype had been eaten, thus preventing simple statistical analysis. By doing this, it will be appreciated that the bias was, thereafter, in favour of that phenotype which had been eliminated previously, and it was found that on the majority of occasions the more conspicuous of the two forms were all taken before any of the others. This behaviour was common to five species of birds to a greater or lesser degree, as will be seen from the figures in table 4 (plate I, fig. 3, and plate II, figs. 1, 2, 3 and 4).

(iii) *Recapture results*

Releases were undertaken on fourteen occasions in all, making a total of 969 individuals, 473 being *carbonaria* and 496 *typical*. I recaptured 30 *carbonaria* and 62 *typical*. For all types of release we got back 12·5 per cent. of the *typical* form, but only 6·3 per cent. of the *carbonaria*. For various reasons about to be discussed, the releases on three days should be excluded from this total as they are unduly biased in one way or another. This gives a figure of 799 releases

TABLE 5

Release experiment figures for Biston betularia *(males only).*
Deanend, Dorset, 1955

Date (1953)	Releases			Total	Catches			Total	Recaptures			Total
	C	T	I		C	T	I		C	T	I	
(13.6)	(37)	(38)	(9)	(84)	...	...	...	...	...	...	...	...
14.6	8	17	2	27	4	17	2	23	(4)	(1)	(1)	(6)
(15.6)	(8)	(25)	(1)	(34)	2	27	5	34	2	9	(3)	14
(16.6)	(22)	(40)	(0)	(62)	1	34	2	37	(0)	(0)	(0)	(0)
17.6	...	...	...	...	7	58	3	68	(7)	(7)	(0)	(14)
18.6	42	65	(3)	110	0	30	1	31	0	1	0	1
19.6	39	72	0	111	2	26	1	29	2	6	0	8
20.6	24	57	0	81	1	44	2	47	1	3	0	4
21.6	42	29	0	71	1	13	2	16	1	4	0	5
22.6	...	...	...	...	5	13	1	19	5	4	0	9
23.6	...	...	...	...	...	No releases		...	...	No captures		...
24.6	...	...	...	...	...	No releases		...	...	No captures		...
25.6	82	43	0	125	1	11	0	12	0	0	0	0
26.6	...	...	...	...	3	8	1	12	2	2	0	4
27.6	51	28	0	79	0	8	0	8	0	0	0	0
28.6	22	22	0	44	1	20	0	21	1	5	0	6
29.6	17	18	0	35	0	14	0	14	0	5	0	5
30.6	24	11	0	35	4	11	1	16	3	6	0	9
1.7	...	...	...	...	2	9	0	11	2	2	0	4
2.7	...	...	...	...	0	7	0	7	0	0	0	0
3.7	...	...	...	...	...	...	...	...	...	...	...	...
4.7	55	31	0	86	...	...	...	...	...	...	...	...
5.7	...	...	...	...	0	9	0	9	0	7	0	7
Totals	473	496	15	984	34	359	21	414	30	62	4	96

	C	T	I	Total
Wild Deanend population . Per cent. phenotype (fig. 11) .	(4) (Possible escapes)	297 *94·60*	17 *5·4*	318
Release after 1 day of self-determination Per cent. phenotype . .	2 ...	4 ...	(1) ...	
Per cent. return of releases .	*6·34*	*12·50*	*(26·67)*	

for the 11 correct days : 406 being *carbonaria* and 393 *typical*. I got back 19 *carbonaria* and 54 *typical*, being 4·68 and 13·74 per cent. respectively (see tables 5 and 5A).

4. DISCUSSION AND RELEASE PROBLEMS

Various types of release techniques were undertaken with the object of finding the best way of subjecting as many individuals as possible, under natural conditions, to maximum predation for the longest time. I propose, therefore, to discuss these in some detail, and to give reasons for excluding three sets of figures from the table due to the unsatisfactory nature of the releases.

I used 84 *betularia* in the first experiment (13/6/55). These were released on only twenty trees, the reason for this small number of release points being that I had been unable to locate and prepare the other trees in the area. The result was that I produced a high concentration of moths on comparatively few tree trunks (an average of 4 per tree), nor were the two forms on every occasion released in equality per tree. The late afternoon check showed that in nearly

TABLE 5A

Deanend recaptures, 1955

Date	Observed			Total	Expected		
	C	T	I		C	T	I
(13.6)	(6)	(3)	(3)	(12)	(5·29)	(5·43)	(1·29)
14.6	1	7	2	10	2·96	6·30	0·74
(15.6)	(0)	(1)	(0)	(1)	(0·24)	(0·74)	(0·03)
(16.6)	(8)	(8)	(0)	(16)	(5·68)	(10·32)	(0)
17.6	...	...	...	...	...	...	...
18.6	2	8	0	10	3·81	5·91	0·27
19.6	1	2	0	3	1·05	1·95	0
20.6	2	4	0	6	1·78	4·22	0
21.6	4	4	0	8	4·73	3·27	0
22.6	...	...	...	...	...	...	...
23.6	...	...	...	...	...	...	...
24.6	...	...	...	...	...	...	...
25.6	2	2	0	4	2·62	1·38	0
26.6	...	...	...	...	...	...	...
27.6	1	5	0	6	3·87	2·13	0
28.6	0	7	0	7	3·50	3·50	0
29.6	3	8	0	11	5·34	5·66	0
30.6	2	1	0	3	2·06	0·94	0
4.7	0	7	0	7	4·47	2·52	0
Totals	32	67	5	104	47·40	54·27	2·33

every case the moths were either all present or all absent per tree. Subsequently, by direct observation, Dr Tinbergen and I found that a concentration of releases increased the predation risk for all present, even though the birds took the more conspicuous ones first. It will be noted that on this occasion we recaptured 4 *carbonaria* and 1 *typical* (expected—near equality). It is possible that, apart from a faulty release technique, a further point may have played a part in the production of these figures. The birds in this wood were unlikely to have had any previous experience of the Black Peppered Moths, and it is conceivable therefore that at first some of them did not recognise them as an article of diet. Dr Tinbergen did, in fact, record a similar incident in one of the Birmingham 1955 experiments. A Wren

(*Troglodytes troglodytes* Linn.) flew on to a tree trunk on which was released a very conspicuous *typical* (Birmingham frequency 10 per cent.) and after scrutinising it closely it flew away without attacking it. It is, however, possible that the noise of the ciné camera disturbed it at this point.

The next release (14/6/55), which was considered satisfactory, was conducted with a greatly lowered concentration. Twenty-seven *betularia* were, in fact, put on to 23 trees.

The release on the 15th was designed to test whether the presence of a *carbonaria* on the same tree trunk as a *typical* lowered the latter's expectation of survival. Apart from the 8 male *carbonaria* released, females had, on this occasion, to be used also (because of a temporary lack of *carbonaria* males), so that each of the male *typicals* had a black moth on the same tree trunk. Two trees, however, were used as controls, and on these two *typicals* were released on each, with no accompanying melanics. The late afternoon examination (6 p.m.) gave the surprising result that no *betularia* of any form were to be found on any of the release trees, with the exception that one of the control trees (without a *carbonaria* being present) had two *typicals* on it. The following night, out of 37 *betularia* caught at light and assembling traps, none were from the releases of the 15th. The next night, however, I recaught one *typical* (out of 68) from this release. This would seem to provide additional evidence to the statement I made in my original paper (p. 336), " From this it would appear that, when a conspicuous insect had been found, it at once put other insects in the immediate vicinity at a disadvantage because of the bird's active seachings." For these reasons I feel that the release conducted on the 15th should not be included.

The following day (16/6/55) a release was undertaken between 5 and 6 p.m., long after the maximum predation time of birds. The object was to test whether, having excluded predation, the design of experiment favoured unduly one phenotype more than another. Twenty-two *carbonaria* and 40 *typical* were released. Of these, 7 *carbonaria* and 6 *typical* were retrapped the same night (expected— 4·61 to 8·39). It will be noted that this represents the return of nearly a quarter of our releases on the 16th. I am unable to account for the increased proportion of *carbonaria* recaptures over *typical*, which occurred this night, but in view of the absence of predation it suggests that the recapture arrangements did not unduly favour the return of the *typicals* more than the *carbonaria*. We have, however, already shown that in the Birmingham experiments there was no difference in the proportion of the three phenotypes which were collected, firstly, at mercury vapour light traps and, secondly, at assembling traps containing females of all three phenotypes (pioportions of *carbonaria*, light and assembling, 85 per cent. to 86 per cent., and *typical* 10·8 to 10·4 per cent.). Furthermore, we are able to report similar findings in this present set of experiments (see table 6). In view of these facts, and that this release was not designed to reflect the degree of selective predation, and that little in fact could have taken place, it is better to extract the results, along with those of the other two previously mentioned, from those which are about to be considered.

It can be seen from this that the act of predation is no simple response to a single stimulus. It involves, apart from insect cryptic efficiency, such other considerations as insect density, bird conditioning, and searching intensity per trunk, stimulated by an immediate previous experience of finding a conspicuous insect. All other releases were in fact conducted in a uniform manner (with the exception of one other satisfactory method used). In these, on every occasion, there was one phenotype released per tree, and the experiment was conducted over a larger area of woodland. Furthermore, as in the Birmingham experiments, other species of moths which were inhabiting the wood were released within the area at the same time, to minimise

TABLE 6

Comparative methods of collecting at M.V. light and assembling traps. Deanend, 1955

Phenotypes	Carbonaria	Typical	Insularia	Total	
M.V. light—					
Totals . . .	14	166	12	192	
Percentage . .	7·29	86·77	5·94	100	
					414
Assembling—					
Totals . . .	20	193	9	222	
Percentage . .	9·01	86·94	4·05	100	

the effect of conditioning. This, of course, involves a great deal of extra work, but it is necessary. One further point was noted, that the same trees must not be used as release points on each day, as the birds became conditioned to them.

The " other method " of release referred to was used successfully on 18th June. This took place just before sunrise, between 4 and 4.30 a.m. Forty-two *carbonaria*, 65 *typical* (and 3 *insularia*) were allowed to fly out of their separate boxes which had been previously warmed on the engine of my car. The majority flew and took up positions on the boughs and trunks of nearby trees. I, therefore, used many release points within the area. This method was not repeated because it is necessary to get each insect airborne over a very short period of time, which was difficult due to the coldness of the morning, so that by the time the last few flew, birds were active and, in fact, a Spotted Flycatcher (*Muscicapa striata* L.) chased and caught two *typical betularia*. A too early release, on the other hand, would involve a number of the moths coming to the various traps in action from the previous night. With the exception of the two *typicals* taken by birds, it appeared that this release was satisfactory. One *carbonaria* and 6 *typical* were subsequently recovered.

We have produced evidence that, in undertaking any release experiments involving the use of cryptic insects which normally pass the day concealed on their appropriate backgrounds, due regard must be taken of such factors which affect predation as density, proximity of an individual which has been scored conspicuous, bird conditioning for recognition of a particular species, or for the place of release. To avoid all these complications, individual releases, undertaken over a large area containing many trees, are essential.

5. CONCLUSIONS

We are now in a position to review firstly, two separate series of release experiments conducted in an industrial district : secondly, to compare figures obtained from these with the data from a similar release undertaken in an unpolluted and heavily lichened wood in Dorset.

In regard to the Birmingham experiments : in the second of the two series which were carried out, scoring for crypsis was not repeated as it was unnecessary ; neither the trees nor the phenotypes having altered since 1953. Direct observation on bird predation in each case showed that the *typical* light form was eaten more frequently than *carbonaria*, and the deficiency of this light form in our recapture figures can be attributed in each case to selective elimination by birds, as such other considerations as sampling errors, a different life span or migration rate for each phenotype, can be ruled out of the repeat experiment for the same reasons as given in 1953.

On comparing the Birmingham figures for crypsis with those of Deanend Wood, Dorset, we found a complete reversal. Over 97 per cent. of the *carbonaria* in the former location were scored inconspicuous, whereas 89 per cent. of the *typicals* were adjudged conspicuous. In Deanend Wood, of the *carbonaria*, all were scored conspicuous, whilst of the *typicals* all were inconspicuous. Furthermore, of these, 85 per cent. were given the highest mark for cryptic efficiency.

Consequently the observed bird predation on both occasions in Birmingham showed elimination in favour of *carbonaria*. In 1953, a total of 18 *betularia* were kept under continuous observation, half being *carbonaria* and half *typical*. All the nine *typicals* were observed to be eaten by Robins and Hedge Sparrows, but only 3 *carbonaria*, the remaining 6 were never discovered and, in fact, survived the day up to 7 p.m. In the recent work, Dr Tinbergen recorded that a pair of Redstarts and their young took 43 *typicals* to 15 *carbonaria* during experimental releases in which both black and light forms were used in equality (table 2).

On the other hand, in Deanend Wood, Dorset, the reverse was observed : 5 species of birds took 190 *betularia* whilst being watched (table 4). Of these, 164 were *carbonaria* and 26 *typical*. It must be accepted, therefore, that the *carbonaria* has an approximate 6 : 1 advantage in Birmingham, and the reverse was true for Deanend. In regard to the recaptures, on each occasion in Birmingham I got back twice as many *carbonaria* as *typicals*, but in Deanend I recaptured three times as many *typical* as the melanic (text fig. 1*a*). Furthermore, if the collecting techniques employed were comparable in each case, it would appear that the predation intensity was greater at Deanend. Fewer individuals of each phenotype survived. This is also reflected in the nightly recapture totals (assuming, once again, that our collecting efficiency was comparable). In the 1953 large-scale Birmingham experiments, the average return within 24 hours was 19 *betularia* per 100 releases. For Deanend, it was 9 per 100. It is, however, the selective predation and not the total predation with which we are concerned in these present investigations.

6. SUMMARY OF ALL THREE EXPERIMENTS

1. The Peppered Moth, *Biston betularia*, is one of about seventy species of moth which are at present in the process of changing their populations from light to dark individuals. The common Industrial Melanic = form *carbonaria* is black, and another = form *insularia*, which is not an allelomorph, varies from light to heavily speckled specimens (plate II, fig. 6).

2. This paper records two complementary series of experiments, involving the release of nearly 2000 marked moths, to test the relative camouflage or cryptic advantages of the normal light-coloured *betularia* and its melanic form *carbonaria*. This was carried out in the first place near the industrial area of Birmingham where the *carbonaria* form represents about 87 per cent. of the population. Secondly, a similar experiment was undertaken in a heavily lichened and pollution-free wood in rural Dorset, where *carbonaria* does not normally occur or, if it does, at a very low frequency. (The other melanic, *insularia*, though mentioned, was used in too small numbers to have significance.)

3. The first series was a repeat of similar work I carried out in 1953, and fully corroborates the conclusions previously published (Kettlewell, 1955).

4. On each occasion, the more conspicuous of the two forms was deficient in numbers amongst the recaptures ; *typical betularia* in Birmingham and *carbonaria* at Deanend Wood, Dorset.

5. (i) Scoring for conspicuousness as recognised by Man, and (ii) direct observation of the released insects showed that birds were responsible for their elimination, both in polluted and unpolluted countryside, and this took place selectively in each case, and in an order which varied according to the camouflage efficiency of each phenotype in relation to its background.

6. In unpolluted and heavily lichened countryside melanic forms are maintained only by recurrent mutation, and are rapidly eliminated because of their conspicuousness.

7. In industrial areas this limitation no longer exists, in fact it is the pale-coloured *typical* which is now eliminated. This applies also to areas far to the east of them, because of the prevailing westerly wind, where large areas of England, subject to pollution " fall-out ", are deficient in lichens.

8. Predation alone is responsible for the fact that in the Birmingham district I got back only 50 per cent. of the *typicals* that were expected from the proportions of the two forms released. In contrast, at Dean-end, it was the *carbonaria* form which was deficient. In fact I re-captured only 67 per cent. of the number expected.

9. The difference in cryptic coloration alone could be responsible for the rapid spread of the Industrial Melanics. There are also, however, other character and behaviour differences between them and their *typical* forms. These are at present the subject of investigation.

Acknowledgments.—I wish to thank the Nuffield Foundation, who have enabled me to undertake this work, also Dr N. Tinbergen for his observations and records whilst filming the experiments. I am grateful to Dr E. B. Ford, F.R.S. for his advice and to Dr P. M. Sheppard for his constructive criticism.

7. REFERENCE

KETTLEWELL, H. B. D. 1955. *Heredity, 9,* 323-342.

APPENDIX

Table IA (p. 288) reflects a different method of analysing the 1953 recaptures, to that shown in the previous paper. The original recapture figures (Kettlewell, 1955, Table 5) record the number of marked individuals which returned each night. The present table takes into account the number of days each individual had been in the wild. Thus a recaptured insect showing three marks is entered under each of the three releasing days separately.

Plate I

Fig. 1.—*Typical betularia* (left) and its melanic *carbonaria* (right) at rest on lichened tree trunk, Deanend Wood, Dorset.

Fig. 2.—*Typical betularia* and its melanic *carbonaria* at rest on lichen-free tree trunk near Birmingham.

Fig. 3.—Song Thrush, *Turdus ericetorum* L., examining tree trunks from the ground with a *carbonaria* in its beak.

Plate II

Fig. 1.—Nuthatch, *Sitta europæa* L., in the act of taking *typical betularia* from lichened tree trunk, Deanend Wood, Dorset. This species took 40 *carbonaria* to 11 *typical* while under observation.

Fig. 2.—Spotted Flycatcher, *Muscicapa striata* L., about to take *carbonaria* from oak trunk, Deanend Wood, Dorset. This species was seen to take 81 *carbonaria* to 9 *typical*.

Fig. 3.—Robin, *Erithacus rubecula* L., with *carbonaria* in its beak taken from lichened tree trunk, Deanend Wood, Dorset. There were 3 *typicals* on this trunk at the moment of this photograph being taken. This species took 12 *carbonaria* to 2 *typical* whilst being watched.

Fig. 4.—Yellowhammer, *Emberiza citrinella* L., searching tree trunk, Deanend Wood, Dorset. A pair took altogether 20 *carbonaria* and on no occasion whilst under observation did they discover the *typical* form which, on every occasion, was offered in equal numbers to the black.

Fig. 5.—Male Redstart, *Phœnicurus phœnicurus* L., with *typical betularia* in its beak in a wood near Birmingham. This species took 43 *typical* to 15 *carbonaria* whilst under observation.

Fig. 6.—*Typical Biston betularia* L., its melanic *carbonaria* Jordan, and f. *insularia* Th-Mieg, another melanic.

SELECTION FOR SEXUAL ISOLATION WITHIN A SPECIES

G. R. KNIGHT, ALAN ROBERTSON AND C. H. WADDINGTON

Institute of Animal Genetics, Edinburgh

Received March 17, 1955

Two mechanisms have been advanced for the origin of reproductive isolation between species. Muller (1939), dealing in the main with barriers to crossing in the later stages of species divergence, such as hybrid inviability and infertility, suggests that these arise almost by chance as a product of change in the genetic background either by genetic drift or as adaptation to different biological situations. This would lead to accelerating divergences as the process continues, or, as Muller puts it, "ever more pronounced immiscibility as an inevitable consequence of non-mixing." Dobzhansky's suggestion (1937), which is perhaps complementary rather than antagonistic to Muller's, is that when sufficient divergence between two species has arisen so that the hybrids are less well adapted for any available habitat than either parental type, there will be selection for sexual isolation. That is to say—if mating can take place and if the resulting hybrids are inviable or infertile, then natural selection will operate to reduce the chance that mating will occur, either by reducing the chance of encounter or the chance of mating with members of the other species when they are encountered.

Some writers, in discussing the mechanism proposed by Dobzhansky have suggested that "natural selection will favour any mechanism which prevents the wastage of gametes involved in unsuccessful hybridisation." This seems to be unduly teleological. Natural selection will only tend to suppress crossbreeding if those individuals which hybridise will in consequence pass on fewer gametes in the form of pure-bred offspring. It would seem probable that this would be more often the case in females than in males. In *Drosophila melanogaster*, for instance, females seem reluctant to mate again for a period of two or three days after an effective mating. If the first mating has been heterogamic, this will reduce the number of purebred offspring that she will produce in her lifetime. Gestation in mammals will have a similar effect. But the male, who must on the average have the same number of effective matings in his life as the female, is usually capable of many more if willing females are available. It follows then that willingness to cross-breed, which may merely be a sign of greater general sexual activity, will not necessarily reduce the number of purebred progeny that a male will leave. If Dobzhansky's mechanism for the establishment of sexual isolation is correct, it follows that it should be in the main a matter of female preference. Merrell (1954) has recently presented evidence that it is the female which exercises discrimination in matings between *D. pseudobscura* and *D. persimilis.*

Koopman (1950) has shown that selection leads to an intensification of the sexual isolation between these two species. Using marked stocks of the two species, he selected continually for purebred flies—the progeny of parents that had mated homogamically. He showed that the proportion of hybrids emerging declined dramatically after a few generations of selection. More recently, Wallace (1950) and King (private communication) attempted to demonstrate the production of sexual isolation by selection within a species. They used two stocks of *D. melanogaster,* from widely separated localities, which had each been marked by a different recessive gene. After 12 generations, when the experiment was first reported, little change in the proportion of wild-type flies emerg-

Reprinted by permission of the authors from EVOLUTION, **10,** 14–22 (1956).

ing had been observed, but in subsequent generations the proportion declined significantly, showing that sexual isolation had been to some extent established. This was confirmed by observation of individual matings.

Our own experiment on very similar lines was started before we were aware of Wallace's work, and as our work was slightly different in conception, we decided to proceed with it. In Wallace's experiment, the mutants were used solely as markers, the stocks because of their origin presumably differing in many genes. As it happens, we had used in our work stocks marked with the autosomal recessive genes, ebony and vestigial, which has been extracted from a population in which the two had been segregating for many generations. The original stocks making up this population were actually those used by Rendel (1951) in his work on the effect of light on the mating of these mutants. Our two foundation stocks, both of which contained a considerable amount of genetic variability, were thus probably genetically very similar except for the marker genes. These genes were chosen because of the ease of scoring but they do react differently to light and, as Rendel has shown, ebony males mate more frequently in the dark than in the light.

In the first experiment of this type that we carried out, there appeared in the seventh generation some flies that were both ebony and vestigial, indicating that in previous generations either a non-virgin female or else a wild-type heterozygote had been used as a parent with the result that each mutant stock was contaminated with the other gene. Theoretical consideration of the effect of this showed that the proportion of double recessive flies should increase by a factor of four each generation until they reached a level of 11% of all flies emerging. At that point, the proportion of flies in each mutant stock that were heterozygous for the other gene would be $\frac{2}{3}$. There would then be a continual inter-change of genes between the two stocks. In addition, one-third of the apparently pure mutants used as parents would be derived from heterogamic matings, thereby reducing the selection for sexual isolation. We therefore discarded the line and started afresh with stringent precautions against non-virginity, parents being collected over a 7 hour period. In the two experiments presented here in detail, no double recessive flies were ever observed.

DESCRIPTION OF EXPERIMENTS

Box Experiment

Two mutant strains of *D. melanogaster* homozygous for the genes ebony and vestigial respectively were used. They had been extracted from the same population, after segregation for many generations. At the start, 54 males and 54 virgin females from each of the stocks were put together into a breeding box (size $18'' \times 18'' \times 7''$) which contained 10 unstoppered $\frac{1}{4}$ pint bottles of maize meal–molasses–yeast–agar medium. Flies were etherised for counting, but were not put into the box until three hours after complete recovery from anaesthesia. The box was then placed in a constant temperature room at 25° C. All phases of the experiment were done at this temperature. The box was always put in the same part of the room, where, due to the direction of the light, two sides of the box near the edge were in slight shadow. The ebony flies, immediately the box was positioned, migrated towards the light source, that is, towards the shaded edge. After some time, the majority of them moved more freely about the cage.

After six days of mating, the ten food bottles were removed, cleared of any flies which remained inside, and stoppered. The parents were discarded. The count of the next generation was started five days afterwards, i.e., on the eleventh day after the parents were put into the box. Three types of flies emerged; hybrids from heterogamic matings, and the two mutants ebony and vestigial from homogamic fertilizations. For 3½ days every fly which emerged was counted. The culture bottles were completely cleared at 10 A.M. Flies which emerged by 5 P.M. on the same day were segregated and mutants were kept in separate vials to be used as parents for the next generation when 1 to 4 days old. When insufficient virgins were obtained, those collected were bred with their own kind, and the experiment carried on from their progeny. In the box experiment, this was done three times in 38 generations.

In order to ensure that any changes in external conditions had not affected the course of the experiment, controls were done on the box experiment in the later generations. Parent virgin flies were obtained from the original stocks and put into a box of identical proportions to the experimental one. The control box and the experimental one received exactly the same treatment throughout. This was done seven times between the 25th and 35th generations.

Jar Experiment

An experiment on similar lines was run in conjunction with the cage one. A 2 lb. glass jar containing approximately 1″ of food was used as the breeding chamber. The number of parent flies employed in this case was between 20 and 30 of each sex of the mutants. Again, it was sometimes necessary to mate the virgins with their own kind to produce sufficient numbers for the next preferential mating. This was done three times in 33 generations. From generations 1 to 12 the parent flies were still under ether when put into the jar, as it was thought that they might otherwise escape. This was found, however, to be unsatisfactory. So from the 13th generation onwards the parents were introduced into the jar three hours after recovery from the ether. The jar was put into the same constant temperature room and at the same time as the box. Thereafter, all operations, such as clearing parents from the jar, counting and segregating flies of each generation, etc., were carried out at the same time and in an exactly similar manner to the box experiment.

Because of the small capacity of the jar compared with that of the box and the fact that there was little or no variation in the light within the jar, it was assumed that any tendency towards an eco-

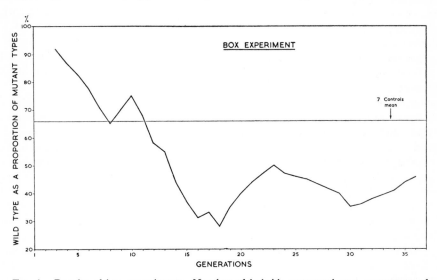

FIG. 1. Results of box experiment. Number of hybrids expressed as a percentage of sum of ebony and vestigial emergences.

497

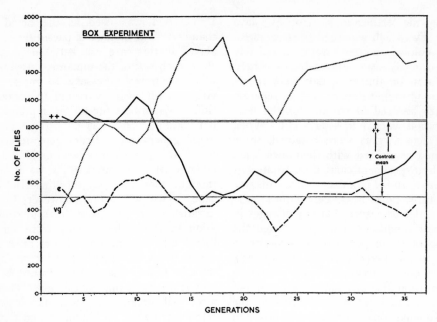

FIG. 2. Results of box experiment. Numbers of 3 types of flies emerging shown separately.

logical isolation between the ebony and vestigial flies would be eliminated.

RESULTS

One of the first impressions at the start of the experiments was of the great fluctuation in results from generation to generation. The jar experiment was in fact started to try to remove this by having all flies developing in one food mass. Our criterion of isolation has been the ratio of wild-type flies, produced by heterogamic matings, to the total number of mutants produced by homogamic matings. The standard deviation of this ratio due to chance fluctuation, determined from the mean square difference between successive generations, was 0.16 for the box experiment and 0.24 for the jar. This fluctuation is equal to that produced by random sampling of 160 units and 70 units respectively from a population made up of two types of objects with equal frequency. The total count was actually of the order of 2,000 flies in both cases. But the number of female parents was 108 and 50 in the box and jar respectively.

The observed fluctuations suggest that the effective units are the initial inseminations of the individual females. In this respect, it is of interest that of the individual platings of females taken from the box after six days of mating, 660 gave offspring all of the same type and only 75 had mixed offspring. However, whatever the reason, it is still true that too many flies were counted each generation and a sample of a quarter of the size that we took would have been quite adequate.

Box Experiment

The results of the box experiment are set out graphically in figures 1 and 2. The graphs are moving averages over 5 generations to smooth out fluctuations. In figure 1, the number of hybrids is expressed as a percentage of the sum of the ebony and vestigial emergences. Figure 2 shows separately the numbers of the three types of flies emerging. From the first to the eighteenth generation a more or less steady decline in the percentage of hybrids is noted. The lowest percentage of hybrids in any individual generation was 10.3% at the eighteenth, with emergences of $++$ 246, e 736, vg 1640. Only once afterwards, at the 23rd generation, does the vestigial line graph fall as low as the control mean for this mutant. Thereafter the values remain high for vestigial emergences. The hybrid figure drops, and is lowest between the 16th and 18th generations, only rising a little and slowly towards the end of the experiment. During the whole 38 generations the emergence values for ebony alternate slightly above and below the figure for the control mean. This suggests that the sexual isolation, after the 18th generation, is due mainly to the increase in the number of homogamic matings of the vestigial flies.

The average values for the seven control generations are also shown in figures 1 and 2. The proportion of wild-type flies to mutants averages 0.66, compared to the proportion in the selected population at the same period of 0.38. The figures for the individual mutants show that the change is due to a decrease of wild-type flies and an increase of vestigial.

It has been shown by Rendel (1951) that ebony reacts to light intensity in its mating behaviour. It seemed possible that the sexual isolation was due to an accentuation of this response. Towards the end of the experiment, therefore, duplicates of the selection box were made up from parents from the selected stock but were kept instead in complete darkness. The ratio of wildtype to mutant offspring was 0.48 compared to 0.46 for

TABLE 1

Controls ♀	Inseminated by	
	e	vg
e	71	69
vg	41	63
Selected stocks		
e	151	108
vg	77	142

the three contemporary generations in the light. It seems therefore that the demonstrated sexual isolation is not concerned with phototropic response. However, there were many more ebony flies in the dark boxes—in fact the average of the three tests (1102 flies) had only once been exceeded by a single generation in the light, and the average in the last few generations of the latter was about 650. There was correspondingly a shortage of vg flies, but the proportional effect was not so great. This agrees with Rendel's observation that ebony males show greater sexual activity in the dark.

Between the 20th and 30th generations, the females were placed in individual vials after they had been removed from the box, and their progeny were examined on emergence. This was done with 6 generations of the selected stocks and with three of the controls. The results in terms of effective matings are given in table 1.

There is a slight tendency to homo-

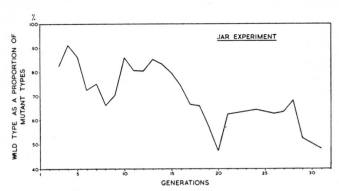

Fig. 3. Results of jar experiment. Compare figure 1.

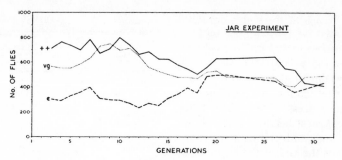

FIG. 4. Results of jar experiment. Compare figure 2.

gamic mating in the controls but the heterogeneity χ^2 is only 2.15. In the selected stocks the tendency is much more marked and the χ^2 value is 27.14. This is confirmatory evidence that some degree of sexual isolation has been obtained in the selected population.

It might have happened that this type of selection, picking out always the mutant flies, would have affected the segregation ratio by selecting those genes favouring the survival from egg to adult of the mutant types. However, a check based on several thousand flies at the end of the experiment showed no differences between control and selected stock in the segregation ratio for either mutant.

Jar Experiment

The results for the jar experiment are given in figures 3 and 4. In the jar, the light intensity was much more uniform than in the box and in addition the flies were more confined—the volume of the jar being of the order of $\frac{1}{50}$ of that of the box. Here again there is a decline in the proportion of wild-type flies as the experiment proceeds, although the proportion at the end is a trifle higher than in the box experiment. However, the ratio of wild-type to mutant flies has declined from 80% to between 50% and 60%. As was noted above, there was a change in method in the middle of this experiment. Up to generation 12, flies were put into the jar etherized but afterwards they were put in an active state. This change does not appear to have affected the sexual isolation. In the five

generations before the change, the average ratio of wild-type to mutants was 0.86 and in the five after the change it averaged 0.80. It may however have affected the separate types. The numbers of vg and wild-type flies decline by about one-third as a result of the change, whereas the ebony count is unchanged. The subsequent change in the wild-type/ mutant ratio appears in this case to be due to an increase in the number of ebony flies. Control experiments were not carried out on the jar population, as the latter was subsidiary to the main experiment in the box.

Sexual Preferences in Inbred Lines and Closed Populations

It is convenient to present here a small amount of data on sexual preferences between lines and populations chosen at random, with a bearing on the "chance" occurrence of sexual isolation. These experiments were carried out by the usual "male choice" method in which males are given equal numbers of two types of female, one of which is recognisable—in our case by a spot of silver paint. The females are then examined for the presence of sperm in the seminal tract. In the first case, two wild-type inbred lines of completely different origin were used, given in our stock list the symbols W20 and K7. The results are given in table 2, which shows the proportion of females inseminated. In all cases, the ♂♂ were equal in number to the ♀♀ of each of the separate lines.

A similar experiment was then done

using lines which, although of common origin, had been selected in different directions without inbreeding for 20 generations for number of chaetae on the 4th and 5th abdominal sternites. There was no overlap in chaetae count between the high and low lines used, so that this character could be used for identifications. The results are given in table 3, for matings between one high line, H1 and two low lines, L4 and L5.

In these rather meagre results, there is little suggestion of sexual isolation having developed by chance in either the inbred experiment or in that with the selected lines. In the latter, it is of interest that the selection for the quantitative character has caused a differentiation in mating ability. The H1 ♂♂ are poorer than those from the two low lines but on the other hand the high ♀♀ seem to be better. But this seems to be a general change in sexual drive, not specifically adapted to the other sex of the same line. Wallace (1955 in press, and personal communication) has also tested whether the mere isolation of two populations is sufficient to cause sexual isolation to arise between them. His populations had been separated for 80–100 generations, and differed in certain morphological characters (primarily abdominal pigmentation). In an extensive series of tests, no tendency towards preferentially mating could be detected nor does there seem to have been any evidence of

TABLE 3

♂	H1 ♀	L4 ♀	Duration of mating
H1	3/10	1/9	30 mins.
L4	9/14	3/14	30 mins.
	H1 ♀	L5 ♀	
H1	11/20	5/19	60 mins.
L5	20/24	17/25	60 mins.

differences in the intensity of general sexual drive.

DISCUSSION

Our results may be summarised in the statement that some sexual isolation developed when we selected for a tendency towards homogamic matings, but that none was found to have arisen by chance in a few lines which had been selected for abdominal chaeta number or inbred. Laboratory experiments on evolutionary mechanisms can, of course, only be indicative and not demonstrative—they can show what might happen in wild populations, rather than what has happened. As far as they go, our experiments lend support to the mechanism suggested by Dobzhansky rather than that discussed by Muller. But when attempting to apply these results to occurrences in nature, one must bear in mind the ways in which artificial populations may fail to imitate conditions in the wild.

It is perhaps misleading to put Muller's hypothesis of the chance origin of sexual isolation in antithesis to that of Dobzhansky, which attributes it to the action of selection. In all probability, both mechanisms have operated in the wild in different cases. Some evidence supporting Dobzhansky's hypothesis comes from Dobzhansky and Koller (1938) who found, in an analysis of crosses between *Drosophila pseudoobscura* and *D. miranda,* that the isolation was greatest between races close to each other in their range. King (1947) has similar evidence from the *guarani* group. However, even between races of the two species widely

TABLE 2

♀s marked	♂	W20 ♀	K7 ♀	Duration of mating
W20	W20	22/23	11/25	40 min s.
	K7	17/23	9/25	40 min s.
W20	W20	17/19	16/20	70 mins.
	K7	4/20	1/19	70 mins.
K7	W20	9/10	5/10	30 mins.
	K7	8/14	9/14	60 mins.
K7	W20	10/20	2/19	30 mins.
	K7	10/20	5/20	45 mins.

separated in origin, the isolation was considerable. One has the suspicion that sexual isolation is common between species which have never had the opportunity to crossbreed, though the evidence is rarely conclusive since seldom if ever do we know the full evolutionary history of the populations.

It is perhaps not surprising that differences in sexual behaviour arose in the experiments involving selection, but were not found in the comparison of populations which has originated independently. If they had occurred in the latter, they could only have appeared by chance, or as a correlated response. It might be expected that random changes in sexual behavior would be slow, even though they arose as a secondary response to an adaptive change in the population. Mating involves the cooperation of the two sexes and it seems unlikely that a genetic shift in the population causing a change of sexual behaviour in the female, perhaps by a modification of the pattern by which a male recognises an animal of his own species, would also change male behaviour in a compensating manner (although an exception to this might be in habitat preference). An individual with aberrant sexual behaviour is not likely to leave many progeny. A population gradually changing its genetic situation could only change its pattern of mating by the selection of males capable of responding to the altered female behaviour. This must constitute a brake on the change of mating behaviour either by chance changes in the genetic situation or even as a correlated response to an adaptive change. This will be particularly true of inbred lines in which selection between potential mates is small or non-existent. Reproductive behaviour, excepting perhaps choice of habitat, would therefore be more stable than other physiological systems to genetic changes.

Both the hypotheses that we have discussed demand the development of a previous geographic isolation before sexual isolation can be established. In this sense, the selection hypothesis is perhaps clumsy, since in the formation of a new species showing sexual isolation with the parent species it demands first a geographic isolation and then an overlapping of the species range so that members of the two species can be selected for refusal to crossbreed. It seems to us that sexual isolation instead of being a consequence of geographic isolation, may be a contributory factor in its establishment. The spread of a population into new territory will often involve the occurrence of genotypes with new hereditary habitat preferences. The existence of such preferences amongst Drosophila stocks has recently been shown by Waddington, Woolf and Perry (1954). In organisms such as birds, in which rather sudden changes in geographical or ecological range are well-known, learning may play a part, but this may also have an important genetic component. In the genetic constitution of a sub-population which has broken out of the original species boundaries and is spreading into new territory, one must expect to find that a number of adjustments are occurring simultaneously. There is most likely to be, in the first place, an evolution of a new system of habitat-preferences and/or of general activity; in the second, the adaptive characters and general fitness of the migrating group will be attuned to the new circumstances which it has to meet. Both these necessary modifications of the gene pool will be made more easily if the genetic constitution of the sub-population is prevented from continual intermingling with that of the original stay-at-home group. Thus any tendency for preferential mating within the migrating group, and sexual isolation between it and the main population, will acquire selective value. It seems rather probable that a species may be able to spread into new territory even if no sexual isolation develops between the main population and the migrating one; but if the increase in species-range demands considerable adjustment of the genotype to fit the new environment, the evolution of some degree of mating-barrier will undoubtedly be of considerable advantage. Our experiments show that the necessary genetic variability is likely to be present in a population; and the fact that the change of environment involves alterations to the behaviour pattern of the migrating animals makes it more likely that their preferences for sexual partners as well as for habitats, will exhibit evolutionary flexibility. Thus species-spread and sexual isolation will tend to act synergistically.

Summary

1. Partial sexual isolation (between two stocks of *D. melanogaster* differing only in marker genes) has been established by selection of the offspring of flies mating with their own type. This has been demonstrated by a reduction in the number of cross-bred offspring found and also by examination of the progeny of individual females.

2. In a small series of tests, no tendencies towards preferential mating were found to have arisen by chance in a sample of lines which had been inbred or selected for number of abdominal chaetae, although there were differences in intensity of sexual drive.

3. Changes in reproductive behaviour brought about by selection are more likely to affect female than male behaviour. Willingness to cross breed, in a male, will not materially reduce the number of his pure-bred offspring but in a female it usually will.

4. It is argued that selection pressure against cross-breeding of two partially separated populations, although probably effective when it occurs, is not likely to be the only mechanism by which sexual isolation between taxonomic groups develops in nature. It is suggested that an important part in the origin of such isolation may be played by the factors (e.g. changes in hereditarily controlled behaviour patterns) which bring about the spread of an initial panmictic population into new geographical or ecological situations.

Literature Cited

Dobzhansky, T. 1937. Genetics and the Origin of Species. Columbia Univ. Press, New York.

Dobzhansky, T., and P. C. Koller. 1938. An experimental study of sexual isolation in Drosophila. Biol. Zentral., **58**: 589–607.

King, J. C. 1947. Interspecific relationships within the guarani group of Drosophila. Evolution, **1**: 143–153.

Koopman, K. F. 1950. Natural selection for reproductive isolation between Drosophila pseudoobscura and Drosophila persimilis. Evolution, **4**: 135–148.

Merrell, D. J. 1954. Sexual isolation between Drosophila persimilis and Drosophila pseudoobscura. Am. Nat., **88**: 93–100.

Muller, H. J. 1939. Reversibility in evolution considered from the standpoint of genetics. Biol. Rev., **14**: 261–280.

Rendel, J. M. 1951. Mating of ebony, vestigial and wild-type Drosophila melanogaster in light and dark. Evolution, **5**: 226–230.

Wallace, B. 1950. An experiment on sexual isolation. D.I.S., **24**: 94–96.

Waddington, C. H., B. Woolf, and M. Perry. 1954. Environment selection by Drosophila mutants. Evolution, **8**: 89–96.

DROSOPHILA PAULISTORUM, A CLUSTER OF SPECIES IN STATU NASCENDI[*][†]

BY THEODOSIUS DOBZHANSKY and BORIS SPASSKY

DEPARTMENT OF ZOÖLOGY, COLUMBIA UNIVERSITY

Communicated January 23, 1959

One hundred years ago Darwin wrote that "... species are only strongly marked and permanent varieties, and that each species first existed as a variety ...." Species of sexual and cross-fertilizing organisms arise mostly through gradual divergence and reproductive isolation of subspecies (= geographic races or varieties). Evidence of this are numerous "borderline cases," in which subspecies have almost reached the degree of divergence and of reproductive isolation met with among species. In turn, the most interesting among "borderline cases" are chains of intergrading subspecies, the terminal links of which coexist sympatrically, in the same territory, with little or no interbreeding taking place. In the territories in which they live together, these divergent forms behave, then, like true species; and yet they appear to be only races if the connecting links are considered. Gene exchange between the terminal links remains possible, and may actually be taking place, via the connecting chain of subspecies.

Several examples of circular chains of subspecies have been observed, chiefly in birds and insects (reviews in Mayr[1] and Rensch[2]). A beautiful case in a species of salamander has recently been added by Stebbins.[3,4] The first instance in the genus *Drosophila* is to be reported in the present article. According to Patterson and Stone's review,[5] the genus *Drosophila* contained 613 described species in 1952. Several race-species borderline cases have been observed, but in none of these have sympatrically coexisting forms been found connected by chains of allopatric races. Since many species of *Drosophila* are favorable as materials for genetic experimentation, the borderline race-species situation may, it is hoped, be analyzed here more fully than has been possible elsewhere.

Position of Drosophila paulistorum among its Relatives.—The five sibling species, *D. paulistorum*, *D. willistoni*, *D. equinoctialis*, *D. tropicalis*, and *D. insularis* are practically indistinguishable by inspection of their external morphology, [6,7] although Spassky[8] recently found slight differences in the male genitalia which enable him to classify living males. The species can, however, be identified by

Reprinted by permission of the authors from PROCEEDINGS OF THE
NATIONAL ACADEMY OF SCIENCES, 45, 419–428 (1959).

their chromosomes, as seen in the cells of larval salivary glands. Furthermore, they are completely isolated reproductively. Sexual isolation is so strong that cross-insemination rarely succeeds, and no viable hybrids are produced except in the crosses involving *D. insularis*. Even these hybrids are wholly sterile. *D. insularis* is known only from some of the islands in the Lesser Antilles, but the other four species are widely distributed in the American tropics, all of them being sympatric in the basin of the Amazon and in the part of South America lying north of the Equator. *D. paulistorum* occurs from southern Brazil to Central America (Guatemala) and Trinidad. In many parts of this large area it is one of the commonest species of the genus, especially in the superhumid tropical rainforest climates.

D. willistoni is a unified species, in the sense that strains of any geographic origin can easily be crossed with strains from anywhere else, and produce fully viable and fertile hybrids. *D. tropicalis* is differentiated into at least two subspecies, the hybrids between which are sterile as males.[9] Nothing is known about possible differentiation of *D. equinoctialis*. The remarkable differentiation of *D. paulistorum* is described below.

Material.—We have in our laboratory strains of *D. paulistorum* from the following 25 localities (the numbers in the following list correspond to those on the map in Fig. 1): (1) Tikal, Guatemala, May, 1958, Sophie Dobzhansky Coe; (2) Lancetilla,

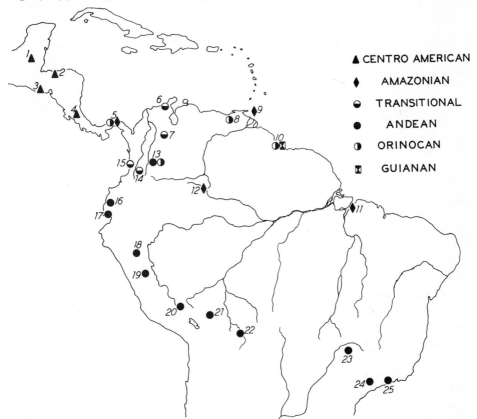

▲ CENTRO AMERICAN

◆ AMAZONIAN

◑ TRANSITIONAL

● ANDEAN

◐ ORINOCAN

▣ GUIANAN

Fig. 1.— Geographic origin of the strains of *Drosophila paulistorum*. The numbers of the localities on this map correspond to those in Figures 2–4 and in the text.

Honduras, May, 1954, W. B. Heed; (3) San Salvador, August, 1954, W. B. Heed; (4) Turrialba, Costa Rica, August, 1956, W. B. Heed; (5) Barro Colorado, Panama, August, 1956, W. H. Heed; (6) Santa Marta, Columbia, September, 1956, H. L. Carson and M. Wasserman; (7) Bucaramanga, Columbia, September, 1956, H. L. Carson and M. Wasserman; (8) Caripe, Venezuela, November, 1956, M. Wasserman; (9) Arima Valley, Trinidad, February, 1956, W. B. Heed; (10) Georgetown, British Guiana, July, 1957, W. B. Heed; (11) Belem, Brazil, July, 1952, Th. Dobzhansky; (12) Içana, Brazil, August, 1952, C. Pavan and Th. Dobzhansky; (13) Llanos near Villavicencio, Columbia, March, 1958, Th. Dobzhansky; (14) Palmira, Colombia, March, 1958, M. Wheeler and Th. Dobzhansky; (15) Buenaventura, Columbia, March, 1958, Th. Dobzhansky; (16) Santo Domingo de los Colorados, Ecuador, March, 1958, M. Wheeler and Th. Dobzhansky; (17) Pichilingue, Ecuador, March, 1958, M. Wheeler and Th. Dobzhansky; (18) Tarapoto, Peru, September, 1956, C. Pavan and Th. Dobzhansky; (19) Tingo Maria, Peru. September, 1956, C. Pavan and Th. Dobzhansky; (20) Urubamba, Peru, September, 1956, C. Pavan and Th. Dobzhansky; (21) Coroico, Bolivia, April, 1958, M. Wasserman; (22) Santa Cruz de la Sierra, Bolivia, April, 1958, M. Wasserman; (23) Ituitaba and Araguari, Minas Gerais, Brazil, August, 1957, M. Breuer; (24) Cantareira, São Paulo, Brazil, January, 1958, C. Pavan; and (25) Angra dos Reis, Brazil, May, 1956, Th. Dobzhansky.

The older strains, the progenitors of which were collected in 1956 or earlier were derived each from a single wild female fertilized in nature. The Peruvian strains (localities Nos. 18–20) are progenies of the populations kept in laboratory population cages for about a year, the founders of which came from several dozen wild strains from a given locality mixed together. The newer strains, started in 1957 and 1958, were prepared as follows. Separate strains were established from each wild female collected in a given locality. These strains were then intercrossed chainwise, i.e., A × B, B × C, ... Y × Z, Z × A. If all crossed yielded fertile F_1 progenies the strains were pooled in a single mixed population from each locality. Sometimes two groups of strains were found, interfertile within but intersterile between groups. Two pooled strains were then established (i.e., Llanos-A and Llanos-B).

First Series of Experiments.—Attempts to intercross strains of *D. paulistorum* yield a variety of results. Some crosses go easily, and produce fertile F_1 hybrids; others fail to give any hybrid offspring; still others produce in F_1 fertile female but sterile male hybrids. Systematic intercrosses were started in the fall of 1956 and in 1957 with the 16 strains then available. The results are summarized in Figure 2.

The experiments were arranged as follows: about a dozen virgin females from one strain and a like number of males from another were placed together in a culture bottle at room temperature. If no larvae appeared in the food within a week, the flies were transferred, without etherization, to a fresh culture bottle, and left there for another week. If no progeny appeared, the cross was considered as having failed; such failures are marked in Figure 2 by the sign *O*. If the progeny did appear, the hybrid flies were allowed to develop, and a dozen or more pairs of them were placed in a fresh culture. If F_2 larvae appeared, the F_1 hybrids were evidently fertile; such fertile crosses are marked in Figure 2 by an *F*. If no F_2 larvae appeared after a week, the parents were transferred to a fresh culture and left

♂ \ ♀	HONDURAS	SALVADOR-A	SALVADOR-B	COSTA RICA	PANAMA-A	TRINIDAD	BELEM	IÇANA	TARAPOTO	TINGO MARIA	URUBAMBA	ANGRA	BUCARAMANGA	SANTA MARTA	CARIPE	PANAMA-B
2. HONDURAS		F		F	O	O	O	O	ST	ST		ST	ST		ST	ST
3. SALVADOR-A	F		F	F	O		O	O	ST		ST			F		ST
3. SALVADOR-B	F	F			O	O	O			ST		ST			ST	F
4. COSTA RICA	F		F		O			O			ST	ST	F	F		ST
5. PANAMA-A	O	O	O	O		F	F	F	ST	O	O	ST	O	O	O	O
9. TRINIDAD		O		O	F		F		O	O	O		O	O		O
11. BELEM	O	O		O	F	F		F	ST		ST		O	O	O	
12. IÇANA	ST	O	O		F	F	F		O	O		ST	O		O	ST
18. TARAPOTO	O	ST	O	ST	O		O	O		F	F		ST			O
19. TINGO MARIA		ST		ST	O	O		F			F	F		O		ST
20. URUBAMBA	ST			O	O		O		F			F		ST		ST
25. ANGRA	ST	ST		ST		O	O		F	F			O	ST	ST	
7. BUCARAMANGA		O	ST	O	O	ST		F	F	F	F			ST	O	O
6. SANTA MARTA	F		F		O		ST	ST	ST		ST	F			F	O
8. CARIPE	O	ST	O	ST	O	O	O	ST	ST	O	ST		O	O		F
5 PANAMA-B	ST	ST	ST		O	O	O		O	ST	ST	ST	ST	F	O	

FIG. 2.—First series of experiments. Outcome of the crosses between strains of different geographic origin. O—no progeny produced; ST—male F₁ hybrids sterile; F—hydrids fertile.

there for another week. The nonappearance of a progeny was taken to mean that one or both sexes of the F₁ hybrids are sterile. Such crosses are marked in Figure 2 by *ST*. Separate experiments showed that the sterile sex is the male.

The geographic origin of the strains, shown in Figure 1, must be taken into consideration in an analysis of the data reported in Figure 2. A group of "Centro-American" strains are easily intercrossed and yield fertile hybrids; these are the strains from Honduras (the locality No. 2 in Fig. 1), two strains from El Salvador (No. 3), and one from Costa Rica (No. 4). The "Amazonian" group consists of strains from Belem (No. 11), Icana (No. 12), Trinidad (No. 9), and Panama-A (No. 5); these strains also yield fertile hybrids easily. A third, "Andean-South Brazilian," group comes from the eastern slope of the Andes in Peru (localities Nos. 18, 19, and 20), and from Angra dos Reis in southern Brazil (No. 25). The strains of this group also interbreed freely. However, intercrosses of strains belonging to the different groups either fail altogether (*O* in Fig. 2) or yield sterile hybrid males (*ST*).

This situation may suggest the existence of three reproductively isolated, although morphologically identical, sibling species: the Centro-American, the Amazonian, and the Andean. This interpretation is excluded by finding four other strains from Santa Marta (No. 6 in Fig. 1) and Bucaramanga (No. 7) in Colombia, Caripe, in Venezuela (No. 8), and Panama-B (No. 5). Figure 2 shows that Santa Marta gives fertile hybrids with the Centro-American group but not with the Andean group; the Bucaramanga strain is fertile with the Andean group, with Santa Marta, but only with Costa Rica in the Centro-American group. Caripe is fertile with Santa Marta but not with Bucaramanga, and produces sterile hybrids or none with the Centro-American and the Andean groups. Panama-B is fertile with Caripe; its females give fertile hybrids with one of the two strains from El Salvador, and its males do likewise with Bucaramanga. Attempts to cross Panama-B to other strains give sterile hybrids or none.

Perhaps the most important fact is that the two strains, A and B from Panama, have refused to cross entirely, despite repeated trials. Since both strains are derived from progenitors collected in Barro Colorado Island, this locality must harbor two sympatric, and yet completely reproductively isolated, populations of D. paulistorum. These populations behave, then, like full-fledged species. And yet they can exchange genes, because each of them can be crossed to other populations with which they produce at least fertile female hybrids. In fact, crosses can be arranged connecting the two Panama populations without yielding any sterile hybrids at all (see below).

The matings which produce no hybrids at all (marked by an O in Fig. 2) fail because of a complete sexual isolation between the strains involved. This has been established by dissection of the surviving females which were exposed for two weeks to foreign males, and examination of their seminal receptacles under a microscope. No sperm was found in the hundreds of females dissected. There is an incomplete sexual isolation also between at least some of the strains which produce sterile hybrids (ST in Fig. 2). We have dissected the females from some of these crosses after the hybrids have appeared, and found usually one or two inseminated females, the rest remaining virgins. This is evidently the explanation of the erratic character of some of the results; thus, the females of the Amazonian strains always refuse to accept males of the Centro-American and Andean groups, but Amazonian males occasionally inseminate some females of the latter two groups. Perhaps, any two strains may eventually be made to produce hybrids. Whether any of the inter-group crosses yielding sterile hybrids are entirely free of sexual isolation remains to be determined.

The nature of the sterility of the hybrid males is also not known in detail. It can, however, be stated that the testes of these males contain no spermatozoa and only abnormal spermatids, and their seminal vesicles are always empty.

Second Series of Experiments.—The experiments reported above made it clear that the species D. paulistorum is broken up into at least three incipient species, plus some connecting, or transitional, populations. In 1958 one of us (Th. D.) was able to collect further material in Colombia and in Ecuador. Drs. M. Wheeler and M. Wassermann of the University of Texas have contributed invaluable material from Panama, British Guiana, and Bolivia; Drs. C. Pavan and A. B. da Cunha have sent new strains from southern Brazil. A second series of experimental crosses has been carried out in 1958, using the same procedure as described above,

♂ \ ♀	GUATEMALA	HONDURAS	COSTA RICA	PANAMA-A	TRINIDAD	BELEM	PANAMA-B	PANAMA-C	LLANOS-A	CARIPE	GUIANA-A	GUIANA-B	SANTA MARTA	BUCARAMANGA	PALMIRA	BUENAVENTURA
1. GUATEMALA		F	F	O	ST		ST	ST	ST	ST	O		F	O		ST
2. HONDURAS	F		F	O	O		ST		ST				F		O	
4. COSTA RICA	F					O	ST		ST		O	ST			O	O
5. PANAMA-A	O		O		F		O		O		O		ST	O	O	
9. TRINIDAD		O				F	O	O	O		O	O		O	O	O
11. BELEM	O	O		F	F			O		O			O		F	
5. PANAMA-B	ST	ST		O				F	F	F	F		ST	O	O	ST
5. PANAMA-C		ST	ST	O	ST		F		F	F	F			O	O	ST
13. LLANOS-A	ST	F				ST	ST	ST		ST	O	O	F	O	O	
8. CARIPE		ST	O	O			F	F	ST		F		ST		F	ST
10. GUIANA-A	O	ST		O		O		F	F	F		O	ST		O	
10. GUIANA-B	ST	ST		O	O		O	ST	O	O			ST		ST	
6. SANTA MARTA		F	O	O			O				O			F	O	F
7. BUCARAMANGA	O	ST				ST		ST	O	ST	O	ST				
14. PALMIRA		F	O	O			O		O				F			ST
15. BUENAVENTURA	ST	ST				O		ST	ST	ST	ST	O	F		O	
13. LLANOS-B	ST	ST		ST		ST	ST	O	O	ST	ST	ST	ST	F		
16. SANTO DOMINGO	F		O	O	ST		ST		F					F		ST
17. PICHILINGUE	ST	ST				O		ST	ST	ST	ST	O	F	ST	F	ST
19. TINGO MARIA	ST	ST				O		O	ST	ST	ST	ST		F		
21. COROICO		ST		O	O		O			O				F		F
22. SANTA CRUZ	ST	ST		ST		O			O		O		ST	F	F	
23. MINAS GERAIS		ST	ST	O	ST			ST								F
24. SÃO PAULO	ST	ST				O		ST		ST	ST	O	ST	F	F	
25. ANGRA		ST		O	O	O		ST						F		F

FIG. 3.—Second series of experiments. Outcome of the crosses between strains of different geographic origin. O—no progeny produced; ST—male F₁ hybrids sterile; F—hybrids sterile.

except that no dissections and examinations of the sperm receptacles were made. The results are summarized in Figures 3 and 4, and in map form in Figure 1.

   (a) *Centro-American group*, Guatemala to Costa Rica. Fully fertile *inter se* and with Santa Marta, Colombia. The strain from Tikal, Guatemala, collected

♂ \ ♀	SANTA MARTA	BUCARAMANGA	PALMIRA	BUENAVENTURA	LLANOS-B	SANTO DOMINGO	PICHILINGUE	TINGO MARIA	COROICO	SANTA CRUZ	MINAS GERAIS	SÃO PAULO	ANGRA
1. GUATEMALA	F	O		ST		ST	ST	ST	ST		ST		F
2. HONDURAS	F		O			ST		ST	F		ST	ST	ST
4. COSTA RICA		O		O	ST	O	ST	ST	ST			ST	ST
5. PANAMA-A		ST	O	O	O	O		ST		ST		ST	
9. TRINIDAD		O	O	O	O	O		ST		ST		ST	
10. BELEM	O		F			ST			ST		ST		ST
5. PANAMA-B	ST	O	O	ST	ST	O		ST		O		ST	
5 PANAMA-C		O	O	ST		ST			ST		ST		ST
13. LLANOS-A	F	O	O	O	O	ST	ST	ST		ST	ST	ST	ST
8. CARIPE	ST	O	F	ST		ST		O	ST		ST		ST
10. GUIANA-A	ST	O			ST			ST	ST	ST			ST
10. GUIANA-B	ST		ST		ST		ST	ST	ST	ST	O		ST
6. SANTA MARTA		F	O	F		ST	F		O		ST		ST
7. BUCARAMANGA				F		O	F		F		F		
14. PALMIRA		F		ST	F	F		F		F			F
15. BUENAVENTURA	F		O		ST		F	ST		ST		F	
13. LLANOS-B	ST	F	F			F	O	F		F		F	
SANTO DOMINGO		F	ST	F					F		F		F
17. PICHILINGUE	F	ST	F	ST		F		ST		ST		ST	
19. TINGO MARIA	ST		F		F				F			F	F
21. COROICO		F		F	F	F						F	F
22. SANTA CRUZ	ST	F		F		F	F					F	
23. MINAS GERAIS				F	F	F			F				F
24. SÃO PAULO	ST	F	F			F			F	F			
25. ANGRA		F		F	F	F			F			F	

FIG. 4.—Second series of experiments. Outcome of the crosses between strains of different geographic origin. O—no progeny produced; ST—male F_1 hybrids sterile; F—hybrids fertile.

by Mrs. Sophie Dobzhansky Coe, yields fertile hybrids also with Santo Domingo, Ecuador. The strain from Costa Rica is fertile with Palmira, Colombia.

(b) *Amazonian group*, Panama to Para. Fertile *inter se*, and with only one other strain, from Palmira, Columbia (Transitional group, No. 14). Amazonian females accept males chiefly from the Andean group, but amazonian males are more successful with females of all other groups.

(c) *Andean-South Brazilian group*, Llanos of Colombia, Andes of Ecuador, Peru, and Bolivia, southern Brazil. There is some incipient differentiation even within this group, since the males from Pichilingue, Ecuador, yield sterile F_1 hybrid sons when mated to Peruvian, Bolivian, or Brazilian females (Fig. 4). Pichilingue females produce fertile hybrids with Peruvian, Bolivian, and Brazilian males. Otherwise this group gives fertile hybrids only with some of the strains of the Group F (Transitional), but sterile ones with other strains of the Transitional and other groups.

(d) *Orinocan group*, Panama, Llanos and Colombia, Venezuela, British Guiana. Fertile *inter se*, except that Llanos-A males produce sterile sons with females of the other strains, and Llanos-A females produce sterile sons with males from Caripe, Venezuela. The Llanos-A strain is also fertile with Honduras of the Centro-American groups, with Santo Domingo of the Andean group, and with Santa Marta of the Transitional group.

(e) *Guianan*, a single strain, Guiana-B from near Georgetown, British Guiana. Thus far, we have succeeded in obtaining fertile hybrids between this strain and only one other, that of the Andean group, from Santa Cruz, Bolivia. Guiana-B males are accepted by females of the other groups except the Amazonian, but the male hybrids produced are sterile.

(f) *Transitional group*, Colombia localities Nos. 6, 7, 14, and 15 (Fig. 1). Fertile *inter se*, except that the strains from Palmira and from Buenaventura are difficult to cross, and when crossed produce sterile sons. This group deserves its name because at least some of its members produce fertile hybrids with at least some members of every other group, except the Guianan group. Here we have, then, a genetic bridge which connects the gene pools of the other groups. A glance at the map in Figure 1 shows that Group F is geographically also bridging the other groups.

Conclusions and Summary.—The geographic distributions of the six groups, or subspecies are, as shown in Figure 1, generally distinct. However, in at least three localities representatives of two groups occur together, sympatrically, and yet remain incapable of interbreeding. These localities are: (1) Barro Colorado Island, Panama, where groups B and D have been found, (2) Llanos near Villavicencio, Colombia, groups C and D, and (3) Georgetown, British Guiana, groups D and E. In all these cases the sympatric populations yield no hybrid progenies, and even no cross-insemination, in laboratory experiments in which they have no possibility of mating within their own race.

Inability of sympatric Mendelian populations to interbreed and to exchange genes is *prima facie* evidence that these populations belong to different species. Nevertheless, we are obliged to conclude that *D. paulistorum* is, considered as a whole, a single species. This is not because its component populations, whether reproductively isolated or not, are not distinguishable by the morphology. The compelling evidence comes from the existence of bridging populations, which do produce fertile hybrids when crossed to other populations which are reproductively isolated from each other. With the strains at our disposal, it may be necessary to make as many as four consecutive crosses in order to connect two otherwise non-interbreeding populations without encountering sterility of, at least, the male hybrids (e.g. between Panama-A and Panama-B). Since female hybrids are mostly fertile, the gene exchange becomes facilitated; generally no more than two consecutive crosses are needed to open a channel for gene exchange. *D. paulistorum* is a single inclusive Mendelian population. No matter to what group a strain giving rise to a favorable mutation or a gene combination may belong, the mutation of the gene combination will, at least potentially, be able to diffuse in other populations and to become the property of the species as a whole. To what extent such a potentiality is actually realized is, of course, a separate question. We hope to be able to shed some light on it by another study.

Comparison of *D. paulistorum* with other race-species borderline case, that of the frog *Rana pipiens*, suggests itself. As shown by the brilliant studies of Moore,[10] the northern populations of this species (from New England) yield inviable hybrids when crossed to southern populations (Texas or Florida). Viable hybrids are, however, formed by geographically adjacent populations. *R. pipiens* is an inclusive Mendelian population, a single species, and, at least potentially, a unit of evolutionary change. One can imagine the situation in *R. pipiens* coming to resemble that in *D. paulistorum*, if the frog populations like those of New England migrated to some territory and met there expanding populations like those of Texas, and both coexisted sympatrically without effective gene exchange. If this were to happen together with preservation of the present genetic connection in the eastern United States, we would be led to conclude that the specific unity of *R. pipiens* is not forfeited. On the other hand, suppose that only populations like the present inhabitants of New England and Texas were preserved and became sympatric without breakdown of reproductive isolation; that would mean emergence of two genetically closed systems, two species. A parallel event would be disappearance of the populations of *D. paulistorum* which now inhabit the northwestern part of the continent of South America (Colombia and, perhaps, Panama). What remained would, perhaps, be five independent species (here, however, a caveat: the populations of central and eastern Brazil having not been studied, we do not know whether the Amazonian and the Andean groups are, or are not, connected there).

Whether two Mendelian populations, or groups of populations, are distinct species or only races is frequently in doubt. Most of these doubtful cases can be resolved unambiguously if sufficient evidence, observational and experimental, becomes available. A minority are, however, true borderline cases; in these the process of species splitting has, on our time level, reached the critical stage of transition from race to species. *D. paulistorum* is one species; it is also a cluster of species *in statu nascendi;* it bespeaks the correctness of Darwin's opinion that "each species first existed as a variety."

The generosity of the colleagues at the University of Texas, particularly Drs. W. B. Heed, W. S. Stone, M. Wasserman, and M. R. Wheeler, and of C. Pavan and A. B. da Cunha of the University of São Paulo, who collected and sent us strains of *Drosophila* from many parts of South and Central America, is gratefully acknowledged. The collecting expedition to Colombia and Ecuador was made possible by a grant from the Rockefeller Foundation, and by the courtesy of the members of the Agricultural Program in Colombia, particularly of Dr. L. M. Roberts. Thanks are also due to Professor and Mrs. F. Hunter of the Universidad de los Andes, Bogota, Colombia.

* To J. T. Patterson, pioneer student of systematics and evolution of *Drosophila*, dedicated on his 80th birthday.

† The work reported here has been carried out under Contract No. AT-(30-)-1151, U.S. Atomic Energy Commission.

¹ Mayr, E., *Systematics and the Origin of Species* (New York: 1942).

² Rensch, B., *Neuere Probleme der Abstammungslehre* (Stuttgart: 1954).

³ Stebbins, R. C., *Univ. Calif. Publ. Zool.*, **48,** 377–526 (1949).

⁴ Stebbins, R. C., *Evolution*, **11,** 256–270 (1957).

⁵ Patterson, J. T., and W. S. Stone, *Evolution in the Genus Drosophila* (New York: 1952).

⁶ Burla, H., A. B. da Cunha, A. R. Cordeiro, Th. Dobzhansky, Ch. Malogolowkin, and C. Pavan, *Evolution*, **3,** 300–314 (1949).

⁷ Dobzhansky, Th., L. Ehrman, and O. Pavlovsky, *Univ. Texas Publ.*, **5721,** 39–47 (1957).

⁸ Spassky, B., *Univ. Texas Publ.*, **5721,** 48–61 (1957).

⁹ Townsend, J. I., *Am. Natur.*, **88,** 339–351 (1954).

¹⁰ Moore, J. A., *Advances in Genetics*, **7,** 139–182 (1955).